CONSTRUCTION TECHNOLOGY

DESIGNING SUSTAINABLE HOMES

TREVOR HICKEY

Gill Education
Hume Avenue
Park West
Dublin 12

www.gilleducation.ie

Gill Education is an imprint of M. H. Gill & Co.

978 07171 4834 9

Design and print origination, Charles Design Associates
Illustrations, Elizabeth Israel

The paper used in this book is made from the wood pulp of managed forests. For every tree felled, at least one tree is planted, thereby renewing natural resources.

For permission to reproduce photographs, the author and publisher gratefully acknowledge the following: © Alamy: 30B, 77, 82T, 82B, 96B, 104TR, 102, 107TR, 108T, 108T, 177TC, 197TL, 368T, 368B; © Alice Clancy/TAKA Architects: 109, 131B; © All-Island Research Observatory (AIRO): 16B, 19R 402; © Aughey O'Flaherty Architects: 130; © Boyle Copper & Zinc Craft Ltd: 188TL, 188TR; © CER/SEAI: 376R; © Ciarán Mackel, Ard Architects: 131TL, 131TR; © Construction Photography: 93CR; © Corbis: 83; © Department Environment, Community and Local Government: 57BL, 57BR, 316; © Development, Economic & Transport Planning, South Dublin County Council: 59; © Dominic Stevens: 120, 145L; © Ecohomes.ie: 148, 149; © Fitzpatrick & Mays Architects: 286; © Fläkt Woods: 345; © Getty Images: 51BL, 51BR, 197CL, 334TL; © Government of Ireland 2012: 14T; © Health and Safety Authority/www.hsa.ie: 91, 92TR; © John Herriot: 353; © Courtesy of GRID-Arendal/www.grida.no/graphicslib/detail/areas-of-physical-and-economic-water-scarcity_1570: 18T; © Maurice Falvey: 349, 392; © Met Éireann: 19L; © METSÄ WOOD: 222TR; © Munster Joinery: 213, 325; © NASA Earth Observatory, Robert Simmon: 10B; © NSAI: 58B, 210; © Ordnance Survey Ireland: 62, 63; © Passivhaus Institut: 322, 328; © Paul Heat Recovery: 342; © Peter Barrow: 351, 354; PVGIS © European Union, 2001-2012: 371; © Radiological Protection Institute of Ireland: 158; © Richard Hatch Photography/McKevitt Architects: 132L, 132R; © Richard Hawkes of Hawkes Architecture Ltd: 176T; © RPP Architects Ltd: 39BL, 39BR; © Ryan Engineering & Project Management: 160R; © Scandinavian Homes Ltd, Galway: 285L; © SEAI: 321; © Shutterstock: 32BR, 73, 93CL, 177TR, 372, 372, 384BL; © SSE Ireland: 355; © Testo Limited/www.testolimited.com: 334R; © Truss Form Ltd. and Wolf Systems: 223; © WFQA: 384BR; © Lloyd Rozema/Wikimedia: 405.

Sustainability checklist from *Rough Guide to Sustainability* by Brian Edwards © 2009, courtesy of RIBA Publishing.

The author and publisher have made every effort to trace all copyright holders, but if any has been inadvertently overlooked we would be pleased to make the necessary arrangement at the first opportunity.

Contents

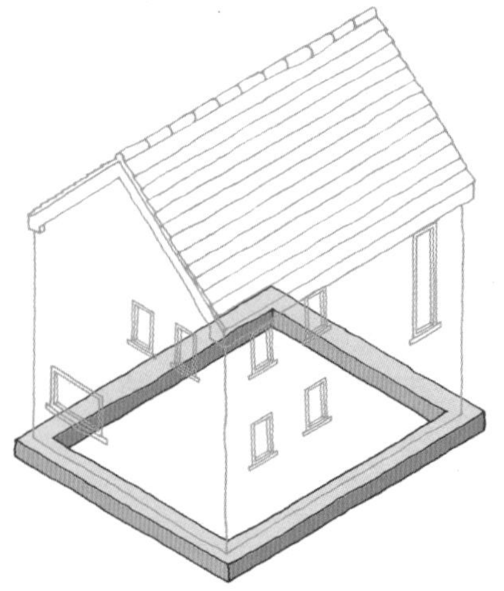

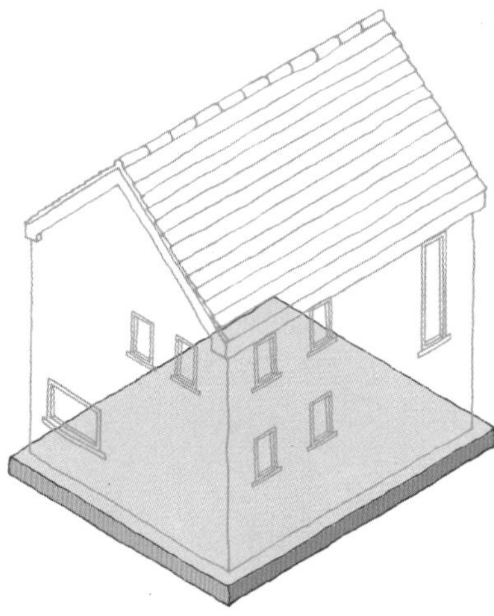

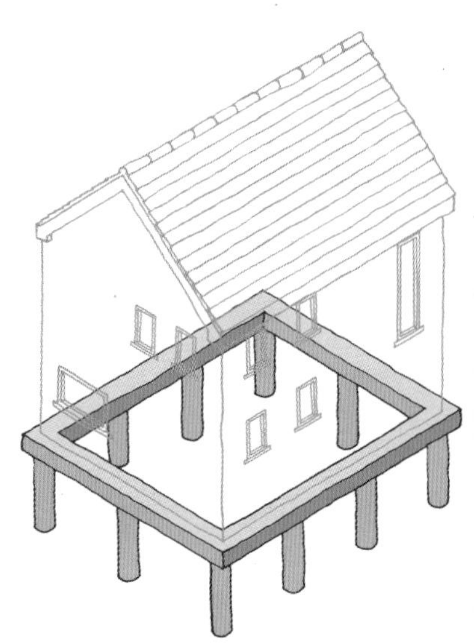

Acknowledgements

The author would like to thank the following people for their assistance in the writing of this book.

Keith Cunningham for the initial detailing of the houses and the structural systems. Keith made a major contribution to the development of the details, the design of the three houses and their site plans – his input is greatly appreciated.

Elizabeth Israel, B.Arch (University of Notre Dame), American architectural designer and illustrator. Elizabeth's artwork is the backbone of this book. Her ability to turn a rough sketch into a technically accurate, yet simple artwork, is second to none.

Tricia Charles of Charles Design Associates, for her wonderful work on the design and layout of the book. Tricia's attention to detail, patience and commitment to the project are really appreciated.

Neil Ryan for his excellent editorial work and commitment to getting every detail right. Also Anthony Murray, Jen Patton, Mairead O'Keeffe, Anita Ruane and everyone at Gill & Macmillan for their professionalism and contributions to the production of this book.

Sean Ó Broin of the State Examinations Commission for his vision and leadership in bringing Leaving Certificate Construction Studies into a new era. There are few subjects that have so successfully responded to the changing context in which they are taught.

The many teachers of Construction Studies who have offered their encouragement and support while the book was being written.

The author would also like to thank all of those people who provided support, information, advice and images for this book, including the following:
Jonathon Barnett
Joe Condon
Scott Cook
Eric Coyne
Niall Crossan
Colm Cryan
Maurice Falvey
Richard Hatch
Richard Hawkes
Des Kelly
Cyril Mannion
Art McCormack
Adrian O'Connor
Tomas O'Leary
Darren O'Gorman
Declan Phillips
Claire Robinson
Jeremy Rynhart
Alan Spillane
Dominic Stevens

To Sinéad, for her constant support, encouragement and patience during the many hours I spent on this project.

To my children, Caoimhe, Emily, Ríonagh & Dómhnall for making life great.

In memory of my dear friend Donal Lynch – a great teacher who saw the best in every student.

Foreword

To the teacher

This textbook provides a new approach to the teaching of Construction Studies. It responds to the changes seen in the subject since the publication of Construction Studies Today in 2006. At that time the construction boom was in full swing and our main focus as teachers was in keeping up to date with the many new systems and products that the industry was adopting. The focus now is on building energy efficient homes. This is evident in the way the industry is moving and in the way leaving certificate Construction Studies is being assessed.

The content is structured into three main areas with a particular emphasis on design. This focus on design is deliberate. If Construction Studies is to remain a valuable part of the curriculum, the role of design in the creation of homes must be made clear. A home must be designed to respond to its site, to meet the needs of the occupants and to provide a comfortable indoor environment while minimising energy consumption and carbon emissions.

The European Union Directive (2010/31/EU) on the energy performance of buildings will change the way homes are built in Ireland in the short term – the way we teach this subject must respond. In this textbook you will find the knowledge that your students require to enter this new period of construction history with confidence.

To the student

This textbook is designed to guide you through what you need to know about residential construction in the Irish context. There are three sections that explore the main areas of knowledge in a logical sequence. The chapters are sequenced to provide you with a gradual buildup of knowledge and understanding. Each chapter contains learning activities that are designed to encourage you to 'think outside the classroom' and explore your own home from a new perspective. When you have completed your study of this textbook you should have gained a detailed understanding of why (and how) homes are designed to provide a comfortable indoor environment without consuming fossil fuels and emitting carbon dioxide.

Introduction

Every home has an impact on the planet. Energy, water and other resources are consumed; carbon dioxide is emitted. Some homes have a greater impact than others. The typical Irish home has a much bigger impact on the planet than homes in most other countries. The average person living in Ireland has a higher rate of carbon dioxide emissions than an average person living in 21 of the other European Union countries.

In the age of climate change and water scarcity, at a time when the environmental and economic cost of energy is rising at a rapid rate, it is no longer acceptable to design and build homes that are adding to this problem. The knowledge, technology and skills exist to build homes that have a very low impact on society and on the planet. It doesn't cost more to build homes this way; it is simply a question of choosing to learn how to.

This text aims to demonstrate the difference between designing and building homes to a minimum standard and doing so to a standard that represents international best practice. The European Union Directive (2010/31/EU) on the energy performance of buildings requires that by 2021 all new buildings are 'nearly zero-energy buildings'. A nearly zero-energy building is defined in the directive as 'a building that has a very high energy performance' and states that 'the very low amount of energy required should be covered to a very significant extent by energy from renewable sources, including energy from renewable sources produced on-site or nearby'.

When it comes to energy-in-use, the Passivhaus standard represents international best practice. It is a scientifically proven concept that is supported by almost two decades of academic research and publication. Over 25,000 buildings around the world are standing evidence that it is possible to design and build ultra low energy buildings using today's technology. The challenge now is to provide the leadership required to make this standard the new norm. Ordinary people building their own homes around Ireland are increasingly doing so... the wider construction industry and the policy makers need to follow their lead.

Throughout this text, emphasis is placed on the why rather than the how. While some knowledge of how things are done is necessary, it is more important to understand why things are done. If we understand why buildings are designed to perform in certain ways we can use this knowledge to improve their design. If we merely learn how they are assembled we cannot advance; we are stuck with yesterday's solutions.

The specific knowledge and skills required to construct a building are learned as part of professional training; for example, when learning a craft trade (e.g. plumbing). This text aims to provide the knowledge required to understand the design principles underpinning why buildings perform – the 'nuts and bolts' of putting a building together can be learned later. Our task now is to learn why homes are designed the way they are; it is not to learn how to build a house. Some of the how will also be learned, but only as part of learning why.

So, this book is about design... the design of homes. Designing a home is about using structure, space, light and artefacts to create a place that makes us feel safe, warm, healthy, protected. A well designed home generates happiness and pleasure – designing a home involves much more than merely providing shelter.

In this text there are detailed drawings of three ordinary houses; a single storey house in a rural setting, a two storey house in a suburban setting and a three storey house in an urban setting. These houses are original designs that have been created to allow the reader to see how the concepts explored in each chapter come together in the design of a complete building. All of these homes are designed to meet the requirements of the building regulations. In addition, the two storey and three storey homes are designed to meet the Passivhaus standard for energy in use. This difference is most obvious in the building fabric.

'Fabric first' is a term used in the construction industry to convey the idea that, when the goal is to reduce energy consumption, the first thing designers and builders should do is get the structure right. In other words, ensure the building fabric is designed to minimise energy consumption. This is exemplified by a building fabric that is highly insulated, thermal bridge free and airtight.

The fabric first principle is clear in the design of the two storey and three storey houses. The standard of thermal performance and airtightness detailing is far above that seen in the single storey house designed to meet the energy conservation requirements of the building regulations.

Hopefully, the benefits of building to a higher standard will become self evident as you read through this text and armed with this knowledge and understanding you will one day create comfortable, low energy homes.

SECTION 1

DESIGN: CONTEXT

Chapter 1 Sustainability

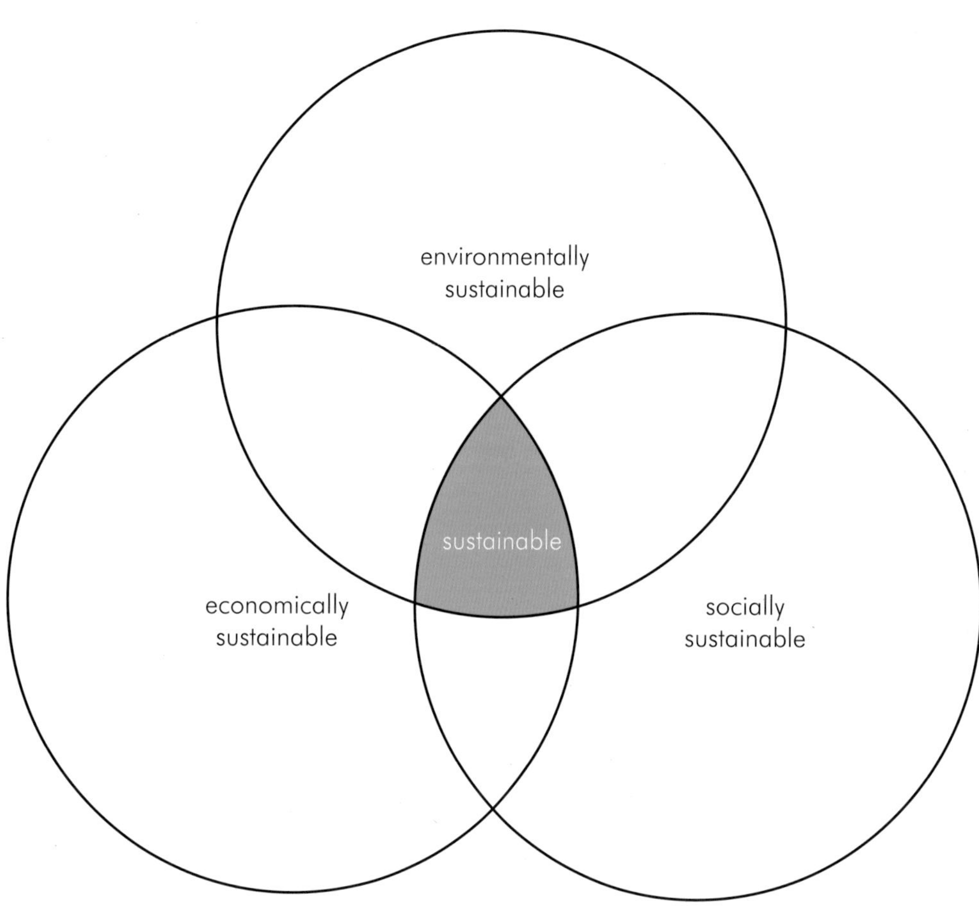

In the past, architects could design buildings that relied on cheap energy that they thought would never run out, and they did so unaware of the damage that carbon emissions cause. They could also use materials from anywhere in the world. They could make these design choices without having to worry about the impact their buildings were having on society or on the planet. This is no longer the case.

Architects are now working in the 'green age'. They are limited by new regulations, a scarcity of resources and high expectations from the people for whom they are designing. The challenge facing today's architects is to build beautiful, functional buildings using materials and resources that are increasingly scarce and expensive.

Sustainability

Sustainability is the capacity to endure. Something is sustainable if you can keep doing it the way you are doing it now without causing harm to society, the environment or the economy.

Sustainability is central to how we design, construct and use buildings. Everyday life takes place in buildings; homes, schools, offices, hospitals, stadiums, theatres and lots of other types of building. We work and socialise in buildings and when we are not in buildings we are often travelling on roads and other built infrastructure.

Today's society is totally reliant on buildings and yet the planet cannot continue to support the level of resources consumed to make this possible. Around half of all non-renewable resources consumed across the planet are used in construction, making it one of the least sustainable industries in the world.

Estimate of global resources used in buildings	
Resource	**%**
Energy	45–50
Water	50
Materials for buildings and roads (by bulk)	60
Agricultural land loss to buildings	80
Timber products for construction	60 (90% of hardwoods)
Coral reef destruction	50 (indirect)
Rainforest destruction	25 (indirect)

1.01 Global resource consumption associated with buildings.

Estimate of global pollution that can be attributed to buildings	
Pollution	**%**
Air quality (cities)	23
Global warming gases	50
Drinking water pollution	40
Landfill waste	50
Ozone thinning	50

1.02 Global pollution associated with buildings.

Sustainability is a complex concept that addresses many interconnected ideas and practices. One of the fundamental concepts is the long-term nature of built structures and their impact on the planet. Buildings are around for a long time so they have long-term impacts. This is similar to the idea that, a bit like when a person is injured, damage can be done in moments but can take a long time to repair.

Typical life expectancy of different aspects of construction	
Building finishes	10 years
Building services	20 years
Buildings	50+ years
Infrastructure (roads, railways)	100+ years
Cities	500+ years

1.03 The long-term impact of buildings.

DEFINITION

Sustainability
An activity is sustainable if it meets the needs of people today without compromising the ability of future generations to meet their own needs.

There are three areas that are usually identified as being fundamental to sustainable development:

- environmental sustainability
- economic sustainability
- social sustainability.

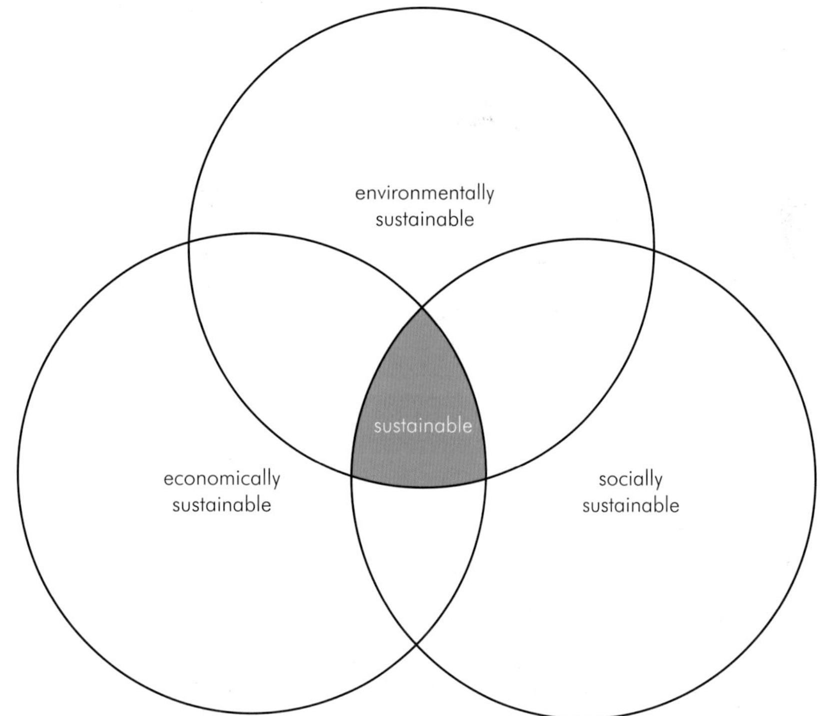

1.04 The three main elements of sustainability.

Sustainable design of buildings

Sustainable design aims to provide a high quality of indoor environment in a way that provides economic prosperity, social progress and environmental protection. Foster & Partners (the world-famous architects) define sustainable design as creating 'buildings which are energy-efficient, healthy, comfortable, flexible in use and designed for long life'.

Sustainable design (also known as 'green building') is a broad concept that considers the impact of a building in several ways, including:

- use of resources – the impact of choosing between different construction materials (e.g. timber, steel or concrete) and between different energy sources (e.g. oil, gas or renewables) and land and water resources
- environment – the construction of new homes must not harm the natural environment (including soil, water, vegetation and the atmosphere); they must be built with environmentally friendly materials and processes and should have low energy consumption and low CO_2 emissions
- society – new homes in urban areas must be part of well-designed neighbourhoods that include a mixture of types of home that are visitable by all (e.g. wheelchair users), with schools, shops, etc. nearby

- economy – new homes must be affordable to build and maintain, and they must also be affordable to live in. This means low energy consumption (lighting and heating costs) and controlled use of water.

If the homes we build in the future are to be sustainable, we will need to think about the bigger picture. This includes the location and orientation of a building, its function and flexibility, its form, structure and life span, its heating and cooling, the materials used; plus the impact that all these elements have on the amount of energy required to build and maintain it and travel to and from it. Only when all of these things are factored in can a home be designed to be sustainable.

Self-assessment sustainability toolkit for architecture students

Theme	Topic	Score	Multiplier	Sub-total
Energy	Orientation		x 4	
	Climate and shelter		x 3	
	Super-insulation		x 3	
	Glazing area		x 3	
	Passive solar gain		x 3	
	Passive solar cooling		x 3	
	Renewable energy		x 4	
	Heat recovery		x 3	
Materials	Waste minimisation		x 2	
	Local sourcing		x 2	
	Re-use (of buildings)		x 3	
	Recycling (of parts)		x 3	
	Embodied energy		x 2	
	Maintenance		x 2	
Resources (land)	Brownfield site		x 2	
	Density		x 3	
	Avoidance of flood plains		x 2	
Resources (water)	Low-water appliances		x 2	
	Grey water recycling		x 2	
	Rainwater collection		x 2	
	SUDS		x 2	
Access	Disabled		x 2	
	Public transport		x 2	
	Cycling		x 2	
	Walking		x 2	
Health	Natural materials		x 2	
	Natural vegetation		x 2	
	Natural light		x 2	
	Stress		x 1	
	Contact with nature		x 1	
Total				

1.05 Sustainability checklist developed by Brian Edwards.

ACTIVITIES

Is the fuel used to heat your home sustainable? Discuss this issue with your classmates. Think about:

- **The environmental test:** Does the fuel produce greenhouse gases which are causing climate change?
- **The social test:** Does the fuel used have a negative impact on society? (Many oil companies have a poor record of exploiting local indigenous people, for example.)
- **The economic test:** Will the fuel continue to get more expensive as it gets more scarce? Will ordinary people be able to afford it?

ACTIVITIES

Creating sustainable buildings involves design, materials and construction. But it also involves how those buildings are used, including how we travel to and from them.

Think about how you get to school each day. Under the three sustainability headings, list and discuss the reasons why your mode of transport is (or isn't) sustainable. Is there a sustainable alternative?

REVISION EXERCISES

1 Write a short summary outlining the impact of the construction of homes on the natural environment.

2 Define the term *sustainability* and give an example of:

a) sustainable travel

b) sustainable energy

c) sustainable use of land.

3 Describe the three principles of sustainability.

4 Outline the factors to be taken into account when designing 'green' buildings.

5 Discuss, using five examples, simple steps that you could take to make your home more sustainable.

CHAPTER 2 Energy Resources and Carbon Dioxide Emissions

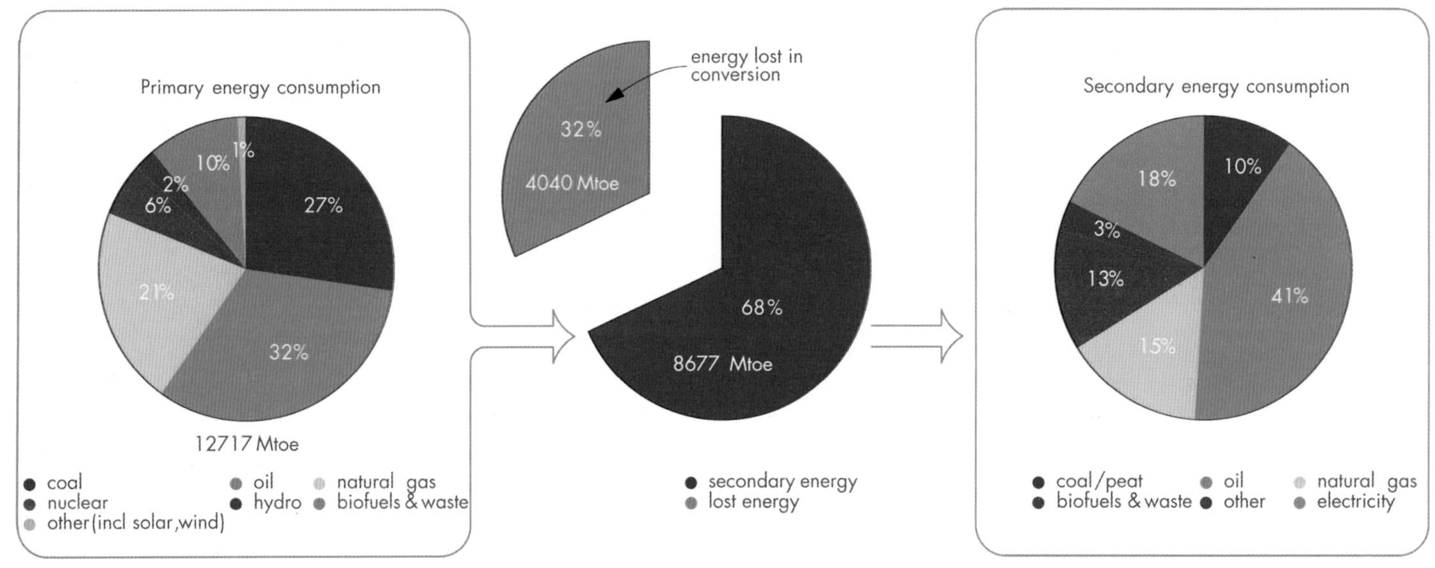

It is important to be aware of the place in which we build homes. The world is a small place and everyday decisions made by ordinary people living in Ireland have an impact on the welfare of the planet and on the lives of people living in other, often poorer, countries.

Our impact on the planet

Humankind is doing irreversible damage to the planet. This damage involves a number of interconnected issues including population growth, energy consumption, water scarcity, global warming and climate change.

Weblink
Population clock
www.census.gov/popclock/

Population growth

World population has exploded in recent years. A person born in 1927 was one of two billion people on earth; a person born in 1999 was one of six billion. The global population will be 9 billion by 2045 and will stabilise at just above 10 billion persons around 2100. Continuing growth in population will increase pressure on the world's food and water supplies, the natural environment and energy resources. Ireland's population has grown by over 64% over the past 50 years.

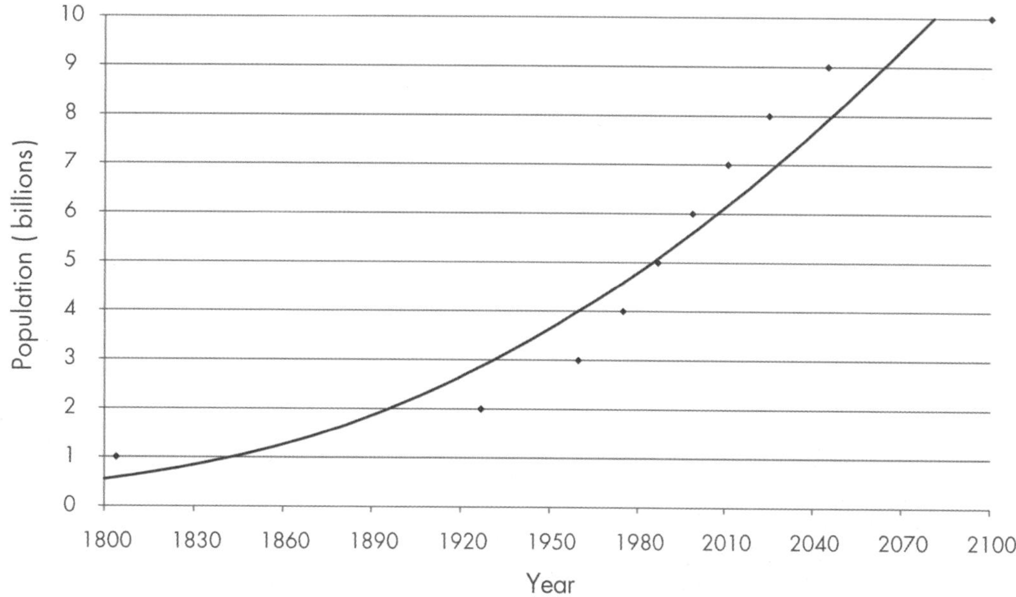

2.01Growth of the world's population (including estimation up to 2050).

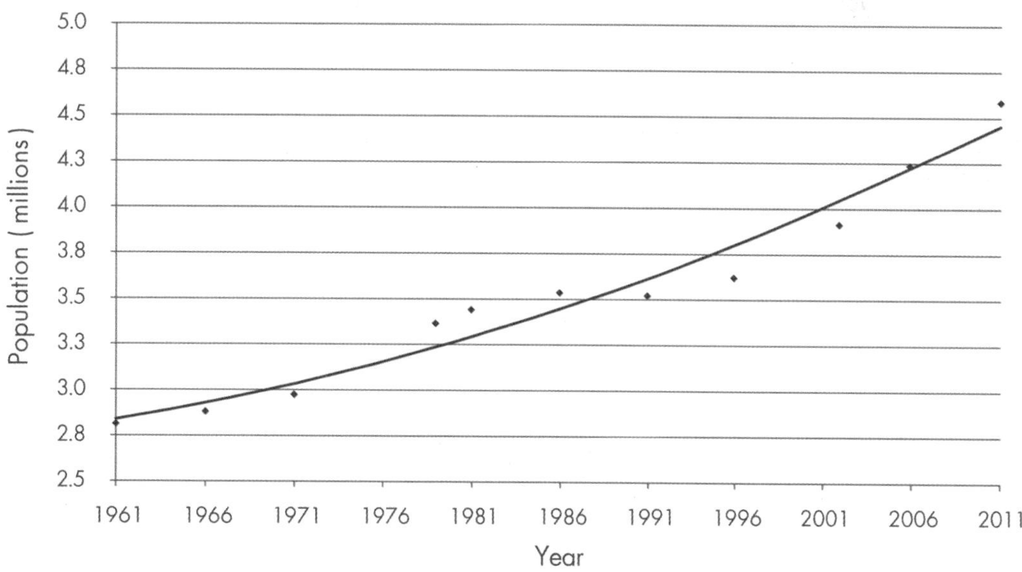

2.02 Ireland's population from 1961 to 2011. All of these people need homes and the resources required for everyday life, such as energy, food and water.

Anthropogenic carbon dioxide increase

Human activities since the Industrial Revolution (c.1850) have caused increasing levels of greenhouse gases in the atmosphere. Burning carbon-based fuels (e.g. coal, oil, natural gas, wood) for factories, homes and vehicles produces greenhouse gases, particularly carbon dioxide (CO_2). In May 2013 the level of carbon dioxide in the atmosphere reached 400 parts per million (ppm) for the first time since recording began in 1955.

Weblink
Current weekly CO_2 level
www.esrl.noaa.gov/gmd/ccgg/trends/weekly.html

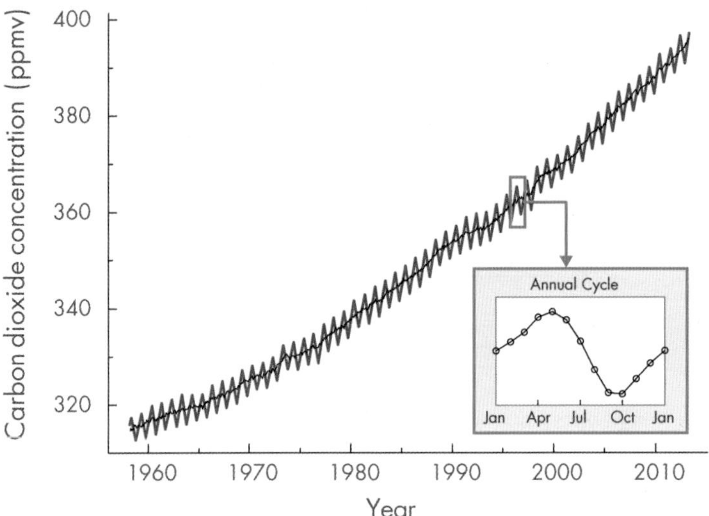

2.03 The Keeling curve of atmospheric CO_2 concentrations measured at the Mauna Loa Observatory, Hawaii.

Global warming

Global warming refers to the recent and ongoing rise in global average temperature near the Earth's surface. It is caused mostly by increasing concentrations of greenhouse gases in the atmosphere trapping more heat and amplifying the warming of the planet (the greenhouse effect).

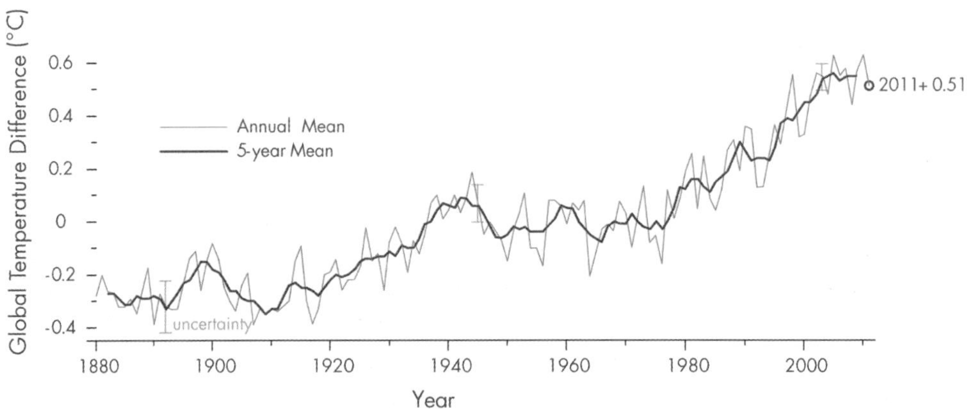

2.04 This graph from NASA, compiled from weather data from more than 1,000 meteorological stations around the world, satellite observations of sea surface temperature and Antarctic research station measurements, shows the gradual increase in average surface temperature.

While average global temperature fluctuates from year to year, scientists focus on the 10-year trend. Nine of the 10 warmest years, since records began in 1880, have occurred since the year 2000. In order to avoid dangerous climate change, average global surface temperature must not increase by more than 2°C over the pre-industrial average.

Climate change

Climate change refers to major changes in temperature, precipitation, or wind patterns, among other effects, that occur over several decades or longer.

Future changes are expected to:

- increase earth's average temperature
- influence the patterns and amounts of precipitation
- reduce ice and snow cover, as well as permafrost
- raise sea level
- increase the acidity of the oceans.

These changes will have a detrimental effect on food supplies, water resources, infrastructure, ecosystems, human health and quality of life. The magnitude and rate of future climate change will primarily depend on the rate at which levels of greenhouse gas concentrations in our atmosphere continue to increase. This depends on the decisions that ordinary people make every day. Some of these decisions have long-term impacts, for example choosing to design and build a more energy-efficient home.

Energy

There are several issues of concern in relation to energy and the sustainability of the way in which homes continue to be designed and built in Ireland. From an environmental perspective, the residential sector is responsible for significant carbon dioxide emissions. Economically, residential energy costs have doubled in recent years and many families are finding it harder to pay their energy bills. Socially, there are many people in Ireland living in energy poverty – this adds to inequality in society and is morally wrong.

Primary and secondary energy

Primary energy demand is one of the key indicators used when measuring the energy performance of a building. The amount of primary energy a building is allowed to consume is limited in the building regulations and in the Passivhaus standard.

Primary energy is energy in its natural form, for example:

- oil
- coal
- natural gas
- uranium
- solar
- wind
- wave.

These raw fuels and other forms of energy can be converted into usable forms of energy called secondary energy. Examples of secondary energy include fuel oil (e.g. kerosene, diesel) and electricity. The conversion of primary energy sources into secondary energy consumes energy as the raw fuel has to be extracted, refined and transported from where it is produced to where it is consumed. Approximately one-third of world energy supplies are lost in conversion from primary energy to secondary energy.

Each form of energy has an energy conversion factor that describes how much primary energy is required to provide a single unit of secondary energy. For most forms of energy this factor is low: for every unit of secondary energy consumed, 1.1 units of primary energy are required.

However, electricity that is produced in a coal-burning power station has a high conversion factor because of the high level of energy consumed to mine the coal, transport it (e.g. from Poland) and convert the energy in the coal into electricity. Energy is used at every step of this process. For electricity the conversion factor is 2.4: for every unit of electricity consumed in the home, approximately 2.4 units of primary energy are required.

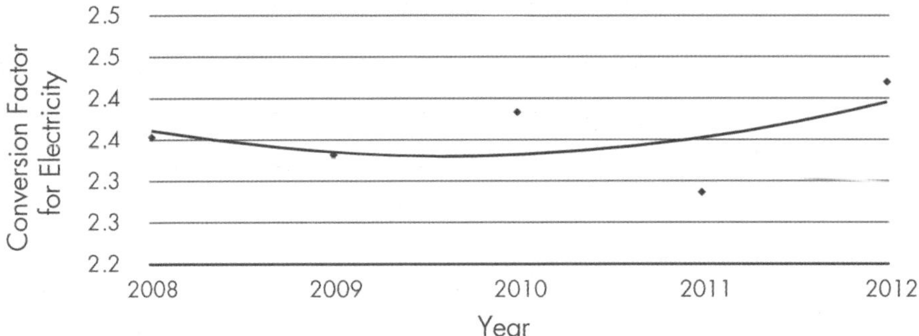

2.05 Conversion factor for electricity (2008–2012).

Worldwide fossil fuel dependency

Carbon-based fuels (e.g. oil, coal and gas) are the primary source of energy worldwide. Renewable energy (e.g. hydro, wind and solar) makes up less than 5% of global energy sources. The International Energy Agency forecasts that by 2035, carbon-based fuels will still represent 75% of the principal energy sources worldwide. Almost one-third of world primary energy is lost in conversion to secondary energy.

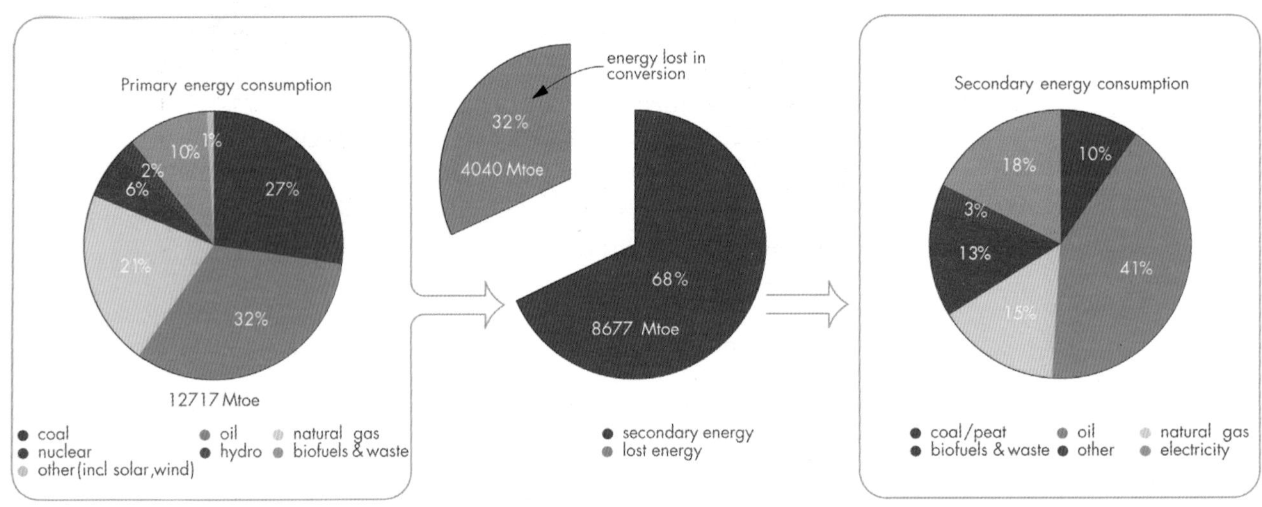

2.06 World energy consumption in 2010, measured in Mtoe (million tonnes of oil equivalent). One Mtoe is the amount of energy produced by burning one million tonnes of crude oil. *Source:* International Energy Agency.

Ireland's energy consumption and carbon dioxide emissions

Over 90% of Ireland's primary energy comes from fossil fuels. This leads to high levels of carbon dioxide emissions. The economic recession caused a dramatic decline in emissions and it is expected that total emissions will not rise above the peak 2009 levels before 2020. This provides Ireland with a window of opportunity to make the changes necessary to reduce carbon emissions in every sector, including the residential sector.

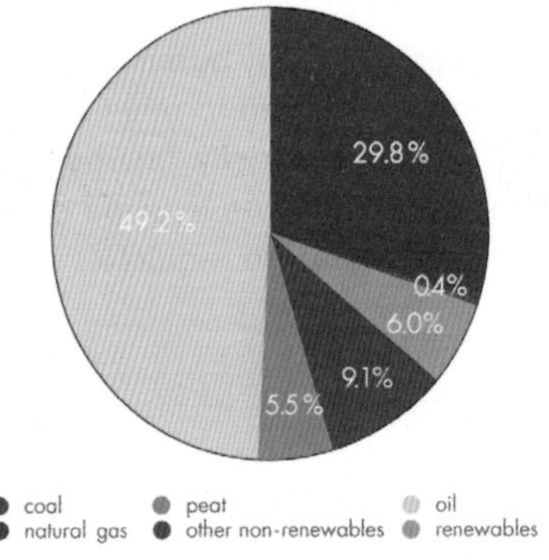

2.07 Ireland's primary energy supply (2011). *Source:* Sustainable Energy Authority of Ireland (SEAI).

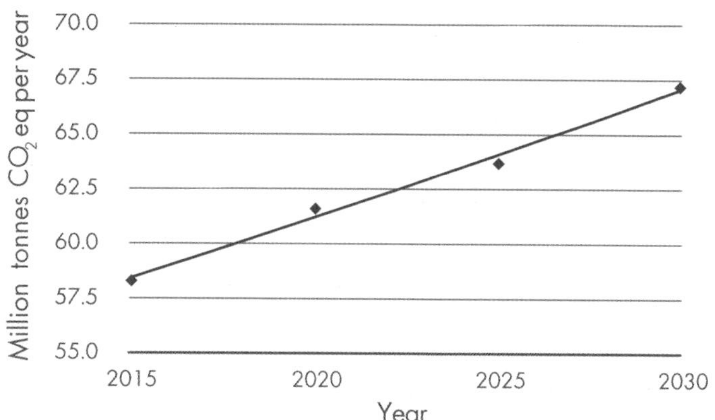

2.08 Ireland's carbon dioxide emissions are expected to rise in the future. *Source:* ESRI.

Residential energy consumption and carbon dioxide emissions

The residential sector (houses, apartments, flats, etc.) is a major consumer of Ireland's energy and a significant contributor to our carbon emissions problem. Housing consumes just over a quarter of all energy used in Ireland and produces just over a quarter of energy-related carbon emissions.

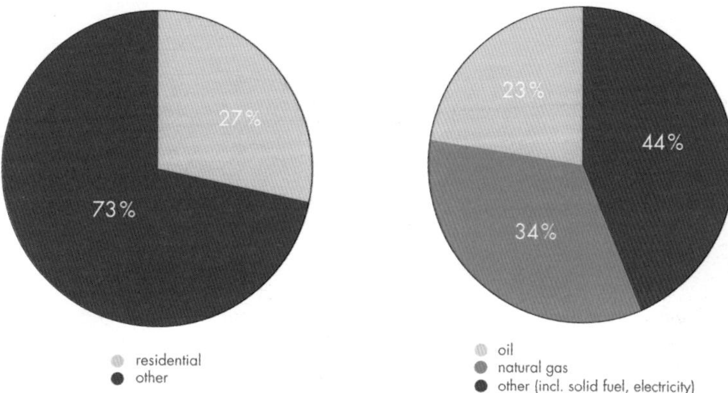

2.09 The residential sector is a big part of the energy consumption and carbon emissions problem.

2.10 Fuel used in heating systems in Ireland.

Ordinary people doing everyday things at home are responsible for a major portion of Ireland's energy consumption and associated carbon emissions. The goal in the future must be to design and build more energy-efficient homes that are less reliant on carbon-based fuels to provide a comfortable indoor environment. This will reduce overall carbon emissions.

Over 98% of homes in Ireland have a central heating system.[1] Of these, almost four out of five (78%) consume oil or natural gas. The carbon dioxide emissions caused by burning heating oil are 25% higher than those caused by burning natural gas. Also oil is much more expensive than natural gas, per kilowatt hour of energy supplied for space heating. This has environmental and economic implications for the sustainability of Ireland's rural communities where oil is the only practical energy source.

[1] 26,390 homes do not have central heating. The total number of permanent private dwellings is 1,649,408. *Source:* Census 2011.

Fuel	gCO_2/kWh
natural gas	205
oil (kerosene)	257
coal	341
peat (briquettes)	356
electricity*	489

2.11 Carbon dioxide emissions. The amount of carbon dioxide emitted varies by fuel type.
* Varies from year to year depending on the fuel mix used at the power generation stations.

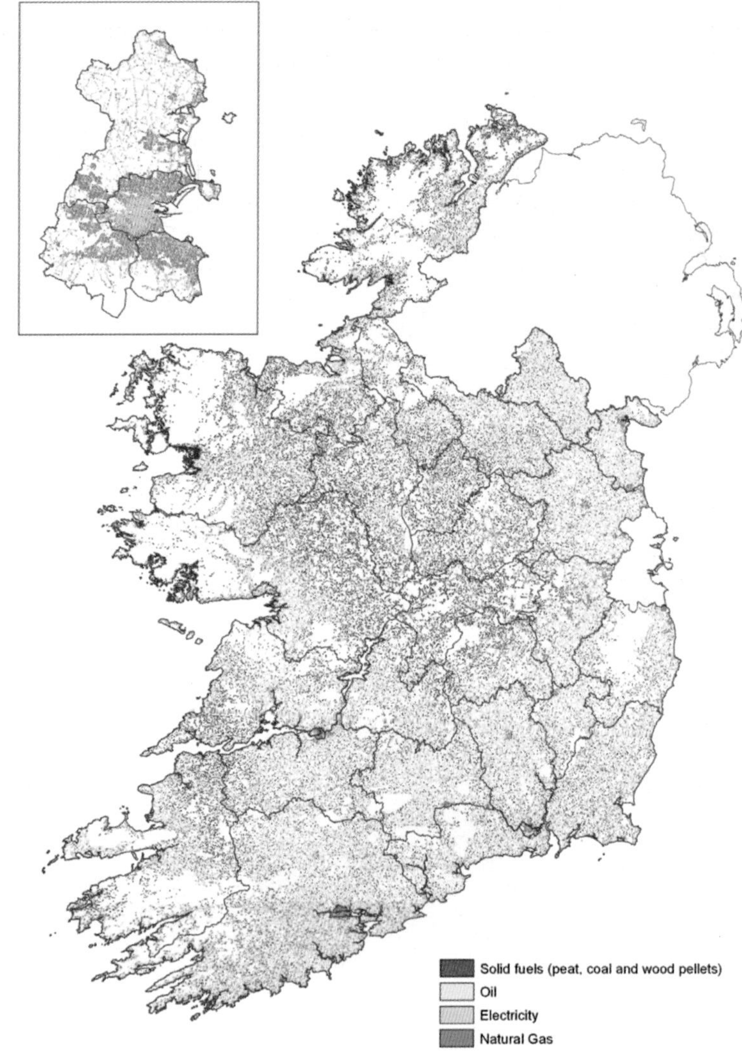

2.12 Fuel used in central heating systems in Ireland (2011). This map highlights the use of gas in urban areas and the consumption of oil and solid fuels in rural areas. *Source: CSO, The Roof Over Our Heads.*

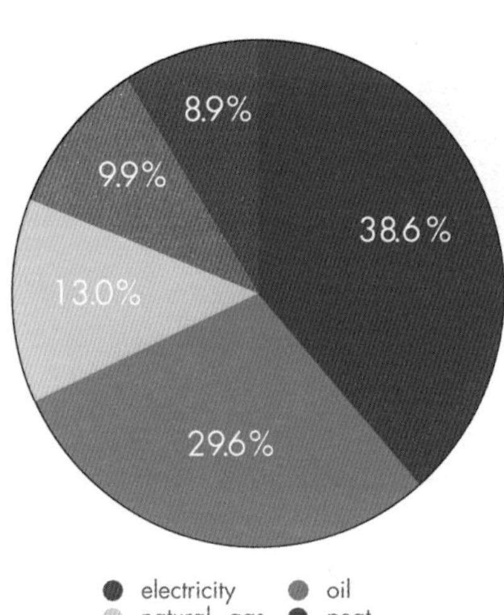

2.13 Residential energy-related CO_2 emissions by fuel (2011). *Source:* SEAI.

Energy use in the home

The amount of energy used in the home, and how it is used, depends on:

- number of people per household
- type of fuel used in central heating systems
- number of light fittings and electrical appliances
- economic status (i.e. poor, wealthy)
- daily habits of the occupants.

An average home in Ireland consumes:

- almost 20,000 kWh of energy per annum, comprising:
  - approximately 5,000 kWh of electricity, and
  - almost 15,000 kWh of non-electrical consumption
- 166 kWh per square metre per annum (242 kWh primary energy equivalent):
  - 124 kWh non-electrical (136 kWh primary energy equivalent)
  - 42 kWh electricity (102 kWh primary energy equivalent).

ACTIVITIES

Discuss energy use in your home with the person who pays the bill. Examine a typical bill to determine the amount of energy consumed on a daily basis. Some utility companies allow customers to track their energy use online. If yours does, take a look at energy use over the past year and compare your home's use to the average figure.

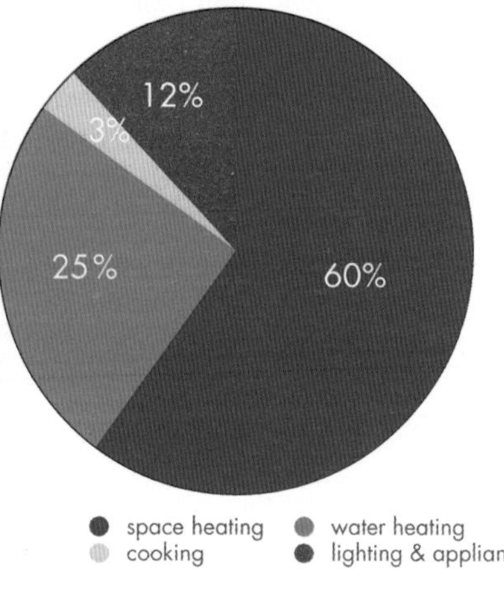

2.14 Energy use in the home.

The average dwelling is responsible for emitting 6.4 tonnes of energy-related CO_2 emissions. Of this, 3.9 tonnes of CO_2 (61%) is from direct fuel use and the remaining 2.5 tonnes is from electricity use.

In the average household, approximately 85% of the energy consumed is used for space heating and water heating. The amount of energy used in the home has increased over time because people like to keep their homes warmer than in the past – average indoor temperature has risen by approximately 5°C over the past 50 years. These changes mean that the residential sector is responsible for a greater proportion of Ireland's energy consumption than in the past. Designing homes that reduce the need to consume fossil fuels to meet the need for space and water heating is essential for the future.

Rising cost of home energy

The cost of energy doubled over the last decade. As the cost of energy continues to rise, it is becoming less economically sustainable to design and build homes that consume large amounts of energy to provide a comfortable and healthy living space.

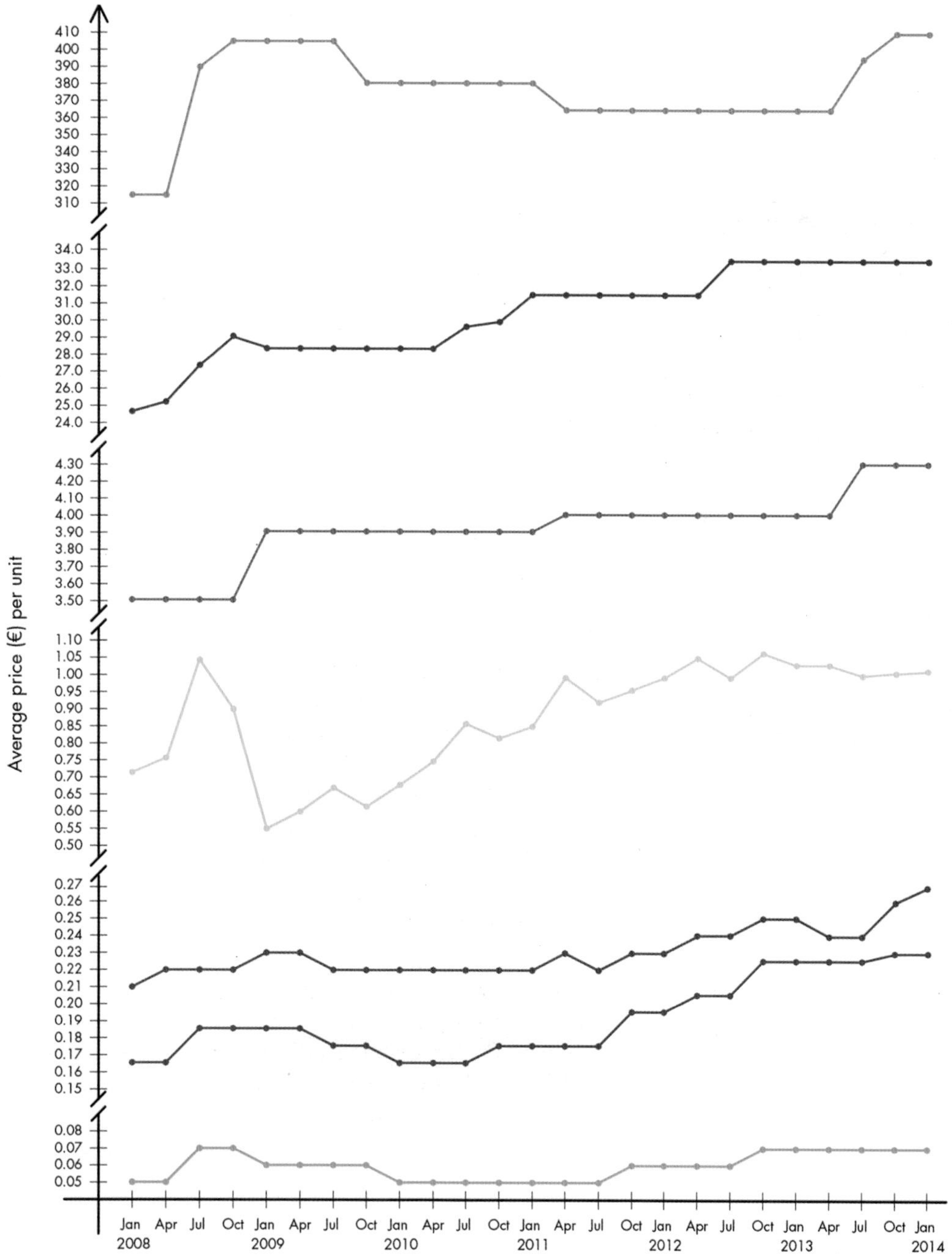

2.15 Residential energy costs 2008–2013: average price (€) per unit. *Source:* SEAI.

Energy poverty

Energy poverty, also known as fuel poverty, is the term used to describe a household's inability to attain an acceptable standard of warmth and energy services in the home at an affordable cost. In practical terms, energy poverty means that a household spends more than 10% of its disposable income on energy. (Disposable income includes all earnings and social benefits minus direct taxes.)

Energy poverty is caused by a combination of high fuel prices, low income and houses that are not energy efficient. It is the most vulnerable people in society who are at most risk by living in energy-hungry homes. For example, children living in cold homes are twice as likely to suffer from respiratory illnesses as those living in warm homes. There is also a strong link between older people dying during the winter and low thermal performance of housing and low indoor temperatures.

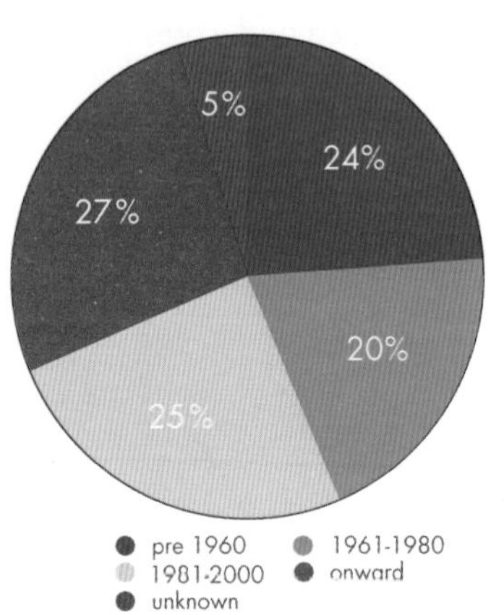

2.16 Housing stock by period of construction.

Building homes that are energy efficient protects people against future energy poverty. Unfortunately, many of the houses that have already been built in Ireland have been built to a very low standard, and they require lots of energy to provide comfort.

There are approximately two million housing units in Ireland. These consist of permanent private households, holiday homes, vacant houses and apartments. Approximately three-quarters of these homes were built before 2000. Around half of the housing stock was built before 1980. This is very significant because the government first introduced requirements for insulation in homes in 1979. Before then, it was common practice to build homes without any insulation in the external envelope (i.e. floor, walls or roof). Upgrading these two million homes to reduce the amount of energy required to make them comfortable and safe for the people who live in them is one of the greatest challenges of the future.

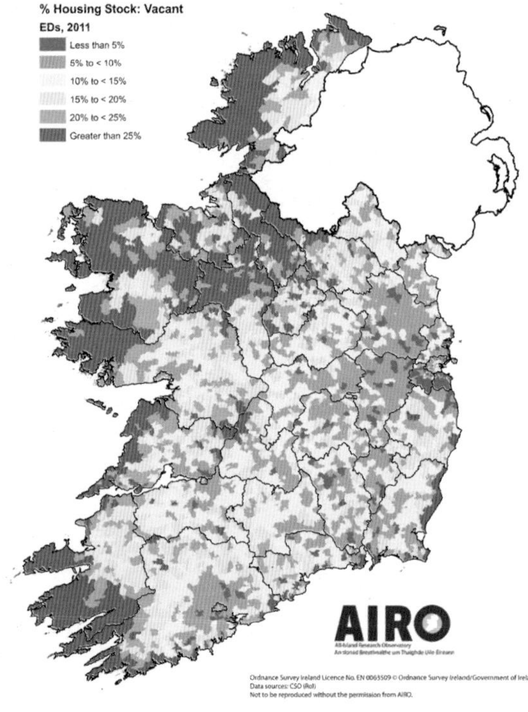

2.17 Unoccupied and unfinished homes in Ireland. *Source*: AIRO.

REVISION EXERCISES

1 Describe briefly the impact that increased carbon emissions are having on the planet.
2 Explain the difference between primary energy and secondary energy.
3 Explain how the housing sector is contributing to Ireland's carbon emissions problem.
4 Describe the factors that should be taken into account when choosing a fuel source for a central heating system.
5 Explain the link between energy poverty and the energy performance of housing.

Water Resources

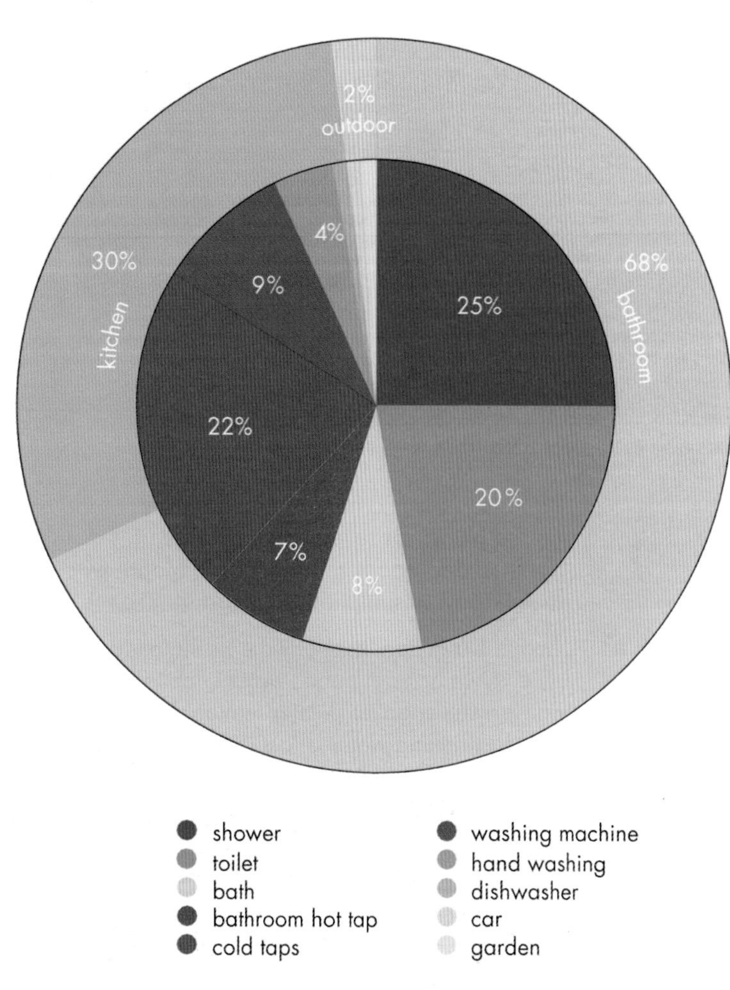

Water is essential to life and is one of our most precious natural renewable resources. It is becoming more and more common for homes in Ireland not to have a reliable supply of water. Future homes have to be designed to meet the needs of the occupants without consuming as much water.

Global water scarcity

Water scarcity is a general term used to describe problems providing a population with a secure source of water. Water use has been growing at more than twice the rate of population increase in the last century. According to the United Nations, around 1.2 billion people (almost one-fifth of the world's population) live in areas of water scarcity. A further 1.6 billion people (almost one-quarter of the world's population) face economic water shortage – this is where a country lacks the necessary infrastructure to take water from rivers and aquifers.

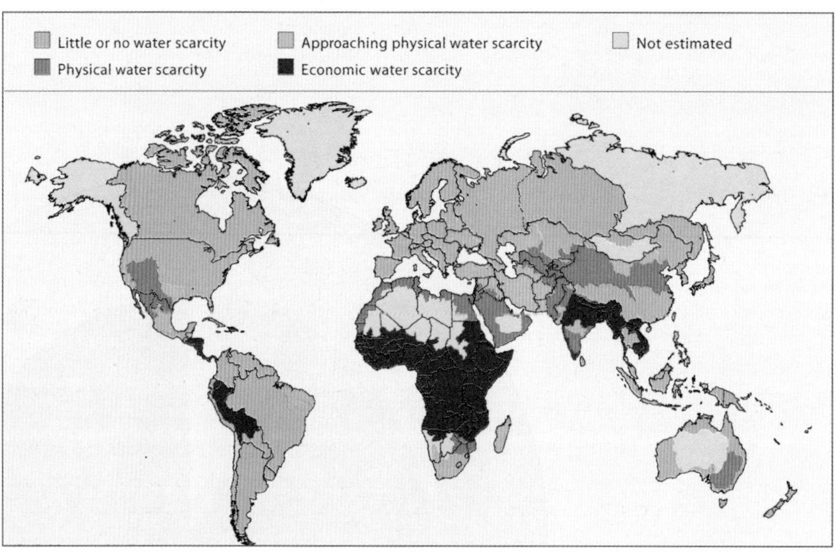

3.01 Global physical economic and water scarcity.

Water scarcity is a natural and a human-made phenomenon. While there is enough fresh water on the planet for seven billion people, it is distributed unevenly and too much of it is wasted, polluted and poorly managed. If a global water crisis is to be avoided, people will have to reduce their water consumption and learn to use the water they do consume more efficiently.

Water scarcity in Ireland

About 1.6 billion litres of water is supplied to Irish households every day. Four out of five people receive water from public water supplies; the rest are served by various group water schemes and private supplies. Water leakage is a serious problem in Ireland. Four out of every ten litres of treated drinking water is lost through leakage in the distribution system.

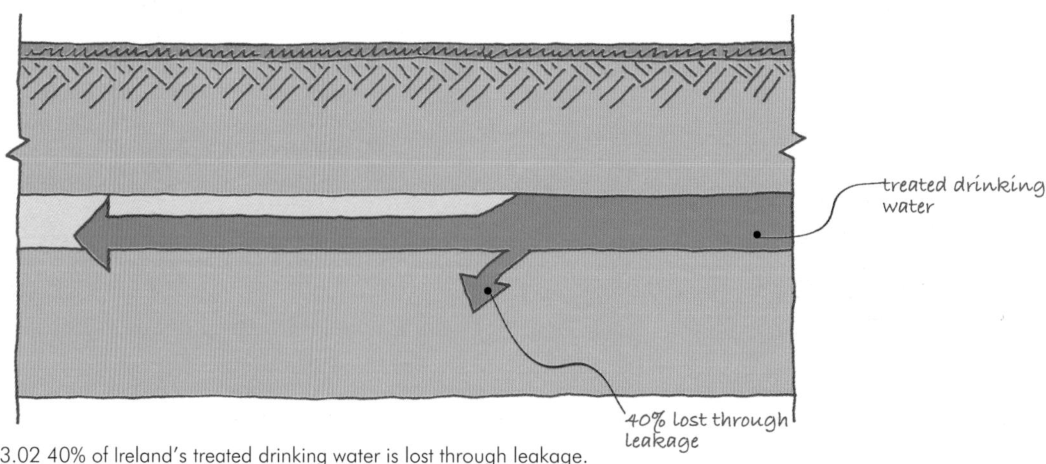

3.02 40% of Ireland's treated drinking water is lost through leakage.

In the future, changing patterns of rainfall will impact on the supply of drinking water and on the level of pollution and contamination in several ways, including:

- **during hot weather** – water shortages caused by drier summers, particularly in the south east
- **during cold weather** –
  - water freezes in the pipes, cutting off the supply – this can also cause pipes to burst
  - when the thaw sets in, the ground moves and pipes can be damaged
- **during wet weather** – flooding of sewage pipes in urban areas causes pollution of nearby rivers.

Water scarcity was significant during the flood events in November 2009 and in the freezing weather events in late 2010/early 2011. The 2010/11 winter was the longest period of severe cold weather in almost fifty years. Most local authorities had trouble maintaining normal supplies to the public. Demand was up to 25% greater than maximum water treatment capacity in most areas. In order to conserve supplies, many water services authorities had to cut off water supplies and reduce pressure in distribution systems, particularly at night. In areas where the supply was lost for an extended period, many people had to rely on tankers providing water.

SUPPLEMENTARY INFORMATION

During times of water shortages, orders can be made to stop or restrict the use of water supplies for:

- watering gardens, recreational parks or sports grounds
- washing cars and trailers (including by commercial carwash facilities)
- filling or replenishing swimming pools, ponds and lakes
- irrigating or spraying crops.

In theory, Ireland receives enough rainfall to meet the water needs of the population. However, the rain doesn't fall where it is needed: the least densely populated areas in the west of the country receive the most rainfall; the most densely populated areas in the east receive the least.

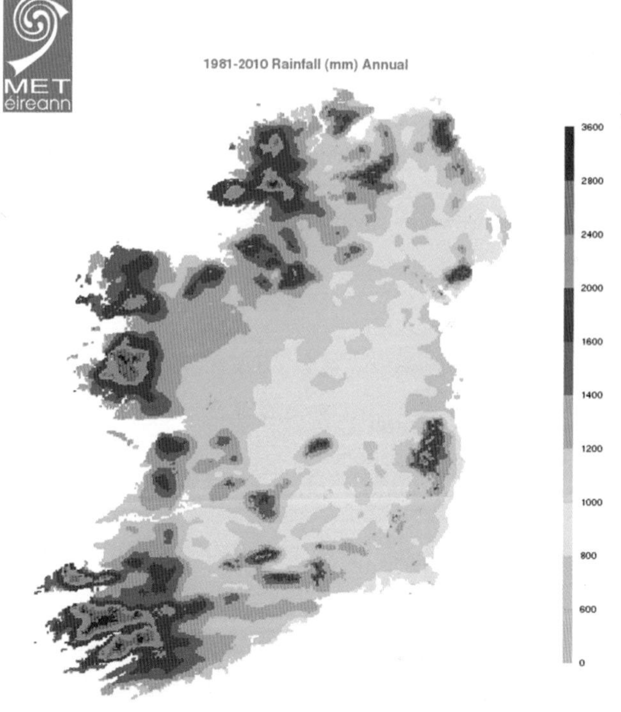

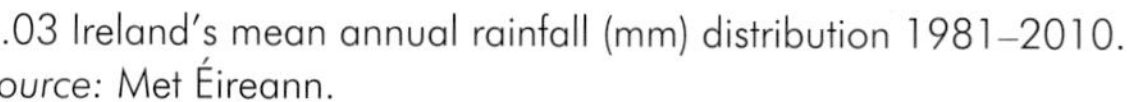
3.03 Ireland's mean annual rainfall (mm) distribution 1981–2010. *Source:* Met Éireann.

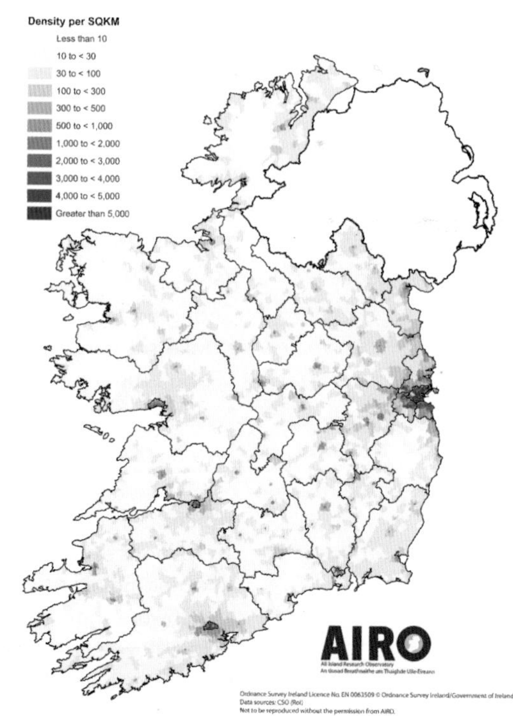

3.04 Ireland's population density (2011 Census). *Source:* AIRO.

Water consumption in the home

Water consumption varies enormously between households. It depends on the number of people in the household and their daily water use habits. The vast majority of water is used in the bathroom, with most water being used for showering and flushing toilets. Water consumption per person in Ireland is around 150 litres per day.

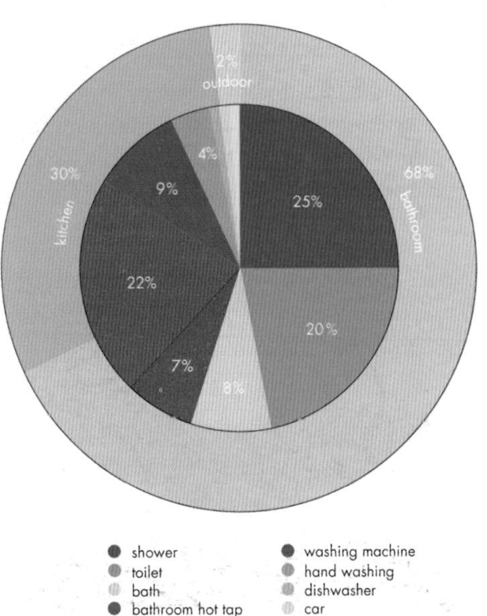

3.05 Water usage in a typical home.

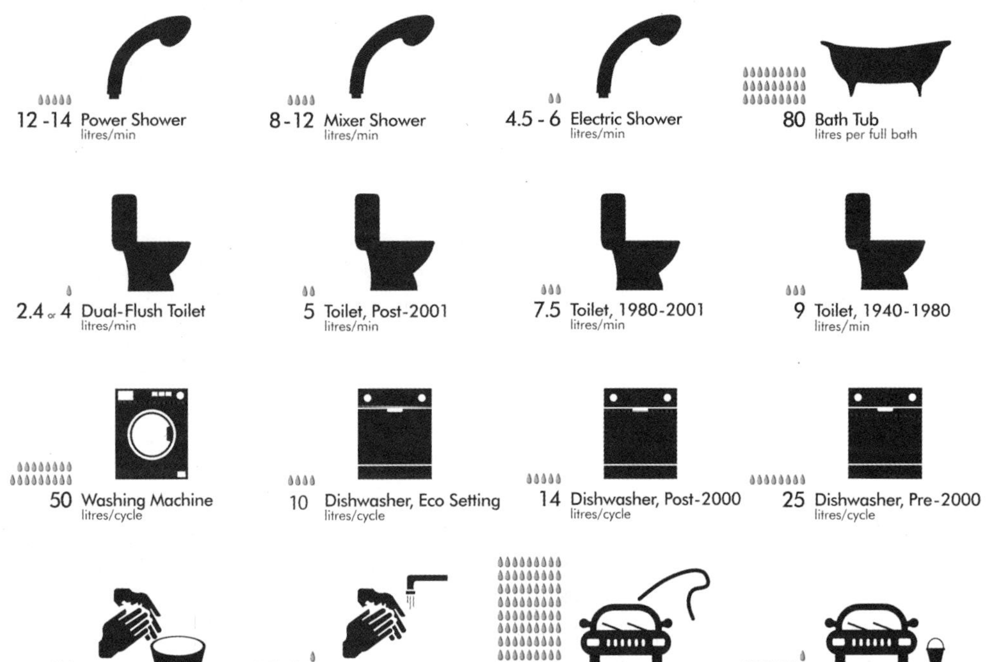

3.06 Typical water usage per appliance.

Weblink
Water usage calculator
www.taptips.ie/water-usage-calculator.html

Reducing water consumption

Changing everyday water use habits and installing water-saving appliances will reduce the amount of water a household consumes.

Behavioural measures

Changing these habits will reduce water consumption:

- take shorter showers
- don't run the tap when brushing teeth
- don't run a washing machine or dishwasher until it is full
- use the 'eco' setting on washing machines and dishwashers
- use a watering can or bucket instead of a hose for outdoor jobs.

Functional measures

Installing these devices will reduce water consumption:

- water meter
- rainwater harvesting
- low-flow 'eco' showers
- dual-flush toilets
- water-efficient appliances (e.g. washing machine, dishwasher)
- trigger valve/nozzle on garden hose.

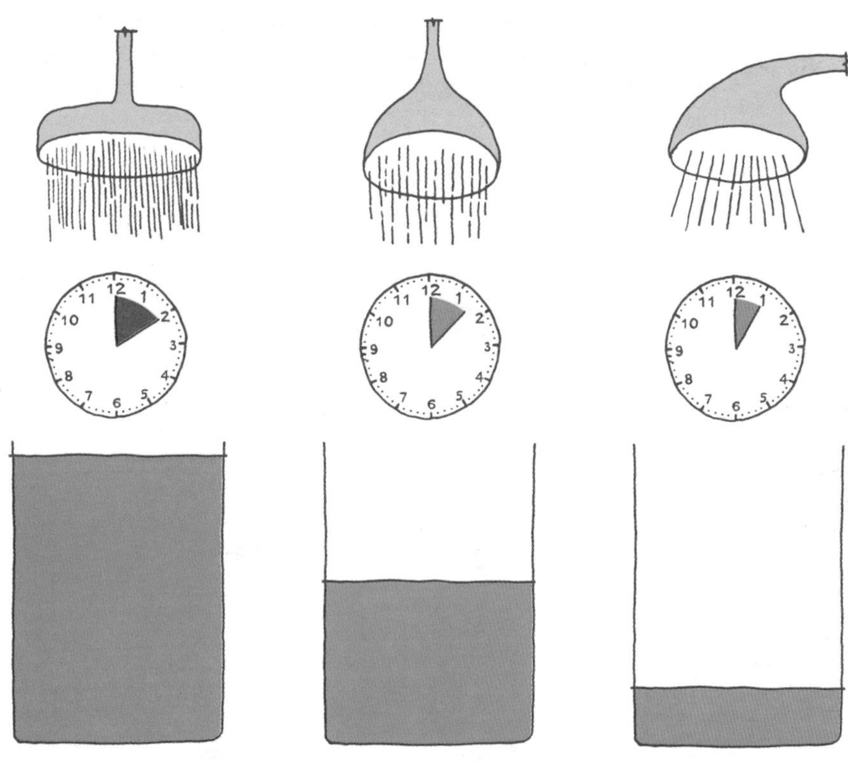

Type	Power shower	Mixer shower	'Eco' shower
Time	10 minutes	7.5 minutes	5 minutes
Flow rate	13 litres/minute	10 litres/minute	5 litres/minute
Water use	130 litres	75 litres	25 litres

3.07 Water consumption: the type of shower and time spent in the shower determines the amount of water used.

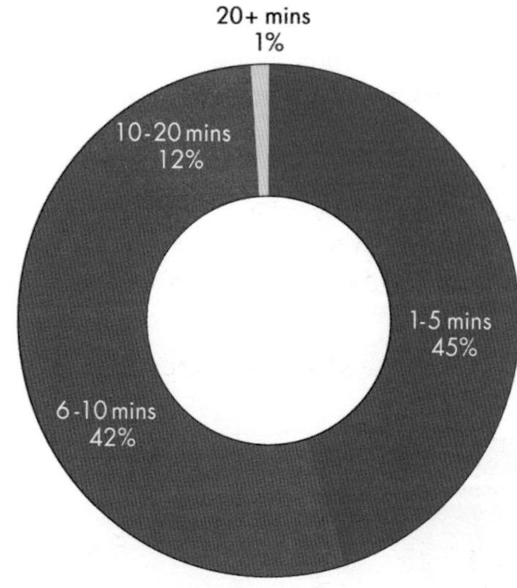

3.08 Average time spent in the shower.

Toilets are the second highest water-using device after showers. One-fifth of a typical household's water is flushed down the toilet. The average person flushes the toilet about 5 times per day or 1,825 times per year. Upgrading a standard toilet to a dual-flush mechanism could cut water use in half.

ACTIVITIES

Examine the toilet cisterns in your home. Figure out how much water is used per flush and calculate your household's annual water consumption.

Type	Traditional Single flush	Standard Single flush	Dual flush
Flow rate	9 litres per flush	6 litres per flush	2.6–4litres per flush
Water used	16,425 litres*	10,950 litres*	5,767 litres**

* based on 5 flushes per day ** based on 3 low flushes and 2 full flushes per day

3.09 Toilet flush volumes per year.

Water metering

Before the introduction of water metering in 2013, Ireland was the only country in the 'developed world' whose citizens did not pay directly for the water they use at home.

It is important that consumers are aware of the value of the water they use. The evidence from other countries shows that, on average, households that pay for their water use 10% less than households that don't. Put simply, water metering reduces water consumption.

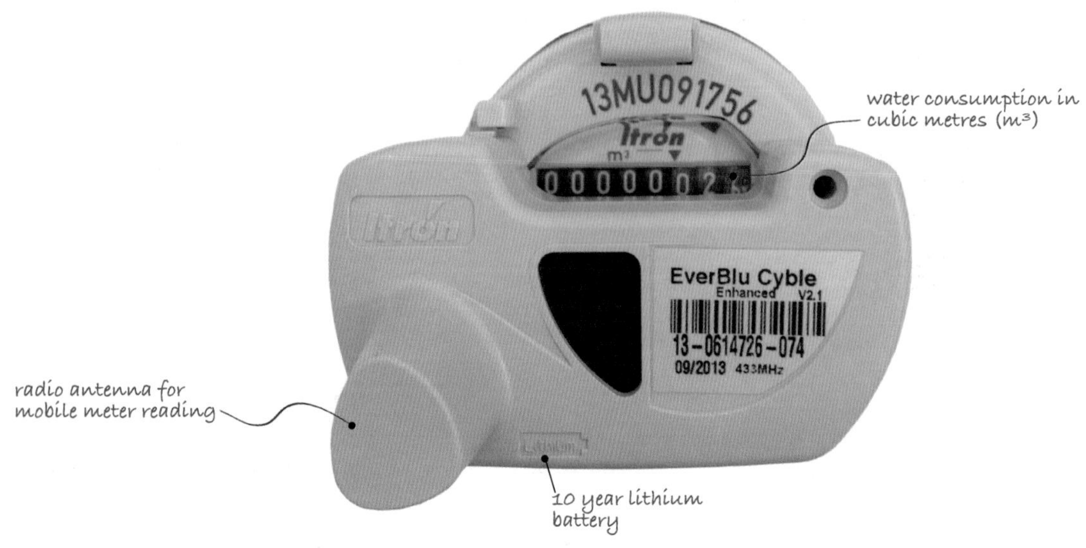

3.10 Water meters measure water consumption in cubic metres (i.e. 1,000 litres).

Measuring water consumption and charging consumers for the water they use has several benefits, including:

- creating awareness of the amount of water being consumed
- reducing water consumption
- giving consumers the information required to regulate their water use
- encouraging consumers to tackle leakages on their property
- balancing the cost so that those who use most pay most.

Every household connected to a public water supply pays for the water they consume. For houses, an individual meter measures how much water is consumed. For flats and apartments, a single meter measures consumption for the group and each household receives a flat rate bill. Approximately one million Irish households have individual meters; the remaining 600,000 have group metering.

Hot water, energy consumption and carbon emissions

Having a reliable, clean supply is only part of the water challenge. Every time a hot water tap is turned on, money is spent, carbon emissions are created and water reserves are depleted. Heating water is the second largest source of energy use in the home (after space heating). The energy used to heat water for devices and appliances emits an average of 970kg of carbon dioxide per household per year. This is equivalent to the carbon dioxide emissions from driving more than 3,170 kilometres in a typical family car.

3.11 Carbon emissions from water heating and water using electrical appliances in the home.
Source: Energy Savings Trust, UK.

Appliance	Temperature (°C)	Temperature rise
Mains	13.4	
Shower	41.0	27.6
Basin hot	55.0	41.6
Kitchen sink hot	55.0	41.4
Bath	44.0	30.6

REVISION EXERCISES

1 Explain the concept of water scarcity.
2 Outline why water scarcity is a problem in Ireland.
3 Describe three low-cost measures that you could be taken to reduce water consumption in your home.
4 Outline the three most effective measures that can be taken to reduce water consumption in the home.
5 Discuss the benefits of water metering.

Urban Design

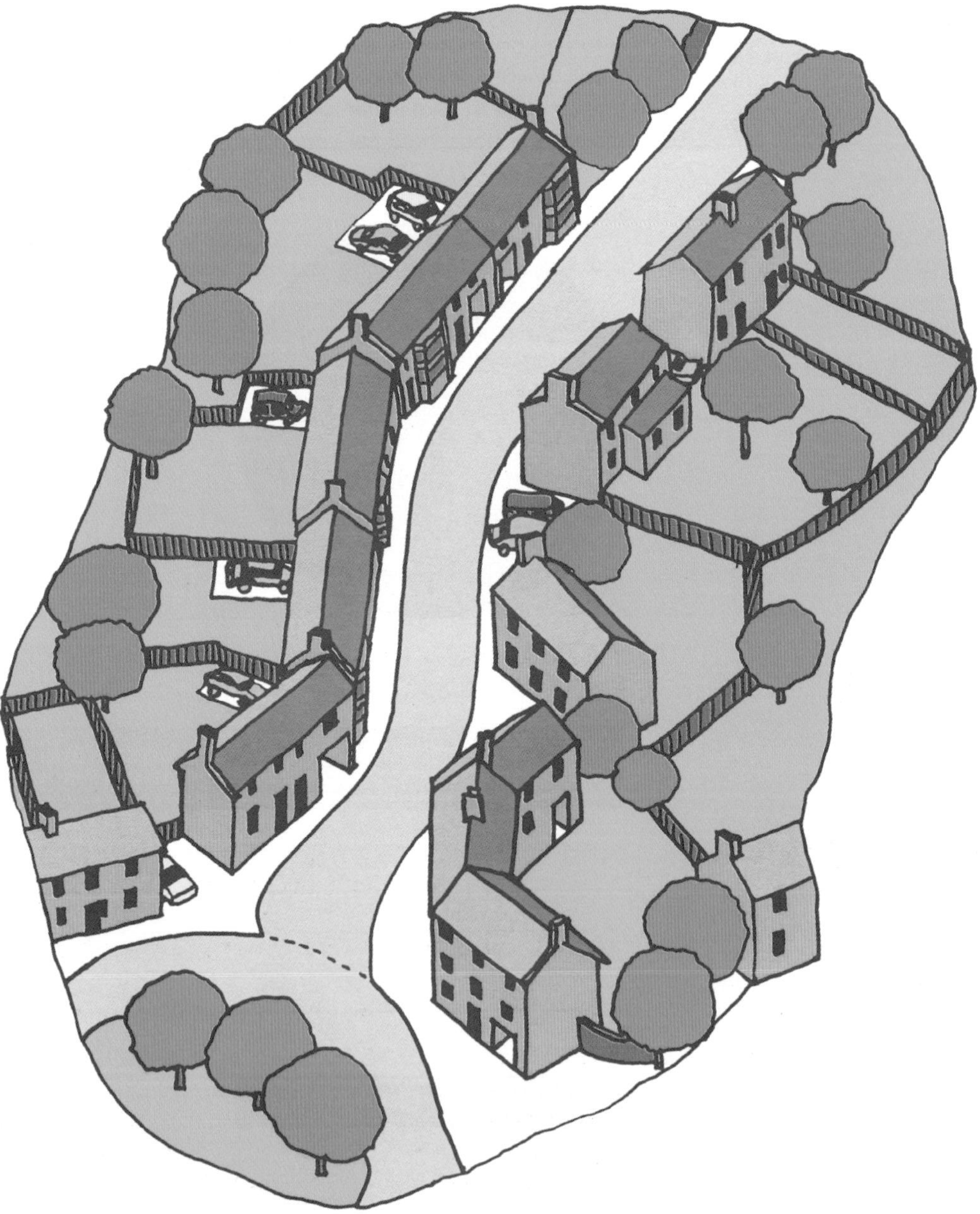

Today 50% of the world's population live in urban areas; by 2040 75% of the world's population will live in urban areas. It is essential that urban centres are thoughtfully designed so as to encourage sustainable lifestyles and provide a high quality of life.

Designing a new area in an urban setting happens on three levels:

1 neighbourhood – the 'big picture' factors, including how well the new neighbourhood will fit into and connect with the existing buildings and infrastructure (e.g. paths, cycle lanes, roads, railways)
2 site – the layout and organisation of the development including the public spaces
3 home – the design of the individual homes and their curtilage.

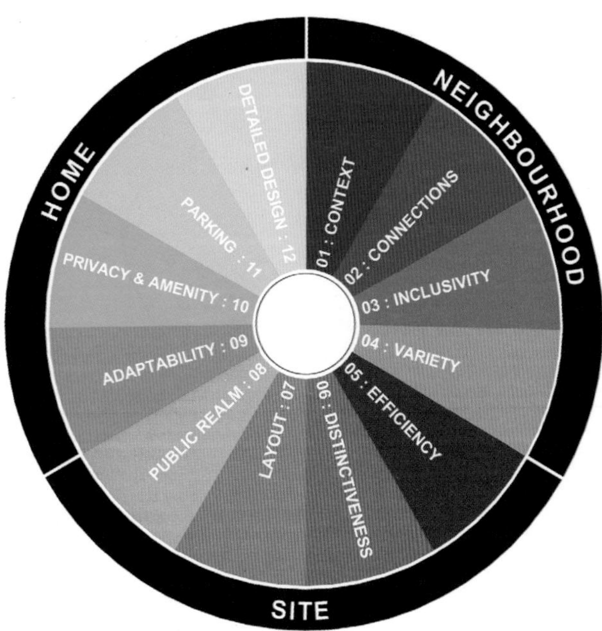

4.01 Urban design: there are 12 criteria to be considered when designing a new neighbourhood. *Source:* Department of the Environment, Heritage and Local Government (2009), *Urban Design Manual: A Best Practice Guide.*

Neighbourhood

There are four elements in neighbourhood design:

1 context
2 connections
3 inclusivity
4 variety.

ACTIVITIES

Talk to someone who uses a bicycle (instead of a car) about the practicalities of living life 'on two wheels'. Prepare a list of questions that you could ask him/her.

Context

Building in context is about ensuring that the design responds to its setting. To do this the development should:

- look as though it has evolved naturally from the surrounding area
- add to the character of the area
- not overpower the existing buildings.

Connections

Making connections is about having easy access to services and amenities that are used regularly (e.g. schools, shops, cinemas, parks, playgrounds, pubs, gyms, health clinics). These links should be convenient and safe to use. They include pedestrian and cycle paths as well as bus routes and connections to train links. Everyday facilities should be within a reasonable distance to encourage residents to walk or cycle.

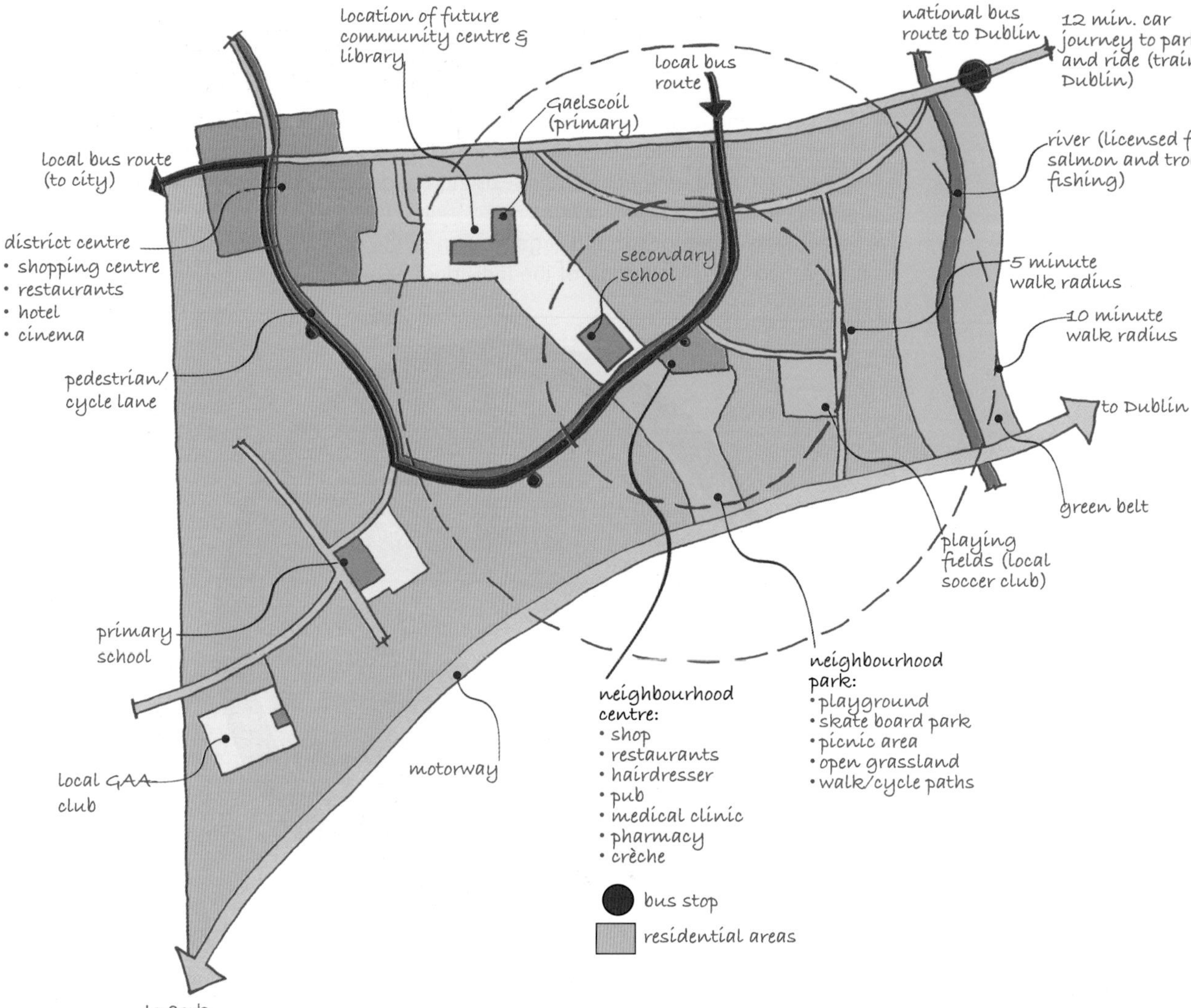

4.02 Connections: this suburban neighbourhood in Castletroy, Limerick has been gradually developed on a green field site over the past 10 years. It includes everyday facilities that are within a 10-minute walk of most homes. (Average adult walking speed on a level surface is approx. 5km/h or 83m/minute.)

Inclusivity

Inclusivity is an important concept that describes the ability of all people to use the neighbourhood on equal terms. This isn't just about providing access for people with a disability; it is about meeting the needs of all people irrespective of ability. This is achieved by designing public spaces that are open and accessible to all. The construction of housing should not create physical or visual barriers that exclude people – and this includes privately managed spaces.

KEY PRINCIPLES

To be inclusive an area should:

- have a mix of homes (detached houses, semi-detached houses, apartments)
- have a layout that is easy to access
- have a range of public, communal and private spaces
- ensure that public spaces are accessible and open to everyone.

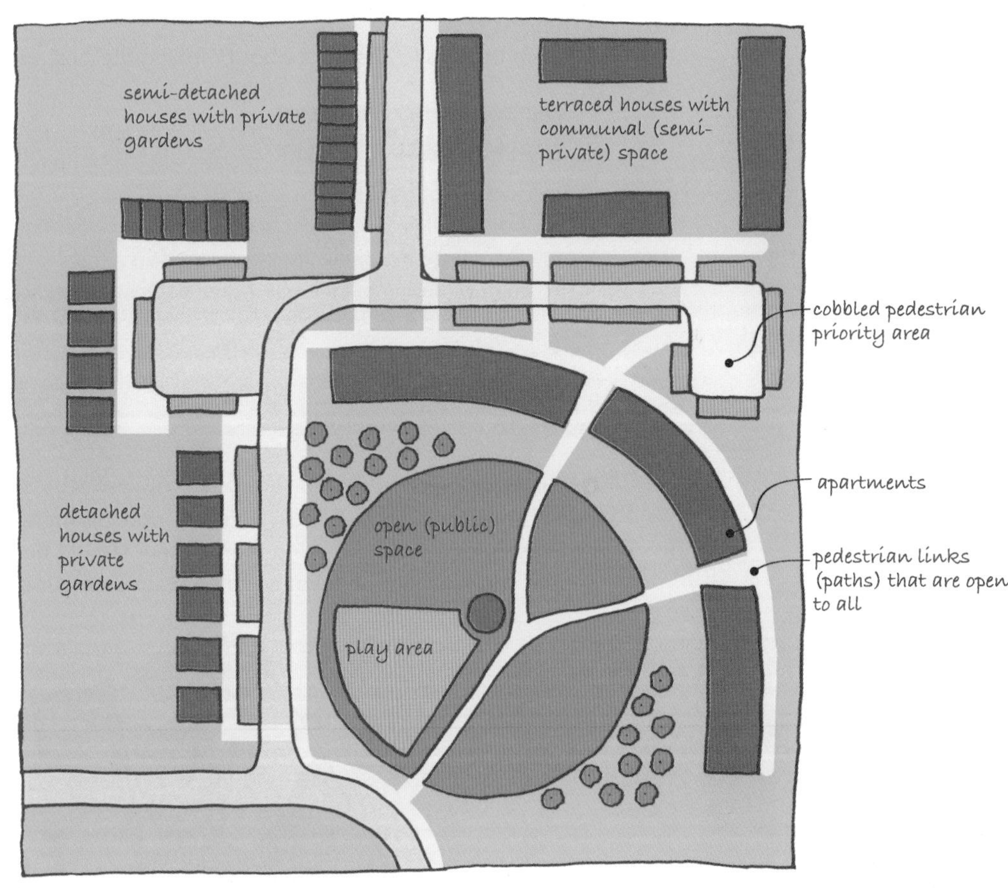

4.03 Inclusivity: a mixture of different types of homes and spaces that provide appropriate levels of privacy while creating public spaces that are easy to access.

ACTIVITIES

'Living in a well-designed neighbourhood improves a person's quality of life.' Discuss this statement with your classmates. Give examples to support your opinion.

Variety

A neighbourhood should include a mixture of residential, retail, commercial and recreational buildings and spaces that allow a variety of activities to take place. This will attract people to the area and lead to an active community and a good quality of life.

4.04 Variety: a mix of residential and commercial units creates a communal garden space while providing much-needed services within walking distance.

Site

Efficiency

Efficient urban site design is about making the best use of the available resources.

KEY PRINCIPLES

Efficient use of resources includes:

- **land** – building high-density residential units (apartments) close to the neighbourhood centre where there are public transport corridors
- **energy** – laying out the site so that each home can optimise solar gain
- **reusing old buildings** – finding new uses for existing buildings so they don't have to be knocked down
- **waste** – providing recycling facilities to reduce the amount of waste sent to landfill
- **drainage** – ensuring that rainwater is collected and reused where possible.

Distinctiveness

Every development should have features and characteristics that make it different and make it interesting for the people living there. There should be landmark buildings and focal points that people can identify. The layout, materials and colour schemes used should create a sense of place.

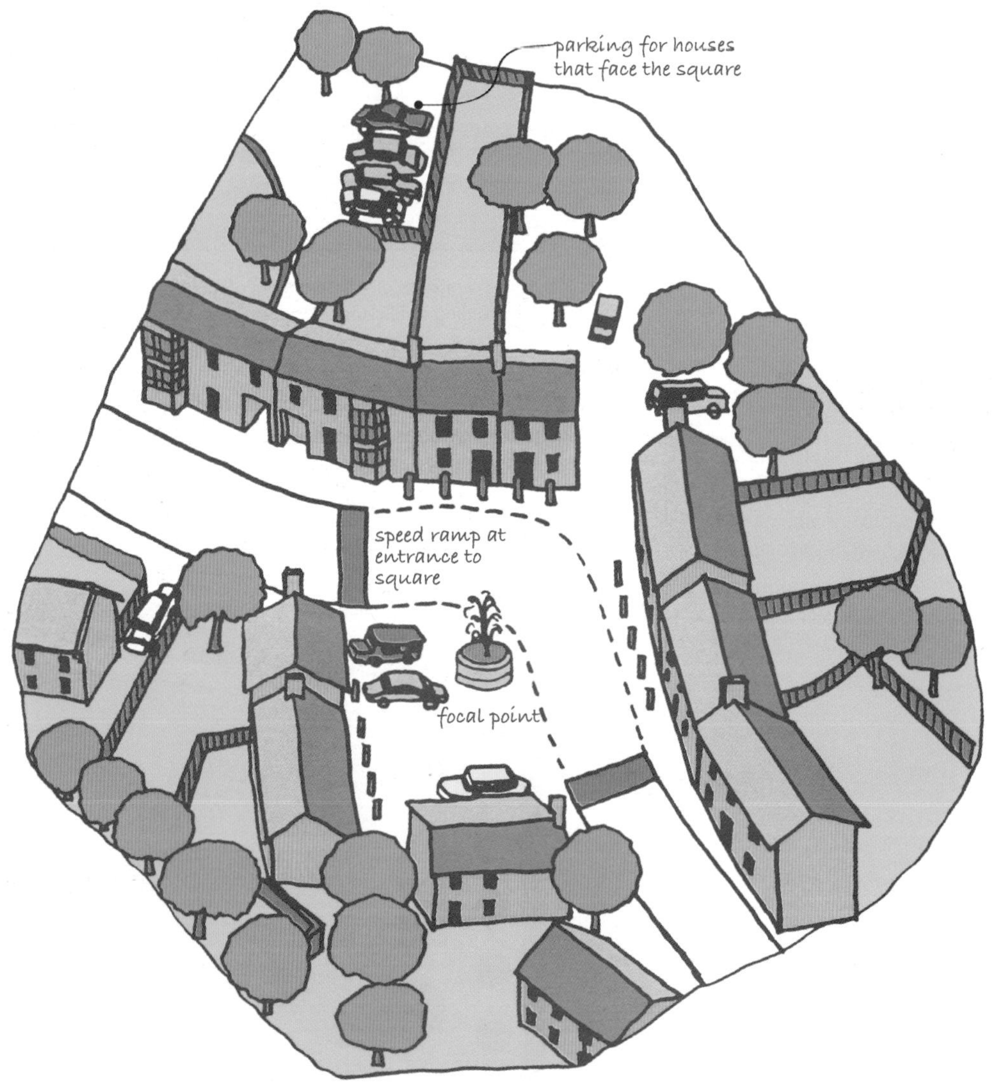

4.05 Distinctiveness: a fountain in a square forms a focal point for the area.

Layout

Good layout of urban developments creates interesting public spaces that encourage outdoor activity. Some houses should open directly onto the street to encourage interaction between neighbours. The streets are designed for people instead of cars and traffic is controlled by layout rather than by traffic lights and speed ramps.

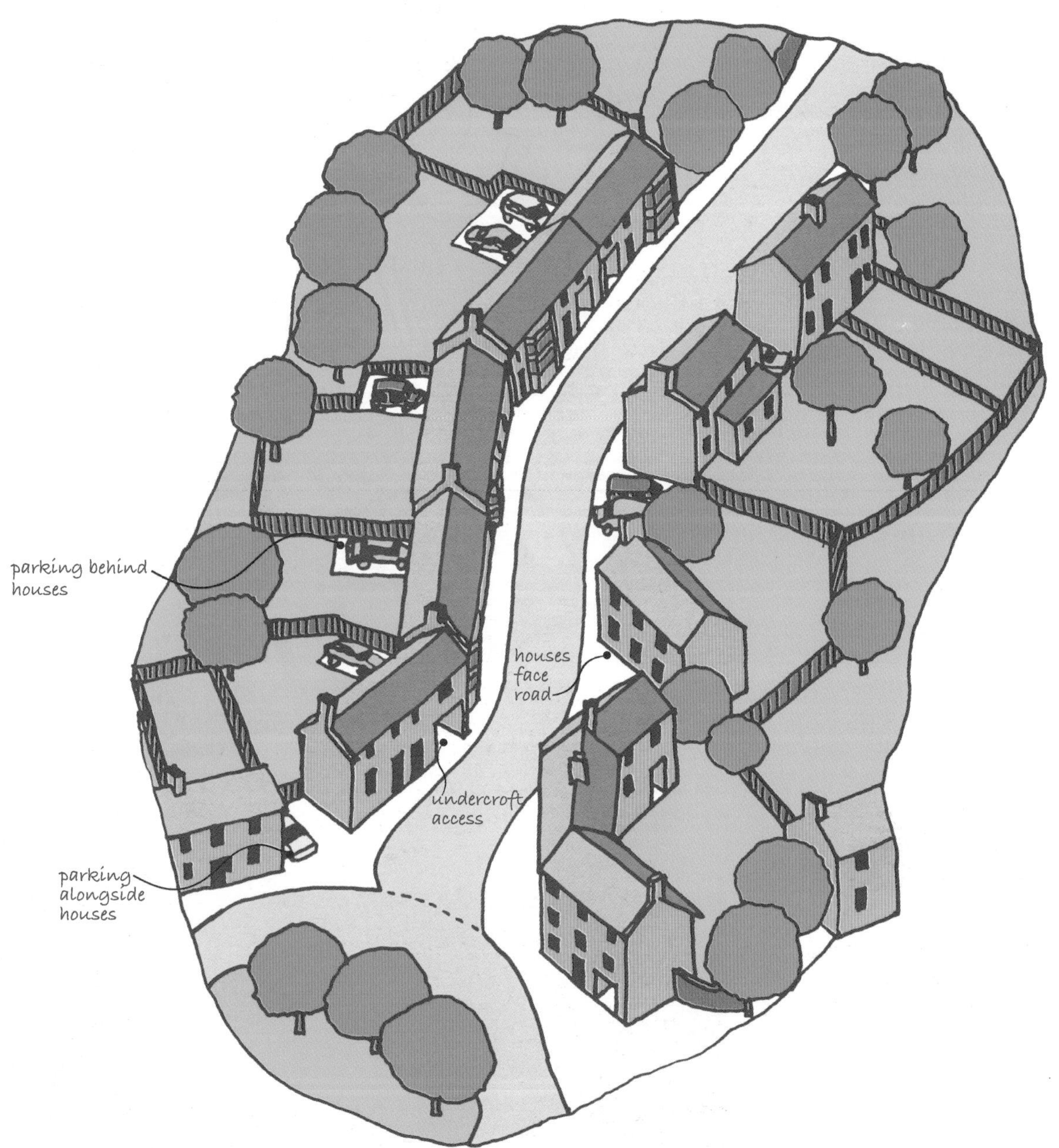

4.06 Layout: an informal urban street curves gently to slow traffic.

ACTIVITIES

'A well-designed site will reduce antisocial behaviour and crime.'
Discuss this statement with your classmates. Give examples to support your opinion.

Public realm

Desirable neighbourhoods have good-quality public spaces that are safe, secure and enjoyable to use. The quality of the public areas is a big factor in a person's overall impression of an area. Neighbourhoods with good-quality public spaces will attract home buyers to the area and will lead to the positive growth of the area by attracting shops, restaurants and other amenities.

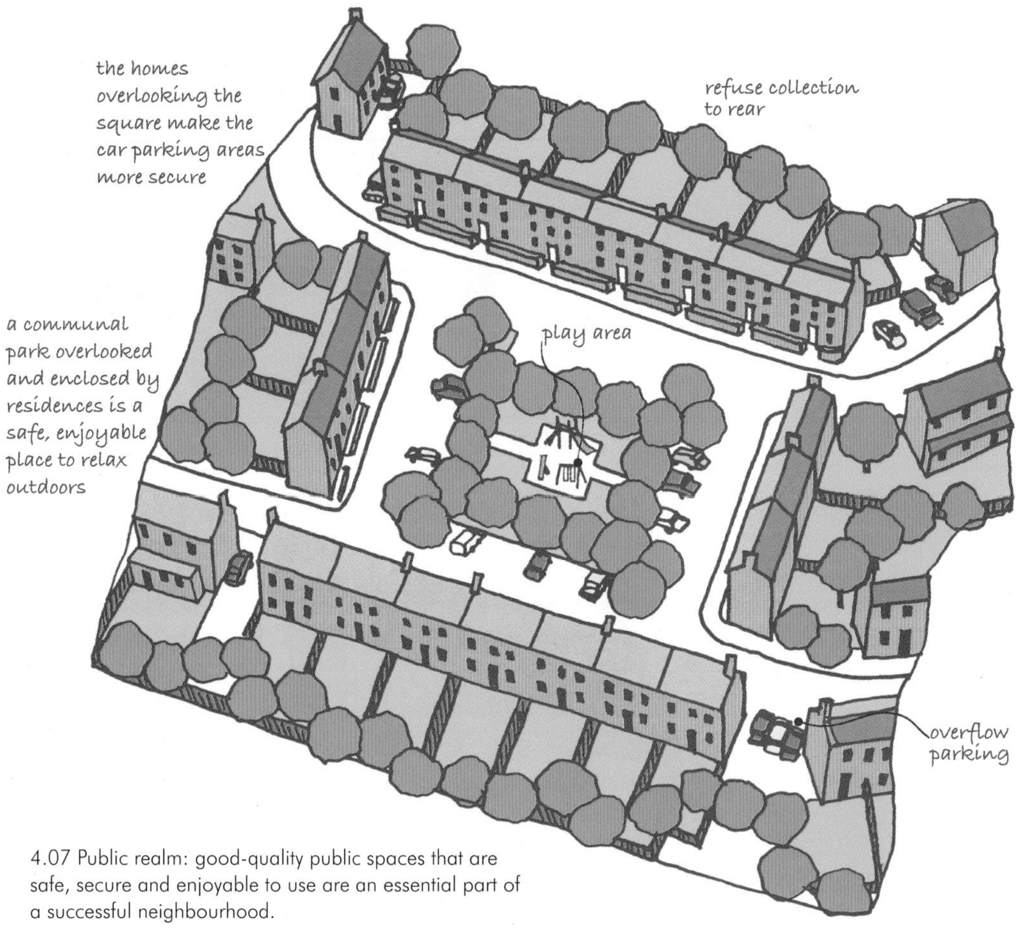

4.07 Public realm: good-quality public spaces that are safe, secure and enjoyable to use are an essential part of a successful neighbourhood.

ACTIVITIES

Carefully study the photograph on the far right. List the features you can see that demonstrate the principles of urban design.

4.08 Detailed design: this residential development of social housing in Fingal, Dublin by DTA Architects, displays a high standard of architectural detailing and a nice use of materials and colours.

Home

There are four elements to home design:

1 adaptability
2 privacy and amenity
3 parking
4 detailed design.

Adaptability

Homes should be designed so that they can grow with the people living in them. As families increase in size or as people get older their needs change; the home should be able to respond to meet these changing needs. For example, if the homeowner decides to work from home, it should be possible to extend the house or convert the roof space to create an office.

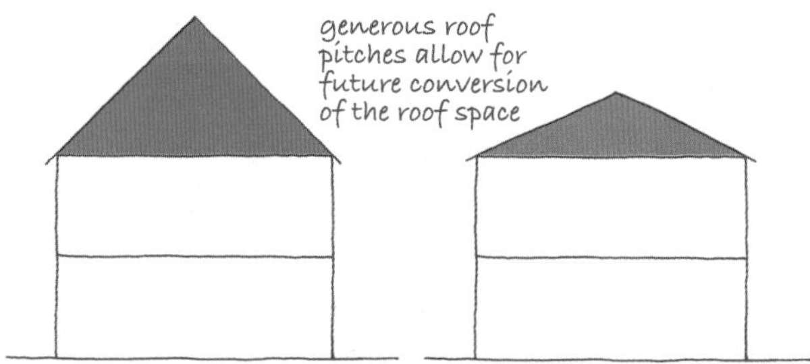

4.09 Adaptability: thinking about the long-term use of a home at the design stage can greatly improve the adaptability of the home in the future.

Privacy and amenity

Every home should allow the people living there to enjoy privacy. This is achieved by ensuring that homes are not overlooked and by creating usable private outdoor spaces. Amenity in this context can mean being comfortable in your home and being free from outside disturbance caused by noise and other nuisances. A well designed home will provide enough space to meet the needs of the occupants.

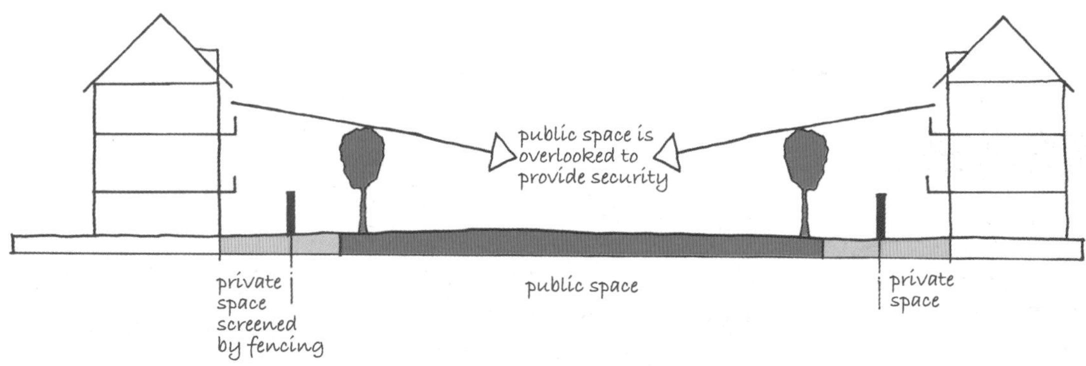

4.10 Privacy and amenity: every home should have some private outdoor space that can be enjoyed without disturbance.

Parking

Secure, convenient parking for cars and bicycles should be provided, without allowing cars to dominate the development.

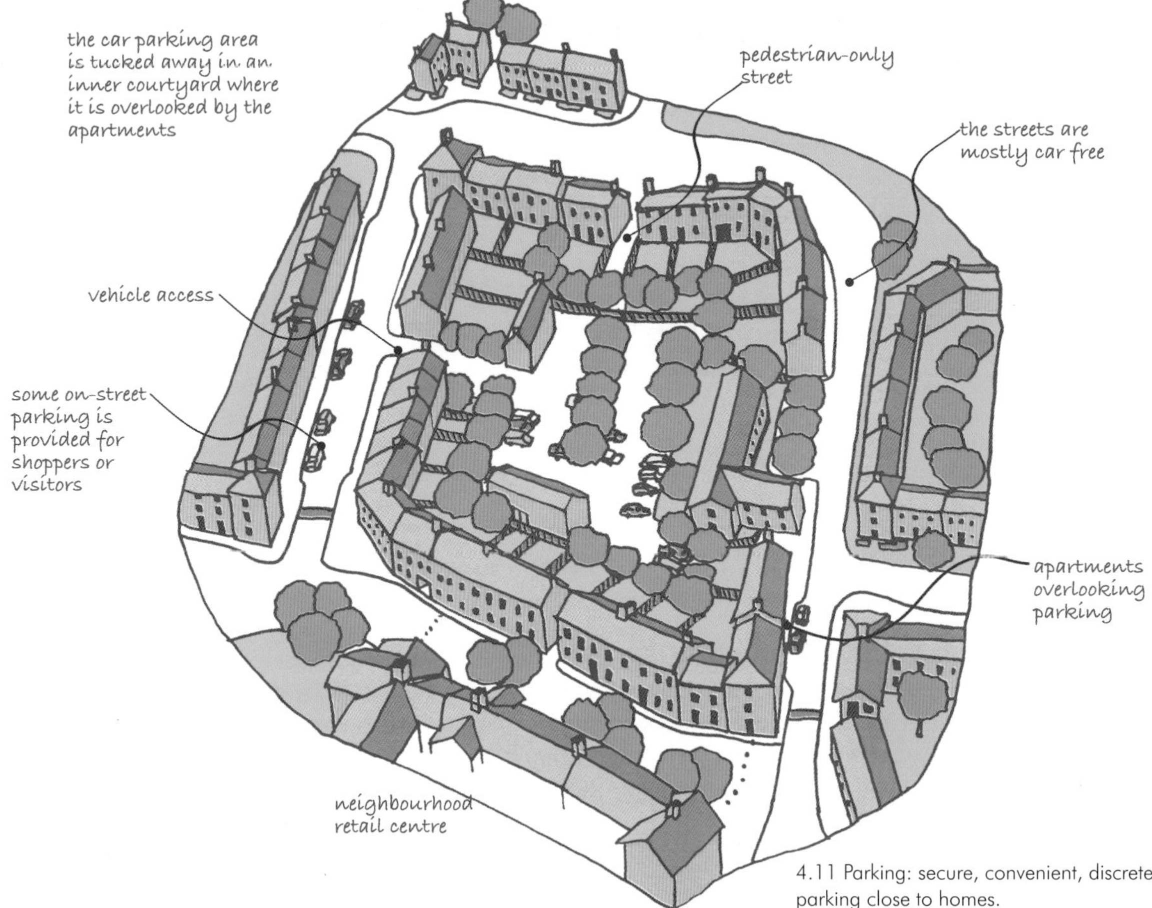

4.11 Parking: secure, convenient, discrete parking close to homes.

Detailed design

The architectural detailing and the quality of the construction materials used in a development have a significant impact on the overall standard achieved. The details and materials should be contemporary and appropriate to the setting. They should set a high standard while respecting the existing character of the area. Small details like street furniture and soft landscaping (planting) have a real influence on the finished quality of a neighbourhood.

4.12 Detailed design: elegant features using high-quality materials will add to the aesthetic appeal of a neighbourhood.

REVISION EXERCISES

1 Why is it important to create a master plan when designing an urban area?
2 Why is transport infrastructure (cycle paths, bus routes, etc.) essential in an urban area?
3 Explain, using neat freehand sketches, the role of inclusivity in urban design.
4 What do public spaces provide to a neighbourhood?
5 Describe one positive feature and one negative feature of an urban area that you have visited.

CHAPTER 5

Rural Design

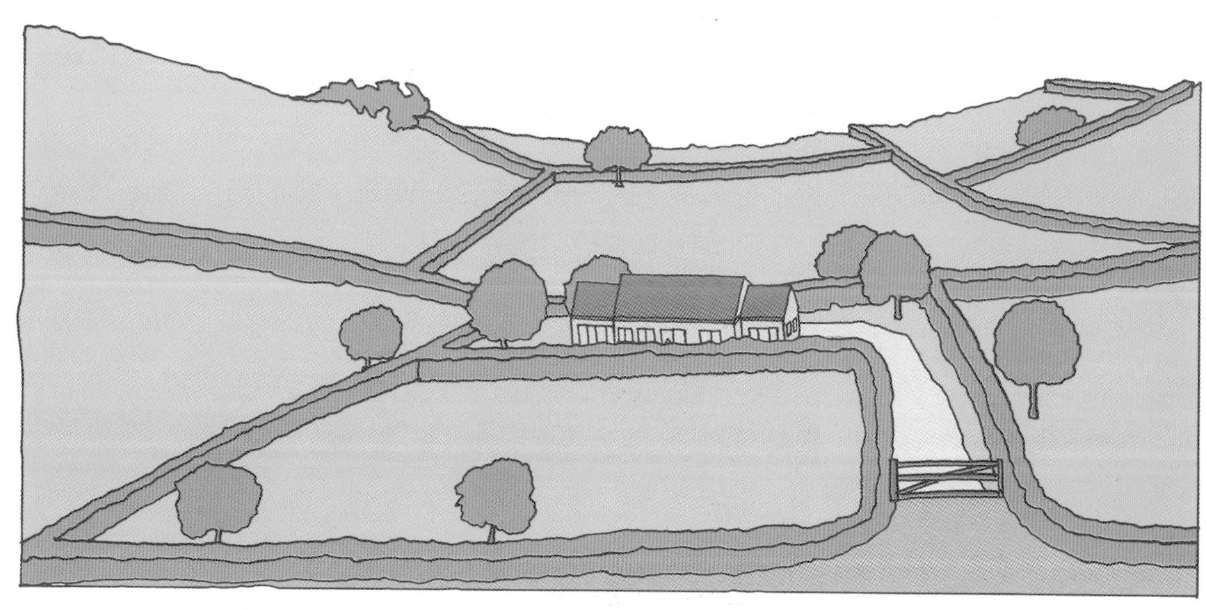

A new house built in the countryside must blend into its surroundings; the house must be designed specifically to suit the area and the particular site on which it will stand. Most county councils in Ireland have guidelines on designing a home for the countryside. The guidelines provide advice on materials, construction details, scale and form; and planting appropriate to the locality. It is essential that these guidelines are followed if the house is to successfully fit into its surroundings.

There are four main elements to rural design:
1 **site selection** – finding a good site
2 **site layout design** – deciding how best to use the site
3 **house design** – designing a house to suit the site and the locality
4 **landscape design** – deciding on planting and other features that will link the house to the land.

In practice, there is a lot of overlap of the different stages in the design process. For example, a lot of thought would go into the house design from the very first visit to the site.

ACTIVITIES

Visit the website of a county council and download a *'rural housing design'* or *'building in the countryside'* guide book. Compare the guidelines with those of other counties downloaded by other students in your class. Look for elements that are common to all and elements that are unique to a particular county.

Site selection

Every site has a unique character. A coastal site overlooking the ocean will have a very different feel from an inland site in a valley. The key is to integrate the design and to make the most of the natural features of the site.

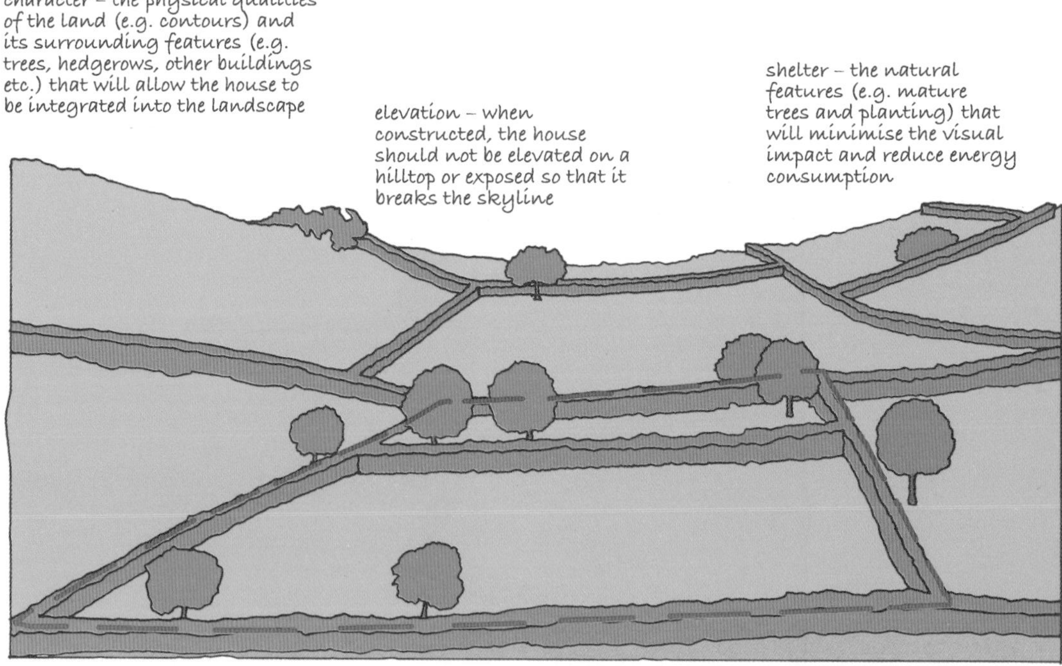

5.01 Site selection: key elements to think about when selecting a site.

Site layout

Once a suitable site has been identified, a detailed site plan must be worked out to ensure that the site is used in the best possible way. A successful site design will make best use of the site for the homeowner, while also limiting the visual impact of the house on the landscape.

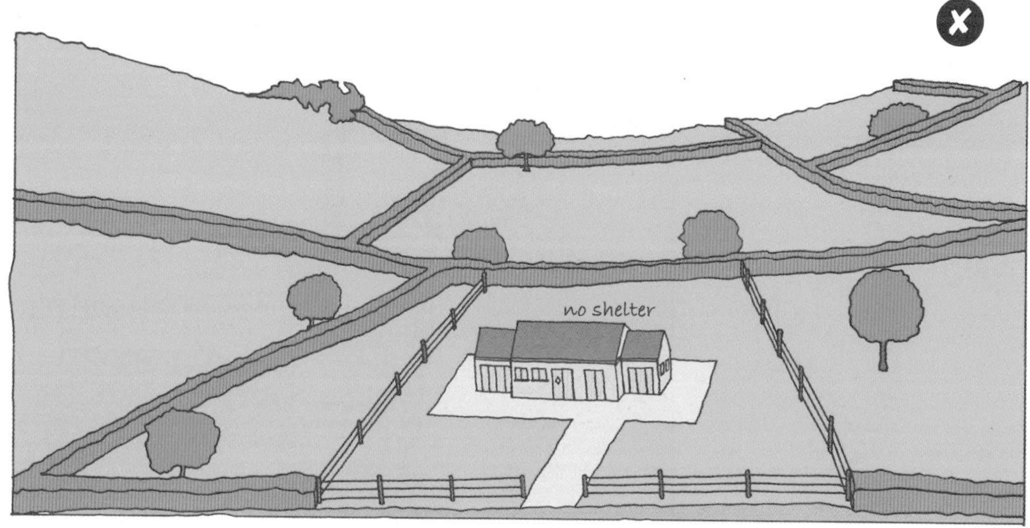

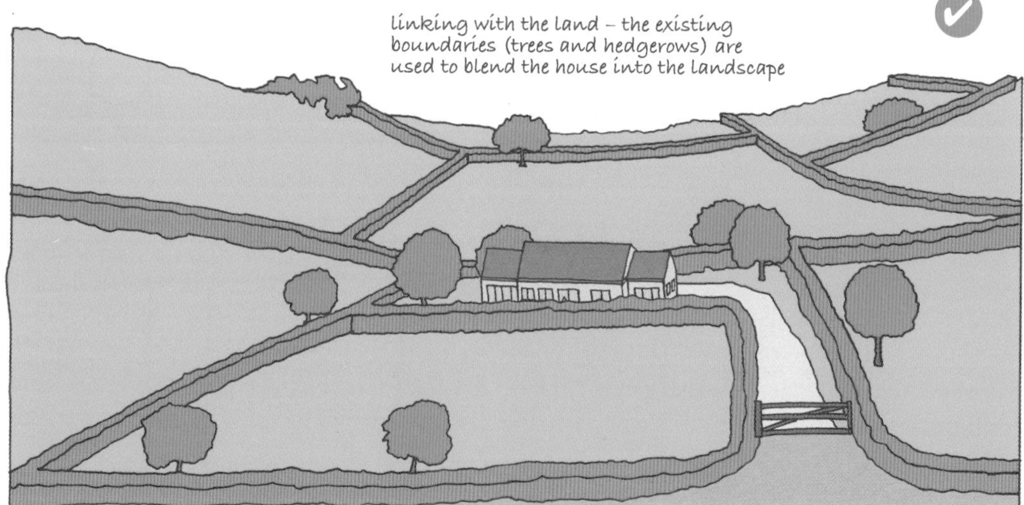

5.02 Site design: minimising the house's visual impact by taking advantage of the site's natural features to blend the house into the landscape.

ACTIVITIES

If you live in a rural area, generate a sketch of your site. Consider how the site is used and evaluate the visual impact of the site on the landscape.

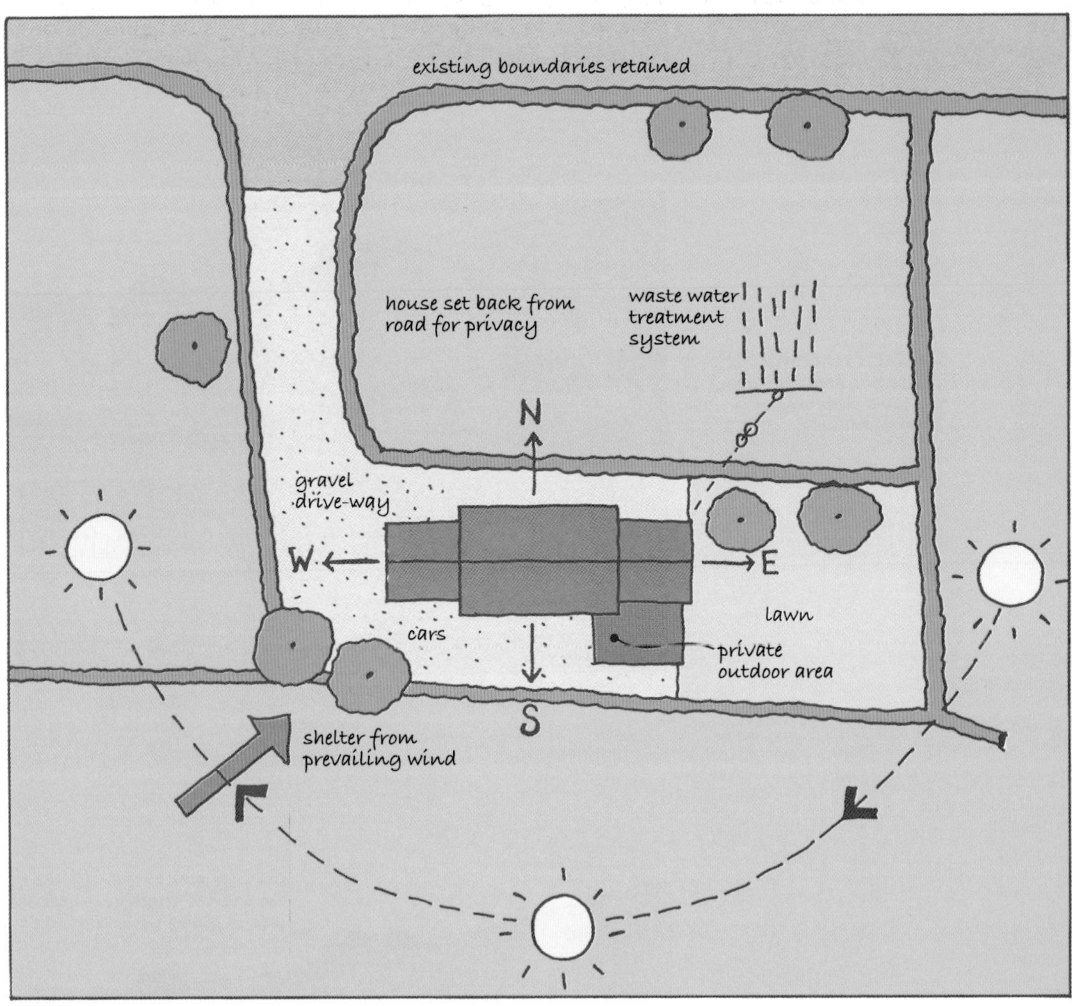

5.03 Site design: making best use of the site to ensure privacy while optimising shelter and solar gain.

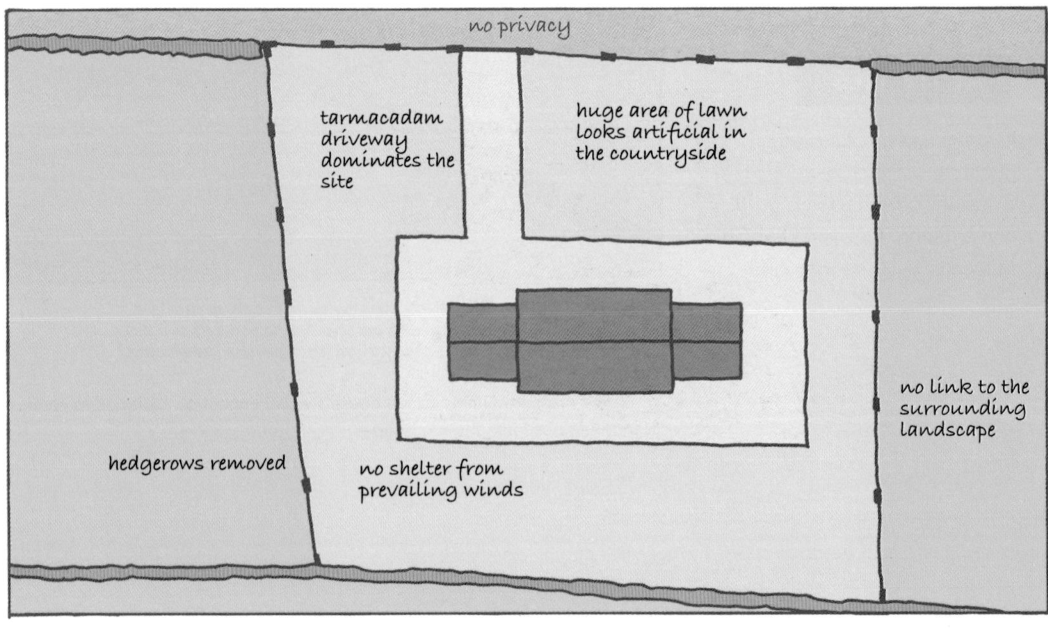

5.04 Poor rural site design.

House design

New house designs should be innovative and contemporary – they should not be old-fashioned. However, it is very important to acknowledge local traditions, so the design should reflect an awareness of the cultural heritage and built heritage of the area. It is best to look around the area at existing houses and buildings to get an idea of the materials and styles that are typical in the area.

KEY PRINCIPLES

If a house is to blend into the countryside, the following elements must be considered:

- proportion – striking a balance between solid (walls) and void (windows and doors)
- scale – the size of the house relative to what's around it (the site, other buildings)
- form – a simple symmetrical shape that reflects the local tradition
- materials (palette) – natural materials (timber, stone, slate) and simple colours
- details – simple, unfussy details with a strong emphasis on quality workmanship.

5.05 Proportion: the solid to void ratio, the height of the building relative to its openings and a simple symmetry all contribute to the proportion of a rural house.

5.06 Scale: this pair of houses demonstrate the difference in scale that has occurred in recent years.

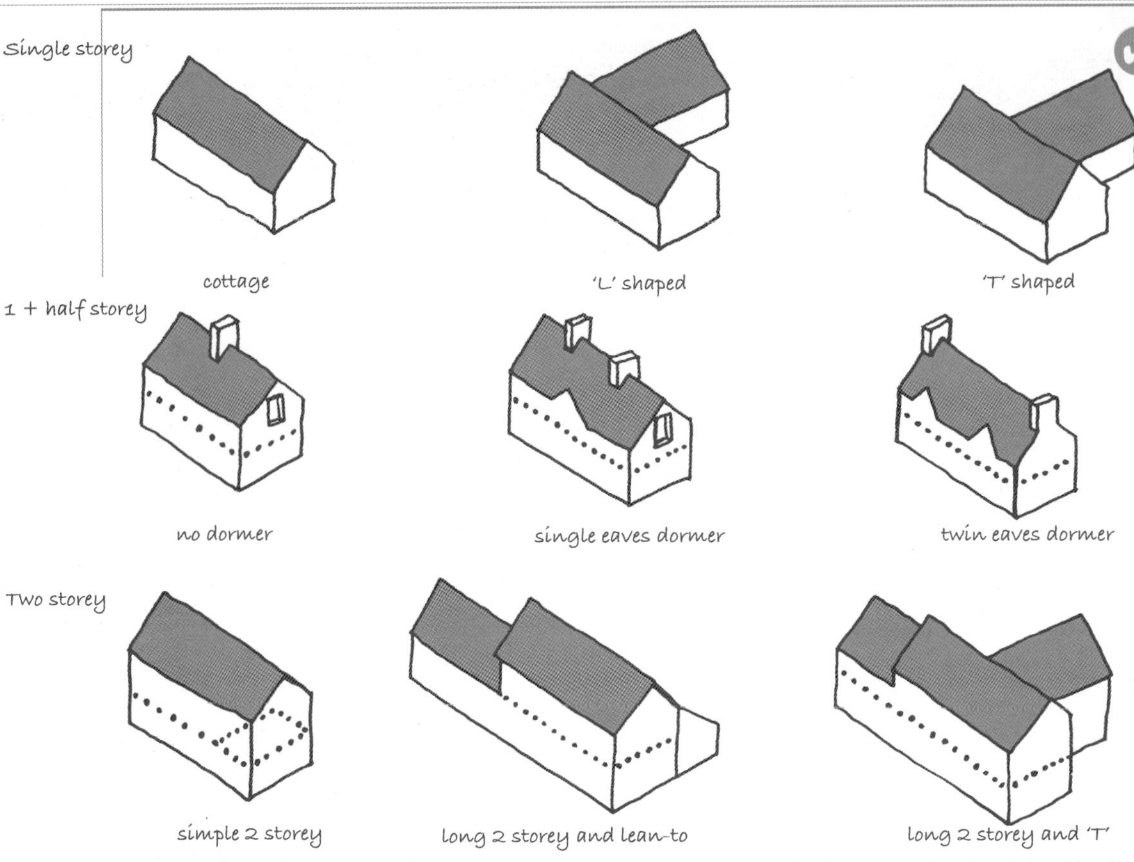

5.07 Form: a simple form best suits the countryside; a house with a narrow plan, flat front, vertical emphasis to gables, low eaves and a sturdy solid feel.

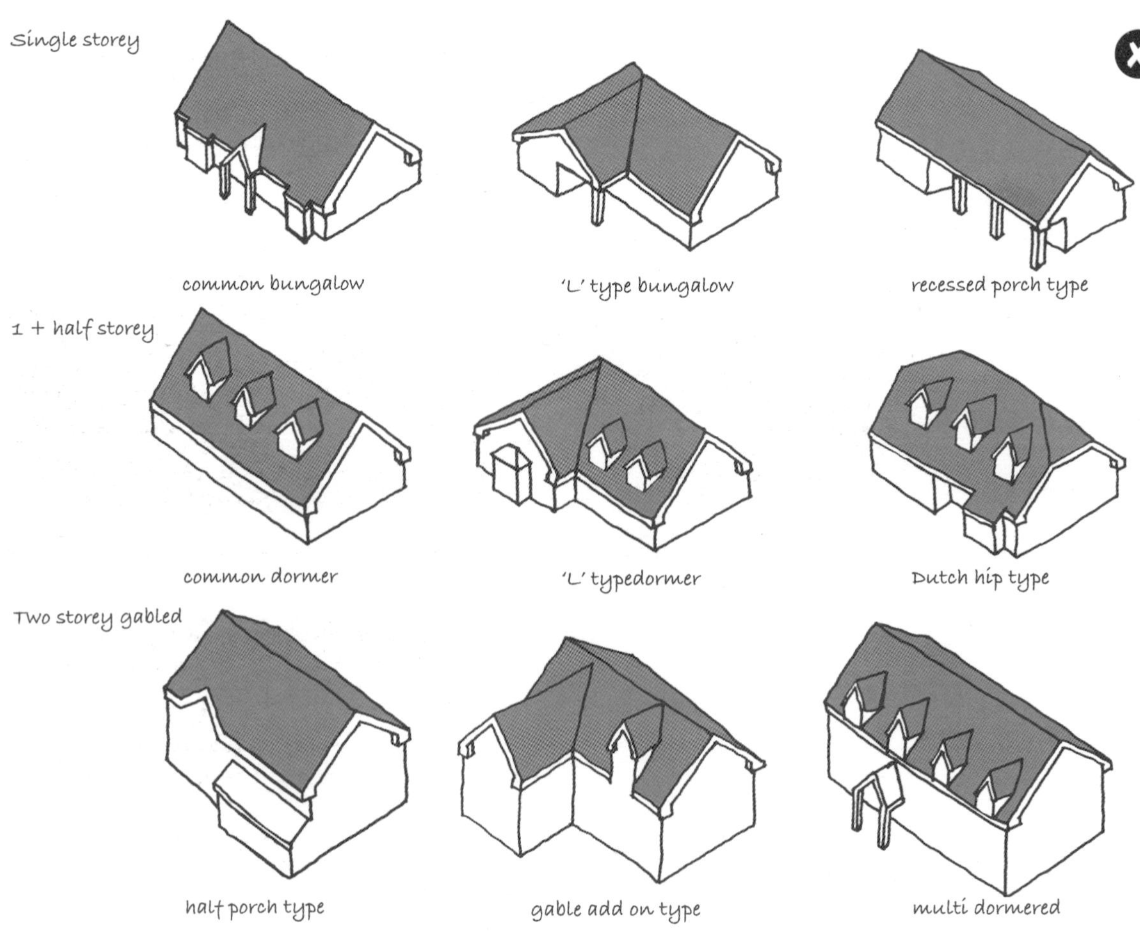

5.08 Form: in a rural setting, deep plan houses lead to excessive ridge heights; this gives the front elevation a top-heavy look (too much roof).

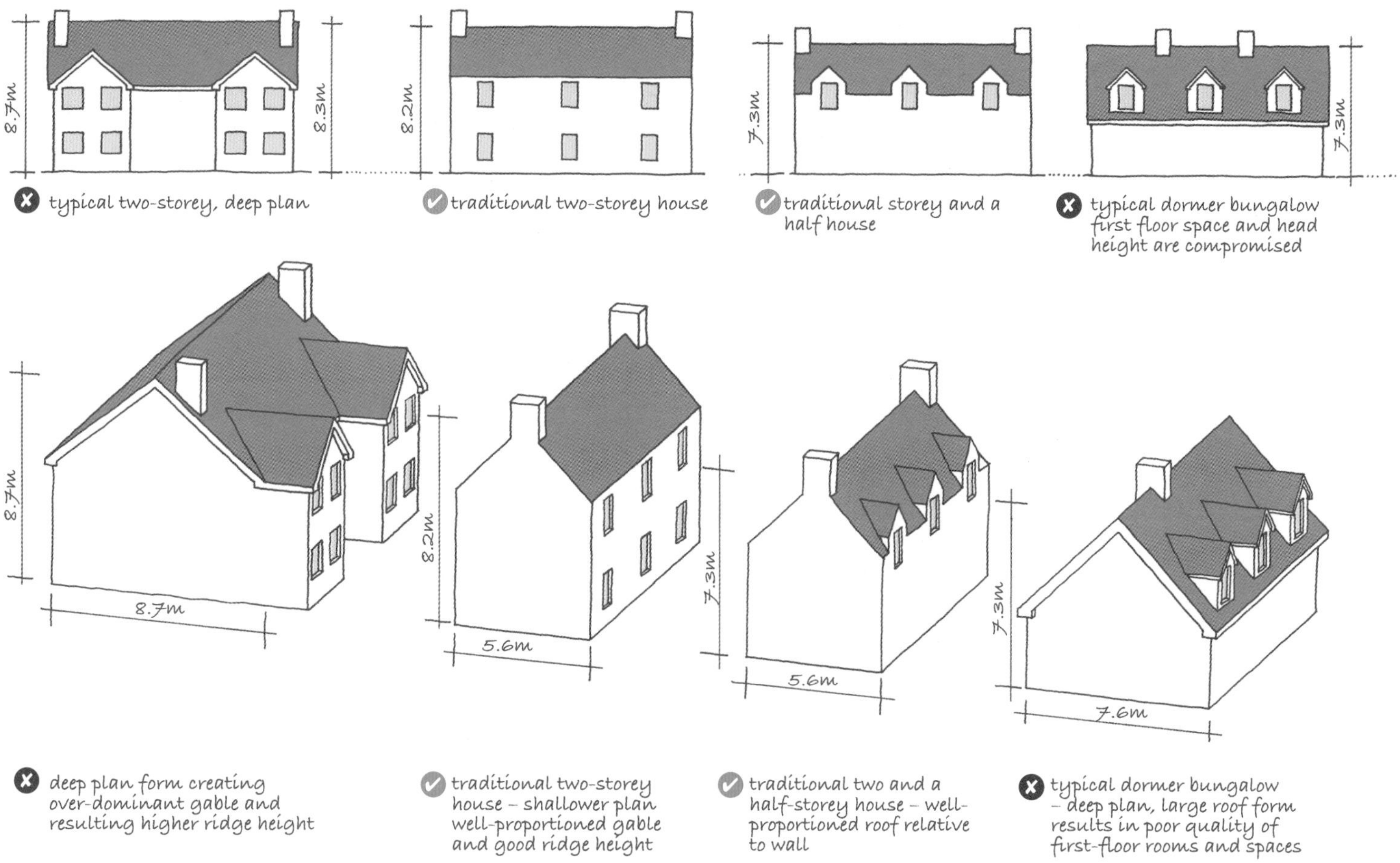

8.7m 8.3m 8.2m 7.3m 7.3m

typical two-storey, deep plan

traditional two-storey house

traditional storey and a half house

typical dormer bungalow first floor space and head height are compromised

8.7m 8.7m 8.2m 5.6m 7.3m 5.6m 7.3m 7.6m

deep plan form creating over-dominant gable and resulting higher ridge height

traditional two-storey house – shallower plan well-proportioned gable and good ridge height

traditional two and a half-storey house – well-proportioned roof relative to wall

typical dormer bungalow – deep plan, large roof form results in poor quality of first-floor rooms and spaces

5.09 Form: shallow plan depth results in a better proportioned form.

5.10 Materials and details: this coastal house at Coney Island, Co. Sligo by RPP Architects demonstrates the use of traditional materials and simple construction details in a contemporary style that sits well in the Irish landscape (view from the sea).

5.11 Materials and details: the same house viewed from the entrance suggests the traditional courtyard layout of a farm in rural Ireland.

Landscape design

Landscape design is the final stage in the process of building a house in the countryside. It is a very important part of the process and it should not be overlooked or set aside. Landscaping augments the natural features of the site by providing additional planting in carefully selected places around the site.

KEY PRINCIPLES

Landscaping is used to achieve the following goals:
- to make the site part of the countryside
- to link the house to the land
- to provide shelter from the prevailing winds
- to provide privacy for the homeowners
- to soften the visual impact of the new house/site.

Creating boundaries

A well-chosen site will have two or three natural boundaries already in place. The challenge is to add to these in a sympathetic way. Two approaches can be taken, depending on the site's characteristics: a walled boundary; or a planted boundary.

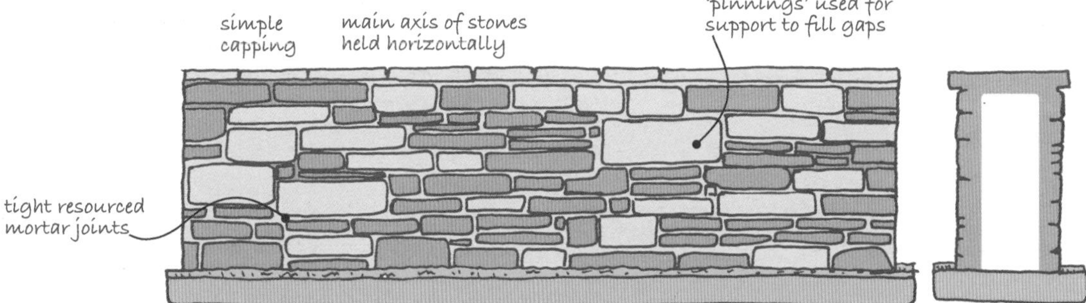

5.12 Boundaries: a simple dry stone wall, built using locally sourced squared rubble.

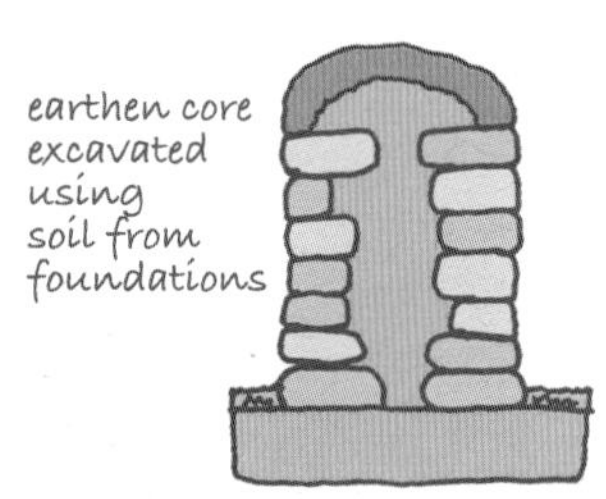

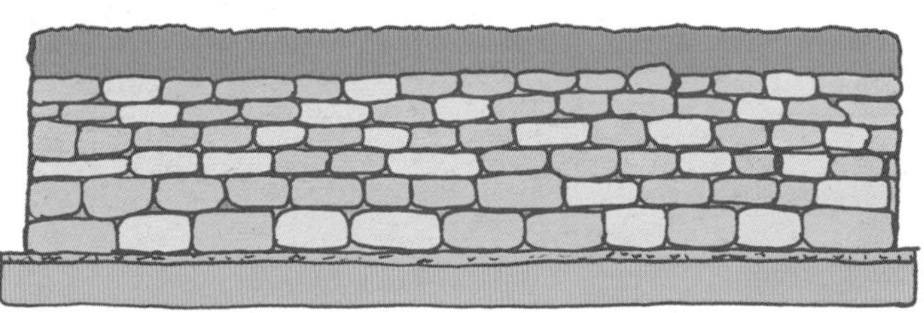
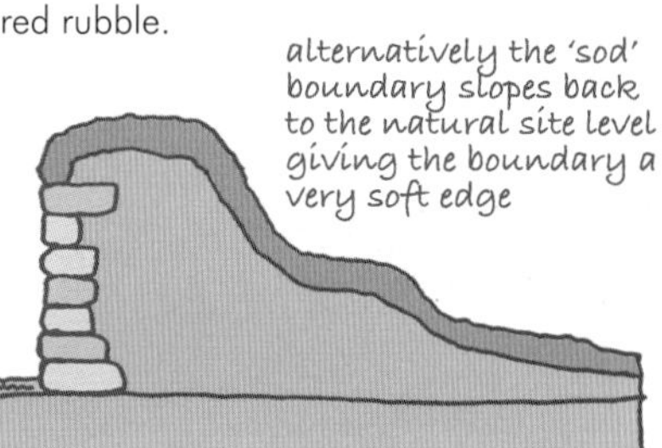

5.13 Boundaries: a stone boundary built using local stone with a 'sod' cap.

As well as being aesthetically pleasing, planted boundaries provide food and shelter for a variety of birds, mammals, insects and other wildlife. Creating mixed hedgerows of native local species of shrubs and trees helps to maintain biodiversity. The use of large single-species hedges should be avoided.

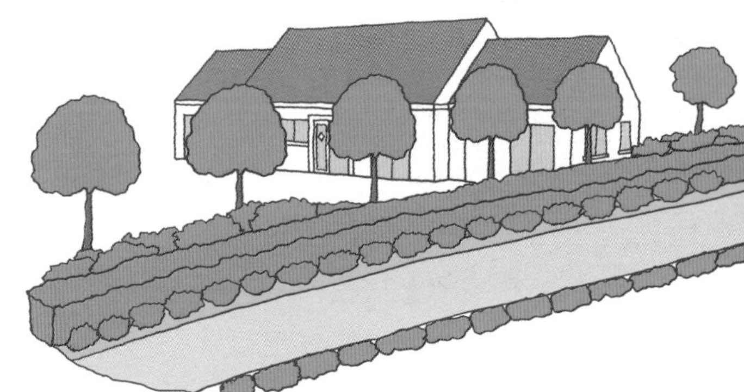

5.14 Boundaries: a planted boundary should include a mix of hedges and trees that are commonly found in the local area.

Creating shelter

Planting is a very effective way of sheltering a house from the prevailing winds. A well-planted screen will consist of layers of wind-tolerant shrubs gradually rising in height with trees in the centre. It is essential that local native species that are common to the area are used. Most counties provide guidance on the species that are appropriate in their area.

5.15 Shelter: a selection of shrubs and trees are used to create a wind shelter.

Creating privacy

Locating the house a reasonable distance back from the roadside will provide some privacy. However, planting is usually required to provide outdoor spaces that are not overlooked by passing traffic. Screens of planting are an effective way to do this.

5.16 Privacy: a screen of native hedging and trees is used to create a private courtyard area.

ACTIVITIES

Look up the website of your local planning authority (e.g. county council) and download a copy of the rural design guidelines. Identify the plant species recommended for use in your area.

REVISION EXERCISES

1 Why does each county have its own rural design guidelines?
2 A family buying a site in a rural setting has a choice of any of eight sites in each of four areas as shown. Outline the benefits and drawbacks of each site and make a recommendation.

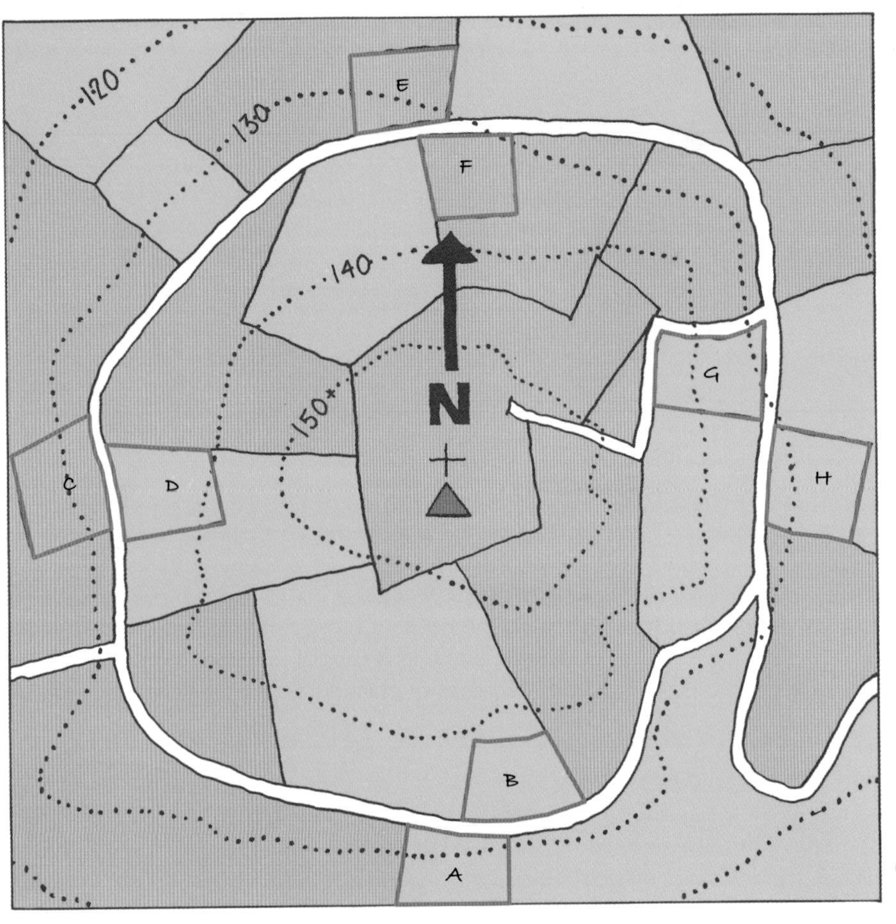

3 Explain, using neat freehand sketches, the importance of site layout when building in the countryside.
4 Explain, using neat freehand sketches, the concept of scale when designing a home that will be built near an existing home in a rural setting.
5 Discuss the relevance of local traditions when designing a home for a rural setting.

CHAPTER 6

Universal Design

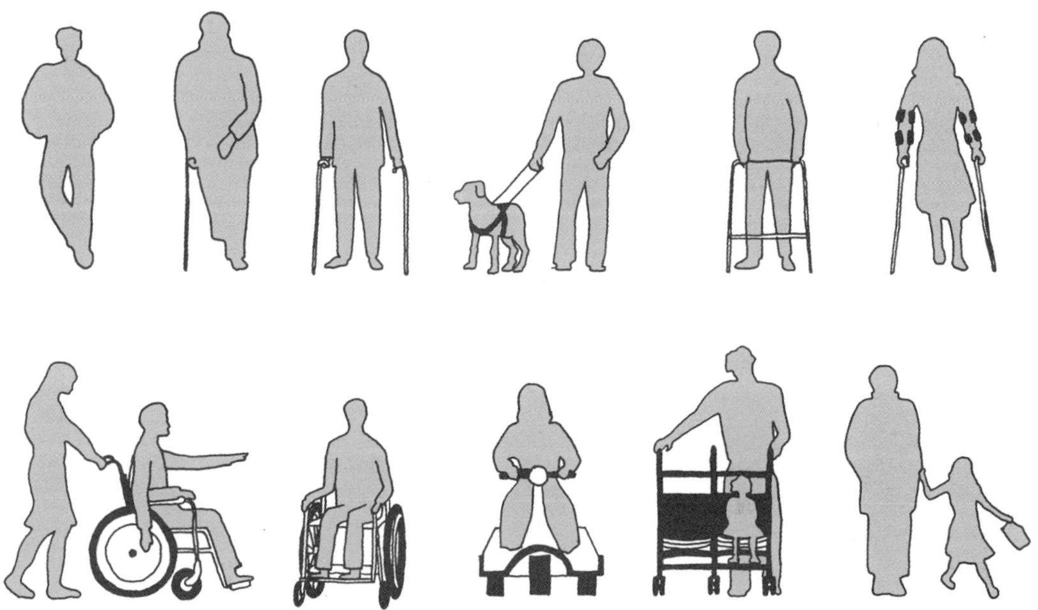

A well-designed home can enable people to have a better quality of life. Simple features can be 'designed in' to improve the way a home works for everyone. The universal design approach encourages a single solution that suits everyone and makes a home better for all users, irrespective of their age or ability. A universally designed home can be adapted to the changing needs of occupants over time and provide everyone with greater choice in where they live.

Principles

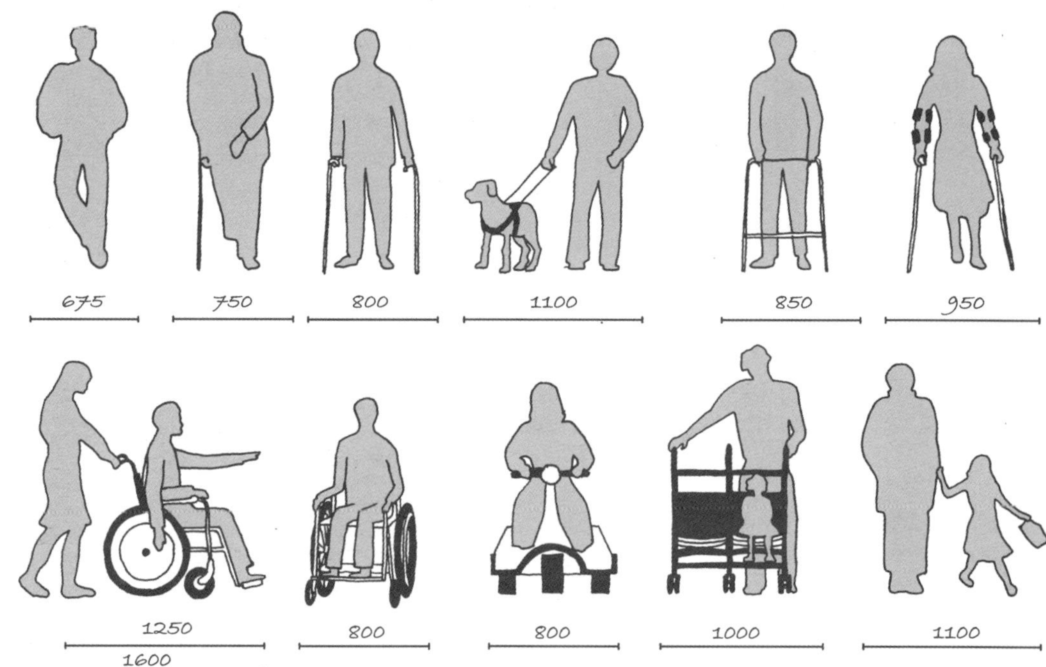

6.01 Space requirements: everyone has different needs. This is essential knowledge when designing circulation spaces (hallways, corridors) and doorways.

A home should be suitable for everyone because everyone is different. Consider the following people:

- a three-year-old child
- a wheelchair user
- a teenager on crutches
- a heavily pregnant woman
- a young man
- a person with impaired hearing
- an elderly person.

Each of these people has different abilities and needs. There is no 'normal' – everyone is unique and has different needs at different stages of life.

DEFINITION

Universal design
The design and composition of an environment so that it can be accessed, understood and used to the greatest extent possible by all people, regardless of their age, size, ability or disability.

ACTIVITIES

Imagine that you have been involved in an accident. You have badly broken your leg and it will be in a special steel support for three months. During this time you will need to use a wheelchair. You need assistance every time you use the bathroom and it is difficult for you to use stairs. How would your home adapt to your new needs?

Sketch the floor plan(s) of your home as it is today. Then sketch a new layout that will make your life easier for the next three months. Consider, in particular, bathroom access and where you will sleep.

Note: do this activity before you read the rest of this chapter.

KEY PRINCIPLES

Universal home design is based on the following principles:

- **access** – everyone should be able to safely and independently approach and enter a house, unaided and in a dignified manner; they shouldn't have to be lifted into the home and they shouldn't have to use a different entrance from everyone else
- **use** – the design and layout of the home should allow everyone the same opportunity to use the home
- **enjoyment** – everyone deserves the right to enjoy their home and to be able to visit others in comfort.

Design brief

Designing a home is about turning words, models and drawings into a building. The process of designing a new home begins with the creation of a design brief – a written description of the home to be built. It usually begins with a site visit and a meeting in which the architect and the client discuss their ideas. The design brief is then prepared by the architect working in partnership with the client.

SUPPLEMENTARY INFORMATION

The design brief includes all the details relating to the home, some of which include:

- **size** – area in m^2, number of floors
- **style** – traditional, contemporary, etc.
- **spaces/rooms needed** – bedrooms, living room, kitchen, etc.
- **energy performance** – Passive House or BER: A1, A2, etc.
- **construction method** – masonry, timber frame, etc.
- **special requirements** – elderly/disabled occupant, etc.
- **materials** – timber windows, plain render, stone, etc.
- **landscaping** – outdoor spaces, planting
- **budget** – money available to complete the project
- **time frame** – completion date.

KEY PRINCIPLES

These are some of the benefits of writing a design brief:

- clarifies the client's thinking: helps the client to turn a fuzzy notion in their head into a clear picture in a drawing or model
- helps to prioritise competing needs and desires: ensures that the most important elements are included first
- uncovers hidden issues: highlights positive and negative things that might not be obvious at first glance
- avoids misunderstandings: writing down the ideas helps to ensure that the client and architect/builder are actually talking about the same thing
- allows the client to express likes and dislikes: it is just as important that the designer is clear on what the client doesn't want as on what they do
- identifies potential problems: conflicting design features are sometimes only seen when everything is written down
- explains how the home will actually be used
- makes it real: writing a design brief will get the client talking about how the home will be lived in
- future-proofs the house: allows the architect to include features that will make the house adaptable in the future
- safety: ensures the home will be safe to use.

Layout

The process of designing the internal layout of a home is driven by the design brief and depends on the needs of the client and the characteristics of the site.

KEY PRINCIPLES

Layout design is influenced by the following factors:

- the size of the family
- the family's lifestyle
- the age, health and ability of each family member
- typical activities (e.g. eating, sleeping, washing, reading, watching television)
- the spaces needed for these activities
- the connections between these spaces
- special requirements (e.g. wheelchair access)
- orientation to the sun
- clustering of rooms to ensure the efficient design of a mechanical heat recovery and ventilation (MHRV) system (i.e. ducting)
- optimal use of the site (e.g. using shelter or capturing a view).

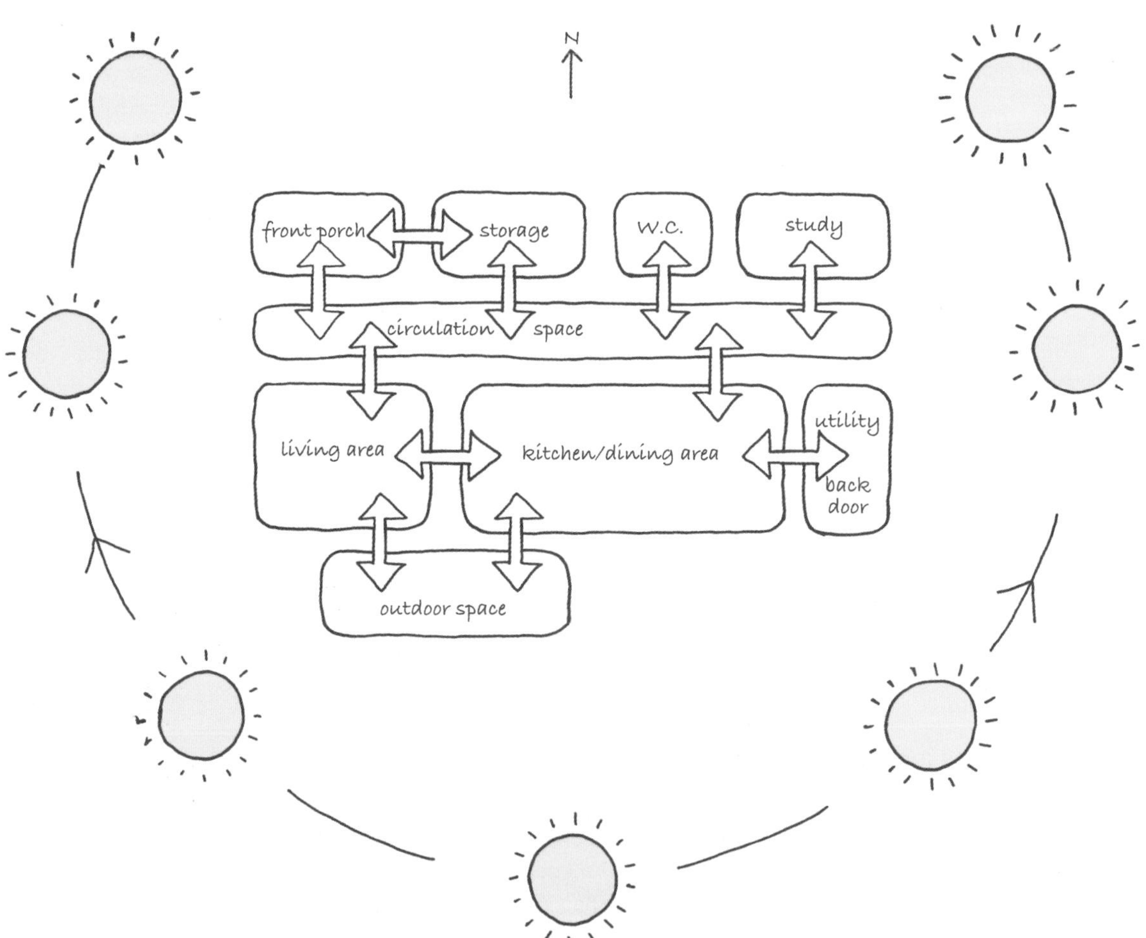

6.02 Layout design: a layout sketch (ground floor) shows a possible arrangement of spaces and the relationship between them.

Once the layout has been figured out, preliminary drawings and a simple card model (called a 'study model') are produced to allow the client to get a feel for what the house will look like when it is built.

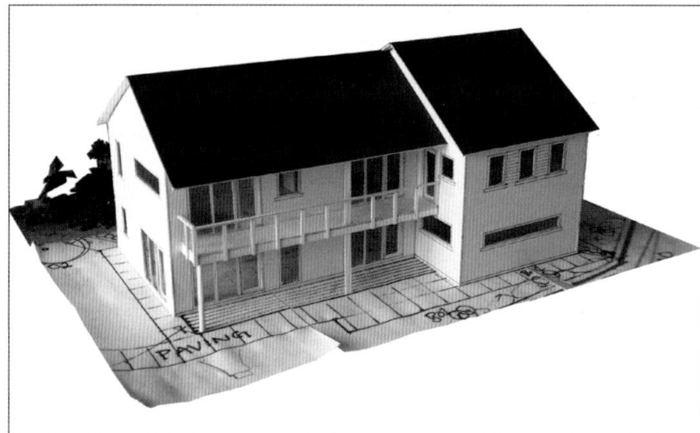

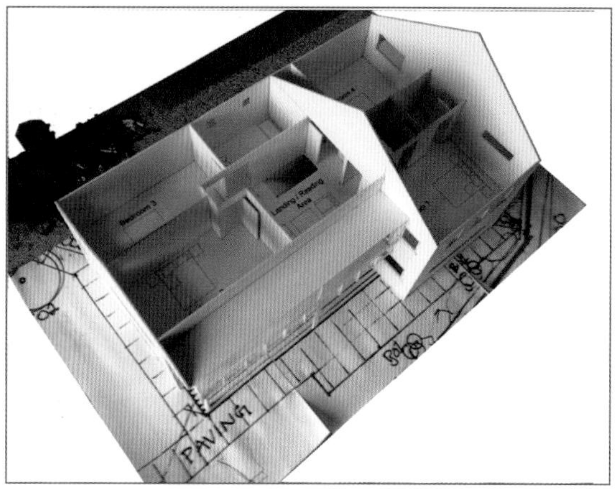

6.03 A simple study model allows the client to 'see' the design. *Source:* Keith Cunningham.

Key areas of the home

The building regulations (Technical Guidance Document (TGD) M) require that specific measures are taken to 'design in' a minimum level of accessibility into every new home. The idea is that every home should be visitable by people with a disability.

These design features include:

- approach – getting from the gate to the door
- access – entering the home
- circulation – moving around inside
- toilet facilities.

However, as well as providing these minimum features it is best practice to take a universal approach to the design of a home if it is to meet the changing needs of all of its occupants.

Approach

The approach to the entrance should ideally be level. Where level access is not possible, a gently sloping surface (with landings at regular intervals) should be provided.

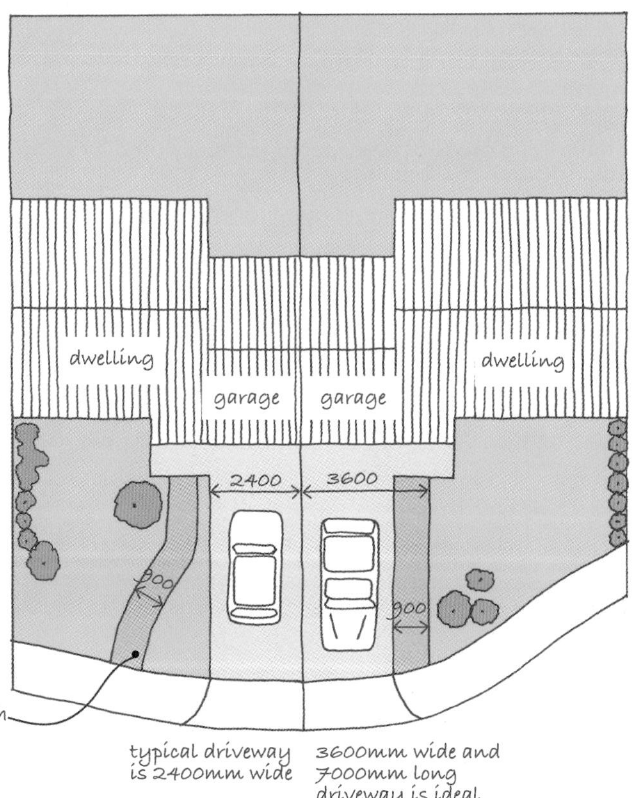

6.04 Approach: the path should be level and well lit at night.

Entrance

The entrance should be well lit and protected from the weather. It should have a level approach and a clear landing area of 1,500mm by 1,500mm. The door should have a minimum effective clear width of 800mm, with 300mm unobstructed space adjacent to the leading edge.

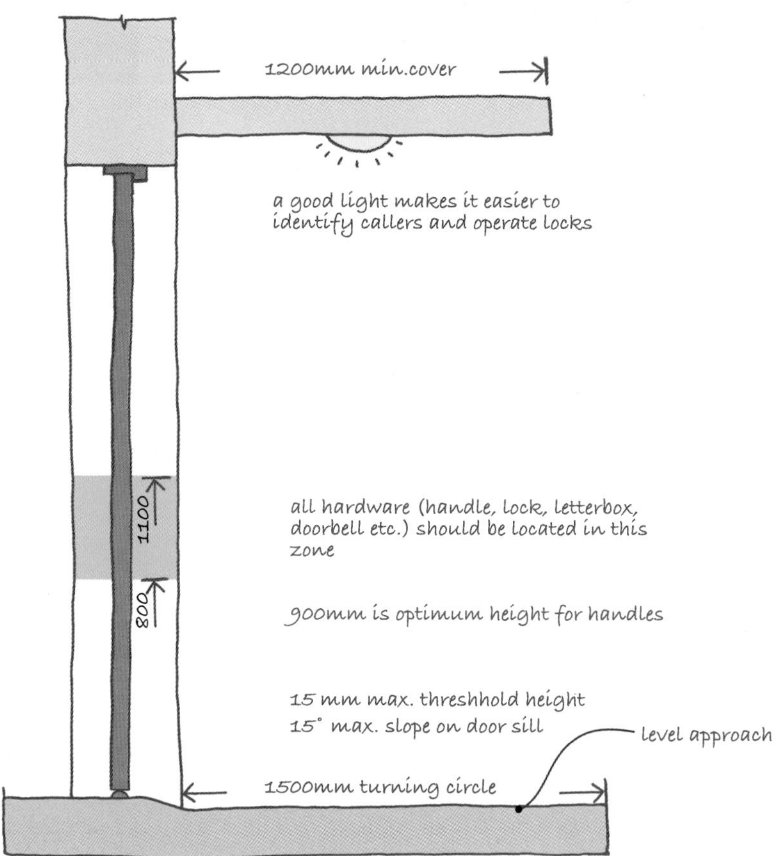

6.05 Access: vertical section through a front entrance. The entrance should have a level approach and be well lit and protected from the weather. Door hardware should be easy to reach for everyone.

Circulation

The main living areas of every home, normally used by visitors, should be accessible to everyone. The minimum requirement for every new home is that people can move freely between the front entrance, hall, living room and guest toilet.

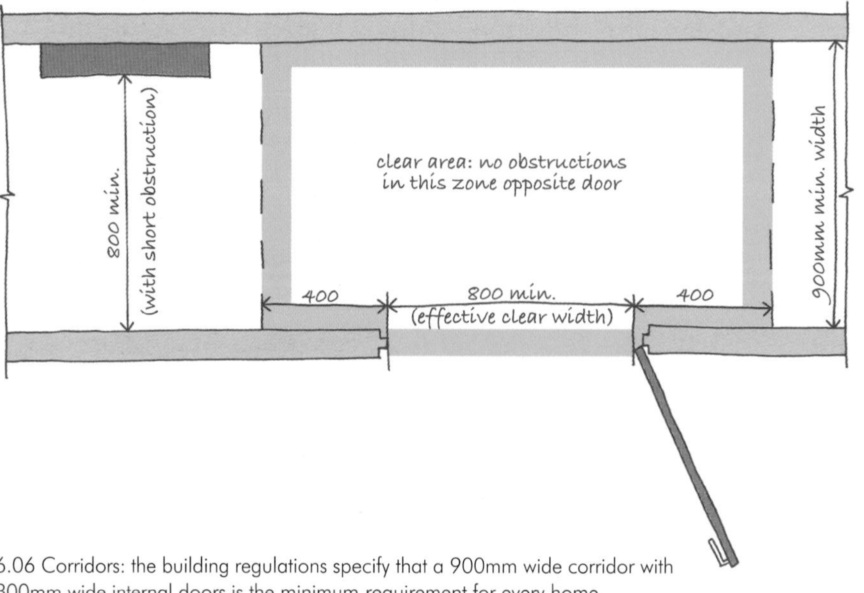

6.06 Corridors: the building regulations specify that a 900mm wide corridor with 800mm wide internal doors is the minimum requirement for every home.

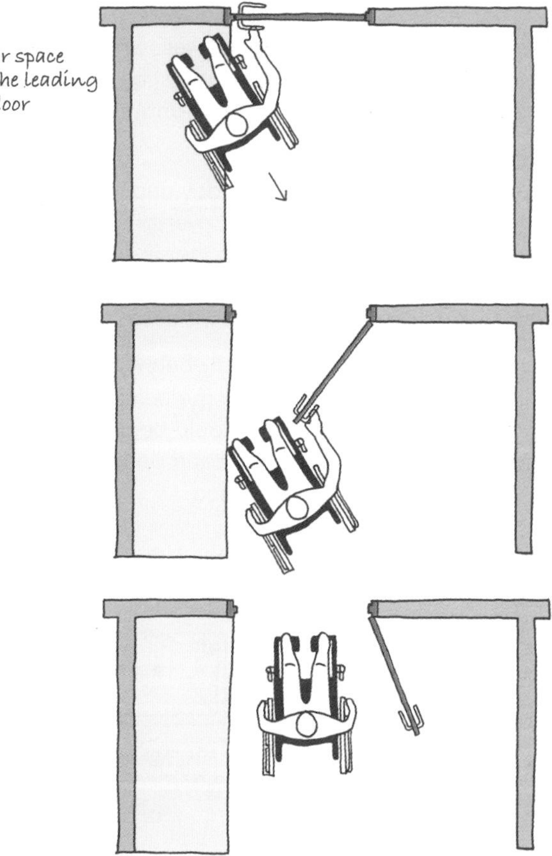

6.07 Internal doors: there should be a clear space beside the door to allow it to be opened by a wheelchair user and the door should open beyond 90°.

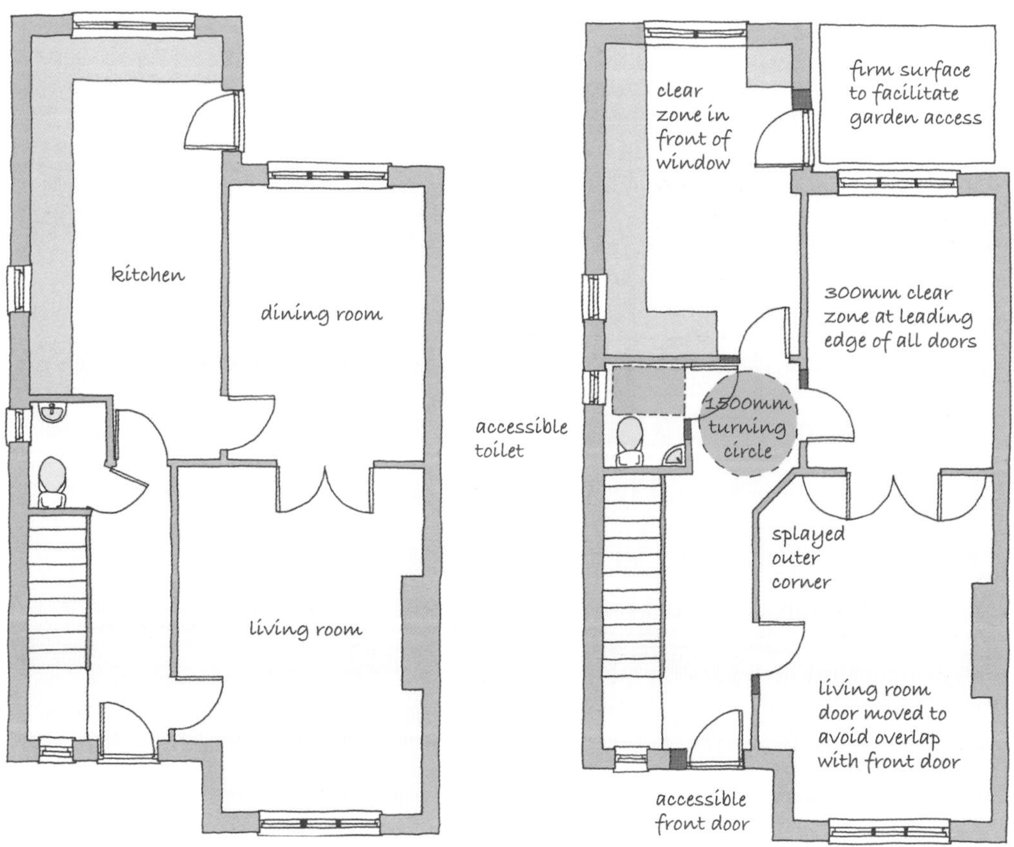

6.08 Circulation: two ground floor layouts of equal area. The layout on the right has been adjusted to improve accessibility.

Kitchen

The kitchen is the most difficult room to design well. Unlike an entrance where a single solution can make the design better for everyone, a kitchen must be tailored to the people using it. There are two approaches that can be taken to kitchen design: dual design and height-adjustable design.

Dual design approach

In a dual design approach, most of the everyday appliances are installed using universal design principles where a single solution is better for everyone. This includes appliances like the fridge, freezer, microwave and dishwasher. However, the sink, hob and work surface are installed twice: a 900mm high work surface with a hob and sink are installed for standing users; while a lower 760mm high sink, hob and work surface are installed for seated users.

A clear knee space should be provided directly below hobs, sinks, and food preparation areas and adjacent to appliances such as ovens, washing machines, dishwashers, refrigerators, and freezers. The remaining appliances that are shared should be installed at heights that suit everyone. For example, a fridge or dishwasher should be raised on a 200mm high plinth. Easy to grip cupboard door handles rather than knobs should be used.

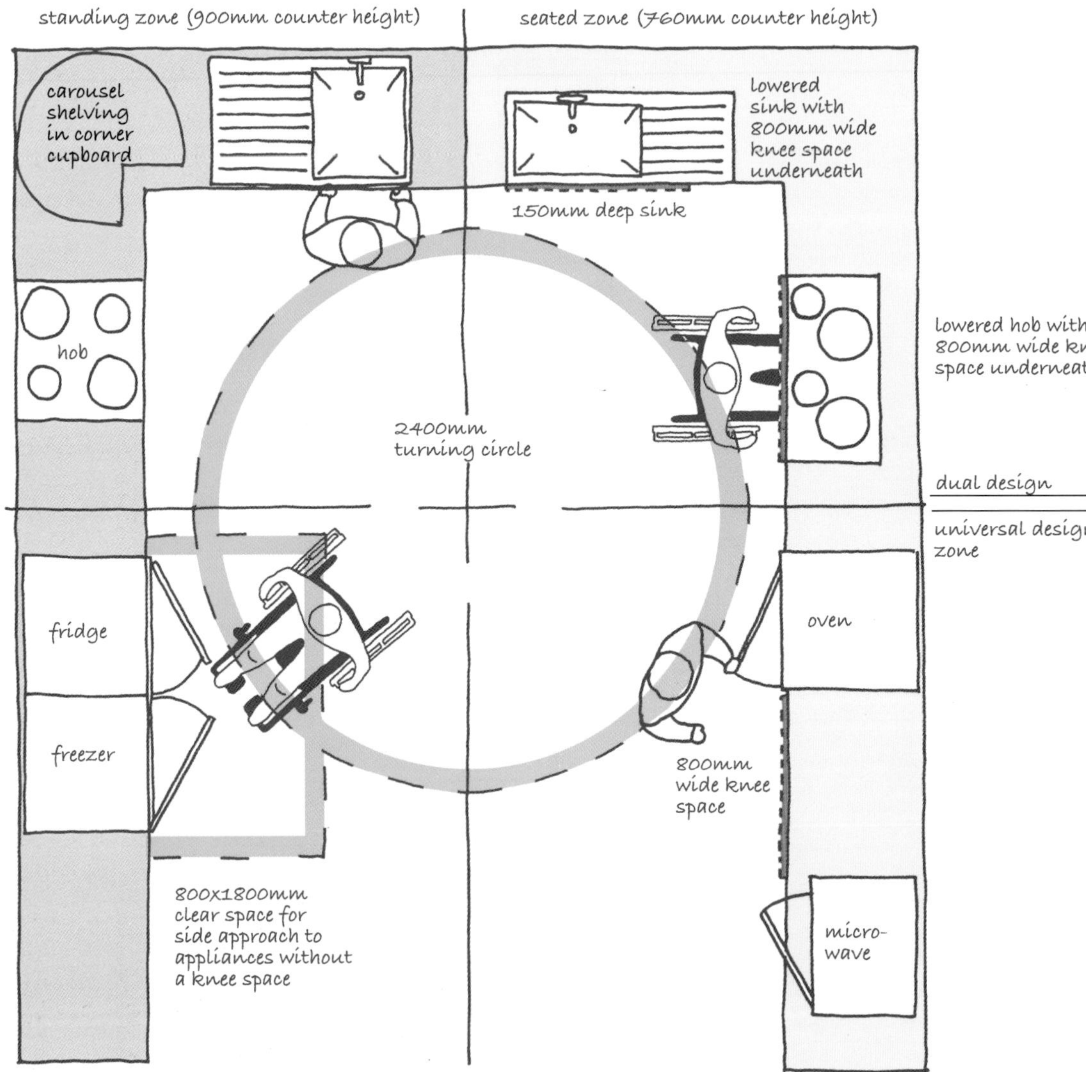

6.09 Kitchen design: a dual design approach for a large kitchen. Two counter heights, two sinks and two hobs are installed to allow for both standing use and wheelchair users.

Height-adjustable design approach

In this approach, a height-adjustable sink, hob and work surface are installed. Their heights are adjusted using simple push button-powered mechanisms. This approach allows for a more compact design and also has the benefit of allowing the user to adjust the height to suit their exact preference. The remaining appliances are installed to suit everyone as described above.

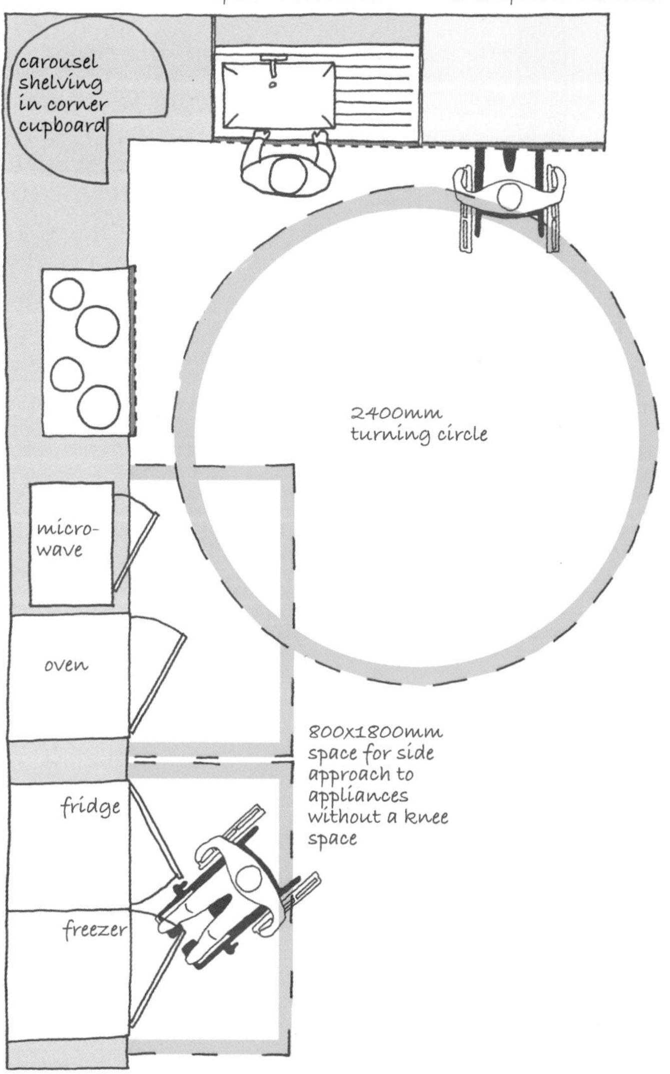

6.10 Kitchen design: height-adjustable design approach. This is a more compact layout for a smaller kitchen.

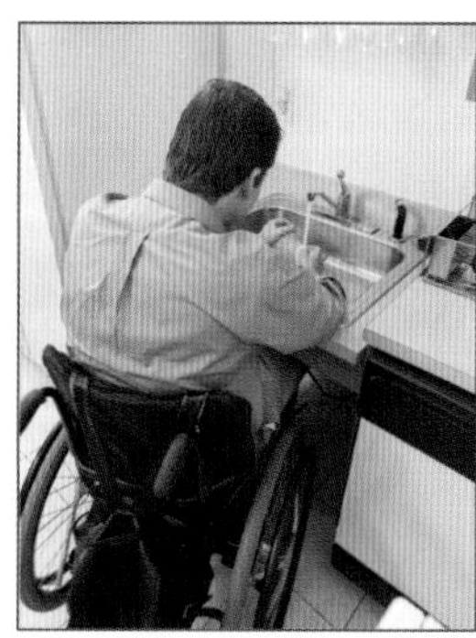

6.11 Height adjustable sink.

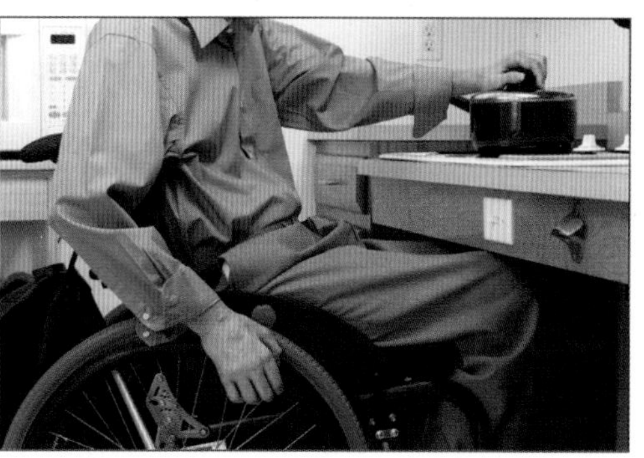

6.12 Height adjustable hob, with knee space below.

Toilets

Every new and refurbished house should have a toilet that is accessible to all. It should be provided at the entrance level (usually the ground floor). The layout should allow for the door to be easily closed with the wheelchair inside. Grab rails are only installed if somebody living in the house requires them.

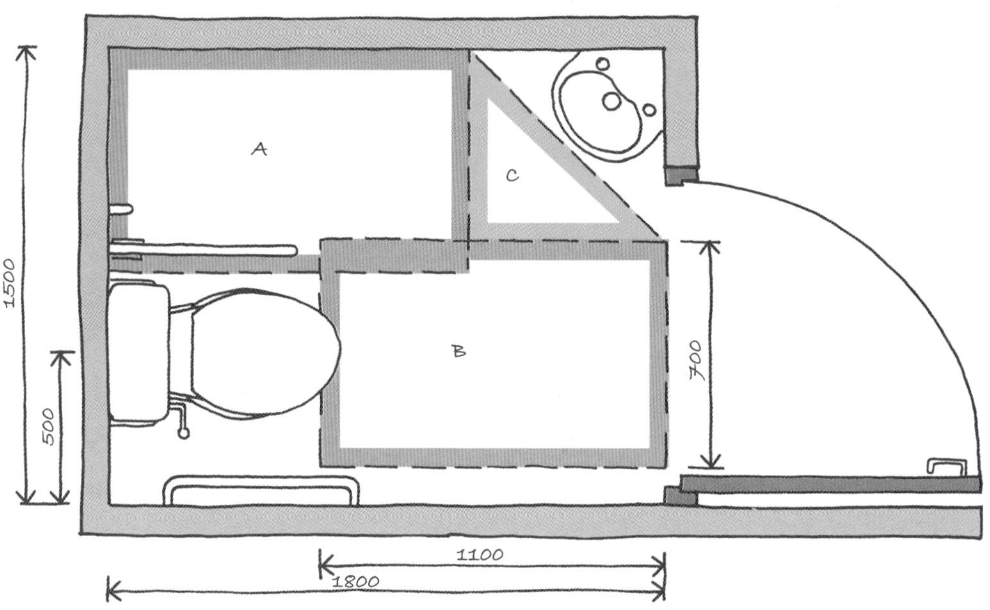

6.13 Toilet facilities: a minimum internal size of 1,500mm by 1,800mm allows two clear areas (A and B) to be included. These areas are required to allow for different transfer techniques from wheelchair to toilet seat. Area C should be kept clear to allow access to area A. Note: the Centre for Excellence in Universal Design (CEUD) guidelines state that the minimum size of area B is 700mm x 1,100mm. The TGD M state that the minimum size of area B is 750mm x 1,200mm.

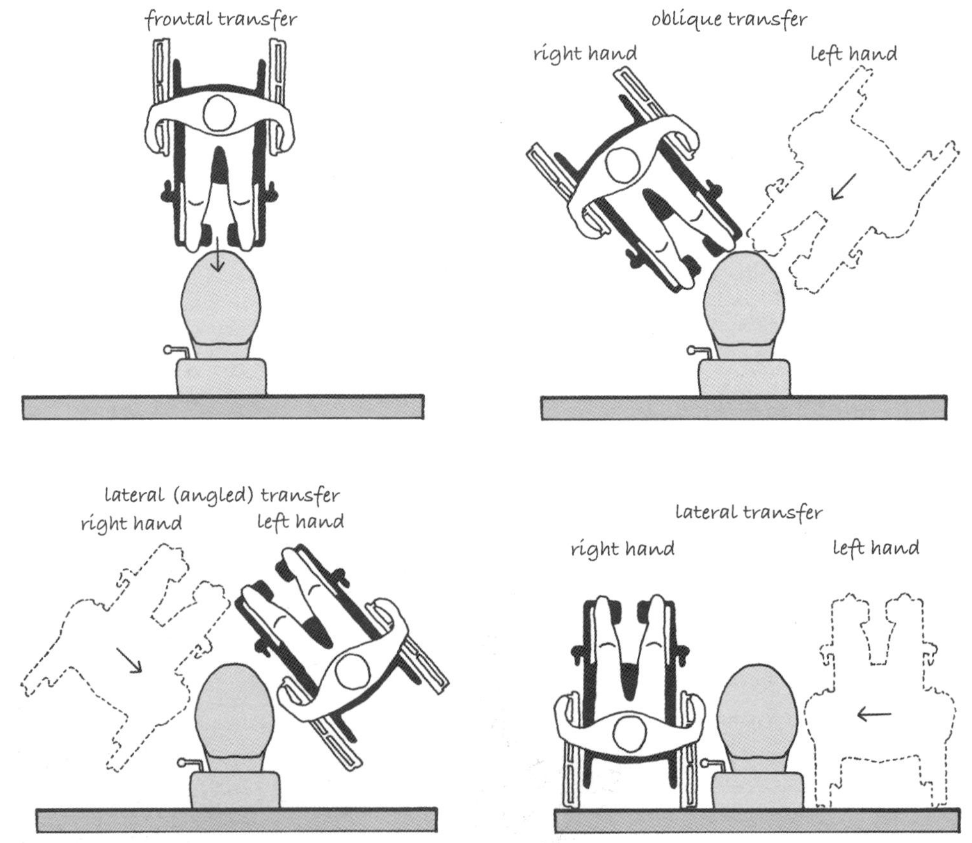

6.14 Toilet facilities: wheelchair users employ various techniques to transfer to the toilet seat; space must be provided to allow for these.

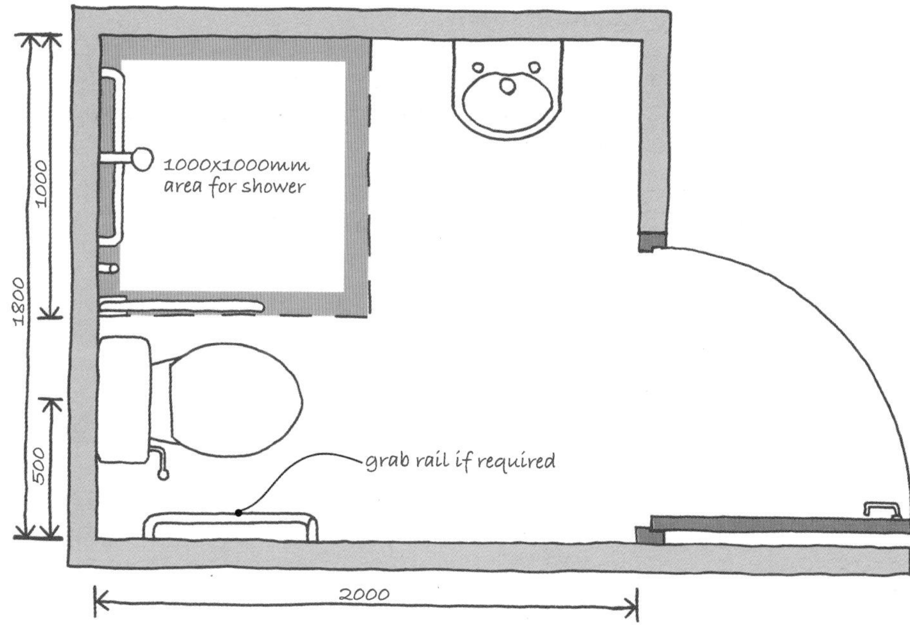

6.15 Toilet facilities: 'best practice' internal size of 1,800mm by 2,000mm. Having a slightly larger space would allow a shower area to be installed should the need arise in the future; if, for example, one of the occupants were unable to access the main bathroom upstairs.

ACTIVITIES

Invite a wheelchair user to visit your class. Prepare a list of questions that you could ask them about the practical challenges they face when doing everyday things at home (e.g. preparing a meal, taking a shower, going to bed, etc.).

Discuss the ways in which their home could be or has been improved to make their life easier.

Note: while it is important to be sensitive when discussing these issues, we should not be afraid to talk about them. It is only when they are discussed that they can be dealt with.

Bathroom

An accessible bathroom should be provided in all new and refurbished houses. The intelligent layout and space provided by an accessible bathroom will benefit all users, especially families with small children. Also, it should not be assumed that people with limited mobility will not use an upstairs bathroom – many people can use stair lifts or similar devices to get upstairs.

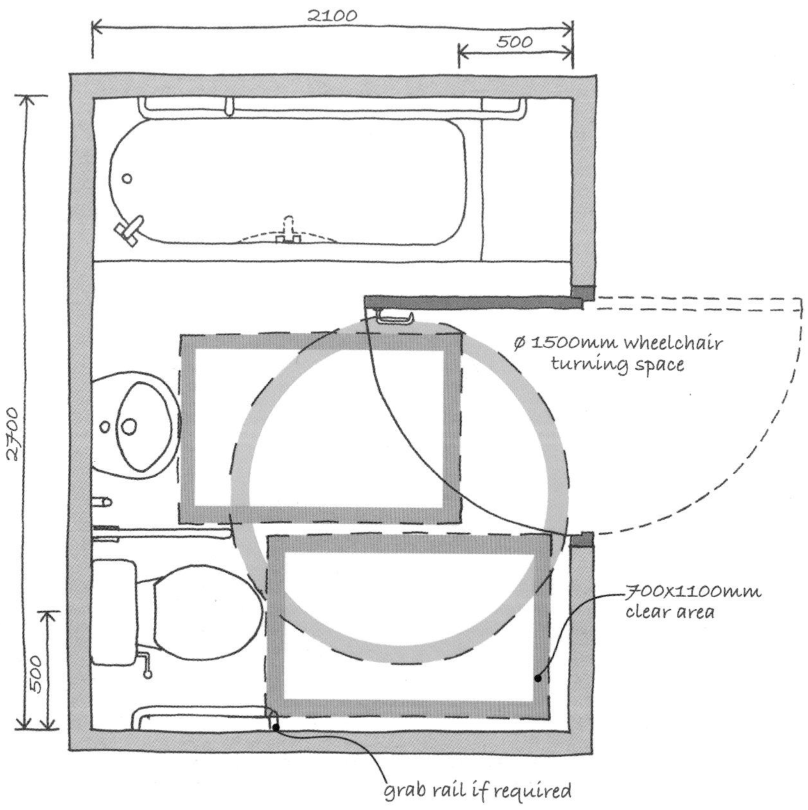

6.16 Accessible bathroom: this layout provides a clear 1,500mm turning circle and also provides a clear area of 700mm x 1,100mm in front of the toilet and the basin. Ideally, the door should swing outwards to maximise space.

Shower room

There are two approaches that can taken to the design of a shower room:

1 A wet room where the entire floor area is tiled (with a slip-resistant tile) and made watertight with a gentle slope (1:60) to a drain in one corner (under the shower head).
2 A flush finish shower tray.

In either case a fabric shower curtain can be installed, if desired.

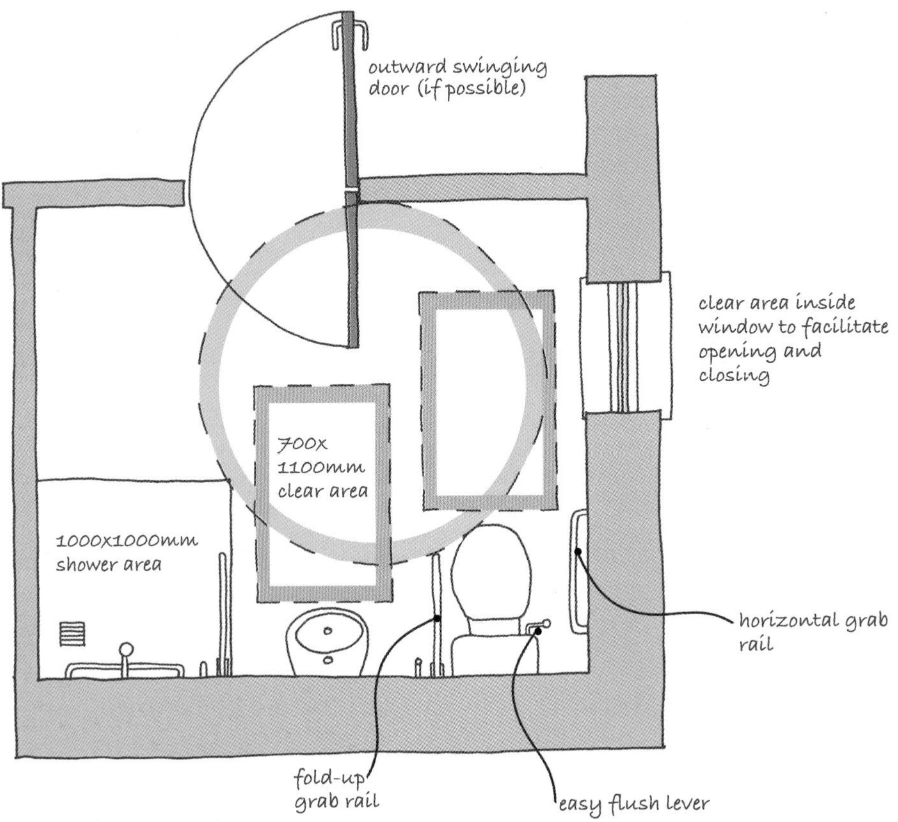

6.17 Accessible shower room: this layout provides a clear 1,500mm turning circle and also provides a clear area of 700mm x 1,100mm in front of the toilet and the basin. Grab rails are only installed if required.

REVISION EXERCISES

1 What is meant by the term 'universal design'?
2 Outline, using a neat freehand sketch, the features of an accessible entrance doorway.
3 Explain, using a neat freehand sketch, how the floor plan of the house shown could be redesigned to make it more accessible for all.

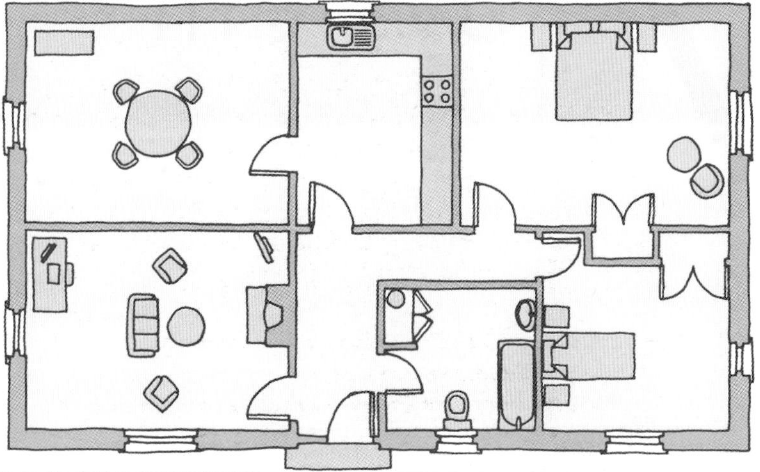

4 A family plans to convert an existing garage into a bedroom with an en suite bathroom for an elderly relative. The bathroom will contain a toilet, hand basin and shower. Explain, using neat freehand sketches, how the principles of universal design can be used to guide the design of the bedroom and bathroom.

5 Generate a neat annotated freehand sketch of a kitchen designed for a young couple, one of whom is a wheelchair user.

CHAPTER 7

Building Control System

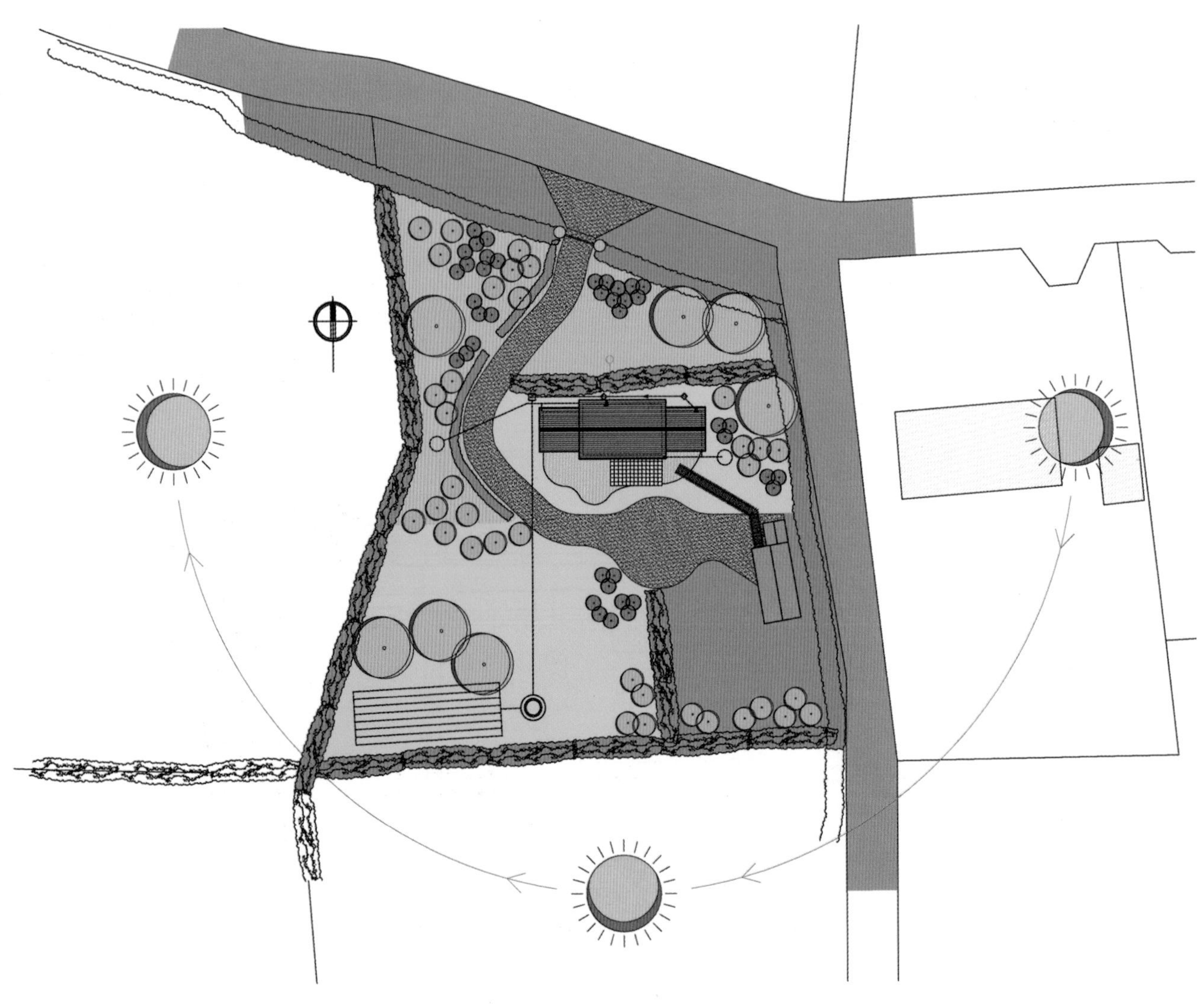

The design and construction of houses in Ireland is controlled by the building control system. The purpose of the building control system is to ensure that every home built in Ireland meets a minimum standard of safety and quality. This minimum standard is described in detail in the building regulations and technical guidance documents.

The regulations were first introduced in 1997 and are constantly updated to improve the minimum quality of homes in Ireland. However, it is very important to realise that the building regulations are a minimum standard. In the important area of energy consumption, the building regulations are improving, but they still do not set a very high standard.

ACTIVITIES

Organise a formal class debate. Pick two teams of three people, three judges and a timekeeper.

The rest of the class are the 'audience'. Each speaker is given two minutes to make their points.

The motion is:
People who are building their own home should be allowed to design their home to any standard they like – there shouldn't be a minimum standard that has to be met.

SUPPLEMENTARY INFORMATION

The building control system comprises five elements.

1 Building Control Act 2007: gives local authorities power to regulate construction in their area and protects certain titles (e.g. 'Architect', 'Quantity Surveyor').
2 Building Control Regulations (1997 onward): requires fire certificates for apartment blocks, requires planning permission for 'changes of use'.
3 EU Construction Products Directive: ensures that construction materials and products are made to harmonised standards so that they can be freely imported and exported to other European countries.
4 Building Regulations (1997 onward): broad statements of design principles that describe the general standards a home must meet.
5 Technical Guidance Documents: provide detailed design information showing how to comply with the regulations.

Technical guidance documents A–M

The Technical Guidance Documents (TGDs) provide detailed information on the design features required to comply with the building regulations. Each document addresses a different area of building design. The documents apply to various types of building, including homes (dwellings). Very detailed advice is provided in each document. When planning permission is sought the design must comply with the regulations that are in force at the time.

It is very important to remember that the requirements of the building regulations (described in the TGDs) are a minimum standard that must be met – the equivalent of a pass grade in an exam. While this is acceptable in most areas (e.g. structure, drainage, stairs), the regulations do not represent best practice in relation to energy efficiency (e.g. thermal insulation, thermal bridging and airtightness). In other words, it is possible to build a home that complies with the building regulations but is not energy efficient.

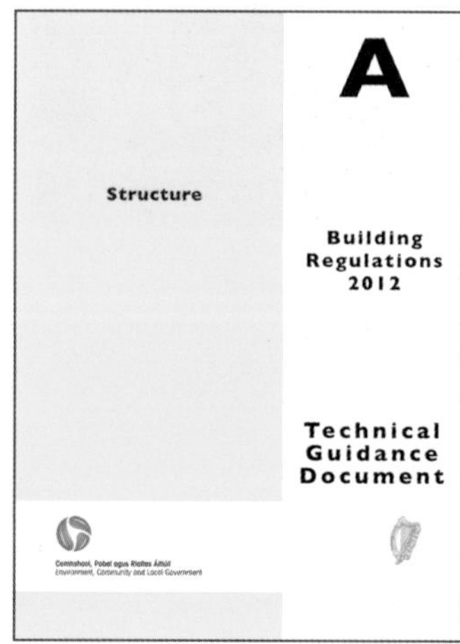

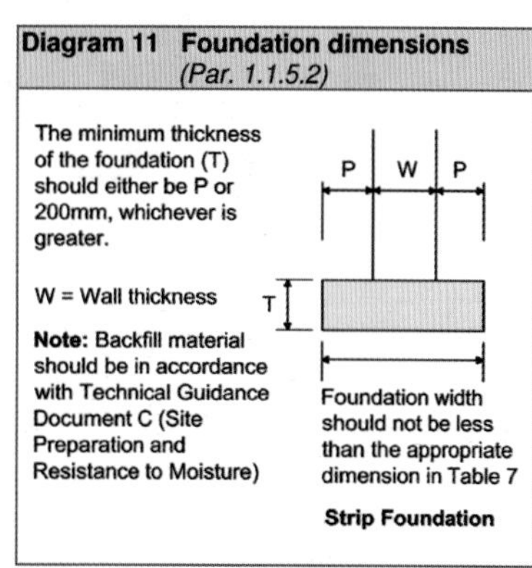

7.01 This sample from TGD A shows the sort of detailed information provided in the TGDs.

SUPPLEMENTARY INFORMATION

Currently there are 12 TGDs covering various areas of design and construction:
- TGD A: Structure
- TGD B: Fire safety
- TGD C: Site preparation and resistance to moisture
- TGD D: Materials and workmanship
- TGD E: Sound
- TGD F: Ventilation
- TGD G: Hygiene
- TGD H: Drainage
- TGD J: Heat producing appliances
- TGD K: Stairways, ladders, ramps and guards
- TGD L: Conservation of fuel and energy
- TGD M: Access and use.

ACTIVITIES

Updates to the regulations are published online: Look up www.environ.ie and check the year of publication of each TGD. Download the latest version of TGD L and look through it.

Certification of building products

Every construction material, product or process used in the construction of a home in Ireland should meet the relevant Irish and European standards. In Ireland, the National Standards Authority of Ireland (NSAI) is the body responsible for product certification. Before a product can be certified, it must undergo a process of inspection and testing to ensure it meets minimum quality assurance standards and any relevant legal requirements. Construction professionals (e.g. architects, builders, etc.) are required to ensure that all construction products they specify or use are certified for use in residential construction.

Since 2013, CE marking is mandatory for most construction products on sale in the European Union (EU). A CE mark denotes that the product has been assessed and meets EU safety, health and environmental protection requirements. If a product is not covered by an EU standard the NSAI can certify the product as having reached the relevant Irish standard and issue an Irish Standard Mark. Alternatively, if a construction material, product or process is new and a national or European standard does not exist yet, the NSAI can issue an Agrément Certificate.

The Agrément Certification system allows new and innovative ways of building homes to be developed while providing consumers with confidence that the construction material, product or process has been independently tested and certified as suitable for use in Ireland.

ACTIVITIES

Visit www.nsai.ie and learn more about certification. Download and compare the Agrément Certificates of two external insulation systems.

Certified Product Name

CERT No. 14/0000

7.02 Certification marks: CE, Agrément Certificate and Irish Standard.

Planning

Planning is the general term used to describe the system that controls how land is used. Planning is controlled by the local government authorities (e.g. city and county councils) to ensure that the right things get built in the right place in the right order. For example, the planning system ensures that when houses are built, roads, cycle lanes, shops, schools and other facilities are also provided in the plan.

7.03 Adamstown, Co. Dublin is an example of master planning; 10,000 residential units with associated transport and community infrastructure were planned.

ACTIVITIES

Look up the development plan for your local area online. Start by visiting the local authority's website; then go to the planning section and find the relevant plan. If you live in the countryside the county development plan will apply. If you live in a small village there might be a village design statement. If you live in an urban area there will most likely be a local area plan for that area.

Planning system

The planning system is based on development plans. There is a development plan for each county as well as a more detailed local area development plan for towns and urban areas. The local planning authority, in consultation with the local community through its public representatives (e.g. county councillors), prepares the development plans.

KEY PRINCIPLES

The planning system is based on the following principles:

- **natural and constitutional justice** – the system must uphold the law
- **sustainable development** – it must ensure sustainable use of land
- **transparency** – it must be open (for example, all documents submitted as part of a planning application must be available to the public)
- **accountability** – the people working in the planning system must be accountable for their actions
- **integrity** – the people working in the planning system must not be corrupt
- **impartiality** – the people working in the planning system must be fair and unbiased in their decisions
- **promotion of the public interest** – decisions taken must always be taken so that the interests of the citizens are placed ahead of all other interests.

When an application to construct a new building is submitted, the development plan is consulted to check whether the proposed building is in keeping with the plan. If the new building does not fit in with the development plan, it will not be allowed to go ahead. Development plans are reviewed and updated every five years.

KEY PRINCIPLES

The development plan provides guidance on:
- types of development that are acceptable in different areas (i.e. zoning)
- areas that are sensitive to development (e.g. green belts)
- buildings and trees to be protected
- traffic safety and road improvements
- water supply and sewage disposal
- environmental issues.

Planning process
Before building a house the client must apply to the local authority for planning permission. A key feature of the process is that it gives members of the public an opportunity to examine the plans and make submissions. This ensures that people have a fair chance to object to an application if they feel it will have a negative impact on their home or amenity.

It is against the law to build a house without planning permission. If this happens, the local authority can apply to the courts for an order requiring the house to be demolished. The court may also impose a fine and/or a prison sentence.

KEY PRINCIPLES

The benefits of requiring people to get planning permission include ensuring that:
- the land owner has given permission for the construction to go ahead
- other people in the area are aware that a house is going to be built
- the house will not have a negative impact on the local environment
- the house is designed to meet the building regulations.

ACTIVITIES

- Visit your local planning office. Ask for a planning permission application form. Read through the form. Make a list of all of the documents required. Note especially any extra information that your local authority requires with a typical application
- Invite a planner to the school to speak to your class about planning in your area. Prepare a series of questions to ask the planner during the visit. Write a summary of what you learned from this visit.

Procedure
Planning permission can be sought in three ways.

1 Outline followed by approval – outline permission is used to establish whether the planning authority agrees in principle with the proposed building, without the need to draw up detailed plans and documents. Approval involves seeking permission to construct the building suggested after outline permission has been received. Detailed drawings and documents are required for approval.
2 Permission – (sometimes called full permission) involves seeking permission in one step. Detailed drawings and documents are required.
3 Retention – this involves seeking permission to retain or keep a building that has been constructed without planning permission. Detailed drawings and documents are required. If the application is rejected the building may have to be demolished.

Full permission is valid for five years from the date the permission was granted. Outline permission is usually valid for three years but this can be extended to five years by the planning authority.

Check the development plan:
- applicant reads the relevant plan to find out what is required in the area.

Pre-planning meeting:
- client/architect meet the planners to discuss plans and seek advice.

Prepare application:
- maps, house plans, percolation test results, application form, etc.

Notice placed in local newspaper:
- submit application within two weeks.

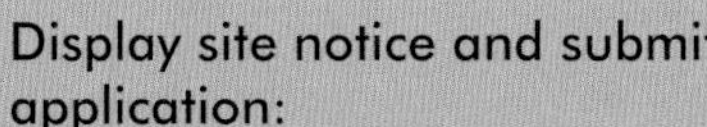

Display site notice and submit application:
- both are done on the same day.

Planners assess the application:
- planners visit the site
- third parties can make observations or objections
- decision made within eight weeks
- planners may request further information (applicant has up to six months to respond).

Applicant is notified of the decision:
- planners usually require certain conditions to be met
- appeals by applicant (or third parties who objected) must be submitted within four weeks.

Final grant issued:
- planners usually require four weeks and three days after the decision (provided there are no appeals).

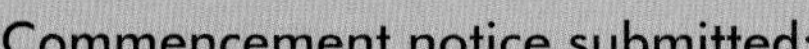

Commencement notice submitted:
- between 14 and 28 days before commencement of work
- work can commence when the planners have received this notice and all conditions have been complied with.

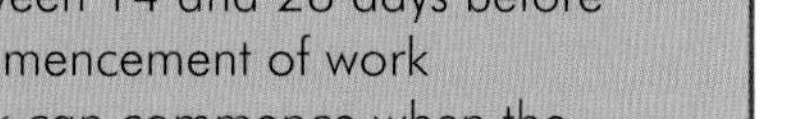

7.04 The typical process for obtaining full planning permission.

Documentation

Several documents must be included in the application to give the planner a clear idea of what the development will look like when it is finished and how it will relate to the site and any nearby buildings:

- site location maps (scale 1:10,560 and 1:2,500)
- site layout plan (scale 1:500)
- house plans, elevations and sections (1:100)
- copy of site notice
- copy of newspaper notice
- letter of consent from landowner
- completed application form
- details of the wastewater treatment system and percolation test results (for rural houses not connected to the public sewer).

Maps/drawings

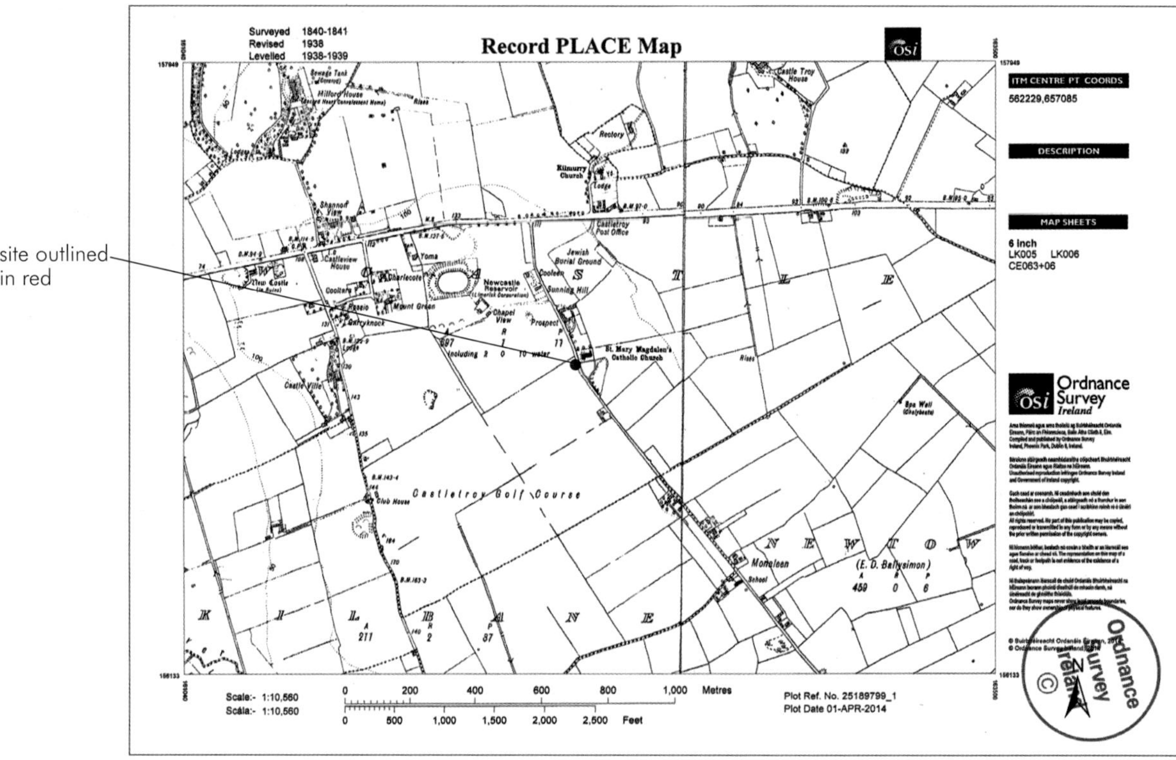

7.05 A typical site location map, 'Record Place Map' (usually printed on paper at scale 1:10,560).

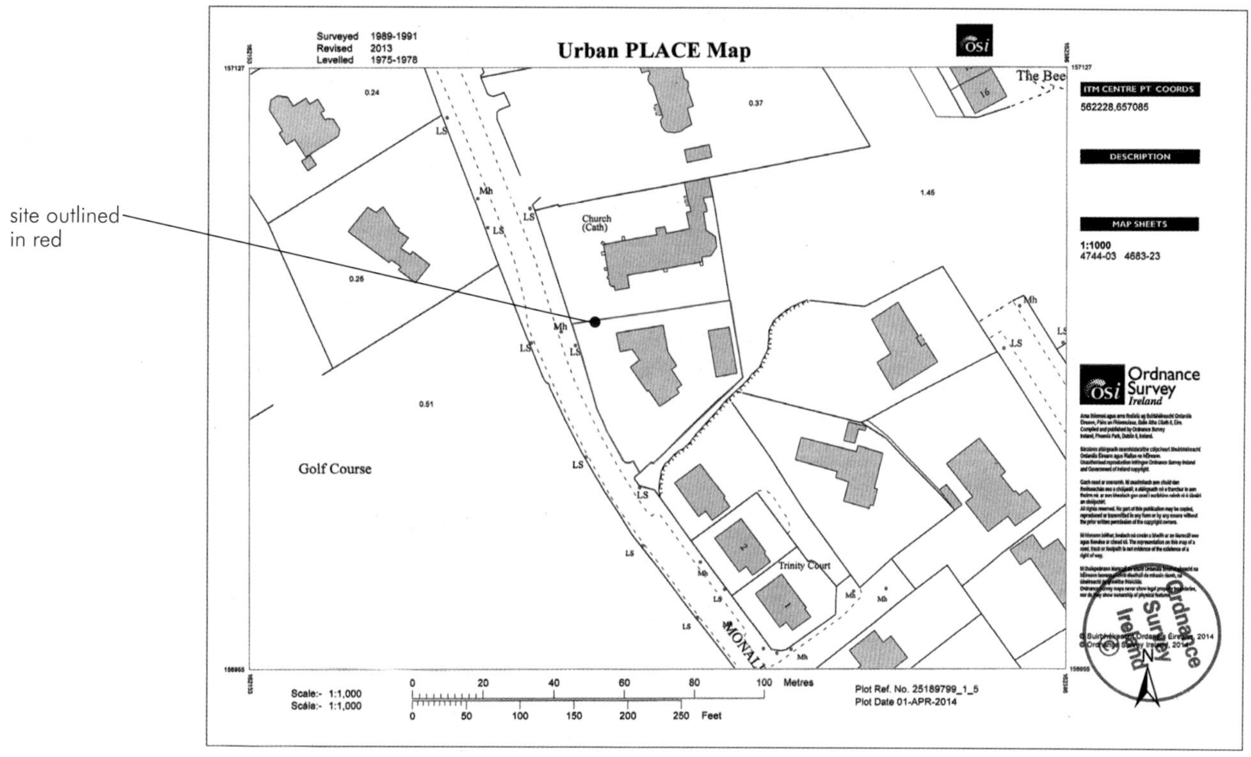

7.06 The same site shown in greater detail on an 'Urban Place Map' (usually printed on paper at scale 1:2,500).

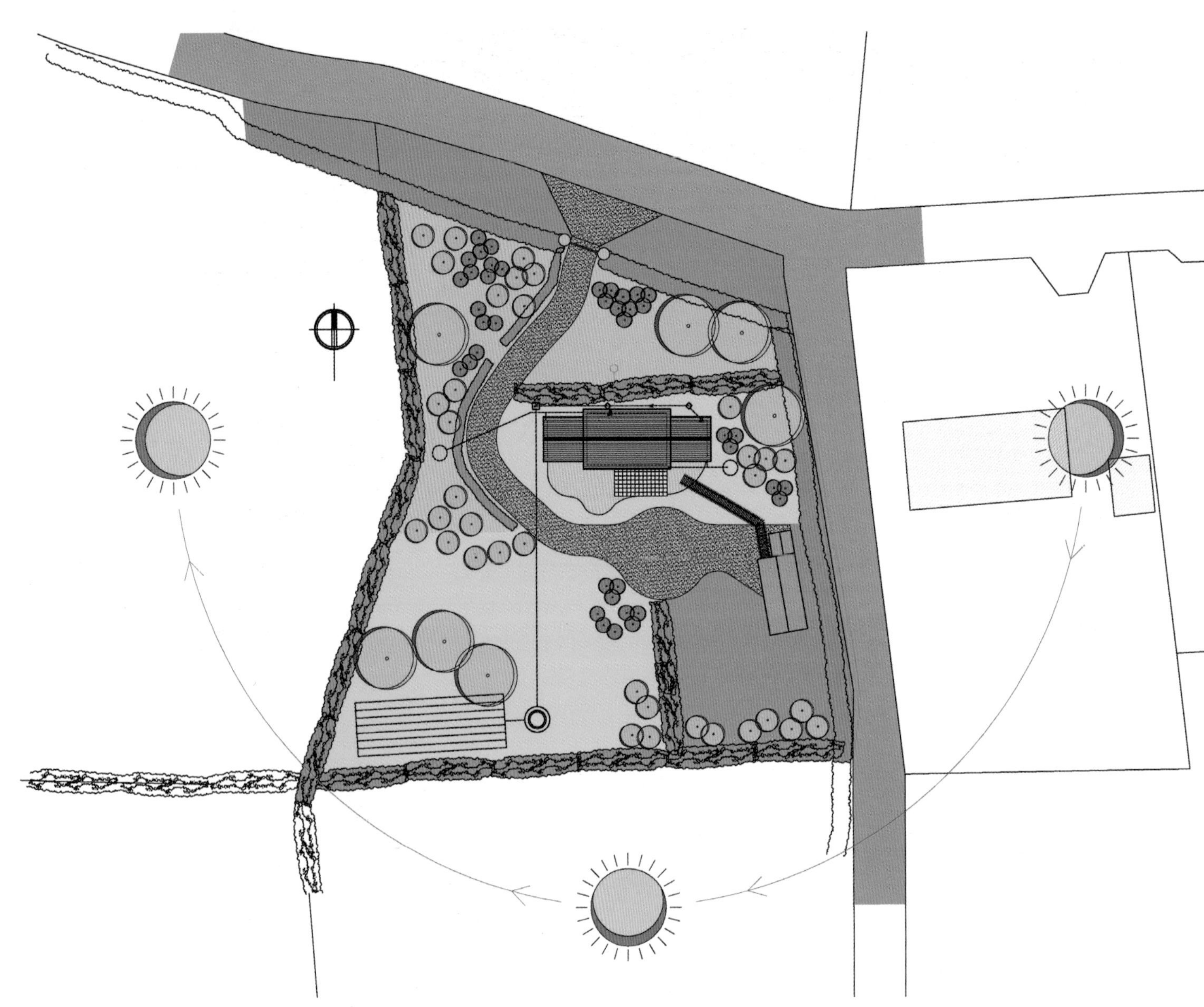

7.07 An example of a site plan for a single house designed for a rural setting (usually drawn at scale 1:500).

7.08 Example drawings of a single storey house designed for a rural setting (usually drawn at scale 1:100 or 1:50).

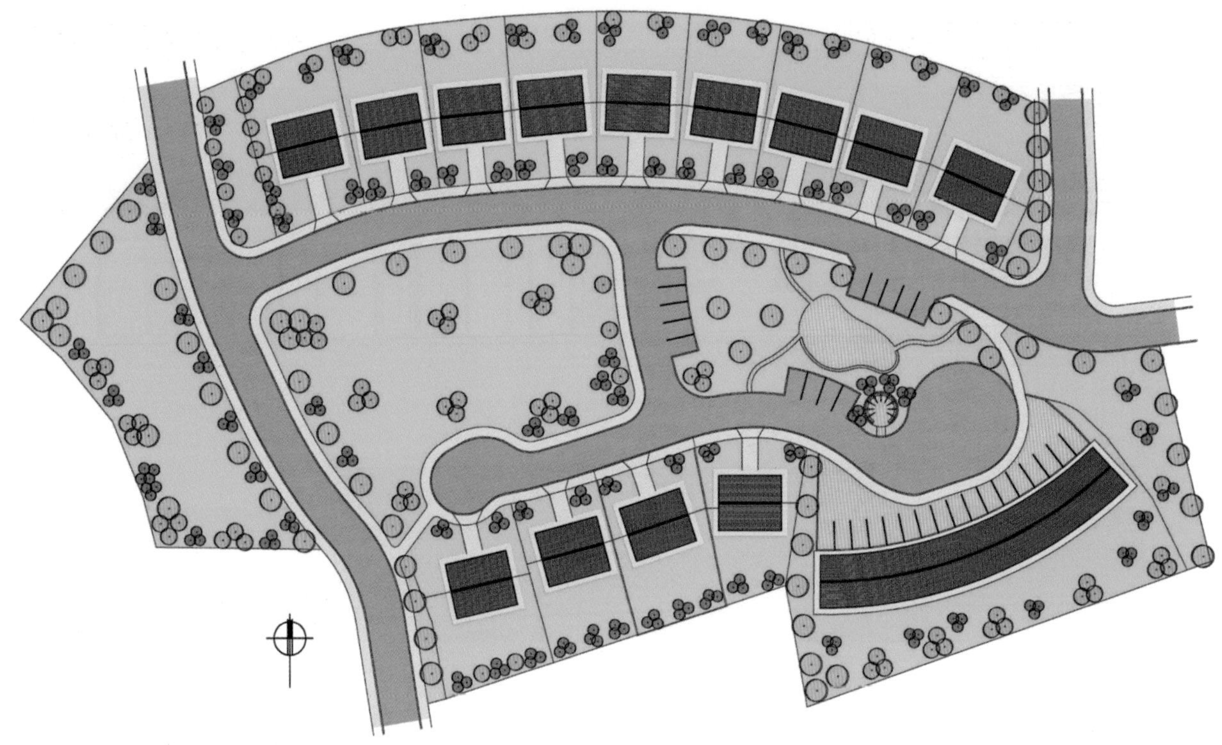

7.09 An example of a site plan for a housing scheme designed for a suburban setting (usually drawn at scale 1:500).

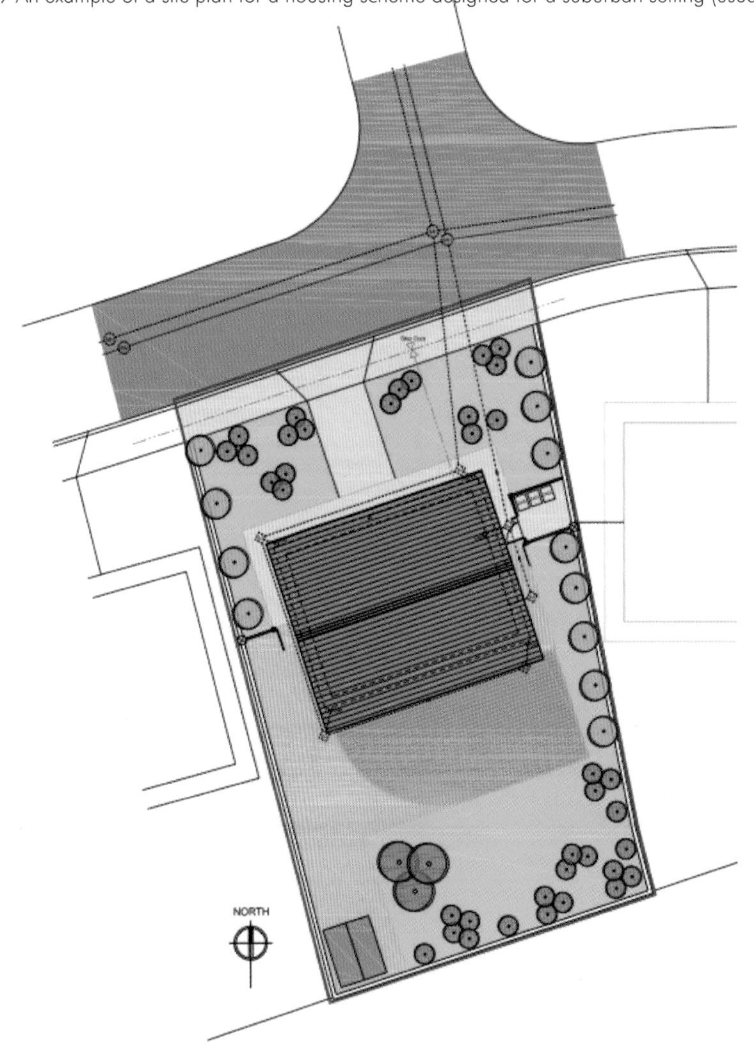

7.10 An example of a site plan for an individual two storey house deigned for a suburban setting (usually drawn at scale 1:250).

7.11 Example drawings of a two storey house designed for a suburban setting (usually drawn at scale 1:100 or 1:50).

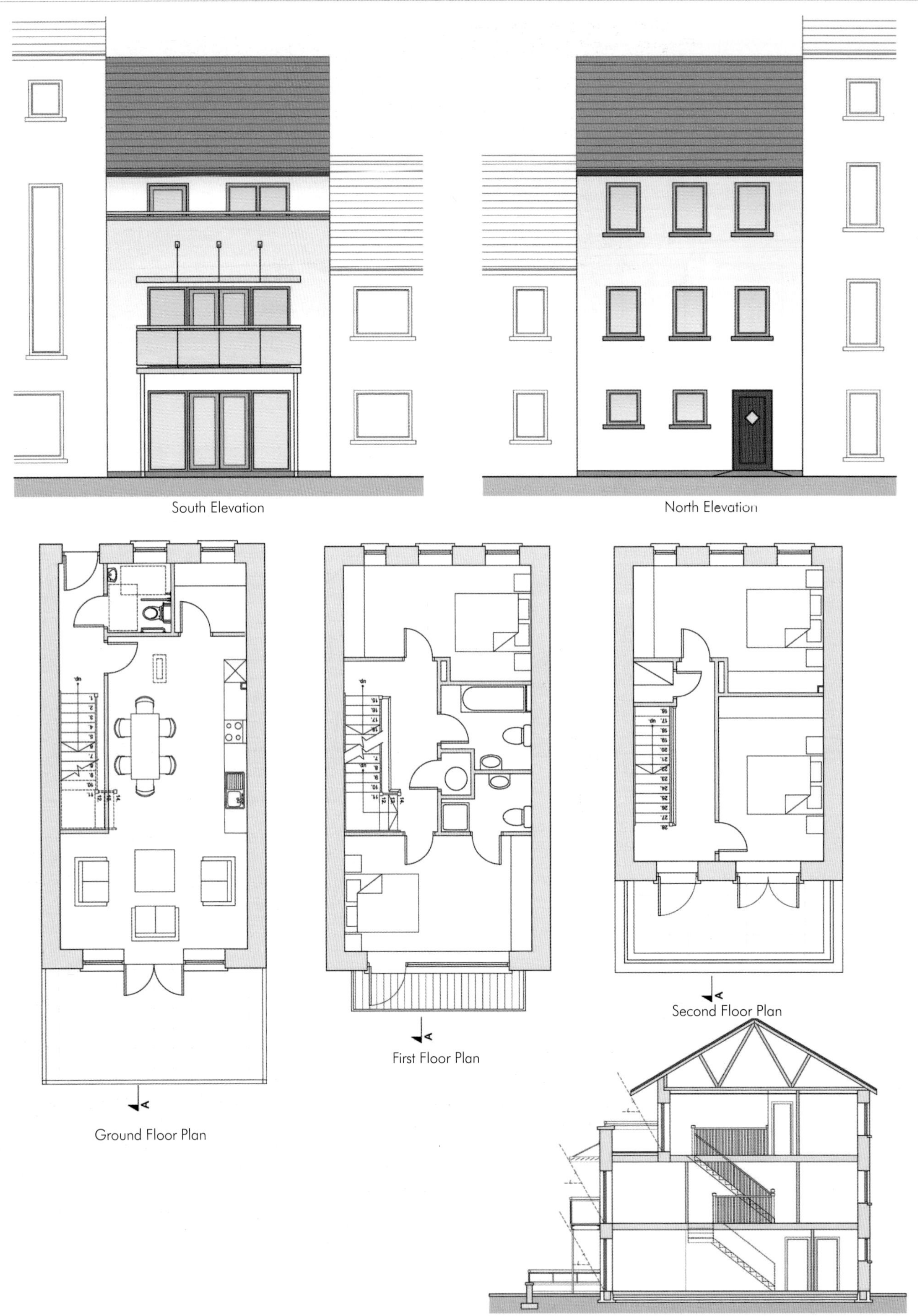

7.12 Example drawings of a three storey house designed for a suburban setting (usually drawn at scale 1:100 or 1:50).

KEY PRINCIPLES

A site layout plan shows:
- proposed house, structures and works
- proposed alterations or extensions to existing buildings
- roads and site boundaries
- distance from existing and proposed structures to roads and boundaries
- approximate height of ground floor level relative to nearby road levels
- buildings and structures on adjoining lands
- existing and proposed water supply and sewage disposal systems
- existing and proposed access to public roads
- position of the site notice.

Objections and appeals

Any person can make an observation or objection to a planning application. An *observation* is made when someone wants to draw the planner's attention to a particular issue but they don't want to object to the proposal.

An *objection* is made when someone wants to prevent some element of the proposal from going ahead. Objections must be made in writing and a fee must be paid. The planners are required to fairly consider the merits of all objections and keep objectors informed of any decisions made. Objections can be made about any aspect of the proposal. For example, a common objection involves a neighbour complaining that windows in the proposed house will overlook their property.

A decision to grant or refuse planning permission may be appealed to An Bord Pleanála. Only the applicant or a third party who previously made an observation or objection can lodge an appeal. However, once an application has been appealed, anybody can make a submission to An Bord Pleanála about the case. The appeal must be lodged within four weeks of the original decision.

ACTIVITIES

- Go to your local planning office's website (e.g. www.lcc.ie/planning). Look up applications made recently in your area. Try to find an application where someone has made an observation or objection. Consider the points made by the third party and imagine yourself in the role of the planner. Make a list of the reasons why you would grant or refuse the planning permission.
- Go to An Bord Pleanála's website (www.pleanala.ie). Read about what they do in the 'About' section. Look up 'new cases' in your local authority area. Browse through a case to get an idea of the process involved. Try to find the inspector's report and read the recommendations. This will give you a good idea of what people who appeal a planning application experience.

Social impact of planning

Decisions made about where to build and what type of housing to build can have a very profound impact on the lives of ordinary people.

Creating communities

In the past, many local authorities decided to build large housing developments of social housing so that every citizen would have a good-quality home. This seemed like a good idea at the time. In practice, however, because these housing estates lacked a mixture of people from different social backgrounds, many of them became centres of high unemployment, crime and other social problems. They also added to the separation of society into homogenous groups (e.g. 'working class', 'middle class'). Sometimes people become trapped in these areas and have a reduced quality of life just because of where they live, not because of anything they have done.

Today the planning regulations require that 20% of every development is set aside for social and affordable housing (Part V, Planning and Development Act 2000). This ensures that people from all walks of life live in every area; this will lead to a more integrated society and should ensure a better quality of life for everybody.

KEY PRINCIPLES

Urban communities should be designed so that:

- people of different social statuses can live in the same neighbourhood
- public spaces are safe to use, especially at night
- there are places where people can live at any stage of their lives (e.g. small units for single people and bigger units for families)
- the resources needed for everyday life are nearby (e.g. shops, schools, employment)
- there are amenities nearby for leisure activities (e.g. parks, cinemas, restaurants)
- the character of the existing area is respected and augmented.

ACTIVITIES

Use the internet to find a story in the media about the social impact of planning decisions/housing developments. These stories are often negative. You might be able to find some positive stories about the regeneration of urban areas (e.g. Moyross, Limerick and Ballymun, Dublin) that have been the focus of negative attention in the past.

Similar mistakes have been made in rural areas. Some people have been allowed to build in isolated rural areas. As these people get older they often don't have the support they need to remain in their own homes. People living in isolated rural areas also find themselves travelling long distances by car for everyday things like buying groceries and going to school. It is essential that the long-term interests of all members of society are considered when making decisions about where and how to build homes.

KEY PRINCIPLES

Rural communities should be designed so that:

- people are part of a community
- there are enough people living in the area to keep the area alive (e.g. schools, GAA teams)
- the resources needed for everyday life are nearby (e.g. shops, employment)
- over-dependence on cars is avoided
- a positive impact is made on the natural environment.

Uncontrolled development

With the growth of the economy from the 1960s onwards, the number of houses built in Ireland grew gradually. However, during the construction boom (c.1998–2008) the number of homes built grew at an excessive rate. The rate at which homes were being built was more than double the rate of population growth.

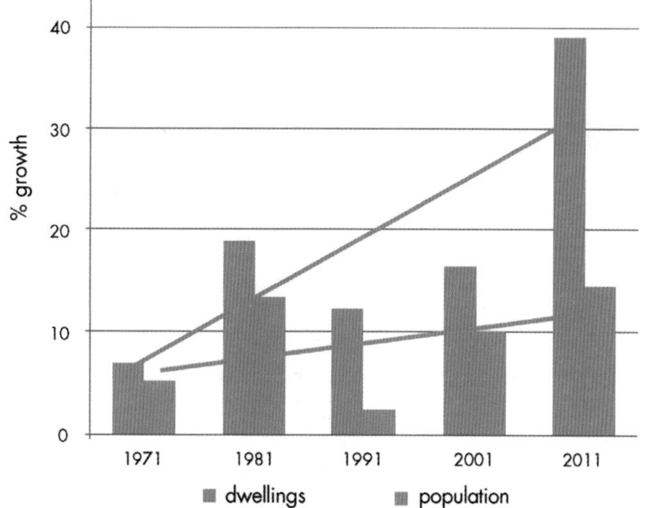

	1961	1971	1981	1991	2001	2011
dwellings	676,400	726,400	896,100	1,019,700	1,220,900	1,994,845
population	2,818,341	2,978,248	3,443,405	3,525,719	3,917,203	4,581,269

7.13 Housing and population growth 1961–2011.

Initially, this rapid growth provided employment, which allowed many people to enjoy a high standard of living. However, the construction of thousands of homes that were not needed ultimately contributed to the 'property crash' and the recession.

This failure of the planning system to control the rate of development has had a very real and lasting negative impact on the lives of many people living in Ireland.

Approximately one-third of Ireland's housing stock comprises individual homes built in rural areas. In 2012, Cork County Council granted significantly more permissions than any other county.

REVISION EXERCISES

1 Why is it necessary to have minimum building standards?
2 What are 'technical guidance documents' and where can they be found?
3 The planning system is based on seven principles. Describe the three principles that you think are most important and explain why.
4 Why is it important to submit such detailed documents when applying for planning permission?
5 Describe one positive and one negative way in which decisions made by the local planning authority have impacted on your local community.

CHAPTER 8

Heritage

Heritage is our legacy from the past, what we live with today, and what we pass on to future generations. Our cultural and natural heritage are both irreplaceable sources of life and inspiration. They serve as points of reference for a people and are fundamental to their identity.

World heritage

The United Nations Educational, Scientific and Cultural Organization (UNESCO) promotes the identification, protection and preservation of cultural and natural heritage around the world considered to be of outstanding value to humanity. Part of UNESCO's work involves maintaining a record of exceptional sites that are of universal value to all people irrespective of where they are located.

UNESCO categorises heritage into:

- **cultural heritage** – monuments, groups of buildings and sites with historical, aesthetic, archaeological, scientific, ethnological or anthropological value (e.g. Skellig Michael or Newgrange)
- **natural heritage** – outstanding physical, biological and geological formations, habitats of threatened species of animals and plants and areas with scientific, conservation or aesthetic value (e.g. Giant's Causeway).

Newgrange

8.01The passage tomb at Newgrange.

The *Brú na Bóinne* UNESCO World Heritage Site in Co. Meath comprises the Neolithic passage tombs at Newgrange, Knowth and Dowth (and many smaller passage tomb structures). These monuments were built over four phases from approximately 3400BC to 2800BC. The passage tomb at Newgrange was built around 3200BC, over 600 years before the Great Pyramid at Giza.

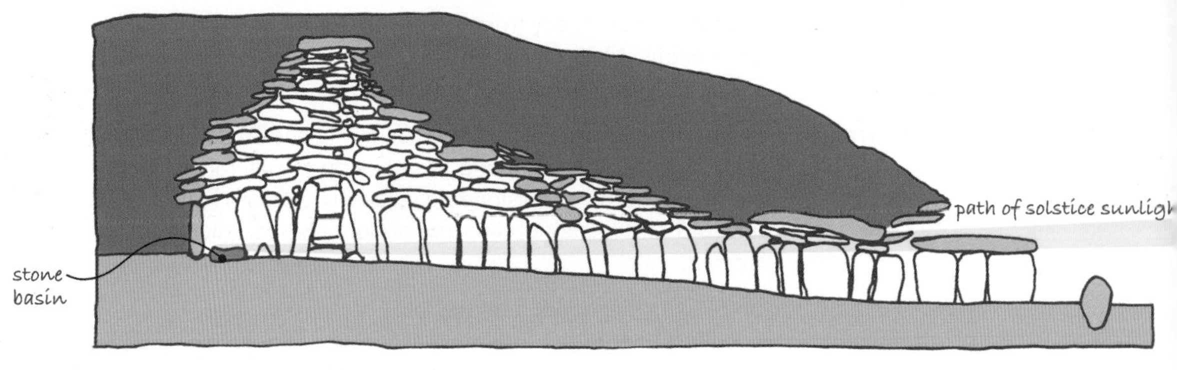

8.02 The precise design of the site allows the rising sun to penetrate into the chamber at Newgrange.

Archaeologists are fairly sure that Newgrange was a tomb. The passage and chamber inside are aligned in a south-easterly direction. A small window-like opening (known as the roof box) above the doorway allows the midwinter rising sun to shine into the central burial chamber at dawn on the winter solstice.

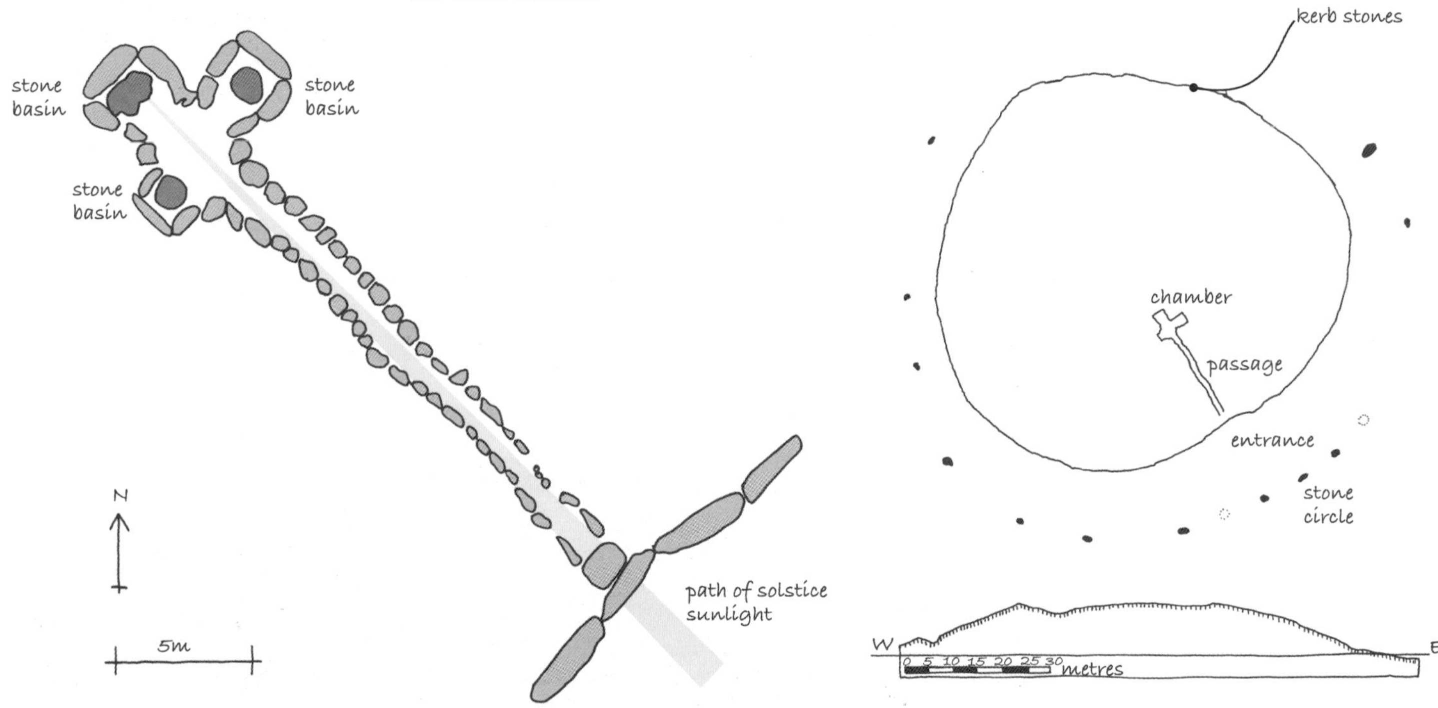

8.03 An aerial view of the site.

8.04 Plan and section of the cairn.

The passage tomb at Newgrange covers an area of just under half a hectare. It is around 11 metres high and has an average diameter of 80 metres. The cairn is encircled by 97 kerbstones and a further 450 similar stones make up the passage and chamber structure. Great effort and time was needed for planning, gathering materials and constructing these monuments. Today we cannot be certain of the construction methods used but archaeologists have suggested it is most likely that log-rolling, wooden scaffolding and earthen ramps were used.

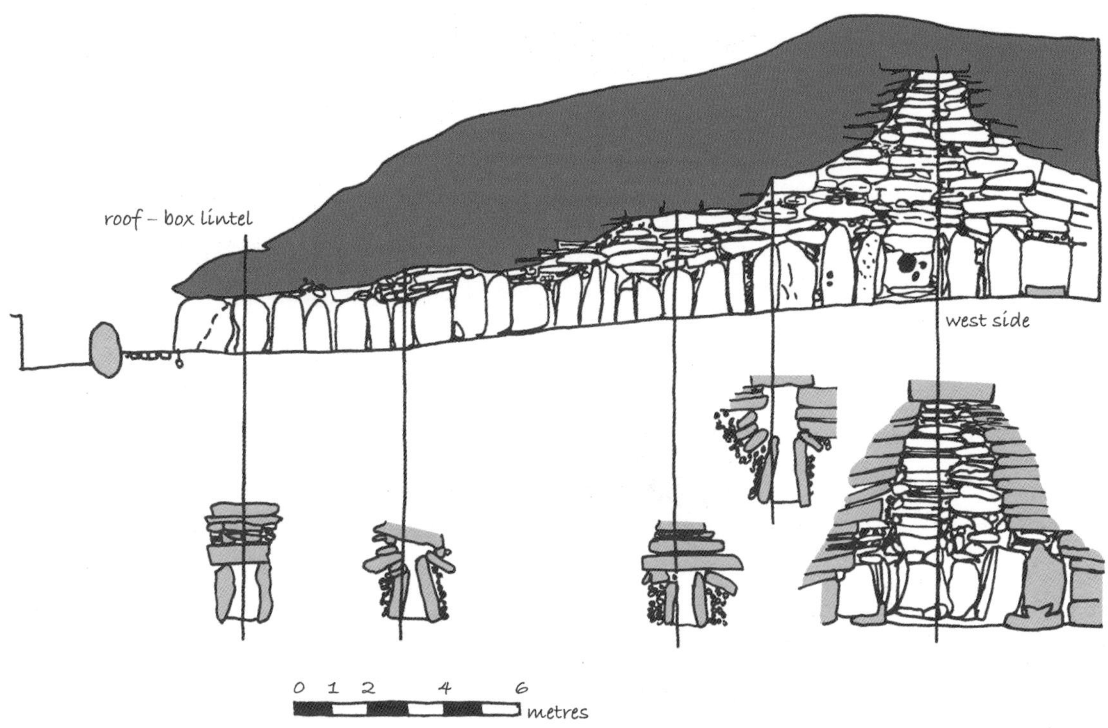

8.05 The passage is a lintelled structure, while the chamber was built using the corbelling technique.

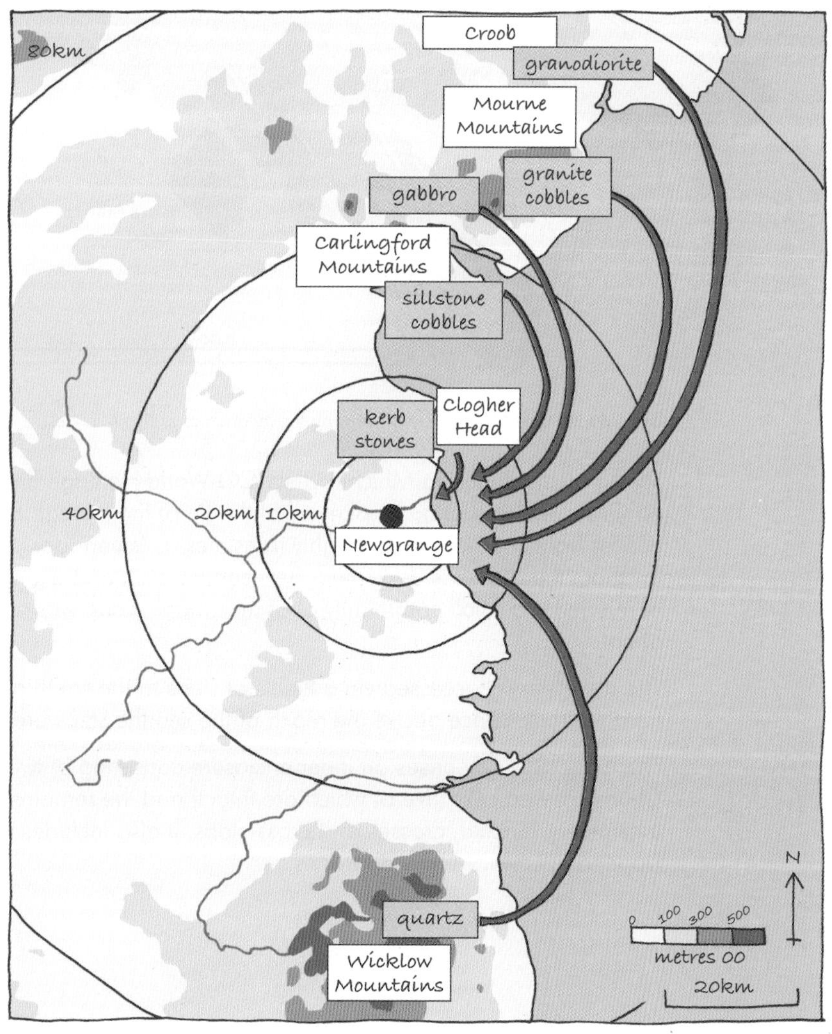

8.06 Sourcing stone: the original builders travelled vast distances to find the various types of stone that were used.

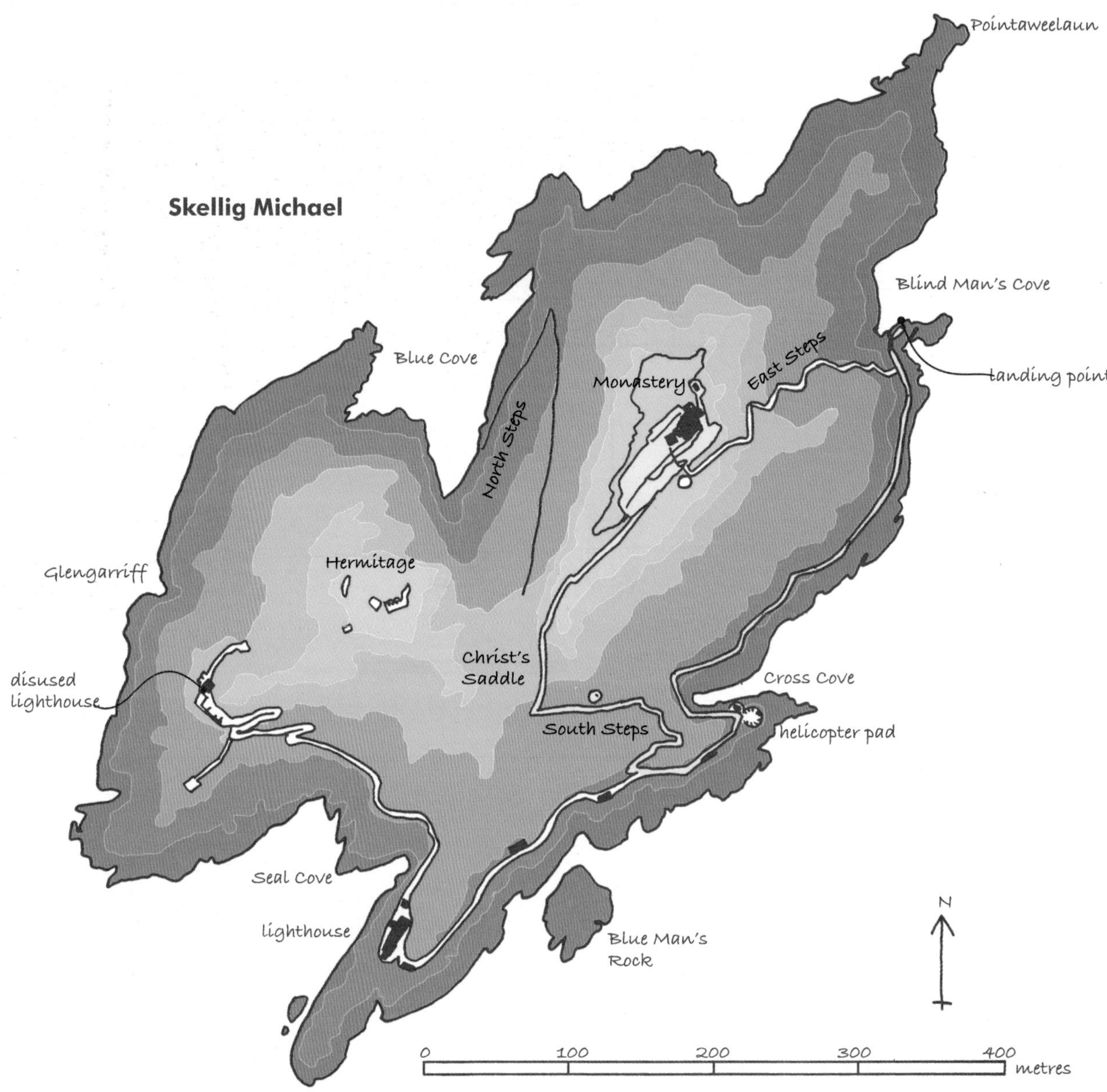

8.07 Map of Great Skellig Island showing the location of Skellig Michael.

Skellig Michael (Sceilig Mhichíl) UNESCO World Heritage Site is an ancient monastery located on Great Skellig Island, 11.6km off of the tip of the Iveragh Peninsula in County Kerry. The name derives from *Sceillic*, which roughly translates as 'steep rock'. Michael is a reference to St Michael, to whom the church is dedicated. Between the sixth and eighth centuries, it was probably a place of refuge for a small community of ascetic monks, and was home to about twelve monks and an abbot.

The monastery is accessed via a flights of steps to the south of the island. The lower steps are cut from the rock. Once above the reach of the sea the steps are constructed of dry stone.

The monastery comprises an inner enclosure consisting of two oratories, a church (St Michael's Church), seven cells (five of which are intact) and the remains of a beehive toilet, water cisterns, a cemetery, leachta, crosses and cross-slabs. It also includes two large terraces referred to as the Upper and Lower Monks' Gardens.

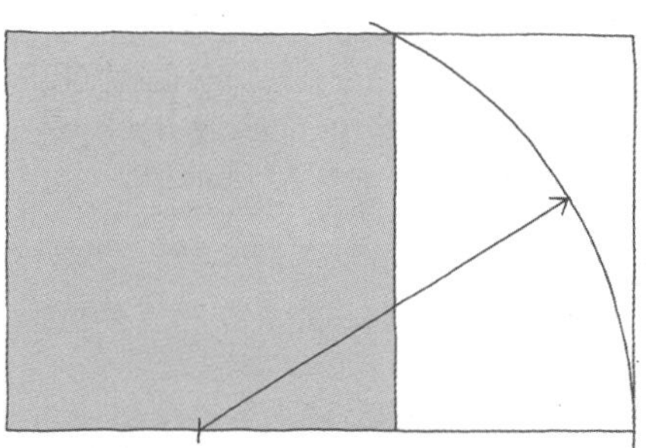

8.14 Golden rectangle: based on the proportional relationship (1:1.618 or 8/5) that has been considered inherently beautiful by architects and builders for centuries.

8.15 A Georgian country house: a simple two-storey symmetrical façade; three bays wide, with a central doorway.

Georgian features

8.16 A Georgian doorcase and door: the fluted columns, detailed frieze and delicate fanlight tracery frame the panelled door.

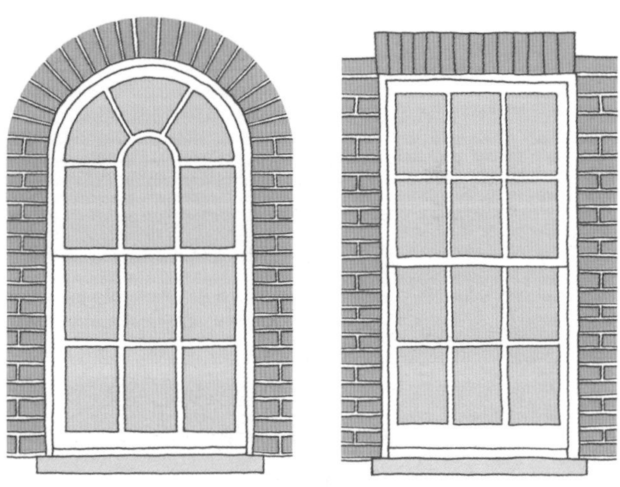

8.17 Georgian windows: the proportion of these windows makes them an appropriate and elegant component of a Georgian-style building. The size of the panes and the thin glazing bars are particularly important.

ACTIVITIES

Visit a heritage building in your locality. If possible, organise a guided tour by someone who has studied the building/area in detail. Make sketches of the building's features and learn about how the building was originally used.

The ornate panelled doors of Georgian houses made a strong statement about the status of a building and its owner. The most decorative and elaborate element of the façade, they provided the architect with an opportunity to assert style and flair.

Each window has vertical sliding sashes that are divided into small panes by narrow glazing bars. Each window has three panes horizontally and, depending on the height of the room, three, four or five panes vertically.

The thin glazing bars and the painted reveals of the windows give them an elegant, bright appearance.

The delicate tracery of the fanlights and the ironwork of the railings and balconies all contribute to the overall appearance of the Georgian town house. In keeping with the classical approach, the scale and proportion of each element of the façade is in keeping with the whole. This gives the typical town house an aesthetically balanced and pleasing appearance. These houses are further enhanced by the wide streets and squares that are a typical feature of Georgian town planning.

Recognising a heritage building

Not all old buildings are a significant part of the built heritage. It is not realistic to say that a building should be preserved just because it is old. The architectural heritage of Ireland includes buildings of great artistic achievement: churches, courthouses, country estate houses and significant commercial buildings. However, of equal importance are the everyday buildings of ordinary people. The key skill is to be able to recognise the important buildings.

8.18 Architectural significance: the Casino (meaning 'small house') in Marino, Dublin is one of the finest eighteenth-century neo-classical buildings in Europe.

8.19 Cultural history: the General Post Office on O'Connell Street, Dublin has great cultural importance because of its historical association with the 1916 Easter Rising.

8.20 Context: each of these everyday buildings in Enniscorthy, Co. Wexford contributes to the overall appearance of the streetscape.

KEY PRINCIPLES

Factors to consider when evaluating a historic building include:

- **architectural significance** – a building that is a good example of a particular architectural style or of a particular architect's work
- **cultural history** – a building associated with a person, group, institution, event or activity that is of historical significance to the area or people
- **context** – a building that contributes to the existing character of the area/streetscape, that occupies its original site, has suffered little alteration, and retains most of its original materials and design features.

Conservation

Conservation is the process of caring for buildings. Generally, the best way to protect a historic building is to keep it in active use. The main cause of deterioration of old buildings is neglect and a lack of basic maintenance, particularly of roofs, gutters and flashings where water can penetrate the building fabric.

Conservation principles

Historic structures are a unique resource which, once lost, cannot be replaced. Good conservation allows new uses to be found for old buildings in a way that protects their character and special interest. Conservation work must be informed by a knowledge and understanding of each building. This requires detailed research and careful study of the building before any work commences. This will usually require the work of a multidisciplinary team of professionals with expertise in architecture, engineering, architectural history and archaeology.

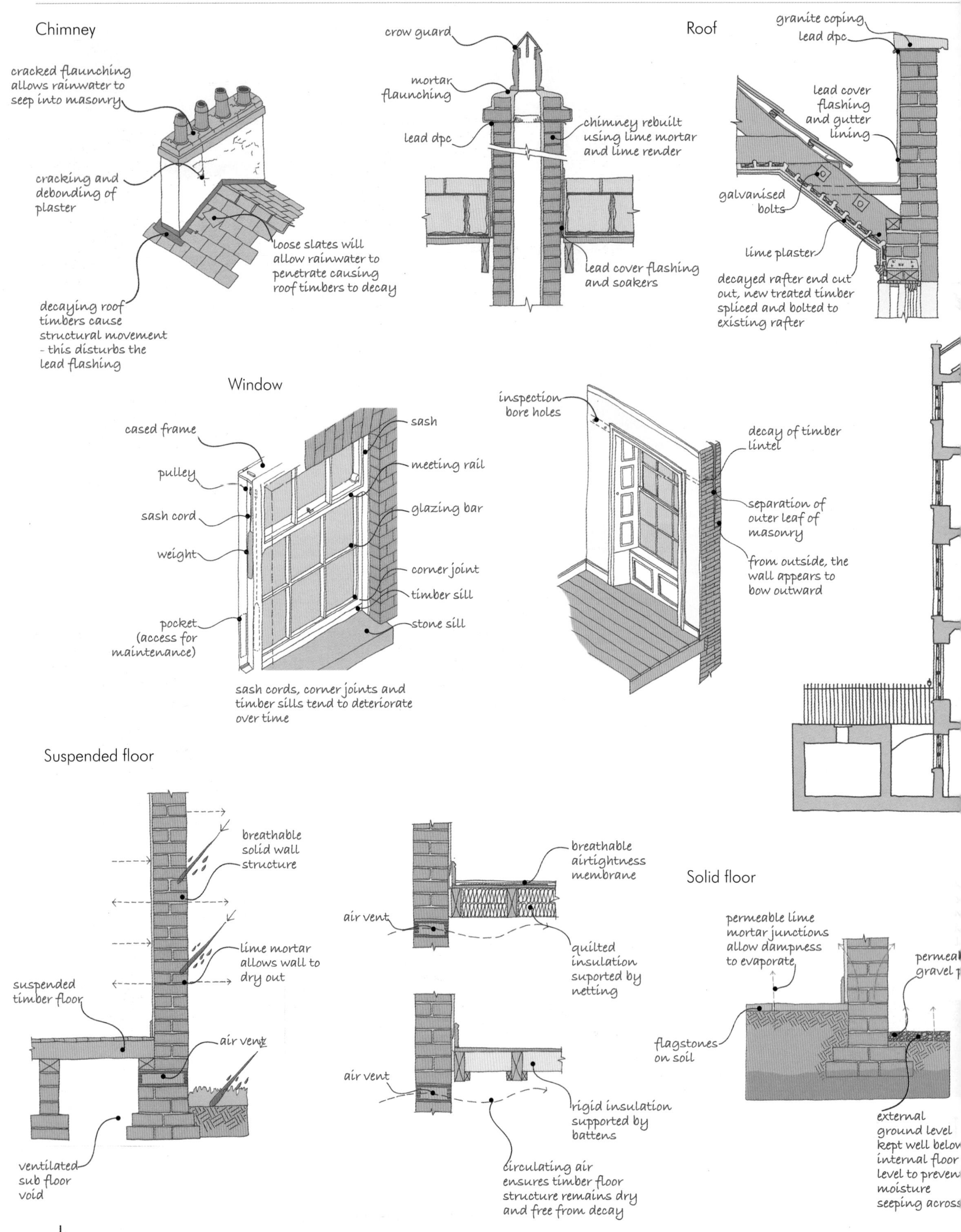
Chimney
cracked flaunching allows rainwater to seep into masonry
cracking and debonding of plaster
loose slates will allow rainwater to penetrate causing roof timbers to decay
decaying roof timbers cause structural movement - this disturbs the lead flashing
crow guard
mortar flaunching
lead dpc
chimney rebuilt using lime mortar and lime render
lead cover flashing and soakers
Roof
granite coping
lead dpc
lead cover flashing and gutter lining
galvanised bolts
lime plaster
decayed rafter end cut out, new treated timber spliced and bolted to existing rafter
Window
cased frame
pulley
sash cord
weight
pocket (access for maintenance)
sash
meeting rail
glazing bar
corner joint
timber sill
stone sill
sash cords, corner joints and timber sills tend to deteriorate over time
inspection bore holes
decay of timber lintel
separation of outer leaf of masonry
from outside, the wall appears to bow outward
Suspended floor
breathable solid wall structure
lime mortar allows wall to dry out
suspended timber floor
air vent
ventilated sub floor void
breathable airtightness membrane
air vent
quilted insulation suported by netting
air vent
rigid insulation supported by battens
circulating air ensures timber floor structure remains dry and free from decay
Solid floor
permeable lime mortar junctions allow dampness to evaporate
flagstones on soil
external ground level kept well belov internal floor level to preven moisture seeping across

Walls

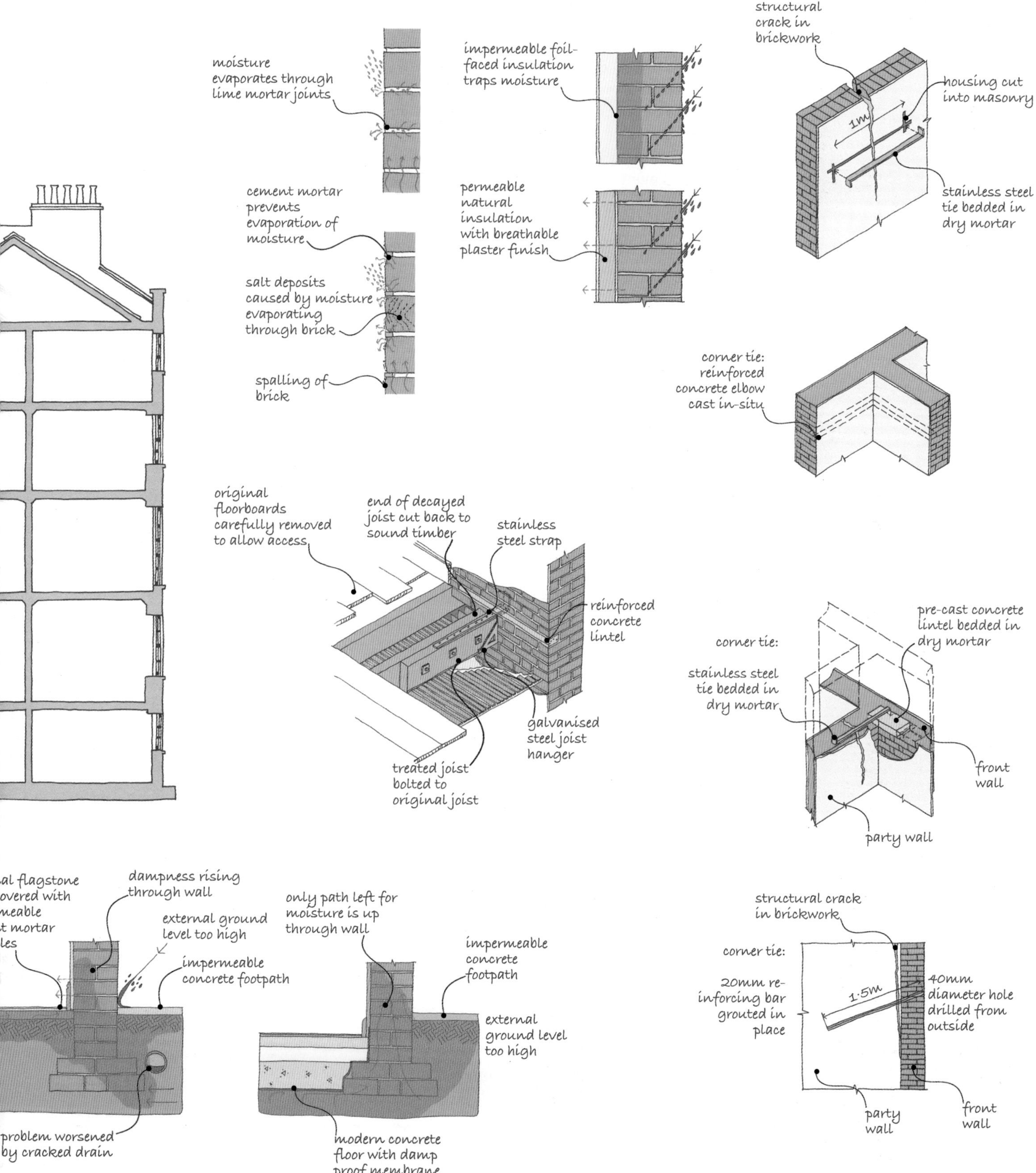

8.21 Conservation: heritage buildings require careful maintenance and repair.

KEY PRINCIPLES

The following principles should inform all conservation work:

- **keep old buildings in use** – find new, appropriate uses for old buildings
- **do the research** – analyse the building fabric and any other evidence (e.g. maps, drawings, documents, etc.)
- **use expert advice** – building conservation is a specialised area that should be led by experts with knowledge and experience of historic buildings
- **promote the special interest** – the features of the building that convey its distinctiveness should be protected
- **minimum intervention** – best summed up by the maxim 'do as much as necessary and as little as possible'
- **respect earlier alterations of interest** – historical alterations and additions to a structure are also an irreplaceable part of the building's history
- **repair rather than replace** – the original building fabric should, whenever possible, be repaired rather than replaced with new materials
- **promote honesty** – repairs should generally be carried out without any attempt at disguise or artificial ageing
- **use appropriate materials and methods** – some modern materials can result in accelerated decay of building fabric, for example replacing lime mortar with cement mortar
- **reversibility** – allows for the future correction of unforeseen problems without lasting damage being caused
- **avoid incremental damage** – it is important to be aware of the potential cumulative impact of minor works to the character of heritage buildings
- **avoid using salvaged materials** – reusing architectural materials from other buildings can confuse the history of a building and create a market for salvaged building materials, which promotes the dismantling of other old buildings, for example the removal of slates or cut-stone elements from a building for reuse elsewhere
- **comply with the building regulations** – apart from a few exemptions, the regulations apply to all works involving new construction, extensions to buildings, material alterations to existing buildings and material change of use of such buildings.

Conservation practice

The building fabric of heritage buildings is designed to be breathable. Typical building materials like clay, lime, brick and stone soak up and release moisture in response to environmental conditions. This principle of absorption and evaporation of moisture is referred to as the 'sponge' principle. Since the 1950s houses have been designed using a cavity wall consisting of an inner wall and an outer wall with a space or cavity between them. This type of wall is based on the 'impervious skin' principle. Instead of absorbing and releasing moisture the cavity wall relies on the total exclusion of moisture. This type of wall, coupled with plastic damp proofing materials, is designed to provide a moisture-proof external envelope.

For builders and architects who have become used to the modern cavity wall approach, working with historic buildings requires a different way of thinking. When modern methods and materials are applied to old buildings, the result is usually a rapid deterioration in the building fabric. The use of cement, concrete, plastic membranes and other vapour-closed materials are a disaster in old buildings because they prevent the movement of moisture. This invariably leads to dampness, mould growth and ultimately structural failure and collapse. It is essential that natural breathable materials are used in the conservation of heritage buildings.

REVISION EXERCISES

1 Explain why old buildings are an important part of our cultural heritage.
2 Describe, using neat freehand sketches, a heritage building from your local area.
3 Explain what this building was used for and why it is an important part of your local heritage.
4 Summarise three factors that influenced the design of vernacular houses.
5 Explain, using neat freehand sketches, the importance of proportion in Georgian architecture.

SECTION 2

DESIGN: STRUCTURE

Health and Safety in Construction

Safety management principles

Many people die and thousands of people are injured on construction sites in Ireland every year. The situation was so bad that regulations had to be introduced to make construction companies introduce safe work practices. While safety on site is still a real problem, many Irish companies now have excellent safety management systems in place.

ACTIVITIES

Visit the Health and Safety Authority (HSA) website www.hsa.ie and download the latest HSA *Annual Report* (it's usually in the *'Publications'* section of the website under the heading *'Corporate'*).

Once you have opened the report, look up the appendix at the back, *'Outcomes of Prosecutions'*. Here you will read about real accidents that happened on construction sites and how the courts dealt with the people responsible.

Select one example, write a brief summary of the accident and explain how you think the accident could have been avoided.

KEY PRINCIPLES

There are three primary reasons why health and safety should be proactively managed on construction sites.

1 **The moral reason** –
- it's the right thing to do
- it is unacceptable that a person should have to risk their life or health to earn a living as a construction worker
- the people who own construction companies should value their workers and take care of them.

2 **The economic reason** –
- accidents are expensive
- when a construction worker gets injured a chain of events is triggered, including –
  - reduced productivity on site
  - hiring replacement worker(s)
  - medical costs
  - sick pay
  - compensation costs
  - fines.

3 **The legal reason** –
- it's the law
- the Safety, Health and Welfare at Work Act 2005 requires employers and employees to proactively manage health and safety
- non-compliance can lead to fines and/or a prison sentence.

SUPPLEMENTARY INFORMATION

The following terms are commonly used in relation to health and safety.

- **Hazard** – any situation with the potential to cause an accident
- **Risk** – the likelihood that the accident will actually happen
- **Risk magnitude** – an estimate of the likelihood of an accident actually happening, how bad it would be and how many people could be involved:
  - risk magnitude = likelihood x severity x number of people
- **Risk control** – any action taken to reduce the level of risk.
- **Risk control hierarchy** – the order in which steps should be taken to reduce risk. Getting rid of the hazard is best (eliminate), using something less hazardous is next best (substitute) and so on.
- **Safety statement** – a written action programme for safeguarding the safety, health and welfare of employees, visitors and other people who might be affected by the work (e.g. passers by). It describes all the hazards to be found on the site and the risks and risk controls required to make the site a safer place.

The Safety, Health and Welfare at Work Act 2005 is the primary law governing health and safety at places of work in Ireland. It is a progressive law because, while most laws are reactive – they punish you when you do something wrong – the 2005 Act is proactive – it requires people to proactively take steps to manage health and safety.

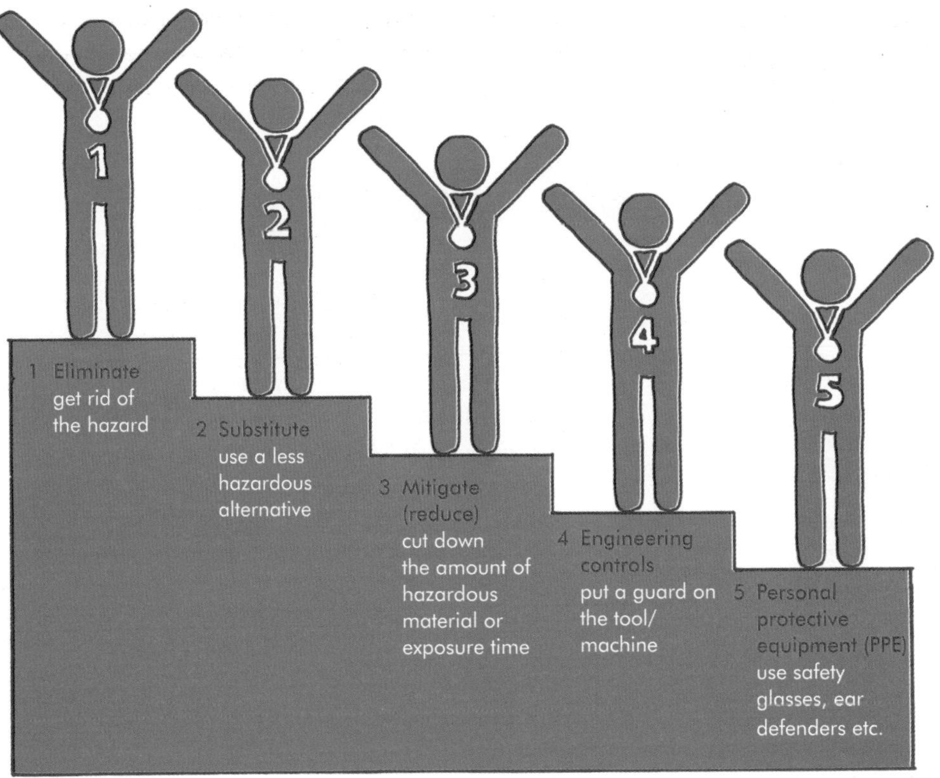

9.01 Risk control hierarchy. *Source:* HSA and t4 guidance document (written for HSA and t4 by the author).

KEY PRINCIPLES

The 2005 Act is based on nine principles:

1 risks should be avoided
2 if a risk can't be avoided it should be evaluated (risk assessment)
3 risks should be tackled at source (risk control)
4 work should be adapted to suit people (monotonous, repetitive work should be avoided)
5 workplaces, machinery, equipment, etc. should be kept up to date with the latest technology (if a better way of doing something is invented it should be used)
6 dangerous materials or systems of work should be replaced by safe or less dangerous materials or systems of work (substitute or reduce)
7 priority should be given to the safety measures that protect most people (favour group over individual protective measures)
8 safety policies should be written that are specific to each workplace
9 workers should be properly trained.

Safety training

All construction workers are required by law to have completed the FÁS Safe Pass Health and Safet Awareness Training Programme. This programme gives the worker a basic knowledge of health and safety so that they are better able to deal with the hazards and risks they will encounter on a construction site.

SUPPLEMENTARY INFORMATION

Safe Pass is a one-day training course comprising twelve modules:

1 promoting a safety culture
2 duties and responsibilities at work
3 accident reporting and prevention
4 working at heights
5 excavations and confined spaces
6 working with electricity, underground and overhead services
7 personal protective equipment
8 use of hand-held equipment, tools and machinery
9 safe use of vehicles
10 noise and vibration
11 manual handling
12 health and hygiene.

In addition to this, some workers must complete specific safety training related to their particular job. This training is called the Construction Skills Certification Scheme (CSCS).

Only workers who have completed CSCS training are allowed to do certain jobs, which include:

- scaffold erection
- crane operation
- plant operation (e.g. tractor/dozer, digger, dumper, excavator)
- roofing and wall cladding/sheeting.

Safe system of work plan

The safe system of work plan (SSWP) is a checklist that can be used on site to help construction workers identify hazards and put risk controls in place. It is a pictogram-based checklist that is quick and easy to use. There is a specific SSWP for house building.

It is designed to be used every day before work starts. The worker looks at the checklist and ticks a box for each hazard that could arise during the job. They then look across the options on the checklist and choose the best risk controls for the job. Once the risk controls are in place the checklist is signed off by the person in charge and the work can begin.

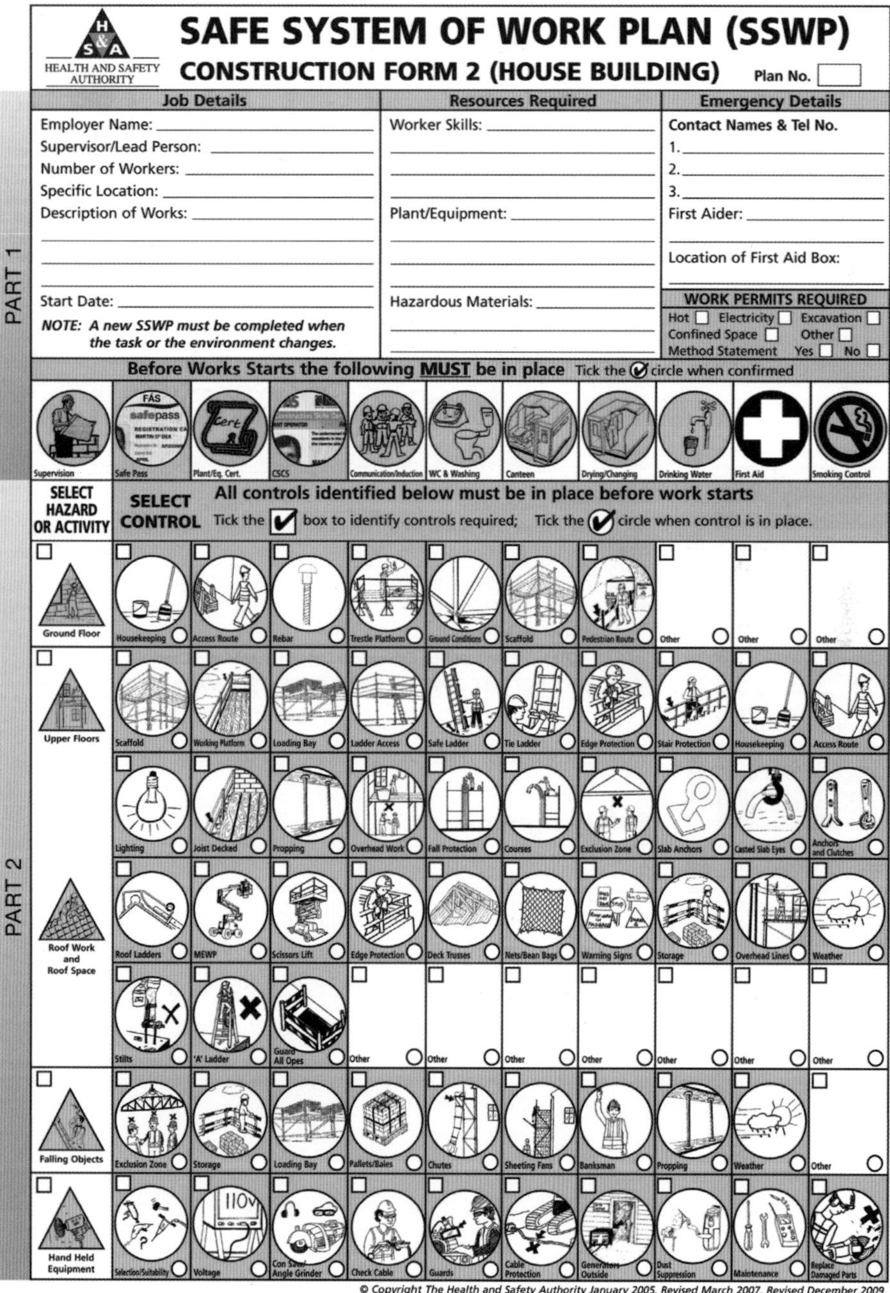

HEALTH AND SAFETY AUTHORITY

SAFE SYSTEM OF WORK PLAN (SSWP)

CONSTRUCTION FORM 2 (HOUSE BUILDING) Plan No. ☐

PART 1

Job Details	Resources Required	Emergency Details
Employer Name: ______	Worker Skills: ______	Contact Names & Tel No.
Supervisor/Lead Person: ______	______	1. ______
Number of Workers: ______	______	2. ______
Specific Location: ______	______	3. ______
Description of Works: ______	Plant/Equipment: ______	First Aider: ______
______	______	Location of First Aid Box:
Start Date: ______	Hazardous Materials: ______	WORK PERMITS REQUIRED
NOTE: A new SSWP must be completed when the task or the environment changes.	______	Hot ☐ Electricity ☐ Excavation ☐ Confined Space ☐ Other ☐ Method Statement Yes ☐ No ☐

Before Works Starts the following MUST be in place Tick the ✓ circle when confirmed

Supervision | Safe Pass | Plant/Eq. Cert. | CSCS | Communication/Induction | WC & Washing | Canteen | Drying/Changing | Drinking Water | First Aid | Smoking Control

PART 2

SELECT HAZARD OR ACTIVITY | **SELECT CONTROL** All controls identified below must be in place before work starts. Tick the ✓ box to identify controls required; Tick the ✓ circle when control is in place.

Hazard / Activity	Controls
☐ Ground Floor	Housekeeping, Access Route, Rebar, Trestle Platform, Ground Conditions, Scaffold, Pedestrian Route, Other, Other, Other
☐ Upper Floors	Scaffold, Working Platform, Loading Bay, Ladder Access, Safe Ladder, Tie Ladder, Edge Protection, Stair Protection, Housekeeping, Access Route
	Lighting, Joist Decked, Propping, Overhead Work, Fall Protection, Courses, Exclusion Zone, Slab Anchors, Casted Slab Eyes, Anchors and Clutches
Roof Work and Roof Space	Roof Ladders, MEWP, Scissors Lift, Edge Protection, Deck Trusses, Nets/Bean Bags, Warning Signs, Storage, Overhead Lines, Weather
	Stilts, 'A' Ladder, Guard All Opes, Other, Other, Other, Other, Other, Other, Other
☐ Falling Objects	Exclusion Zone, Storage, Loading Bay, Pallets/Bales, Chutes, Sheeting Fans, Banksman, Propping, Weather, Other
☐ Hand Held Equipment	Selection/Suitability, Voltage, Con Saw/Angle Grinder, Check Cable, Guards, Cable Protection, Generators Outside, Dust Suppression, Maintenance, Replace Damaged Parts

9.02 Safe System of Work Plan: a sample of the house building form.

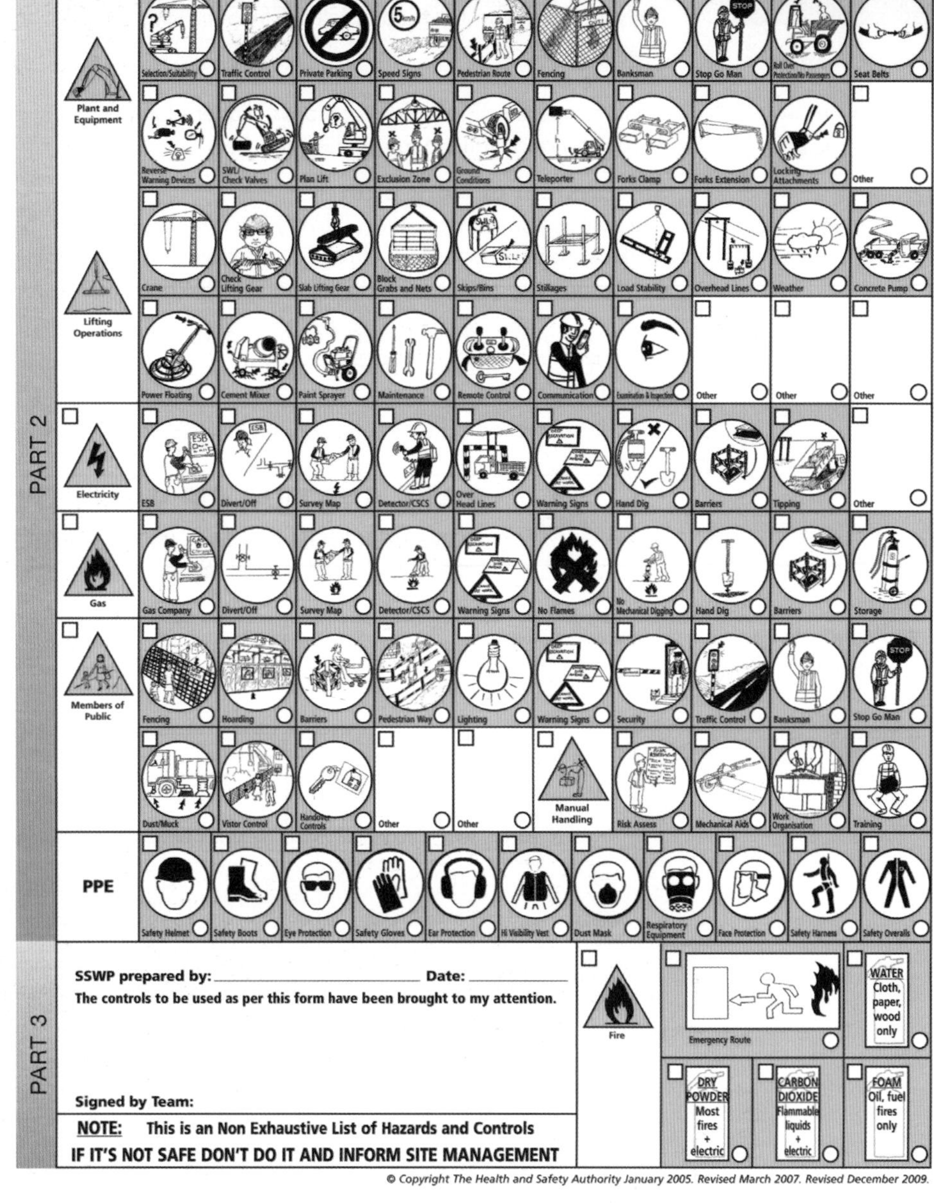

PART 2

HAZARD OR ACTIVITY	CONTROL Tick the ☑ box to identify controls required; Tick the ✔ circle when control is in place.										
Plant and Equipment	Selection/Suitability	Traffic Control	Private Parking	Speed Signs	Pedestrian Route	Fencing	Banksman	Stop Go Man	Roll Over Protection/No Passengers	Seat Belts	
	Reverse Warning Devices	SWL/Check Valves	Plan Lift	Exclusion Zone	Ground Conditions	Teleporter	Forks Clamp	Forks Extension	Locking Attachments	Other	
Lifting Operations	Crane	Check Lifting Gear	Slab Lifting Gear	Block Grabs and Nets	Skips/Bins	Stillages	Load Stability	Overhead Lines	Weather	Concrete Pump	
	Power Floating	Cement Mixer	Paint Sprayer	Maintenance	Remote Control	Communication	Illumination & Inspection	Other	Other	Other	
Electricity	ESB	Divert/Off	Survey Map	Detector/CSCS	Over Head Lines	Warning Signs	Hand Dig	Barriers	Tipping	Other	
Gas	Gas Company	Divert/Off	Survey Map	Detector/CSCS	Warning Signs	No Flames	No Mechanical Digging	Hand Dig	Barriers	Storage	
Members of Public	Fencing	Hoarding	Barriers	Pedestrian Way	Lighting	Warning Signs	Security	Traffic Control	Banksman	Stop Go Man	
	Dust/Muck	Vistor Control	Handover Controls	Other	Other	Manual Handling	Risk Assess	Mechanical Aids	Work Organisation	Training	
PPE	Safety Helmet	Safety Boots	Eye Protection	Safety Gloves	Ear Protection	Hi Visibility Vest	Dust Mask	Respiratory Equipment	Face Protection	Safety Harness	Safety Overalls

PART 3

SSWP prepared by: ______________ **Date:** __________

The controls to be used as per this form have been brought to my attention.

Signed by Team:

NOTE: This is an Non Exhaustive List of Hazards and Controls

IF IT'S NOT SAFE DON'T DO IT AND INFORM SITE MANAGEMENT

Fire

Emergency Route

WATER Cloth, paper, wood only

DRY POWDER Most fires + electric

CARBON DIOXIDE Flammable liquids + electric

FOAM Oil, fuel fires only

9.02 Safe System of Work Plan (continued) : a sample of the house building form.

9.03 Signage at the entrance to a construction site.

Safety signage

There are strict regulations about the use of safety signage in workplaces. These regulations control the shape and colour of safety signs so that they are universal – they look the same everywhere you go. Safety signs are not allowed to have words on them. This is to ensure that the sign can be understood no matter what language the person speaks. This is really important on construction sites where many workers are from other countries (i.e. English is not their native language).

Safe condition

Prohibition

Mandatory

Warning

9.04 Safety signage: there are four types of safety sign.

Personal protective equipment

Personal protective equipment (PPE) is something worn by a person to reduce the level of risk. Construction workers are legally obliged to wear PPE when it is required (e.g. when a blue sign is in place or when they have been told to wear it).

9.05 PPE safety signage: eye protection must be worn.

9.06 A worker wearing PPE.

> **KEY PRINCIPLES**
>
> Every worker should have his/her own set of personal protective equipment, including:
> - hard hat
> - high visibility vest
> - safety boots
> - safety goggles/glasses
> - ear defenders
> - dust mask
> - gloves.

Working at height

Working at height covers a number of issues, including scaffolding, access (getting safely up to and down from the work area), fall prevention and getting materials up and down safely.

Scaffolding

Scaffolding is widely used in the construction industry for working at heights. It is important that scaffolding is erected by personnel certified by the Construction Skills Certification Scheme (CSCS) to ensure that it is stable and secure when in use. Scaffolding must be 'signed off' by a CSCS-qualified scaffolder before it can be used.

> **KEY PRINCIPLES**
>
> The safe use of scaffolding depends on the following principles:
> - safe transfer of the load (i.e. weight of materials and scaffolding) to the ground
> - secure footings to ensure good contact with the ground
> - diagonal bracing of vertical and horizontal members
> - tying the scaffolding to the building at regular intervals
> - correct use of component parts (no modification on site)
> - not overloading the scaffolding.

Braces and ties are used to stiffen and secure the scaffold so that it does not sway. Swaying can cause instability, cracking of welds and over-stressing of the scaffold, which can lead to collapse.

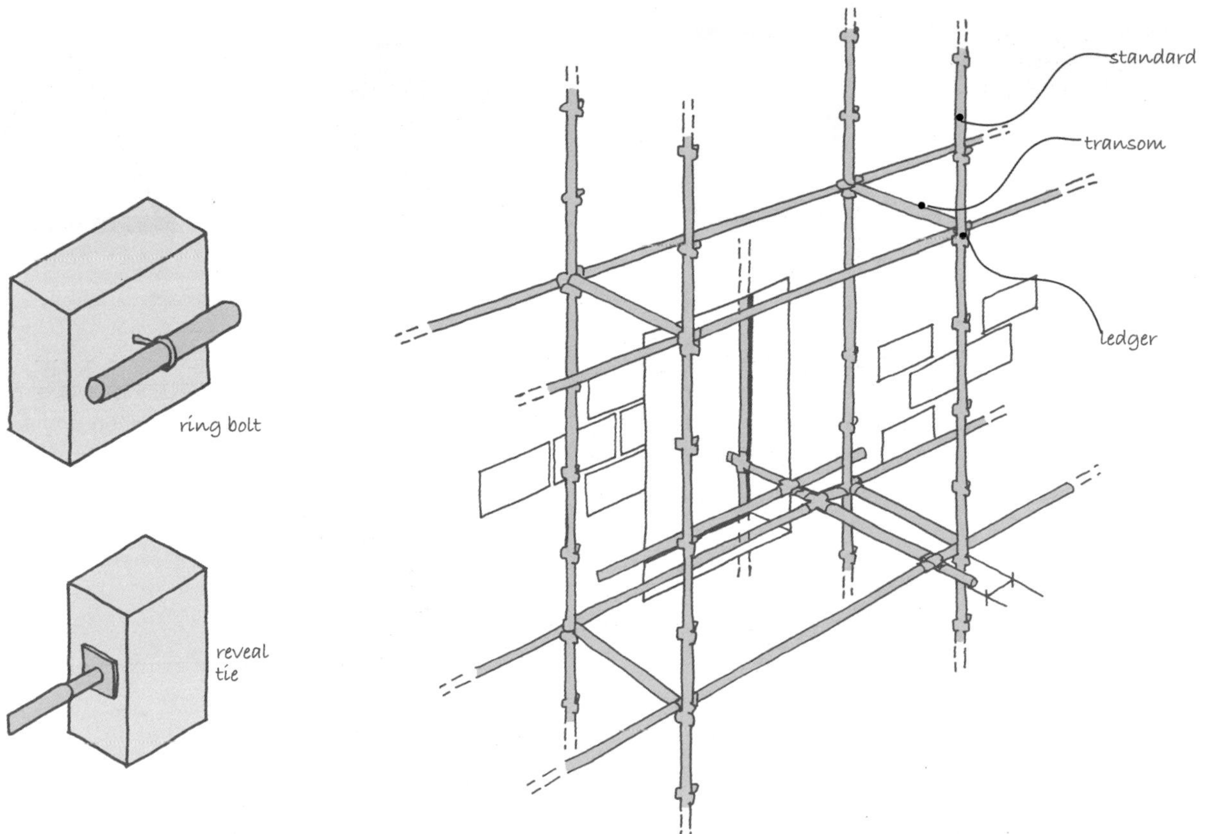

9.07 Scaffolding: main parts.

Working platform

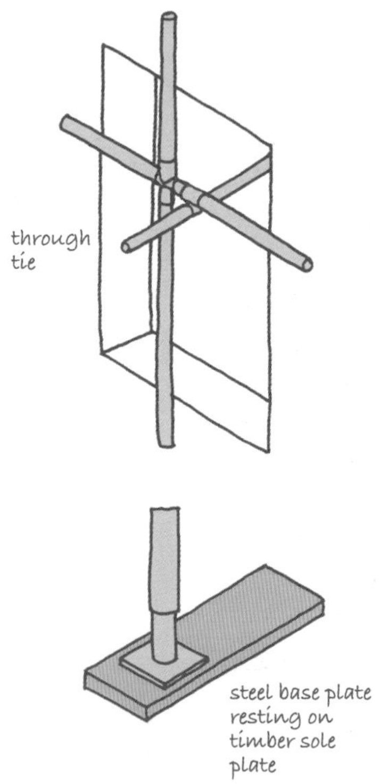

9.08 Scaffolding should be secured to the structure and have a firm footing.

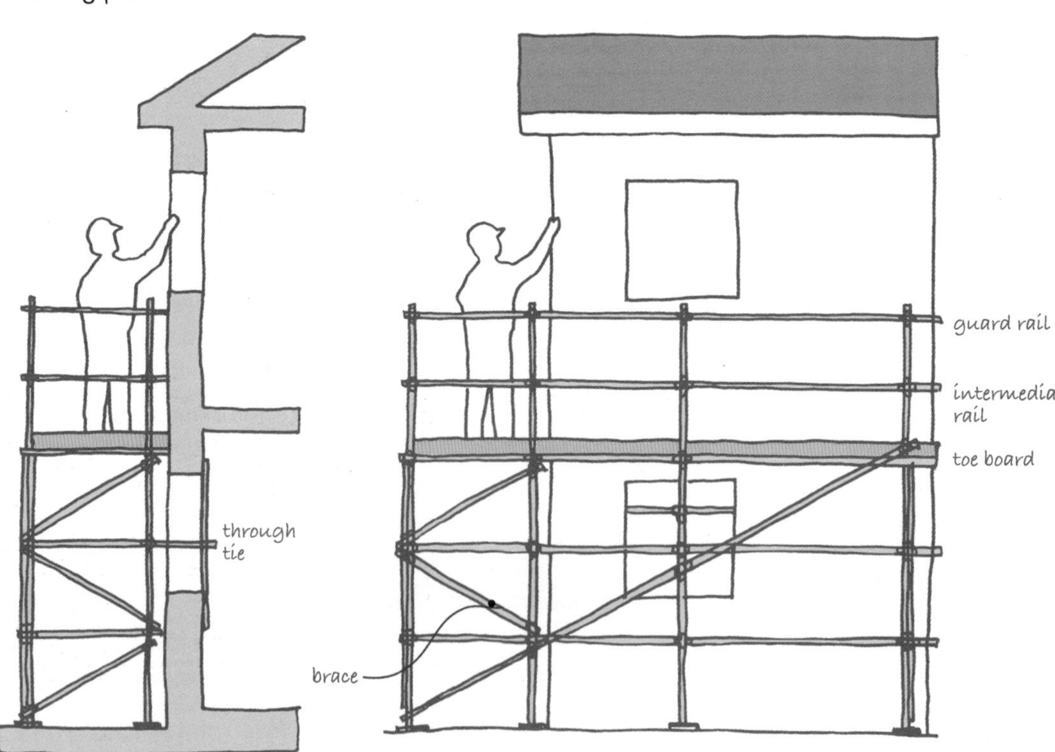

9.09 Scaffolding: correctly erected scaffolding reduces the risk of working at height.

The working platform should be wide enough to allow the workers to move safely along the platform and should also be capable of supporting the loads imposed upon it. It should have a minimum width of 800mm. Above a height of two metres, it is essential that the working platform is fitted with a guard rail, intermediate rail and toe board to prevent workers and materials from falling.

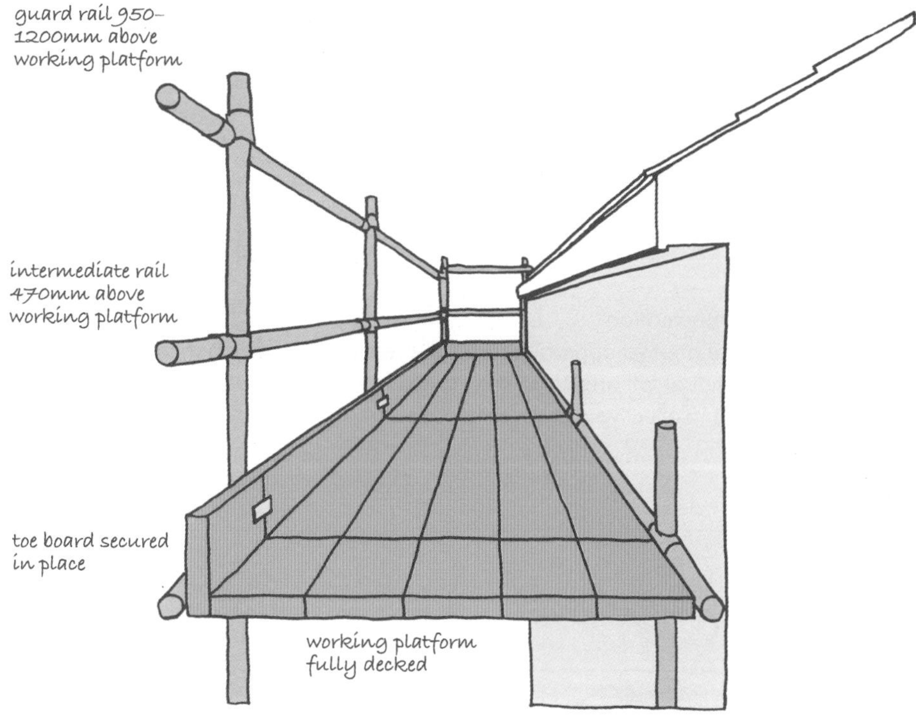

9.10 Working platform: it is essential that the platform is fully decked to prevent falls.

Access to scaffolding

Heights are usually accessed using ladders. When accessing scaffolds, the safest option is to use a ladder access tower.

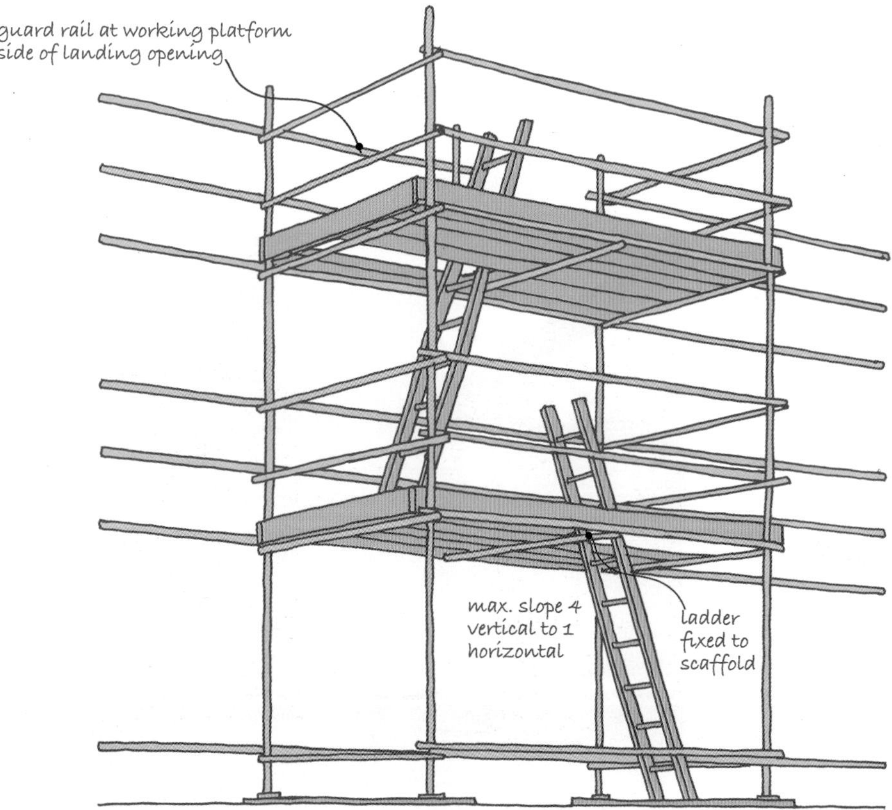

9.11 Ladder access tower: reduces the potential severity of a fall.

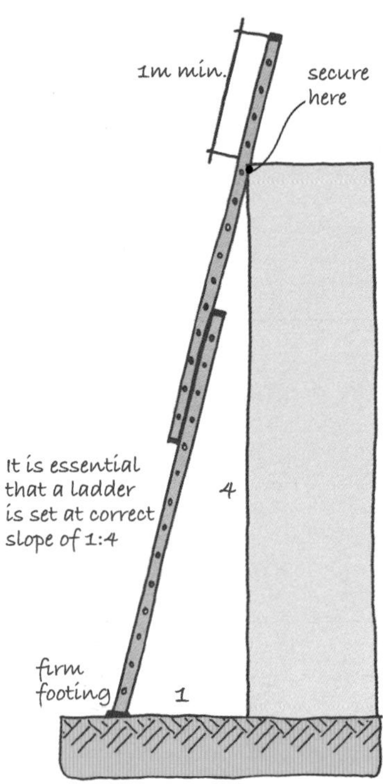

9.12 Ladder guidelines: the correct slope of 1:4 is essential.

KEY PRINCIPLES

When a ladder is used on its own, it is essential that the following guidelines are followed:

- ladder stiles should extend at least one metre above landing area
- the top of the ladder stiles should be secured to the structure
- the slope of the ladder should not exceed four vertical to one horizontal
- the stiles should be supported on a firm footing.

Fall prevention

There are two approaches to fall prevention: individual measures; and collective measures. Individual fall arrest systems consist of a harness worn by the worker which is anchored to a secure point. Collective measures include airbags, bean bags and temporary decking.

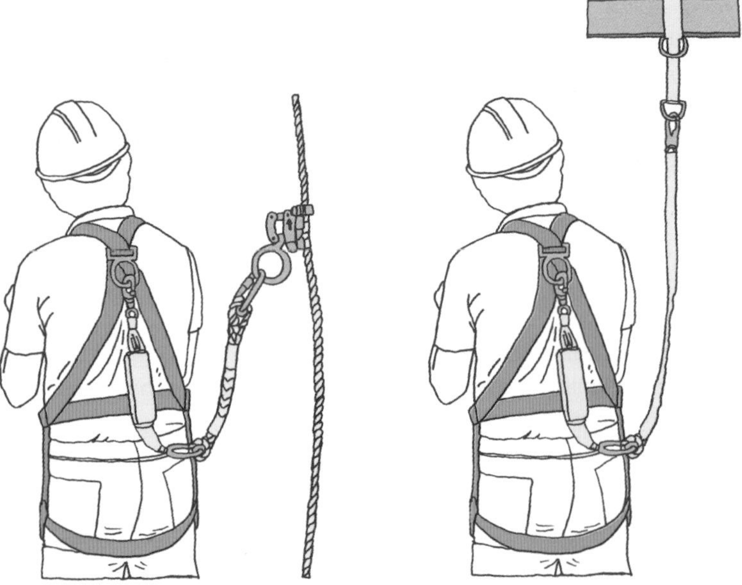

9.13 Fall arrest system: the harness is connected to a lifeline or anchor point by a lanyard with a shock absorber.

9.14 A soft landing bag: air-inflated or polystyrene bead-filled bags that reduce the likelihood of injury from a fall.

Materials lifting

Workers should avoid carrying materials to height by hand. It is much safer to use gin wheels, telescopic lifts or conveyors.

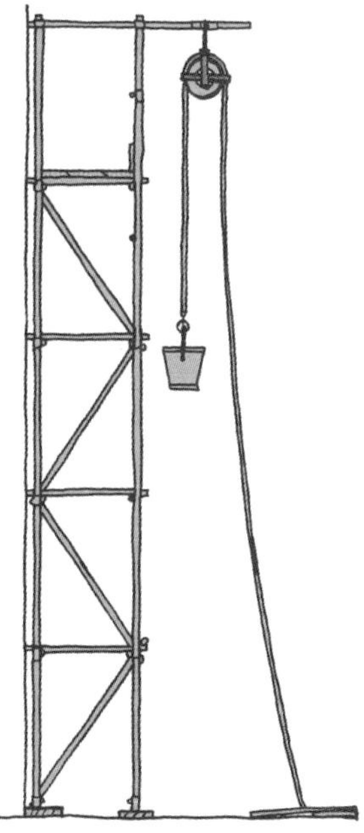

9.15 Gin wheel: useful for lifting small loads (e.g. tools, mortar).

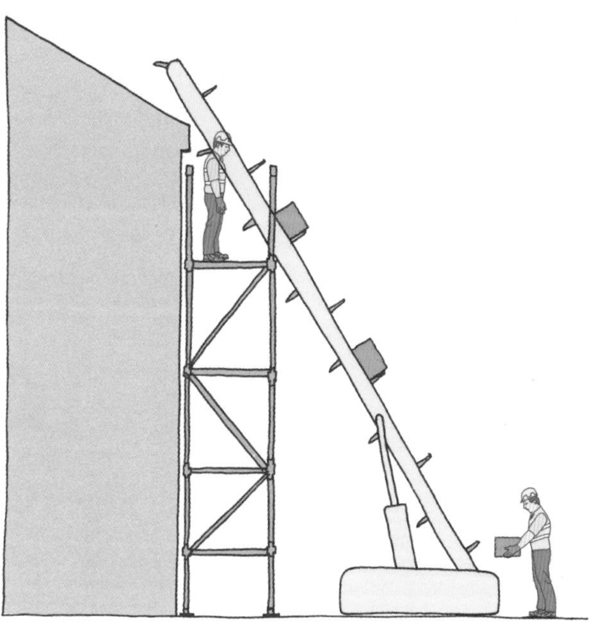

9.16 Elevator or conveyor: useful for lifting large quantities of bricks, blocks or roof tiles.

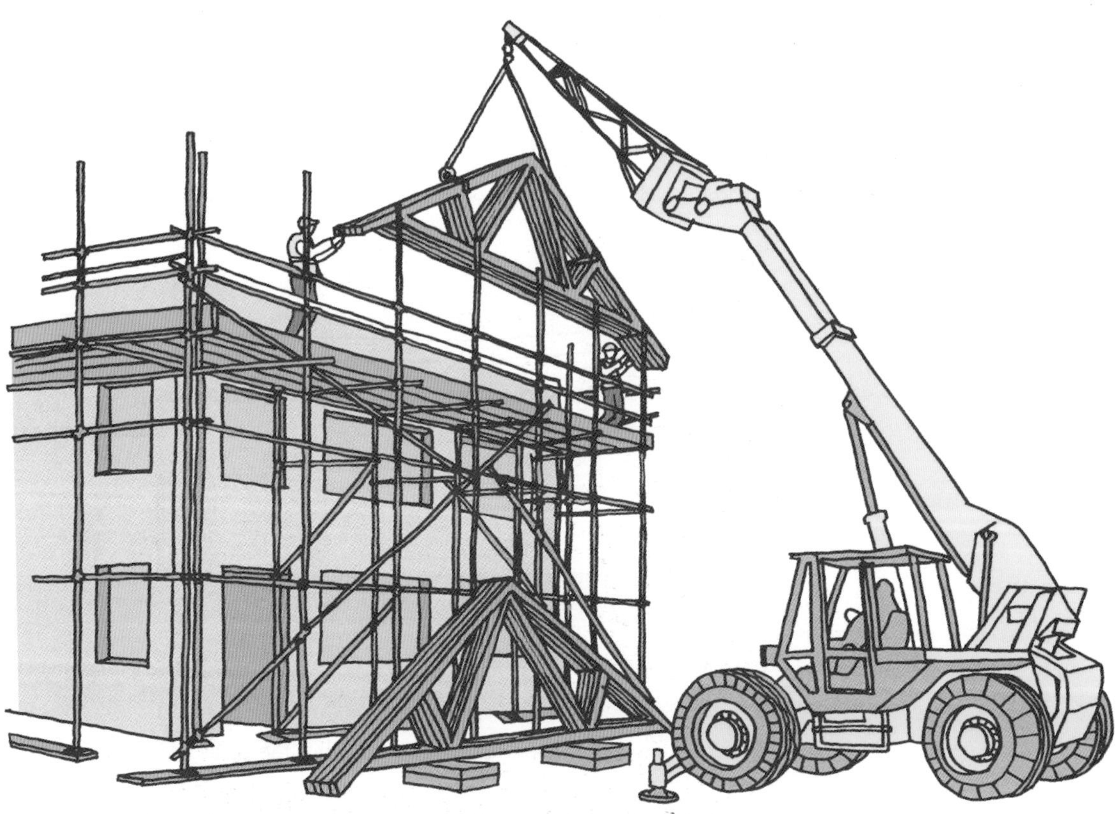

9.17 Telescopic lift: useful for lifting large, heavy or awkward loads (e.g. roof trusses).

Excavation

Excavation is the removal of soil or similar material from an area to facilitate the construction of a foundation or the laying of pipework.

KEY PRINCIPLES

The most common hazards associated with excavation works are:
- contact with underground services (gas, electricity, etc.)
- contact with overhead power lines
- collapse of the excavation's sides, trapping workers
- materials falling on to people working in the excavation
- workers or vehicles falling into the excavation
- workers being struck by machinery
- undermining of nearby structures and buildings
- accidents to members of the public.

9.18 Locating and marking the position of underground pipes and cables using a scanner.

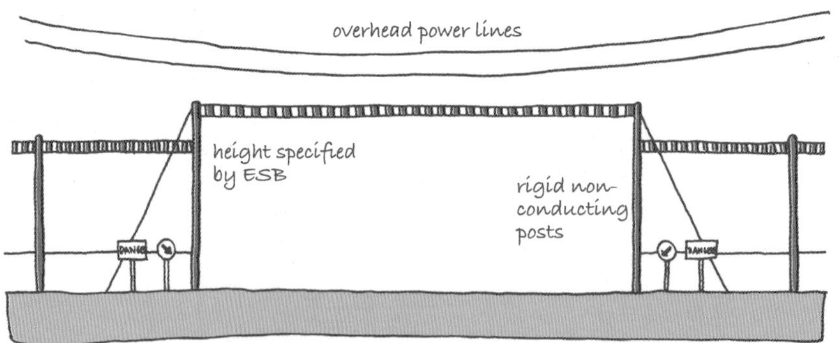

9.19 Overhead power lines: safe routes for site vehicles (e.g. diggers, telescopic lifts) must be clearly marked.

When a trench is dug there is always a risk that the sides of the trench may collapse inward. If a person is required to work in the trench (e.g. when laying pipes) it is essential that steps are taken to ensure the trench is secure. Workers should never enter an unsupported trench greater than 1.25m in depth.

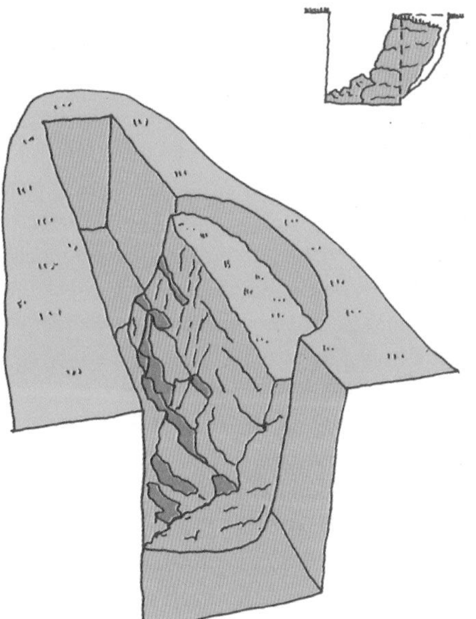

9.20 Collapse of the wall of a trench.

9.21 Excavation safety: a trench box must be used on trenches greater than 1.25m in depth.

Electricity and hand-held power tools

Power tools are commonly used on construction sites because they are faster and easier to use for many jobs around the site.

KEY PRINCIPLES

The hazards associated with hand-held power tools include:
- contact with the tool, causing injury
- noise when the tool is being used
- dust and fumes
- vibration
- electric shock.

KEY PRINCIPLES

Great care must be taken when using power tools to avoid electric shock:
- use battery-powered tools instead of mains-powered tools whenever possible
- only 110V mains powered tools should be used
- mains-powered tools should be protected by a residual current device (RCD)
- all power tools should be double insulated
- the case, cord and plug of mains-operated tools should be checked every day to ensure they are in good condition
- power tools should not be used in wet conditions.

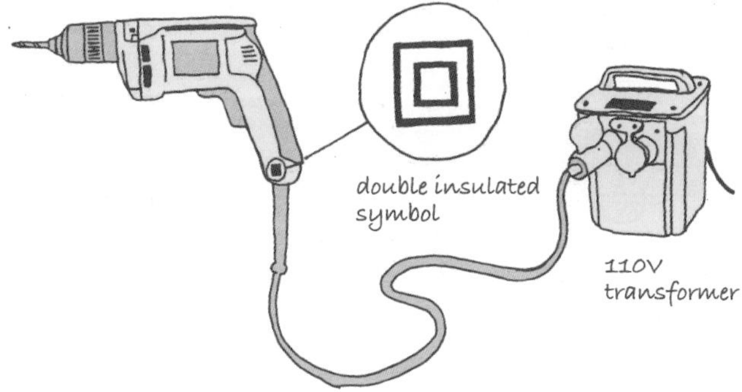

9.22 Power tool safety: 110V double-insulated drill.

Manual handling

Manual handling means lifting any load by hand. Construction workers are prone to back injuries because of the amount of manual handling involved in their work. All construction workers should be trained in manual handling.

KEY PRINCIPLES

To avoid back injury it is important to use the correct manual handling technique:

- **think before lifting** – assess how heavy the object is and check if the path to be travelled is clear
- **adopt a stable position** – get a good stance, with feet shoulder width apart
- **get a good hold** – grip the object tight to the body
- keep the arms tucked in and the load close to the body
- **start in a good posture** – at the start of the lift, slight bending of the back, hips and knees is preferable to fully flexing the back (stooping) or fully flexing the hips and knees (squatting)
- **don't flex the back any further while lifting** – don't straighten the legs before lifting
- avoid twisting the back or leaning sideways
- **look where you are going** – look ahead, not down at the load.

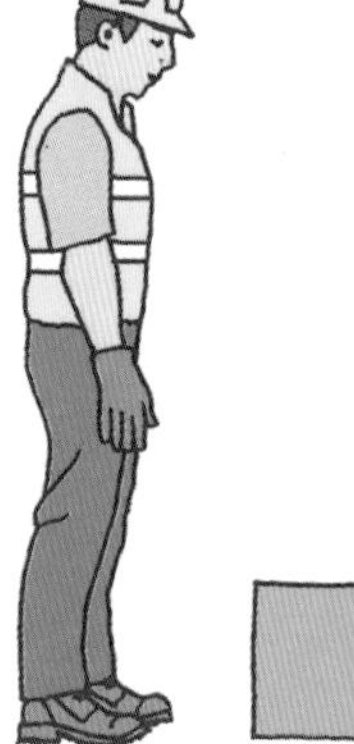

9.23 Manual handling: training in the correct technique is essential.

9.24 Manual handling: using hoists, trolleys, pallet trucks and other mechanical lifting aids greatly reduces the risk of injury.

Site vehicles

Many construction site accidents are caused by moving vehicles.

KEY PRINCIPLES

Accidents involving vehicles can be avoided by following these guidelines:

- all construction vehicles must be properly maintained and used
- strict speed limits should be enforced on site (e.g. 10km/h)
- all workers must wear a high-visibility vest at all times – this makes it easier for the driver to see them
- only workers with the appropriate CSCS training should drive and operate vehicles on site
- clear traffic routes through the site should be marked and controlled by signs, flagmen, or temporary traffic lights
- barriers should be installed beside excavations to prevent the vehicle overturning or the excavation collapsing
- pedestrian paths and crossings should be clearly marked and controlled.

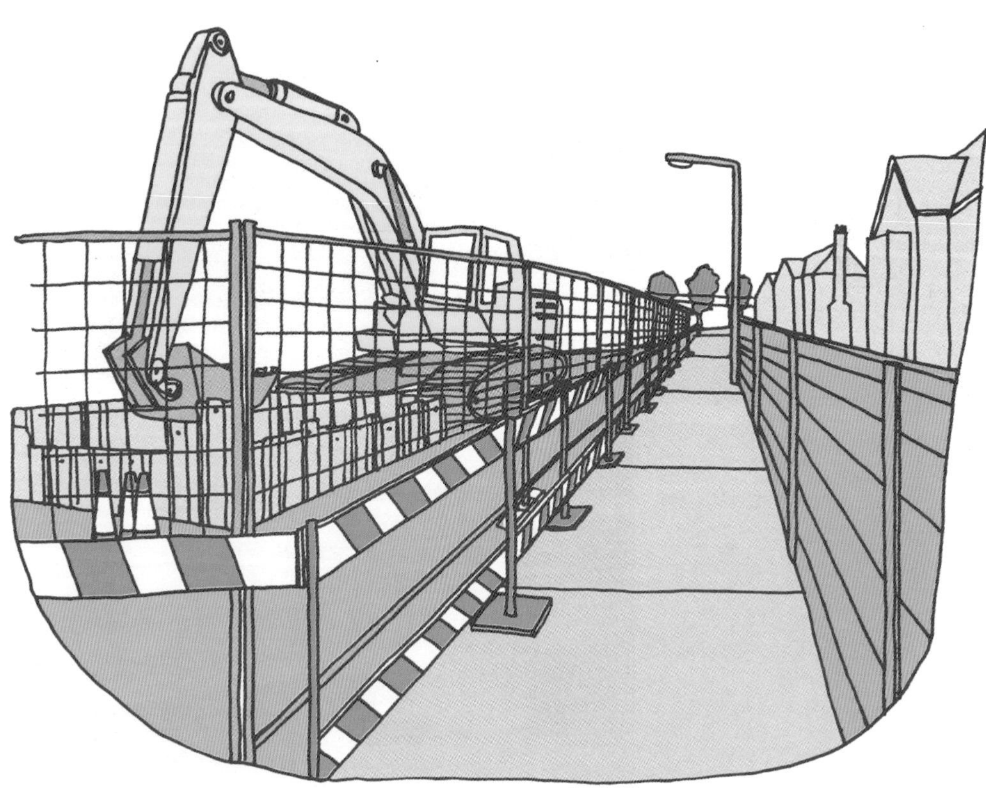

9.25 Site vehicles: particular care is needed when working in public spaces; a safe pathway must be provided for pedestrians.

REVISION EXERCISES

1 Outline the three primary reasons why health and safety should be proactively managed on construction sites.
2 Describe, using examples, the concept of 'risk control hierarchy'.
3 Explain five benefits of providing safety training to construction workers.
4 Describe, using neat freehand sketches, three hazards associated with working at heights.
5 Outline, using neat freehand sketches, the risk controls necessary to address these hazards.

CHAPTER 10

Construction Materials

The structure of a house is essentially a combination of three parts: the foundation/floor structure; the wall structure; and the roof structure. Each of these parts is a complex arrangement of many different construction materials and products. Selecting which to use is a complex and difficult task that needs careful consideration.

KEY PRINCIPLES

The energy consumed in producing, transporting, installing, maintaining and disposing of construction materials and products represents between 10% and 25% of the total lifetime energy consumption of a typical building. However, for low-energy buildings this figure can be as high as 50%. This is a really important point because it means that the impact of building materials is becoming much more important as more energy-efficient buildings are being designed and built.

This idea is also very important for building design because it means that a balance has to be struck between the contribution a material makes to the energy efficiency of a building and the energy cost of producing that material. This is particularly relevant for insulation products. There comes a point at which it no longer makes sense to increase the thickness of insulation in a building because the energy saving achieved during the lifetime of the building or product is outweighed by the energy consumed to produce that insulation product.

Identifying sustainable materials

Every company that sells construction materials and products is aware of the importance of making their products appear as 'green' as possible and most companies promote their system or product as being 'greener' or more sustainable than those of their competitors. However, it is not usually this simple: each material, product or system will have its own good and bad points.

KEY PRINCIPLES

Sustainable construction materials and products can be identified by the following qualities:

- they **are designed for low energy use** – they minimise the energy required to 'run' the home
- they **minimise the use of new resources** – they are made using recovered, reused and recycled materials instead of new materials
- they **use whole unprocessed materials** – materials like solid timber (in the round), natural stone, earth, clay and products that use natural fibres
- they **have a low embodied energy** – the energy used during the extraction/harvesting, manufacture and transport of a construction material
- they **can be reused** – for example, using lime-based mortar instead of cement-based mortar allows bricks to be reused because a lime mortar is softer than the brick and can be cleaned off without damaging the brick
- they **contribute to a healthy indoor environment** – for example, natural paints that do not emit volatile organic compounds (VOCs) and natural fibre (e.g. wool) carpets.

DEFINITION

Embodied energy
Total primary energy consumed from direct and indirect processes associated with a product or service within the boundaries of cradle to gate.

This includes all activities from material extraction(quarrying/mining/harvesting), manufacturing, transportation and fabrication until the product is ready to leave the final factory gate.

While the sustainability of a construction material or product is very important, there are also other factors that have to be taken into account. Each material chosen must be suited to its particular task and should help to ensure that the home is attractive, long lasting and structurally sound.

Embodied energy

Energy is consumed to extract or harvest the raw materials that are used in construction products. More energy is used to transport these raw materials to the factories, where even more energy is used to transform the raw materials into finished construction products. All the energy consumed at each step along the way can be thought of as being 'trapped' or embodied in the final product. All the energy used up to the point where the construction material is ready to be shipped to the consumer is included. The term used to describe this is 'cradle to gate' – meaning from the source of the raw material (e.g. forest) to the factory gate.

Embodied energy is one of the key factors used to assess the sustainability of a construction material or product. Sustainable materials and products have low levels of embodied energy. A material that is locally sourced and is relatively unprocessed will have a low level of embodied energy. Materials that have high levels of embodied energy are generally not sustainable and should be avoided where possible.

10.01 Embodied energy: the picture on the left shows a rolled steel joist being used to support the floor joists across a wide span. However, timber engineered joists, shown on the photo on the right, might have been a more sustainable solution. Steel products have about twice the level of embodied energy and embodied carbon because of the high furnace temperatures used to manufacture steel products.

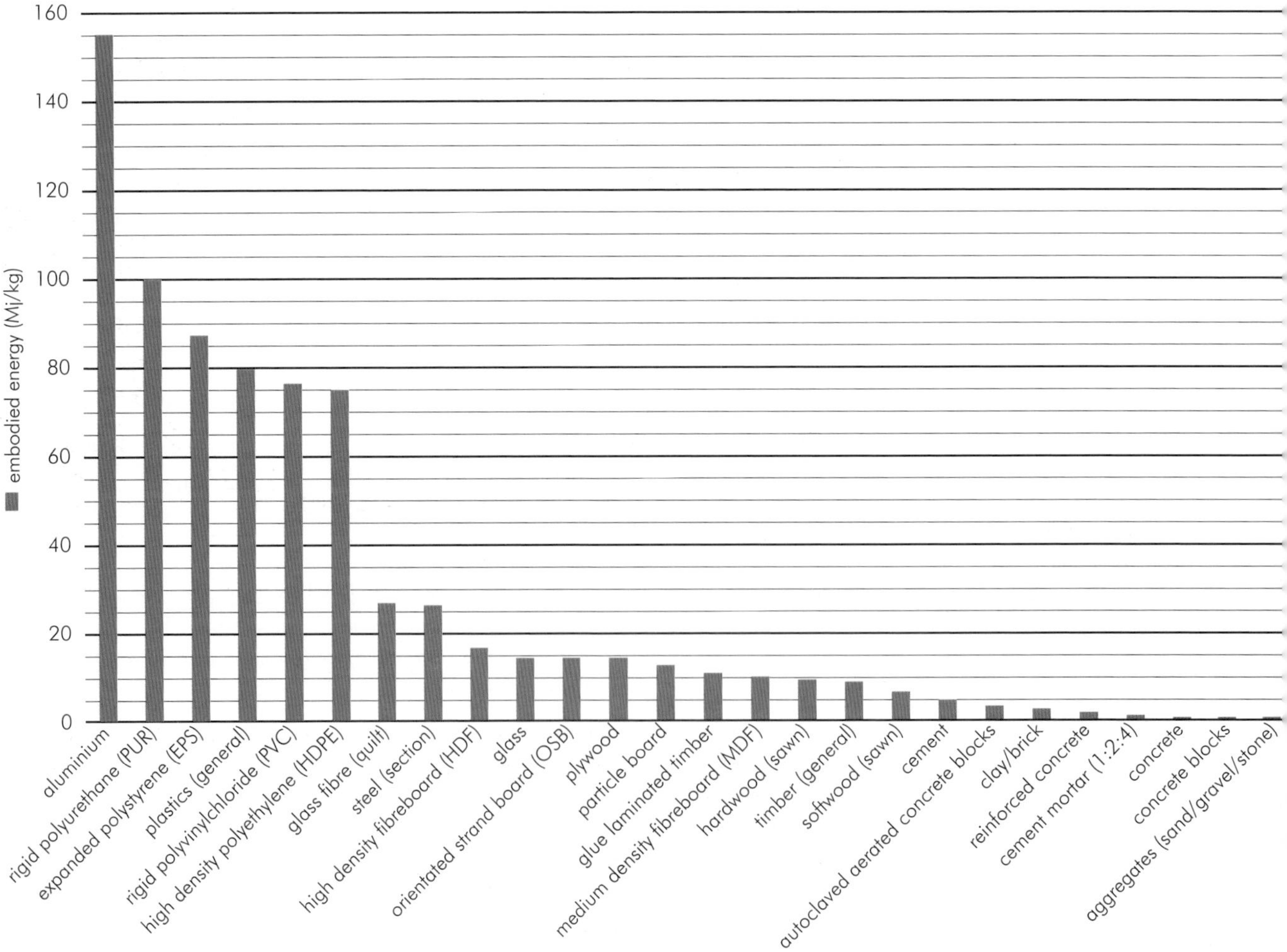

embodied energy (Mj/kg)

160
140
120
100
80
60
40
20
0

aluminium
rigid polyurethane (PUR)
expanded polystyrene (EPS)
plastics (general)
rigid polyvinylchloride (PVC)
high density polyethylene (HDPE)
glass fibre (quilt)
steel (section)
high density fibreboard (HDF)
glass
orientated strand board (OSB)
plywood
particle board
glue laminated timber
medium density fibreboard (MDF)
hardwood (sawn)
timber (general)
softwood (sawn)
cement
autoclaved aerated concrete blocks
clay/brick
reinforced concrete
cement mortar (1:2:4)
concrete
concrete blocks
aggregates (sand/gravel/stone)

10.02 Embodied energy of common construction materials (measured in megajoules of energy per kilogram of material).

KEY PRINCIPLES

The concept of embodied energy provides three guidelines for selecting sustainable construction materials and products.

1 Source heavyweight materials locally: heavy materials like stone, aggregates and bricks should be purchased from local quarries and manufacturers because of the high amount of fuel required to transport heavy materials.
2 Source lightweight materials globally: the proportion of embodied energy that is linked to transport is much smaller for lightweight materials (e.g. aluminium or PVC), especially when compared to the energy used in their manufacture. Many lightweight construction materials compensate for the embodied energy gained during manufacture by saving energy in the building once installed. For example, the aluminium foil used in insulation products saves lots of energy by reducing heat loss.
3 Source materials with a high potential for reuse and recycling: the embodied energy that remains 'trapped' in materials at the end of a building's life should not be wasted by sending the materials to landfill.

Use local suppliers

The benefits of using local suppliers include:

- it reduces the energy needed to transport materials to the building site
- it reduces other environmental impacts, e.g. noise pollution and air pollution
- it supports local businesses and creates employment for local people
- it can revive local building traditions
- it allows new developments to be seen as belonging to the local community.

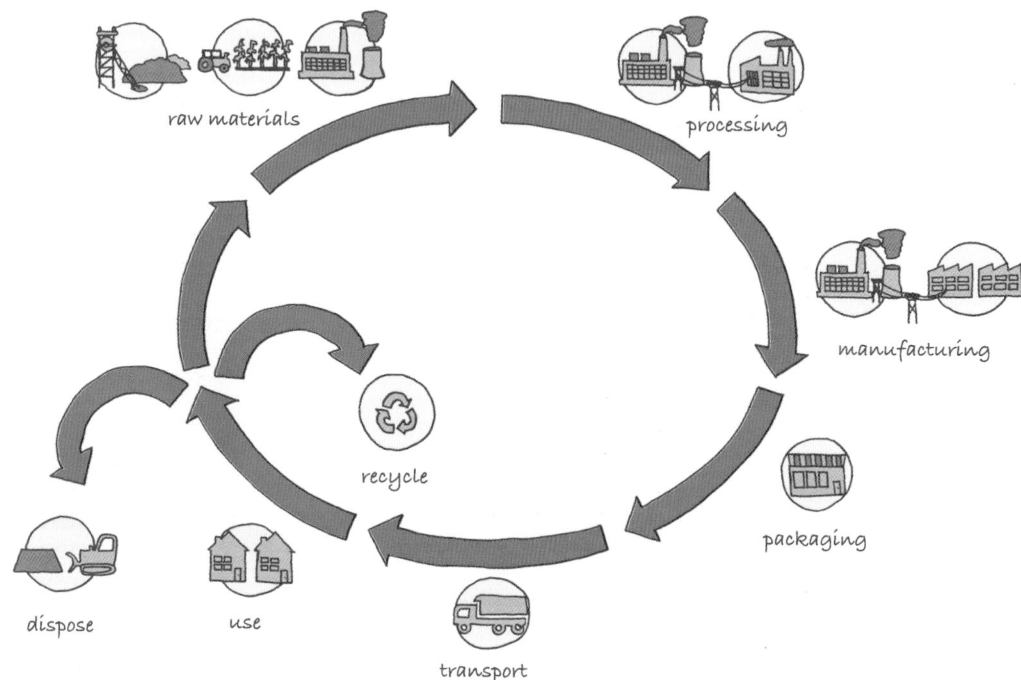

10.03 Life cycle assessment: typical stages in the life of a product.

Life cycle assessment (LCA) is a tool used to calculate the environmental impact of a material or product. LCA takes the into account all associated inputs and emissions, including:

- energy consumption
- greenhouse gas emissions
- resource consumption (e.g. water)
- waste
- pollution (air, water, land).

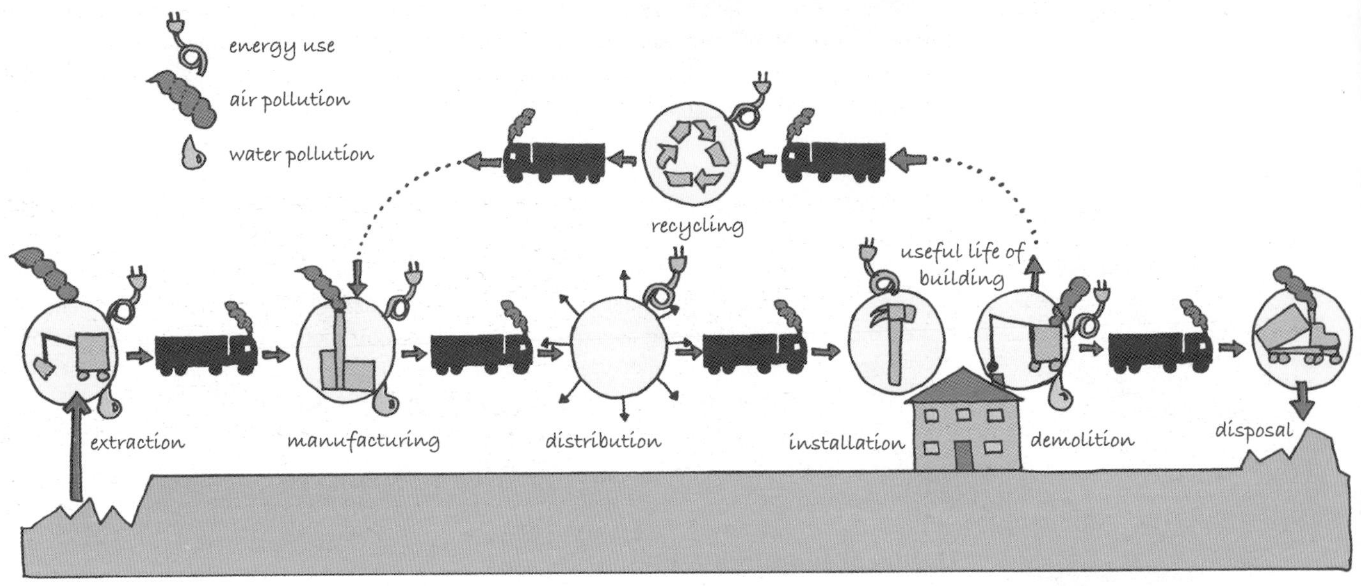

10.04 Life cycle assessment of a building. LCA is commonly used to measure all the environmental impacts of a product or activity; energy is consumed and carbon dioxide is emitted throughout the life of a material.

Over the life cycle of a car, most energy is consumed during the use phase – driving the car uses more energy than making it, delivering it or disposing of it. For a house, most energy is consumed during the material creation phase and the use phase.

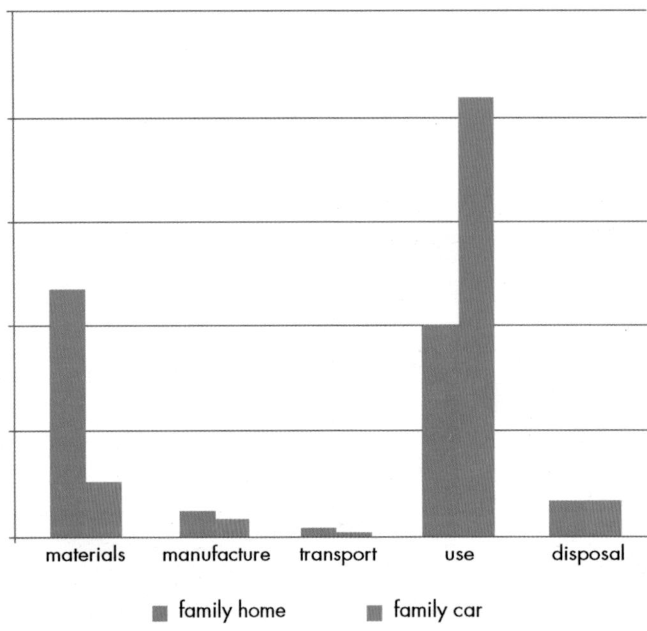

10.05 Life cycle assessment: for a typical house, the 'material creation phase' and the 'use phase' are the most energy-intensive.

Managing waste

Building houses generates waste at every step: when raw materials are extracted or harvested; when these materials are used to manufacture construction products; when construction products are packaged; and so on until the house is demolished and the waste is removed from the site. It is essential that the potential for waste is taken into account when selecting a construction material or product.

10.06 Waste: unlike what has happened in this case, construction waste should be separated (e.g. masonry and rubble, plastic, timber, etc.) so that it can be efficiently recycled.

10.07 Reuse: reclaimed brick ready for reuse in a new building. Reusing these bricks 'saves' all of the energy that went into their manufacture. An average brick contains 1.74 kWh of embodied energy.

Many construction materials and products (e.g. soil, timber, masonry, plasterboard, insulation, steel and glass) can be usefully reused or recycled.

KEY PRINCIPLES

There are four ways (the four Rs) in which construction waste can be minimised.

1. **Reduce** – 'less is more': houses should be designed to use less energy, fewer new materials and fewer resources (e.g. water).
2. **Re-use** – houses should be designed so that their components can be dismantled and reused without the need for substantial remanufacture.
3. **Recycle** – unlike reuse, recycling requires more energy input to convert the material into another useful product. Materials such as steel, copper, aluminium and lead can all be recycled.
4. **Recover** – this is about improving existing resources rather than letting them go unused. For example, a contaminated brownfield site (e.g. a old industrial site) can be recovered by the removal of contaminated soil; and the air quality in a city area can be improved by planting trees or by installing cycle lanes.

Each of these strategies will help to tackle all the various waste streams caused by the construction of homes.

Recycling

Most recycling involves converting or extracting useful materials from a product and creating a different product or material. This can be done in two ways:

1. **downcycling** – the process of converting waste materials or products into new materials or products of lesser quality and reduced functionality. The aim is to prevent waste, reduce consumption of new materials and to reduce energy consumption, air and water pollution and greenhouse gas emissions. An example would be crushing masonry products (e.g. blocks, bricks) for use as fill.
2. **upcycling** – the process of converting waste materials or products into new materials or products of better quality or for better environmental value.

ACTIVITIES

Visit www.containercity.com to learn more about this innovative system.

10.08 Upcycling: Container City, London – a low cost modular construction system that re-uses shipping containers to provide homes, offices, retail spaces, artists' studios, classrooms and various other spaces.

KEY PRINCIPLES

Construction waste can be reduced in many ways, including:

- designing out waste – using standard sizes avoids cutting materials on site
- buying construction materials and products from suppliers who are actively trying to minimise waste in the production process (e.g. wood product companies who use their waste wood to generate the electricity needed to power their factory)
- choosing recycled or reclaimed materials (e.g. reclaimed brick)
- designing buildings that can be easily dismantled (e.g. using screws and bolts instead of nails or glues allows materials to be recovered for recycling and reuse)
- constructing well-built, flexible buildings that are capable of being used in a new way at the end of their first life.

Physical properties

Deciding whether a material is suitable for a structural application depends mainly on the material's physical properties. Many of the systems used in modern houses rely on the technical performance of certain components like breather membranes and airtightness membranes to ensure the structure works as designed.

key physical properties of construction materials

weight
heavy materials require a lot of energy for transport and installation; they also need sturdy structural designs that can support their weight; however, most heavy materials are good at storing heat energy (solar gain)

compressive strength
an expression of how much pressure the material can withstand before collapsing, buckling or crushing; this is very important in vertical load bearing elements like arches and columns

tensile strength
describes how much a material can be stretched before failing; this is very important in horizontal load bearing elements like beams and suspended floors

vapour permeability
how much water will move through a material under diffirent pressure conditions; it depends on the material's moisture content and temperature, and is crucial in the prevention of dampness in structures

thermal capacity
a material's ability to store heat or cold; it evens out the temperature swings in a building and can reduce energy consumption; it is directly proportional to a material's weight

thermal conductivity
a material's ability to conduct heat – used mainly to determine a material's insulating properties – depends on the weight of the material, the temperature, its moisture content and structure

air permeability
how much air will move through a material under different pressure conditions; it depends on a material's porosity (the size and structure of its pores) and its moisture content; air permeability is particularly important when making a building airtight

moisture regulation
ability to absorb and release humidity; closely related to vapour permeability, it also depends on density, porosity and absorption properties; regulating indoor humidity levels improves health and reduces building damage caused by humidity (e.g. growth of moulds and fungi); paint, varnish and wallpaper can have a significant effect on the property

10.

Durability

When selecting a construction material, the likely performance of that material over the lifetime of the building must be taken into account. This performance will depend on a number of factors, including:

- intended use: the function of the material (e.g. window frame)
- exposure conditions: the range of environmental conditions the material or product experiences (e.g. temperature, humidity, water, UV radiation, abrasion, chemical attack, biological attack, corrosion, weathering, frost, freeze-thaw and fatigue)
- expected working life: the period of time the material should continue to work properly, provided normal maintenance is carried out.

Aesthetic properties

Aesthetic qualities such as colour, tone and texture are important if the material is going to be seen. Many natural materials (e.g. timber, stone, brick) have a wonderful feel that gets better with age.

ACTIVITIES

Take a photo of a house that you think is aesthetically pleasing and discuss why you like it with your classmates.

10.10 'House 1' by Taka Architects. The aesthetic qualities of brick are emphasised by the use of 'separated' Flemish bond in the façade of this family home in Donnybrook, Dublin 4.

REVISION EXERCISES

1 Describe, using examples, any five qualities of a sustainable construction material.
2 How does the concept of embodied energy influence the selection of construction materials?
3 Outline the benefits of using local suppliers when building a home.
4 Describe the life cycle of a typical solid timber joist.
5 Explain four ways in which construction waste can be reduced.

CHAPTER 11

Envelope Design Concepts

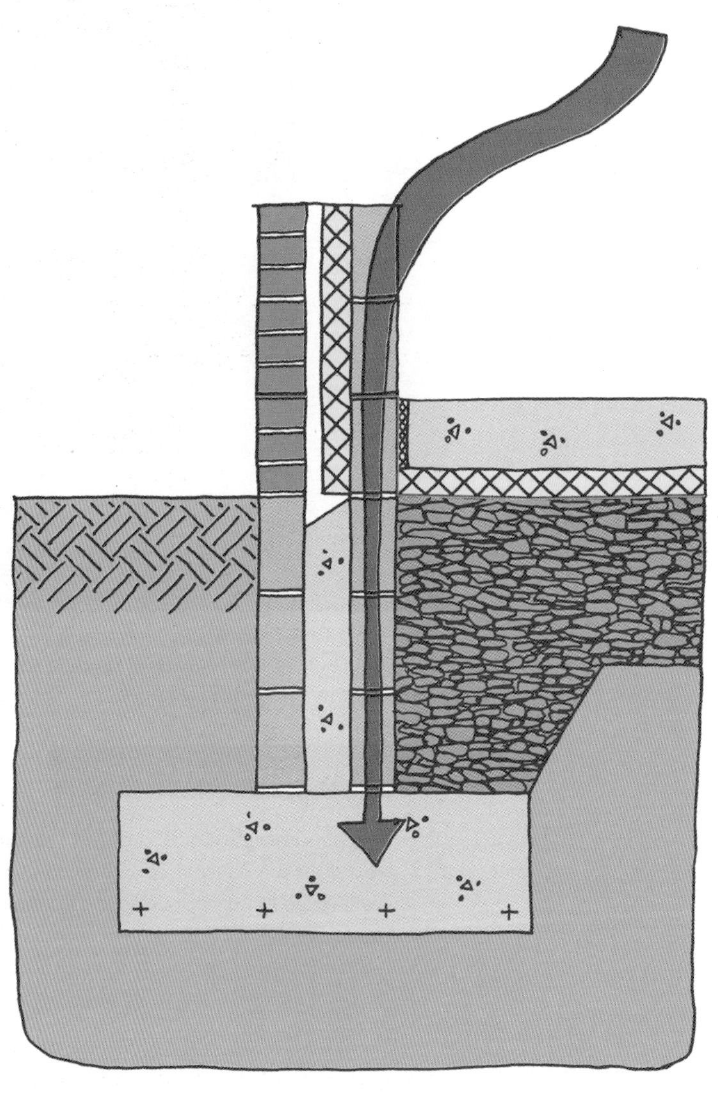

A home is a physical barrier between the internal environment, which we find comfortable, and the outdoor environmental conditions, which tend not to be comfortable. This 'artificial' environment that we like to live in creates differences that the building fabric must be able to withstand.

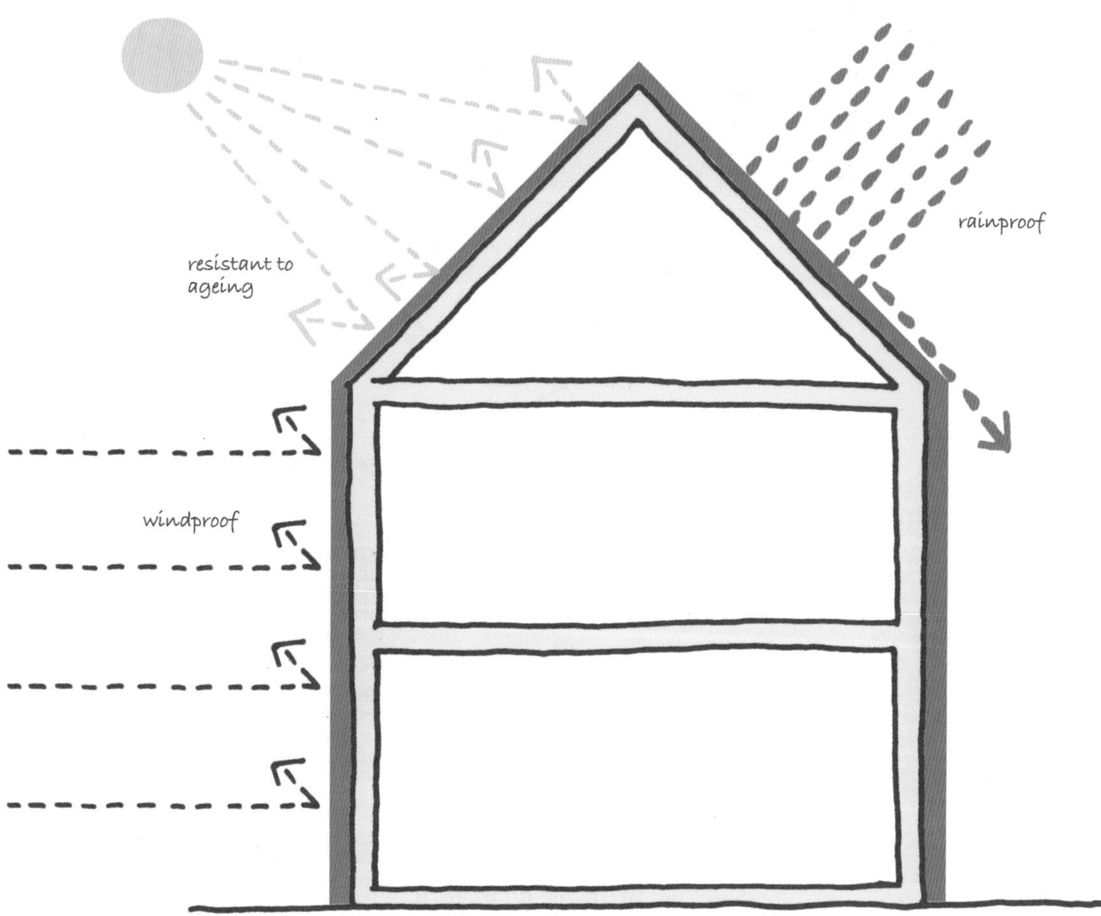

11.01 External envelope: fundamental design concepts.

Human beings have for millennia created shelter for a simple reason; to provide protection from the elements (wind, rain, sun, snow). Construction materials, techniques and technology have evolved as our knowledge and understanding of building physics has improved and new materials have been created. These developments have highlighted several fundamental design concepts that must be understood if a building is going to perform well in various environmental conditions. Unlike a person, who can dress appropriately depending on the weather, a building's fabric does not change with the weather – it must be designed to perform in all types of weather all year round.

Sustainability

The external envelope should be designed to meet the principles of sustainability. This is essentially about:

- selecting sustainable construction materials
- designing the external envelope to be as energy efficient as possible.

Life cycle assessment shows that for houses built to the building regulations the materials-related embodied energy is about 10–25% of overall energy consumption over the lifetime of the building but that for low-energy buildings (e.g. passive house) the materials-related embodied energy consumption can be as high as 50%.

ACTIVITIES

Contact your local builders' providers and ask them what slate products they have for sale and where the products are manufactured.

11.02 Transporting slate from China for roof construction is unsustainable.

Structural stability

Actions is the term used to describe the loads or forces applied to a structure. Every structure constantly experiences a wide range of actions; some of these are static (i.e. they don't change) and some dynamic (i.e. they change over time). The structure must be able to safely transmit the imposed permanent and variable actions to the soil.

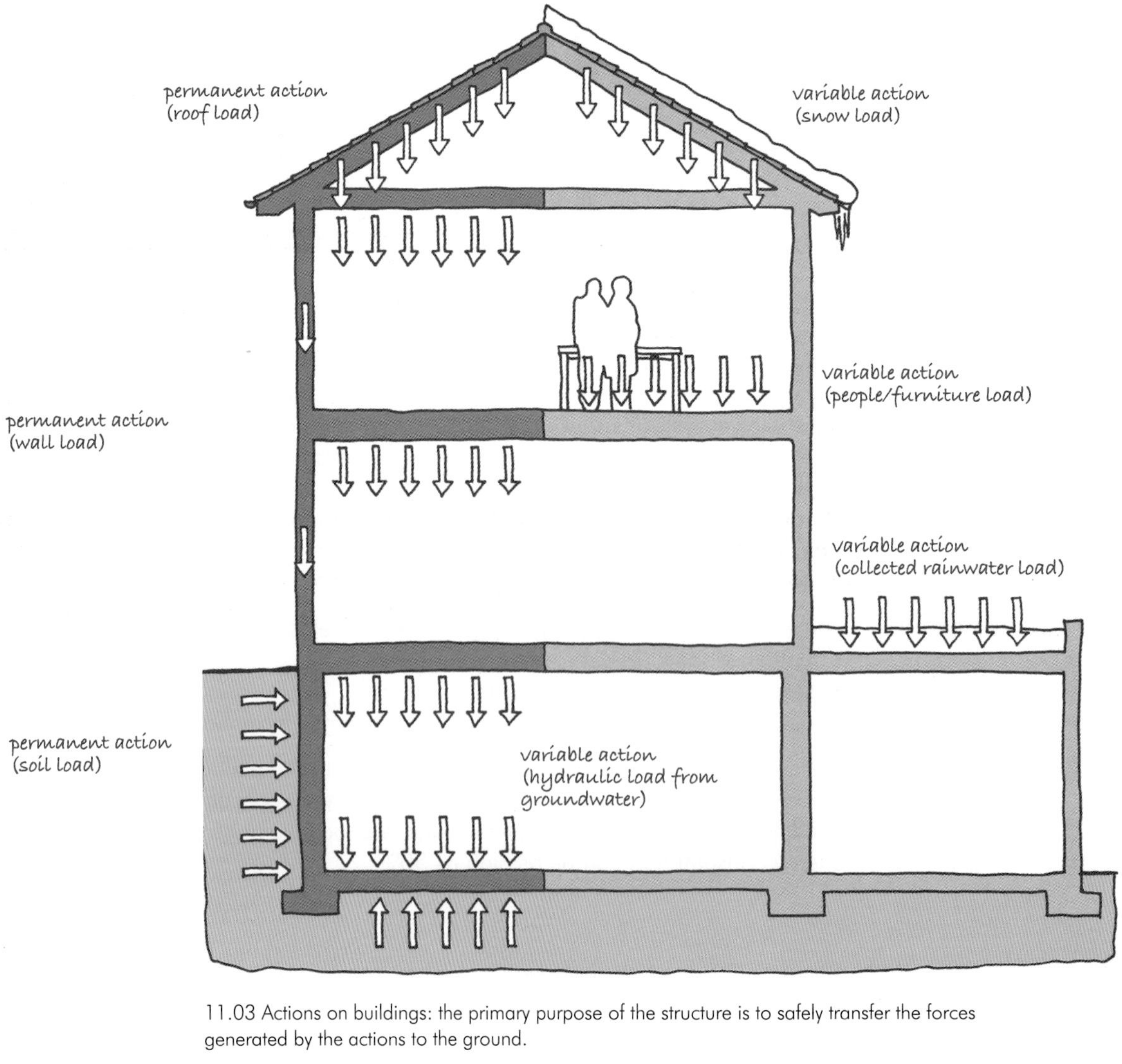

11.03 Actions on buildings: the primary purpose of the structure is to safely transfer the forces generated by the actions to the ground.

SUPPLEMENTARY INFORMATION

- **Load** – the weight or force carried by a structure.
- **Force** – anything that causes an object to accelerate (e.g. a push or pull).
- **Permanent actions** – the weight of all permanent and stationary loads (e.g. roof, floors, ceilings, pipes, electrical cables, soil, etc.) (previously called the 'dead load').
- **Variable actions** – the load generated by movable objects (e.g. people, furniture) and environmental loads (e.g. wind, snow, hydraulic loads from groundwater) (previously called 'live loads').
- **Accidental actions** – exceptional loads caused by unusual events such as fires, explosions and vehicle crashes.

Principle of triangulation

11.04 Triangulation: adding a diagonal brace to a square or rectangular structure greatly improves its structural integrity.

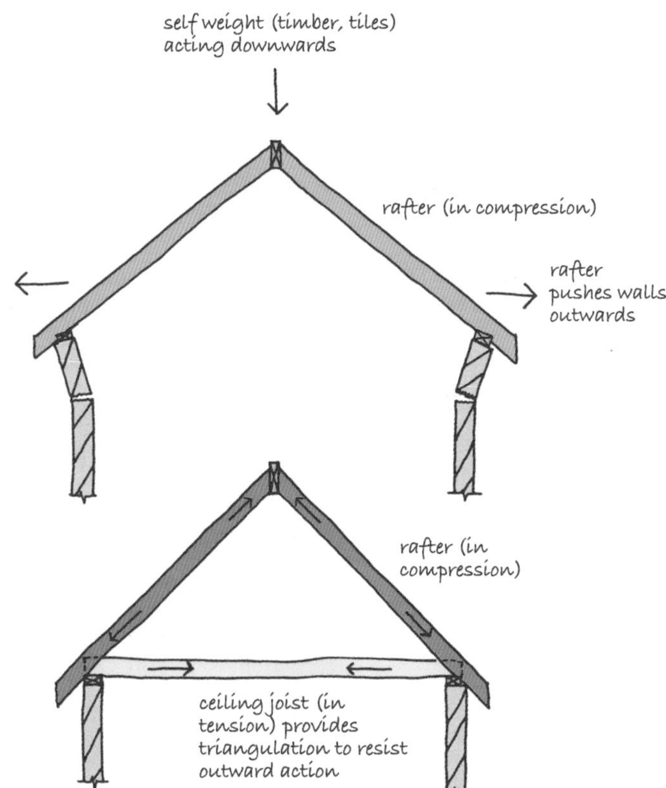

11.05 Triangulation: a pitched roof is made stable using a collar or a ceiling joist.

The principle of triangulation is used in the design of timber frame walls and pitched roofs. A square or rectangular structure is susceptible to racking (i.e. sideways collapse). However, triangular structures are inherently stable. Adding a diagonal brace to a square structure will prevent collapse because it 'converts' the square into two triangles. Fixing a sheet of timber to the surface of a rectangular frame has this effect.

Durability

Walls and roofs must be designed to perform well for the expected lifetime of the building. Traditionally, houses were designed to last fifty to sixty years. With increasing emphasis on sustainability, houses are now expected to last longer.

ACTIVITIES

Visit the Met Éireann website and compare the average meteorological data for a coastal area and an inland area (e.g. Valentia, Co. Kerry and Birr, Co. Offaly).

KEY PRINCIPLES

The main factors affecting the durability of buildings include:

- **maintenance** – a regular maintenance schedule will allow the building to perform as designed (e.g. cleaning leaves out of roof gutters prevents overflow that can damage the building fabric)
- **materials** – some materials are naturally durable; for example, larch and cedar are well suited for use as external cladding
- **detailing** – this is particularly important to prevent rainwater getting into the structure (e.g. roof flashings, window/wall junctions)
- **workmanship** – good detail design and good-quality materials are of little use if they are not installed properly (good workmanship is particularly important in the construction of low-energy housing)
- **local environment** – the level of exposure to wind, rain, temperature changes and humidity – harsh climates cause high levels of wear and tear.

Thermal resistance

Thermal insulation is essential to prevent heat loss through the building fabric. While this might seem obvious, there are thousands of houses in Ireland that have little or no insulation. This is because insulation only became mandatory when the building regulations were introduced in the early 1990s.

The overall thermal performance of the structure is determined by the quality and quantity of the insulation materials used in its construction, the junction details and the quality of the workmanshi

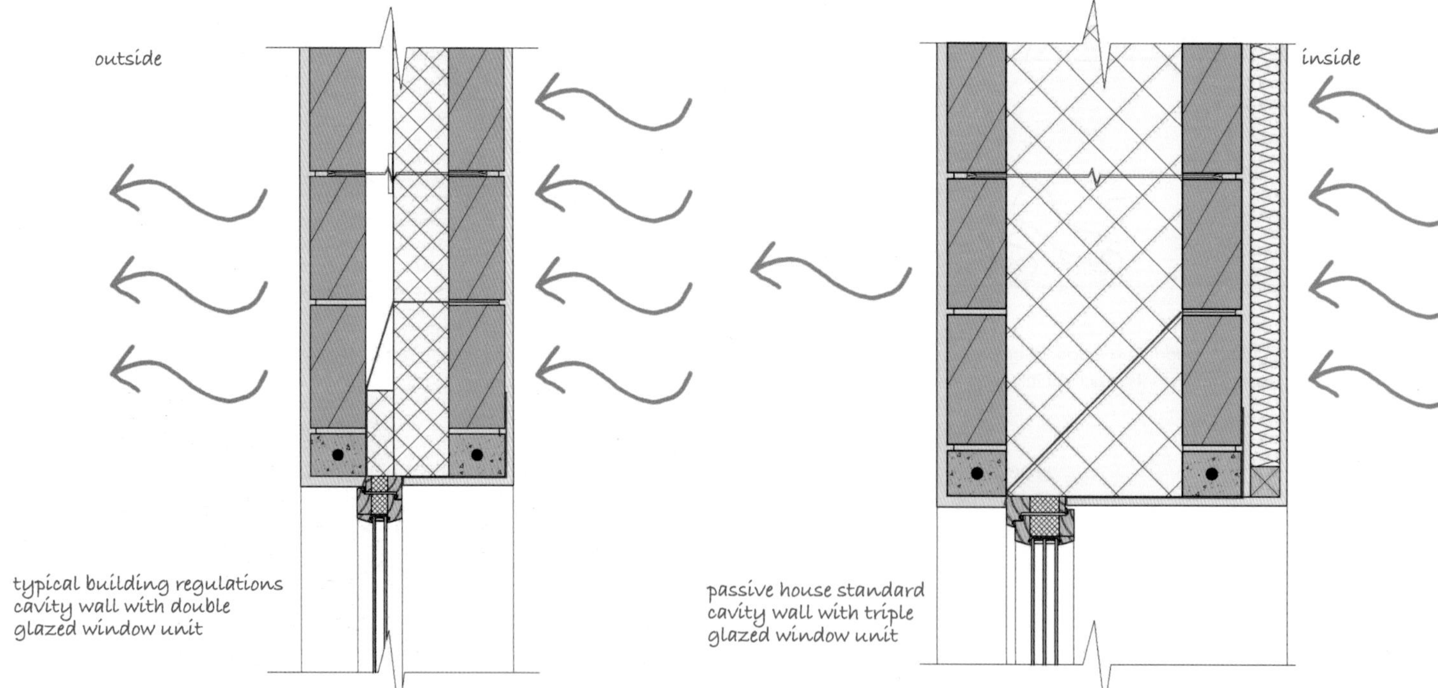

11.06 Thermal resistance: more insulation and better-quality components (e.g. windows) reduces heat loss, energy consumption and carbon emissions.

Thermal bridging

A thermal bridge occurs where the insulation layer is interrupted or 'bridged' by a material of higher thermal conductivity. In older houses thermal bridges have a negligible impact on the overall energy performance of the house because the main structural elements (i.e. walls, floors, roof) are poorly insulated. However, in energy efficient houses (e.g. passive houses) the impact of thermal bridges is very significant and can lead to significant heat losses.

Thermal bridges are usually a result of the building's design – its structural design or geometry:

- **construction thermal bridge** – occurs where the structure penetrates the thermal layer, offering a 'path of least resistance' to the flow of heat
- **geometric thermal bridge** – occurs where the shape of the structure (e.g. a corner) reduces the amount of insulation in the external envelope. This usually results in a change in insulation thickness and is common at junctions (e.g. wall–floor junctions and around windows and doors).

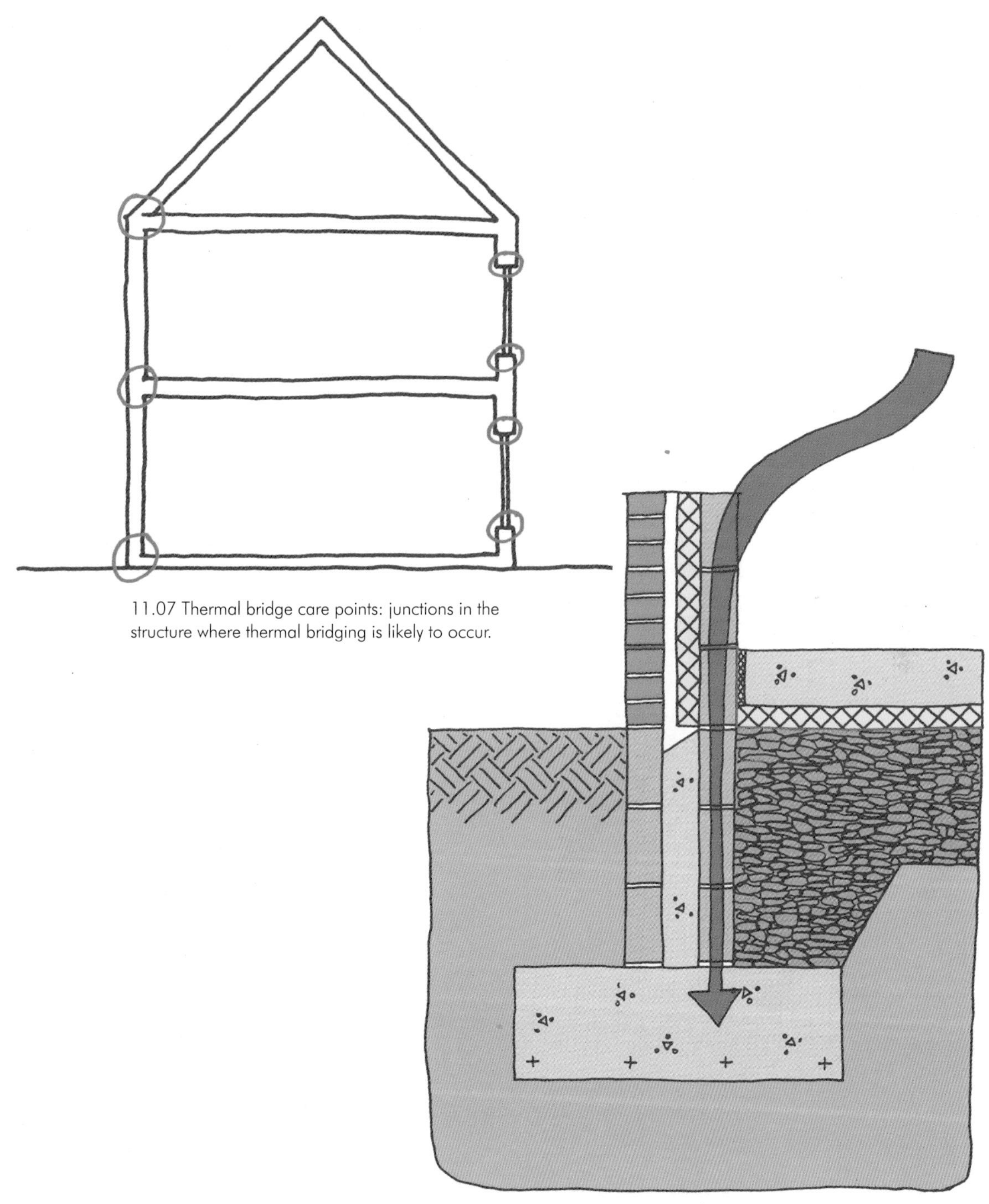

11.07 Thermal bridge care points: junctions in the structure where thermal bridging is likely to occur.

11.08 Construction thermal bridge: in traditional cavity wall systems, heat energy is conducted down through the blockwork.

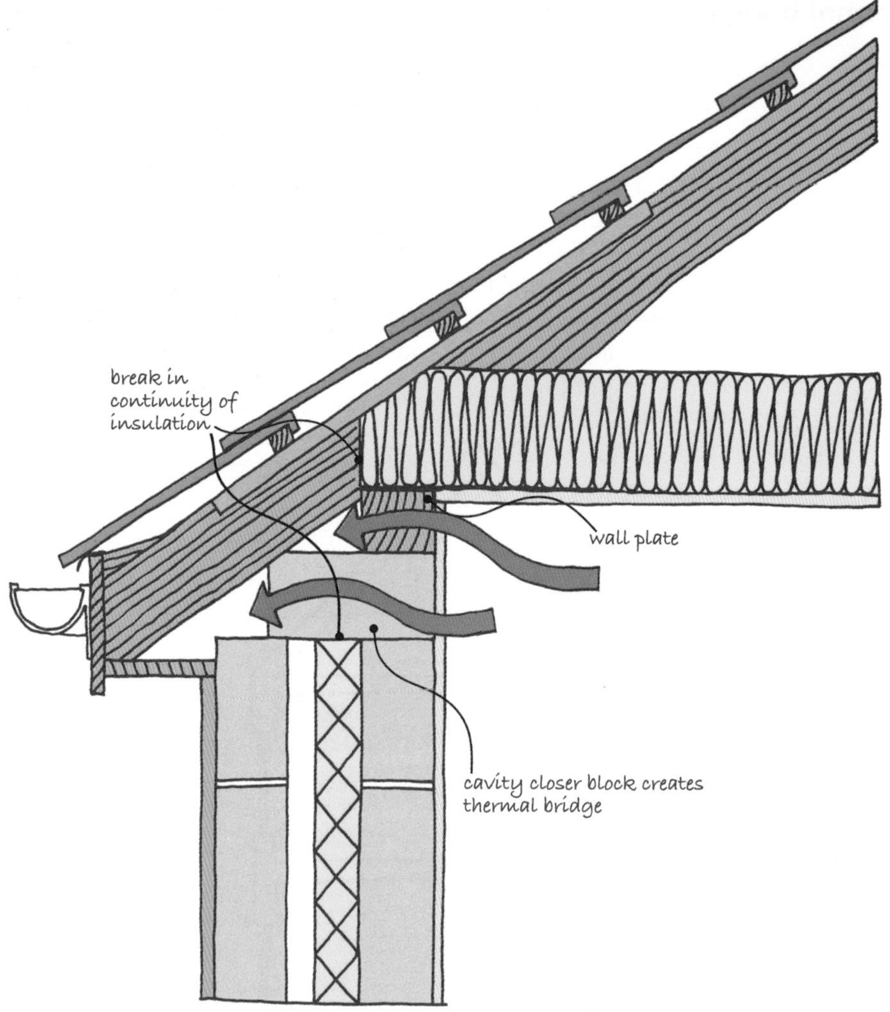

11.09 Thermal bridging: the eaves wall–roof junction is a common thermal bridging problem area because it is hard to dress the insulation down into the tight space around the wall plate and cavity closer.

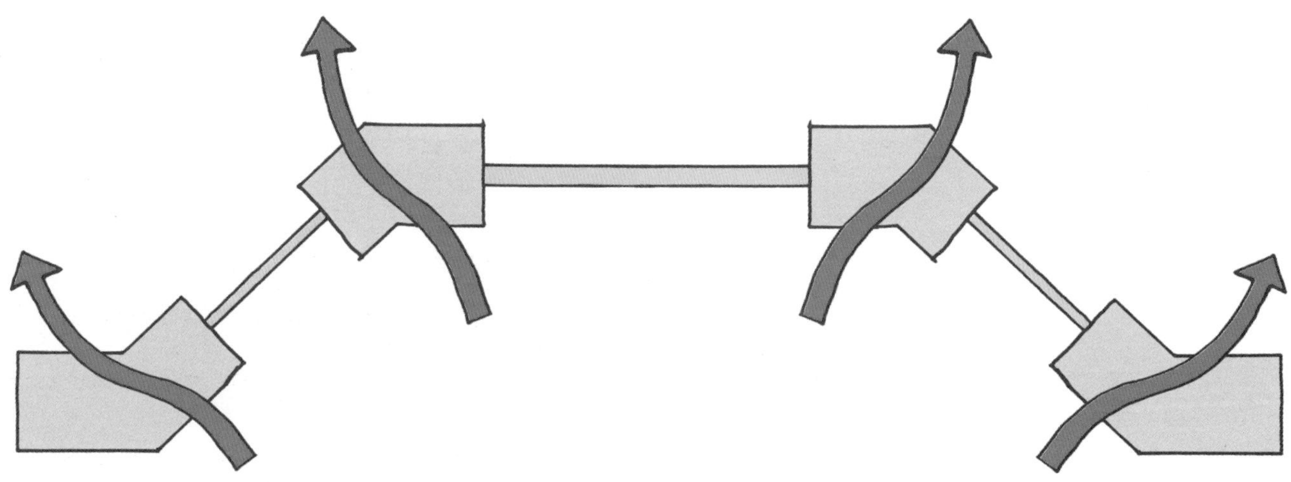

11.10 Geometric thermal bridge: a bay window is a typical potential thermal bridge caused by a change in building geometry and the practical difficulty of installing insulation in a tight space.

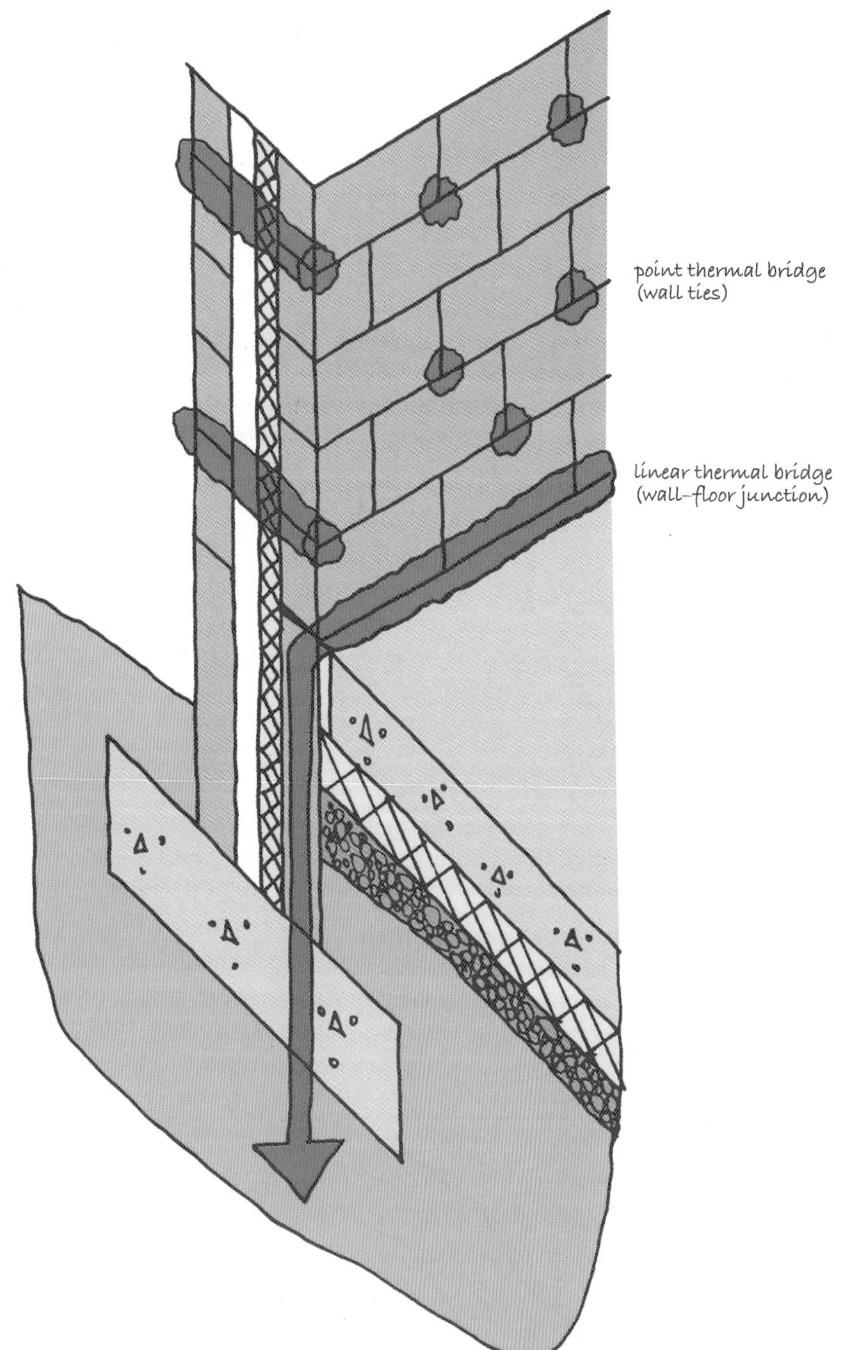

11.11 Linear and point thermal bridges in a traditional cavity walled structure.

The heat energy lost through thermal bridges is added to the heat energy lost through the main structural elements (e.g. floors, walls, roof) to provide an accurate measurement of the total energy loss by thermal transmittance through the building fabric. When measuring thermal bridges two values are calculated:

- psi value (Ψ) – the rate at which energy is conducted through a length of material, measured in watts per metre kelvin
- chi value (χ) – the rate at which energy is conducted through a point in the structure, measured in watts per kelvin.

The building regulations allow for a certain amount of thermal bridging; the amount ranges from zero to 4.88 W/mK depending on the detail. The passive house standard requires the entire structure to be effectively 'thermal bridge free'. The maximum allowable thermal bridge is $\Psi < 0.01$ W/mK.

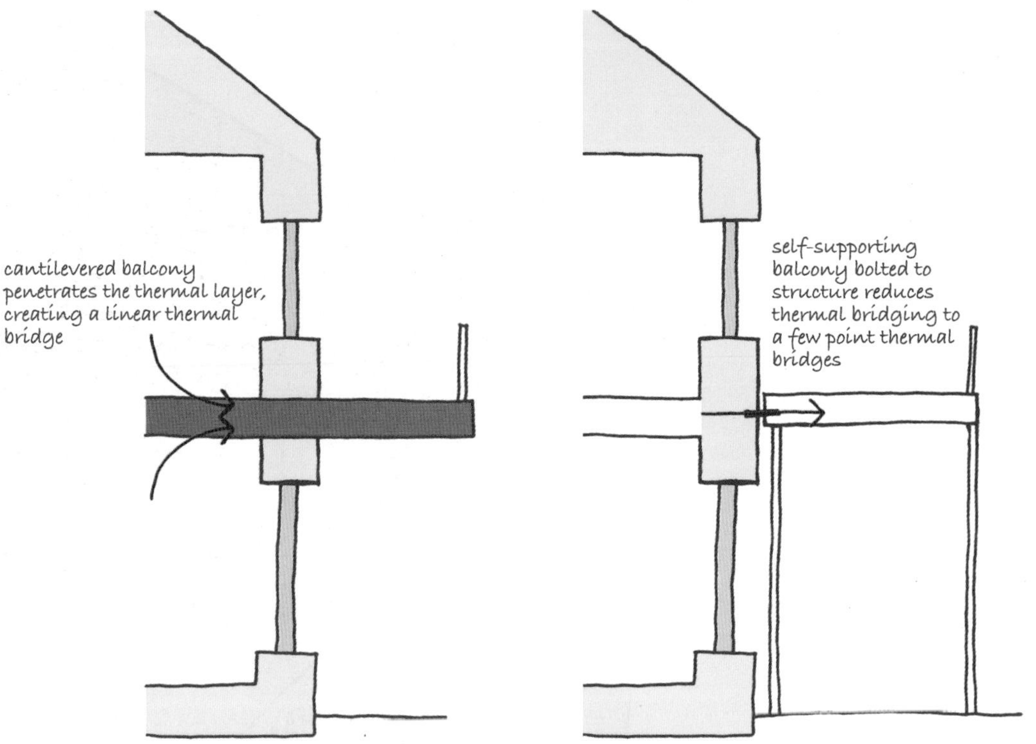

11.12 Designing out thermal bridging.

Where possible, thermal bridges should be 'designed out' at the planning stage. If interrupting the insulation layer is unavoidable, it is best to pierce through (i.e. point thermal bridges) and use materials of low thermal conductivity (e.g. timber instead of steel).

Surface temperature

It is absolutely essential that indoor surfaces are kept warm so as to avoid condensation. Condensation occurs when warm moist air meets a surface that is cool. The moisture in the air cools, forming water droplets on the surface. This moisture leads to dampness and mould growth. In practice, a surface temperature above 12.6°C will prevent mould growth.

Wind resistance

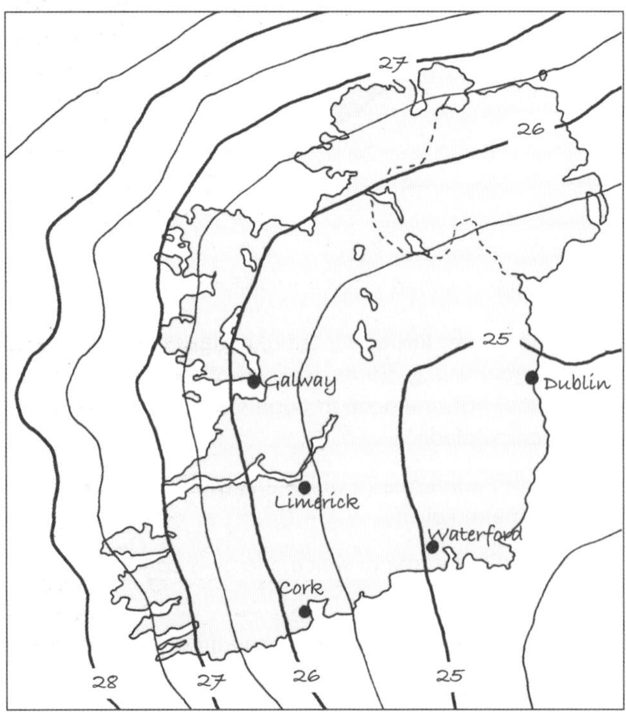

11.13 Wind speeds in metres per second (note: 1m/s = 3.6km/h).

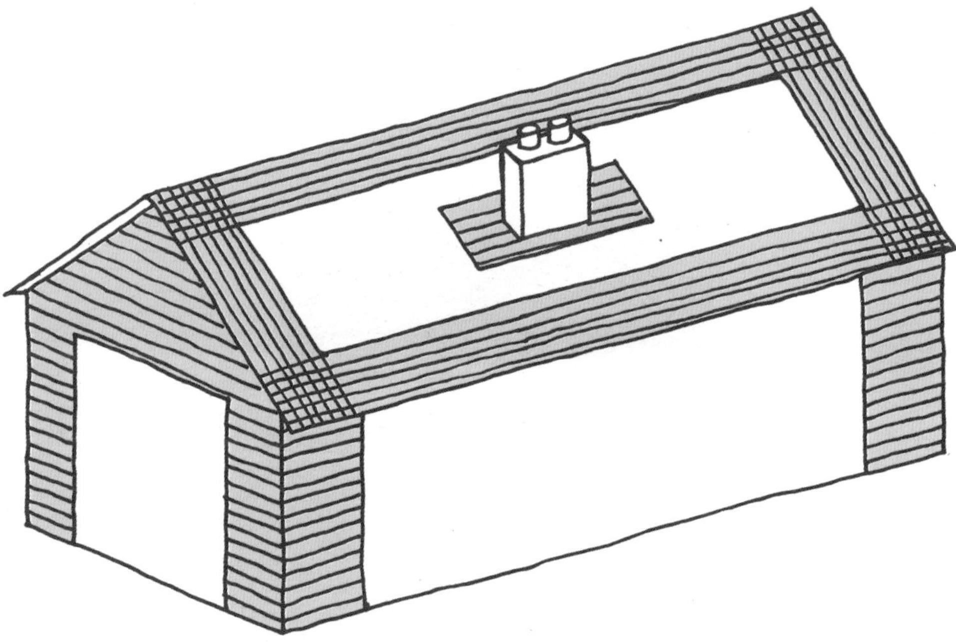

11.14 Wind suction is concentrated in the blue zones on the leeward (i.e. downwind) side of a typical dwelling.

Along the west coast of Ireland the action of the wind, in particular, must be considered. When wind acts on a building the windward faces experience a direct positive pressure. When the wind is deflected around and over a building it is accelerated, creating a lower pressure. This lower pressure creates suction that can lift roof coverings off a building. This suction is greater along the perimeter of the roof and is greatest at the corners. Roof overhangs are also more susceptible to wind lifting – it is important to bear this in mind when designing to prevent overheating in passive houses. Wind speed increases with altitude and on sloped sites (e.g. hillsides).

KEY PRINCIPLES

Wind can cause deterioration of the building fabric in two ways:

- damage to the external envelope (e.g. damaged roof tiles)
- reduction in the thermal performance of the insulation (e.g. thermal bypass).

Most insulants work by trapping air within them, either between their fibres or within their pores. If strong wind penetrates the external envelope it will blow through the insulation, reducing its effectiveness. This is called thermal bypass. A simple way to understand this is to imagine yourself wearing a woolly jumper on a cold, clear winter's day. The jumper traps heat by holding molecules of air between the wool fibres. However, if the wind were to suddenly pick up, the jumper would be of little use; the wind would blow right through it and you would feel cold. Were this to happen you might put on a light jacket (often called a windbreaker) over your jumper. Insulation also suffers from this effect, and it must be protected by providing a windtight layer on the outside of the insulation.

11.15 Windtight layer: a wind-resistant fabric is applied to the outer surface of the structure to prevent thermal bypass. *Source*: Dominic Stevens, www.irishvernacular.com.

11.16 Windtight layer: a wind-resistant material on the outer surface of the structure to prevent thermal bypass.

Moisture resistance

Water can penetrate the building envelope in two ways:
- **wind-driven rain** – the rain is forced into the building fabric by the pressure of the wind
- **water vapour** – water in gas form is forced into the building fabric by vapour pressure.

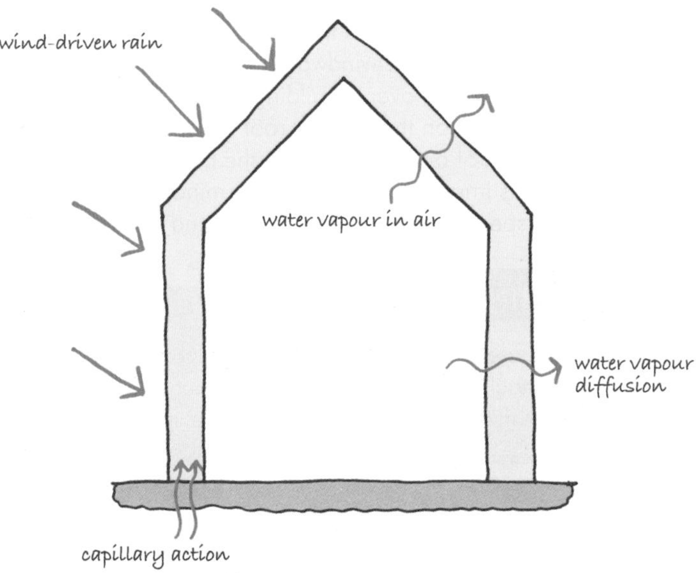

11.17 Moisture penetration: liquid water and water vapour can enter the building fabric through various routes.

The damage that water can do to buildings should not be underestimated. As well as damaging the structure, unwanted moisture can lead to unhealthy indoor living conditions.

Water can cause damage to the external envelope in several ways, including:
- degradation of the structure, particularly timber and steel components (e.g. rot or corrosion)
- reduction in the thermal performance of insulation – many insulants underperform when damp
- mould growth on internal surfaces – fungi need moisture to grow.

Wind-driven rain

Liquid water can enter a structure from the outside through leaks, wind-driven rain or capillary action. Leaks can be avoided through good-quality workmanship and regular building maintenance. Capillary action is avoided by using damp proof courses and membranes. Given Ireland's climate, wind-driven rain is a significant issue.

KEY PRINCIPLES

Wind-driven rain can be handled in two ways:

- **screen** – providing an outer layer that protects the inner building fabric (e.g. roof slates)
- **sponge** – allowing the structure to temporarily absorb the moisture and release it later – requires permeable materials (e.g. lime render).

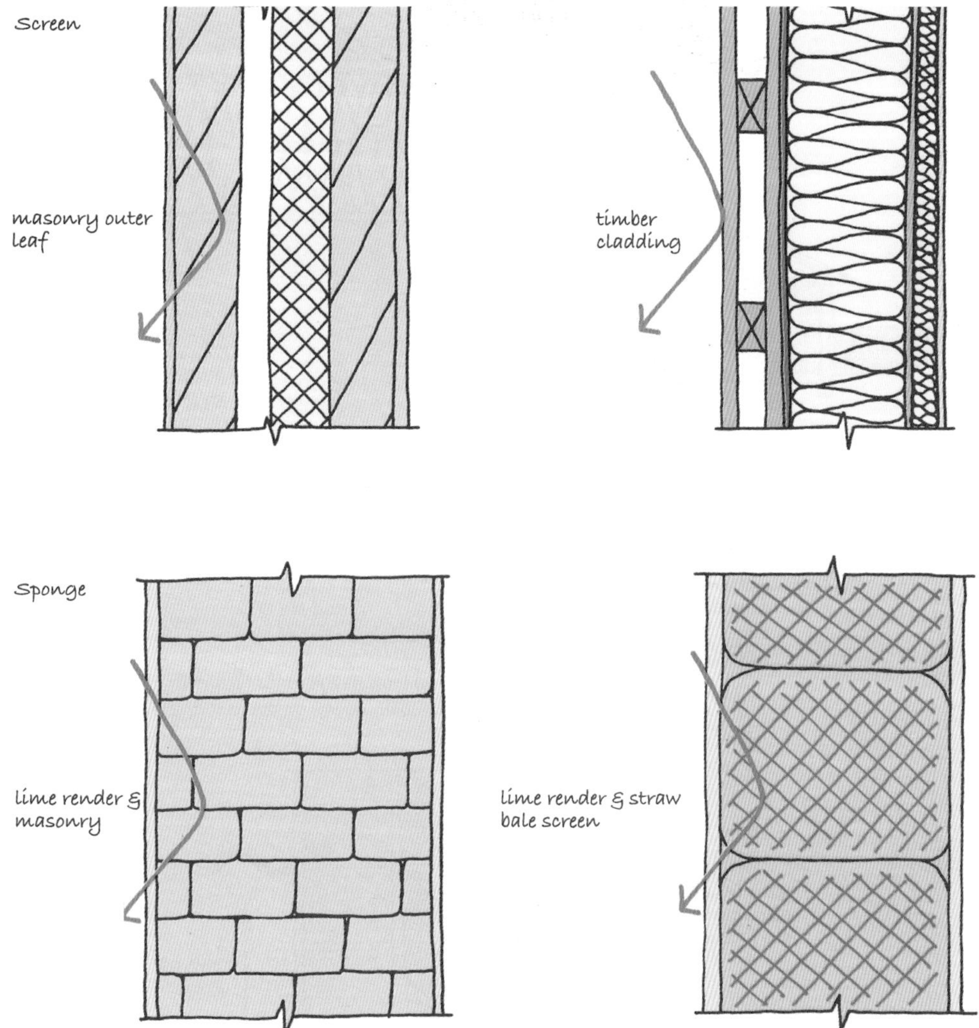

11.18 Rain control strategies: modern systems tend to use a screen, while traditional systems use the sponge approach.

Water vapour

Everyday activities in the home (cooking, washing, etc.) produce water vapour. Water vapour is water in the form of a gas. It should not be confused with steam, mist, fog or clouds – these are all visible because they comprise tiny liquid droplets suspended in the air. When you exhale there is water vapour in your breath that can't be seen. However, when you breathe out on a cold day, the warm water vapour is exhaled into cold, dry outdoor air – this causes the water vapour to condense (cool down and turn into a liquid) and you see your breath as a 'cloud'.

The air inside a house is usually warm, and the warmer the air, the more water vapour it can hold. The higher the indoor temperature, the greater the water vapour pressure will be. Differences in vapour pressure cause water vapour to move from warm areas to cold areas. When a warm body of air is cooled, the water vapour in it will condense to form water droplets. So when the warm water vapour meets a cold surface it condenses on the cold surface. The temperature at which water vapour condensates to become liquid water is called the dew point.

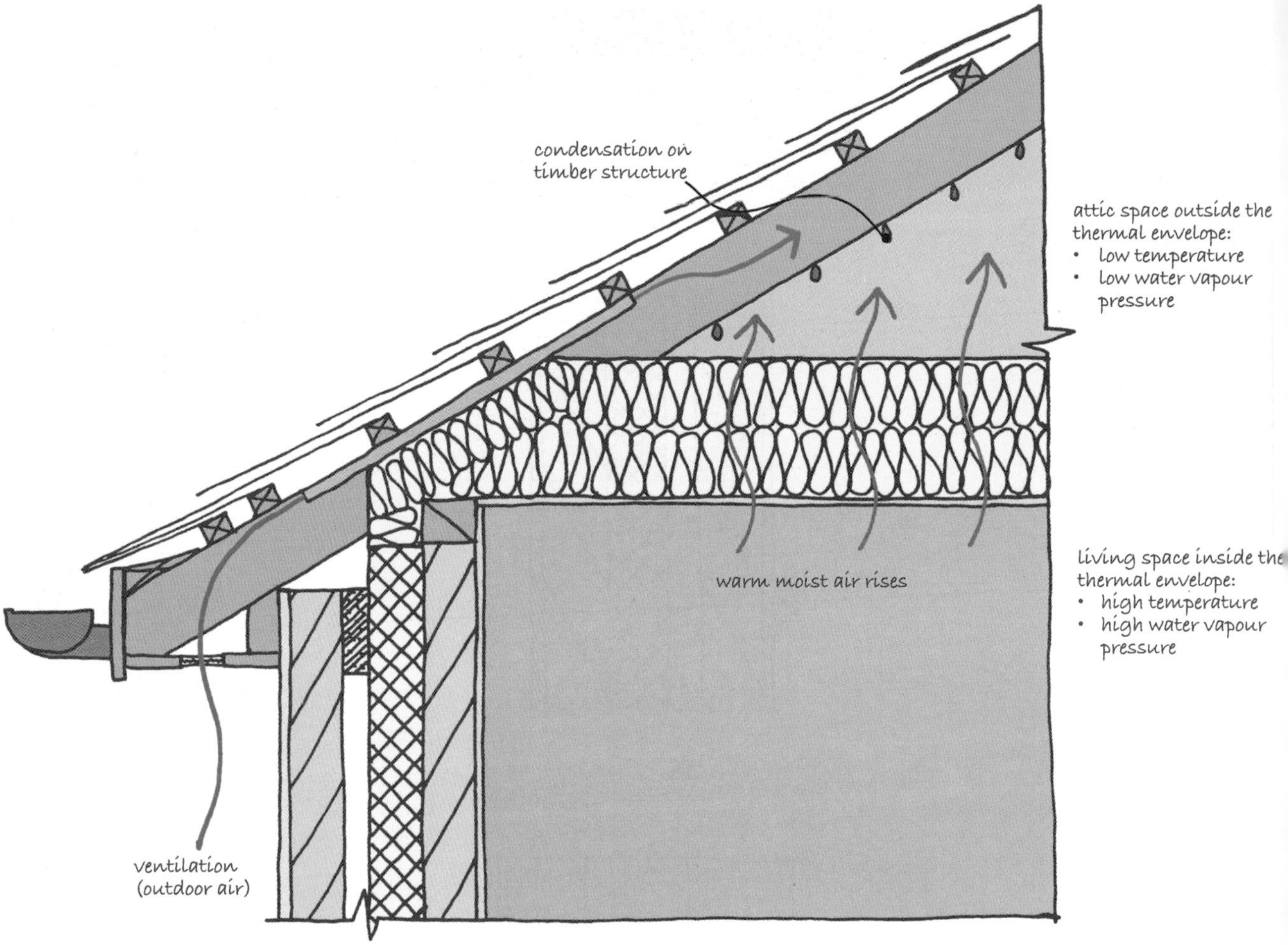

condensation on timber structure

attic space outside the thermal envelope:
- low temperature
- low water vapour pressure

living space inside the thermal envelope:
- high temperature
- high water vapour pressure

warm moist air rises

ventilation (outdoor air)

11.19 Water vapour is driven up through the roof structure by the difference in vapour pressure, causing condensation (and eventually decay) on the roof structure.

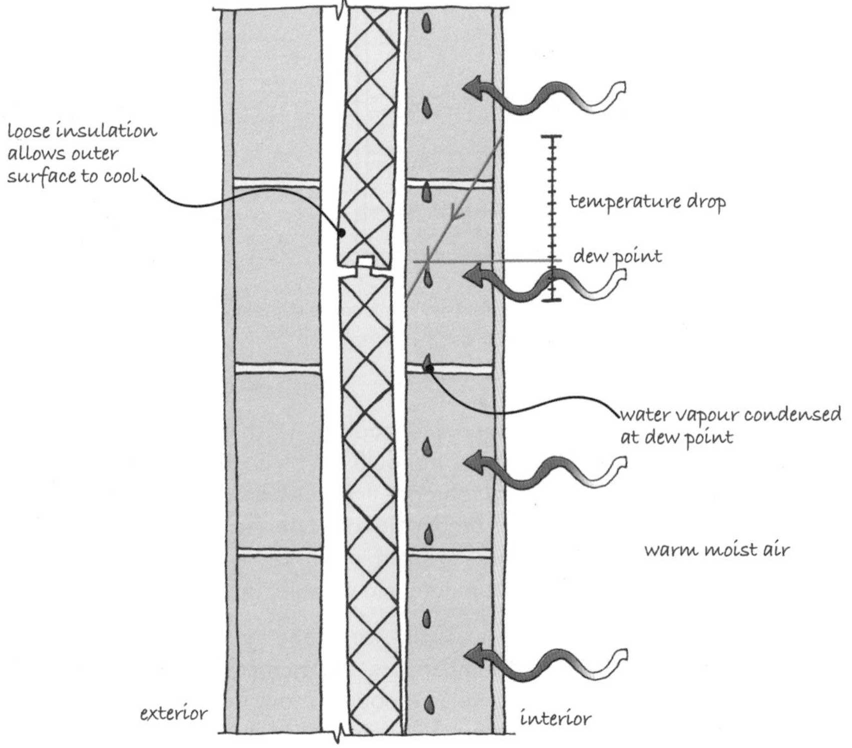

11.20 Interstitial condensation in a concrete cavity wall: the temperature of the blockwork drops from inside to outside; interstitial condensation occurs as the warm moist air moves through the blockwork and approaches the cool outer surface.

KEY PRINCIPLES

Water vapour can be handled in two ways:

- breathable structures:
  - these allow the water vapour to pass through the structure
  - 'vapour open' is also used to describe this concept
  - timber frame systems that include natural insulants (e.g. sheep's wool, wood fibreboard) are breathable.
- non-breathable structures:
  - these do not allow water vapour to pass through the structure
  - 'vapour closed' is also used to describe this concept
  - masonry systems and closed-cell plastic-based insulants (e.g. closed-cell polyurethane/ polyisocyanurate foam) are generally non-breathable
  - insulation products that are foil faced are non-breathable because aluminium foil is vapour closed.

DEFINITION

Interstitial condensation
This occurs in a construction when water vapour moving through that construction comes into contact with a material which is at or below the dew point of the vapour.

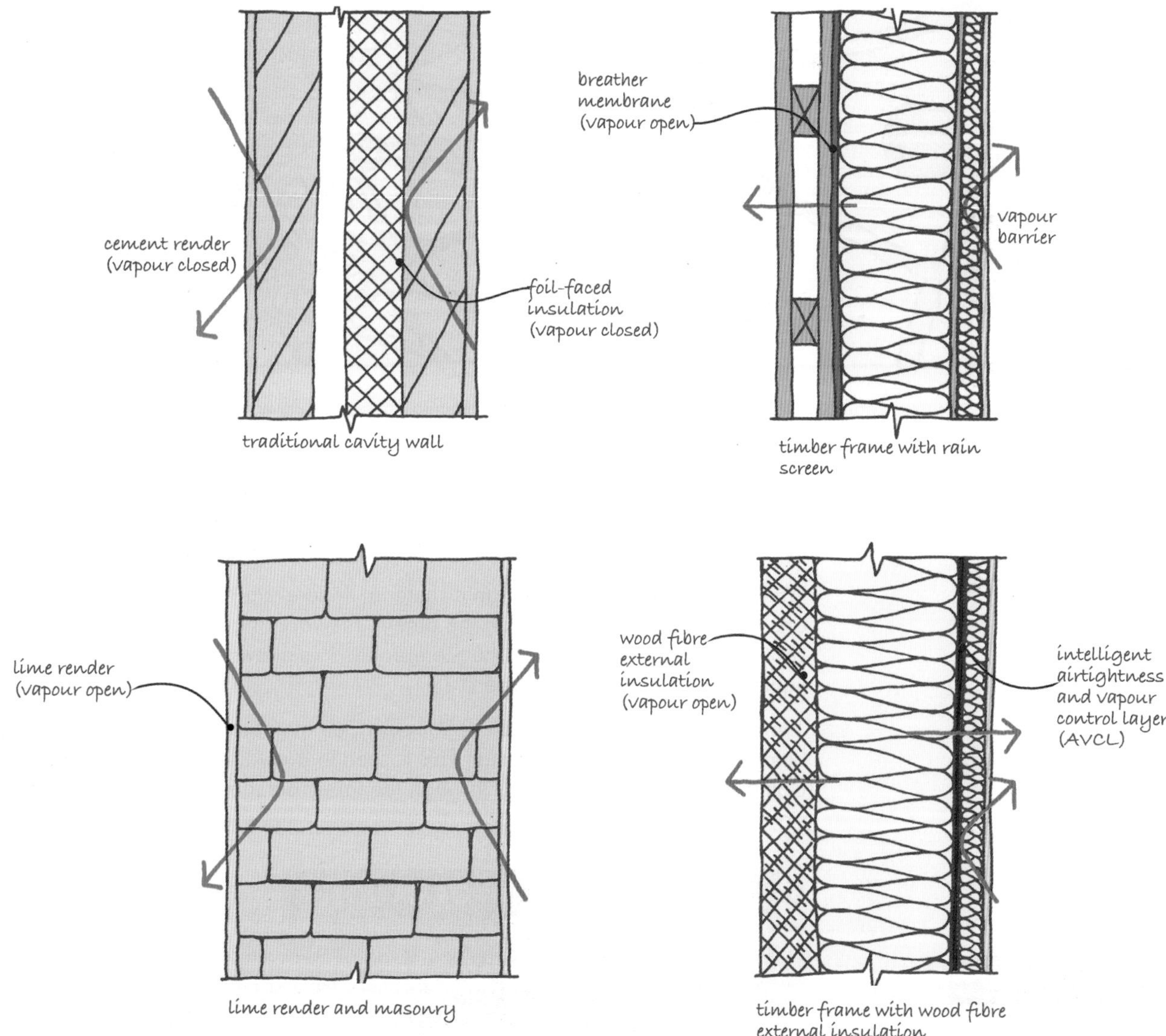

11.21 Vapour control strategies: different structural systems take different approaches to moisture control.

Vapour control materials

Vapour control materials are designed to ensure that the building fabric remains dry.

KEY PRINCIPLES

There are two main types of vapour control material:

- Air and vapour control layer (AVCL) materials resist the passage of air and water vapour. They are typically located on the warm side of the insulation (i.e. near the inner surface of the building).
- Breather membrane materials are designed to be vapour open and allow moisture to escape from within the building to the outside (when the water vapour resistance (G-value) is greater than 0.25 MNs/g and less than 0.6 MNs/g). A breather membrane is typically located on the cold side of the insulation (i.e. near the outer surface of the building).

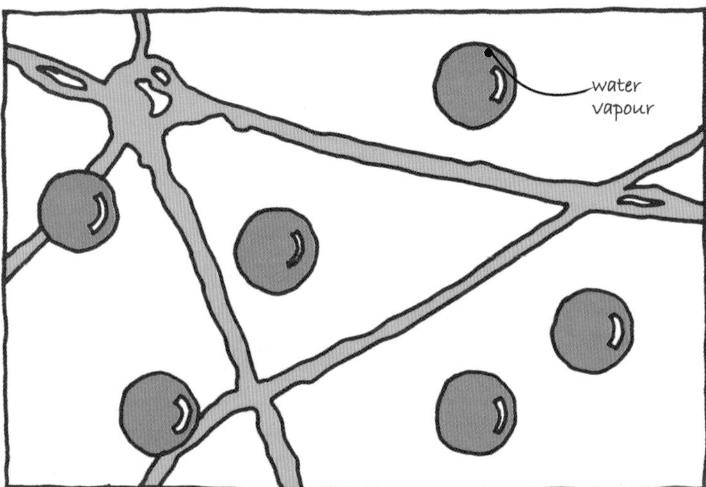

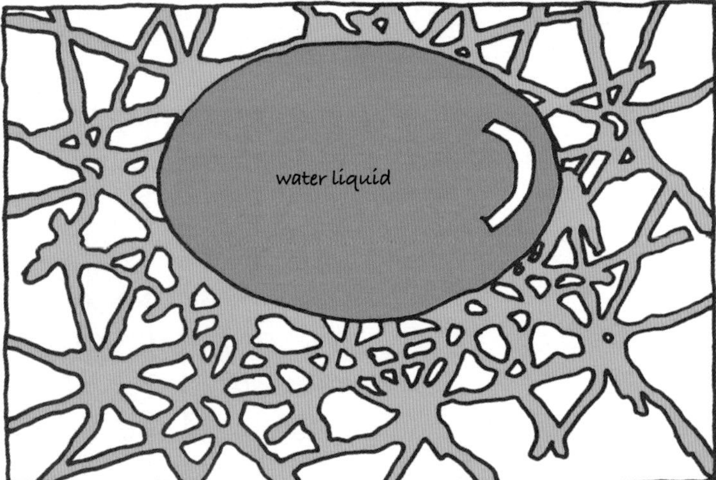

11.22 Breathable materials allow water vapour to diffuse while preventing liquid water from passing through.

Vapour-open or breathable materials allow water vapour to diffuse through while preventing liquid water passing through. The difference between water vapour and liquid water is their molecular density: water vapour is less dense than liquid water. The fibres of the material are so closely spaced that they prevent liquid moisture from passing through the pores (spaces between the fibres).

Water vapour will diffuse through a material if there is a higher concentration of the vapour on one side of the material than on the other – the vapour diffusion is driven by the difference in vapour pressure either side of the membrane. This allows for materials to be designed that are liquid watertight but vapour open.

The same concept applies to air. A vapour-open membrane is impermeable to a body of air while being permeable to water vapour. This is seen in everyday life in the design of breathable outdoor clothing. The wind cannot pass through the fabric but the water vapour can escape, so the wearer stays warm but not sweaty.

SUPPLEMENTARY INFORMATION

Terminology: the terms *vapour barrier* and *vapour check* are commonly used in the construction industry. 'Vapour barrier' is used to convey the idea that a material provides a high level of resistance to water vapour. 'Vapour check' is used to convey the idea that a material provides a lower level of resistance to water vapour. Unfortunately there is a lack of consistency in their use and many people use them interchangeably. Because of the confusion this can cause, it is best to avoid using these terms altogether. The term *air and vapour control layer* (AVCL) should be used instead.

Vapour resistance (G-value) is measured in mega Newton seconds per gram (MNs/g). It is a useful value because it factors in the thickness of the material.

ACTIVITIES

Visit the website of a company that makes outdoor clothing (e.g. Gore-Tex, www.gore-tex.co.uk). Explore the website to learn more about how breathable fabrics are designed.

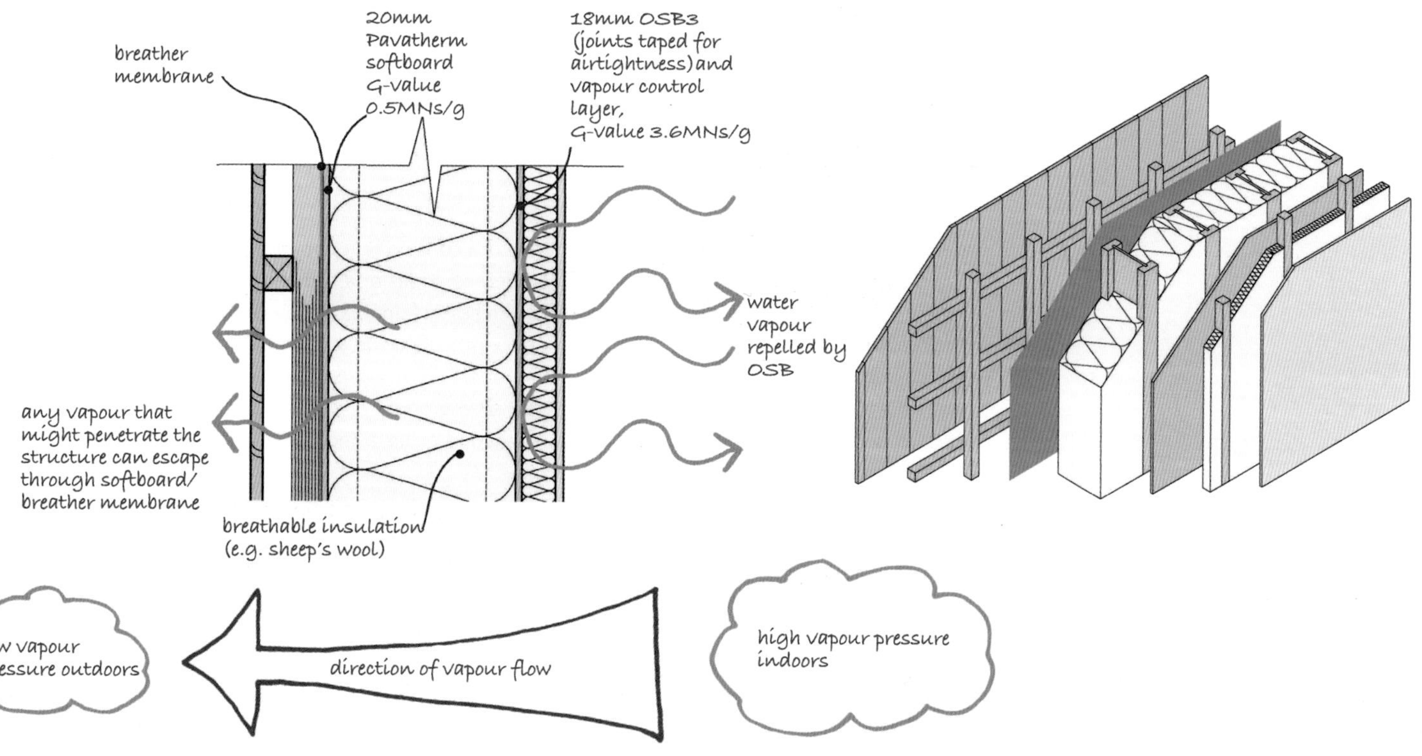

11.23 Vapour-permeable (i.e. breathable) wall structure: the vapour resistance (G-value) of the outer layer should be five times less than the vapour resistance of the inner layer.

Airtightness

Airtightness is the term used to describe the measures taken to control the unwanted movement of air into and out of a building. The air inside a house is usually warm. If this warm air is allowed to escape from the house, cold air will replace it from outside. This effect cools the home and means that more fuel is used to heat the home. As discussed previously, airtightness is also essential to prevent the movement of water vapour, which causes interstitial condensation in the building fabric.

KEY PRINCIPLES

An airtight building envelope is essential to:

- prevent condensation in the construction (interstitial condensation)
- ensure the thermal insulation performs
- improve thermal comfort –
  - ensure an even temperature is achieved throughout the house
  - prevent draughts
  - prevent cold floors – cold air streams on the ground floor (stack effect)
- reduce the amount of energy required to heat the house.
- prevent air pollution of the indoor air
- provide sound insulation
- ensure the ventilation system works
- reduce ventilation heat losses.

Airtightness and ventilation are interdependent elements of building design. A common 'rule of thumb' used in the construction industry is 'build tight and ventilate right', meaning that the building fabric should be airtight and appropriate ventilation should be provided to ensure high indoor air quality. The measurement and calculation of airtightness are examined in the next section; here, the practical measures required to achieve airtightness are explored.

Airtightness completeness

Making a building airtight requires a contiguous airtight layer in the external envelope. The airtightness layer is usually on the inside of the envelope. It is absolutely essential that the airtightness layer is unbroken. This means that every junction (floor–wall, window–wall, wall–ceiling, etc.) is sealed to prevent air movement. Any penetration of the envelope must also be carefully sealed. For example, where drainage pipes for sinks and toilets, and electrical cables pass through the building fabric the airtightness layer must be sealed to prevent air movement.

KEY PRINCIPLES

Making a building airtight requires:

- design – all the details must be worked out before construction commences
- appropriate materials – the airtightness membranes, tapes and sealants must be used as recommended; materials should be used for the correct application (e.g. concrete tape used on concrete); everyday sealants (e.g. expanding foam) cannot be substituted
- compatible materials – the airtightness membranes, tapes and sealants must be suited to each other (it is not advisable to mix and match between brands)
- workmanship – a very high level of commitment and professionalism is required on site to achieve a high level of airtightness –
    - all workers on site must understand the importance of protecting the airtightness layer from damage
    - training is essential – most manufacturers provide training on the correct specification and installation of their products
    - every member of the team must understand the importance of the airtightness layer and ensure that nothing is done to damage or compromise it in any way (e.g. electricians and plumbers need to be particularly careful when installing services that they do not damage the airtightness layer).

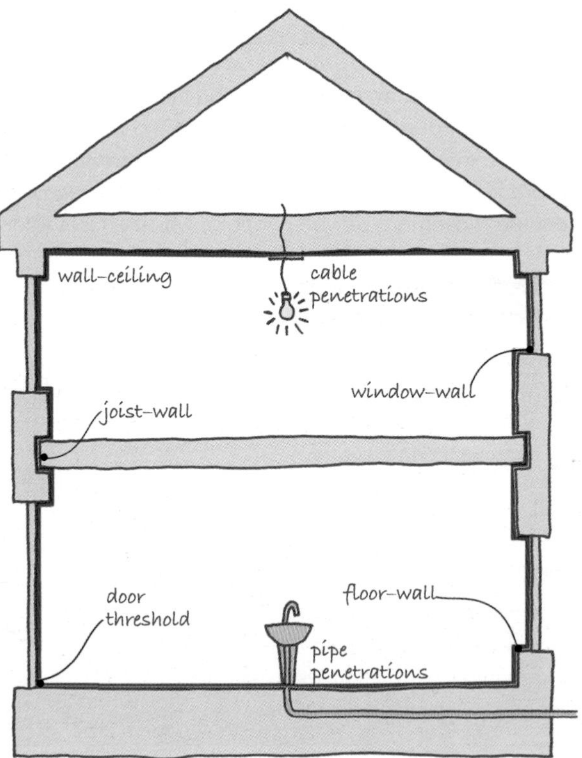

11.24 Airtightness: the airtightness layer must be a single contiguous element of the structure – it should be possible to trace the airtightness layer as a continuous blue line on sectional views. Key detail areas are shown.

Airtightness must be planned for at the design stage. This requires very detailed examination of the design drawings to ensure that it is possible to install an airtight layer. To do this the designer usually works on large-scale (e.g. 1:2) drawings and indicates the specific materials and products that will be used to ensure that every junction in the building is airtight.

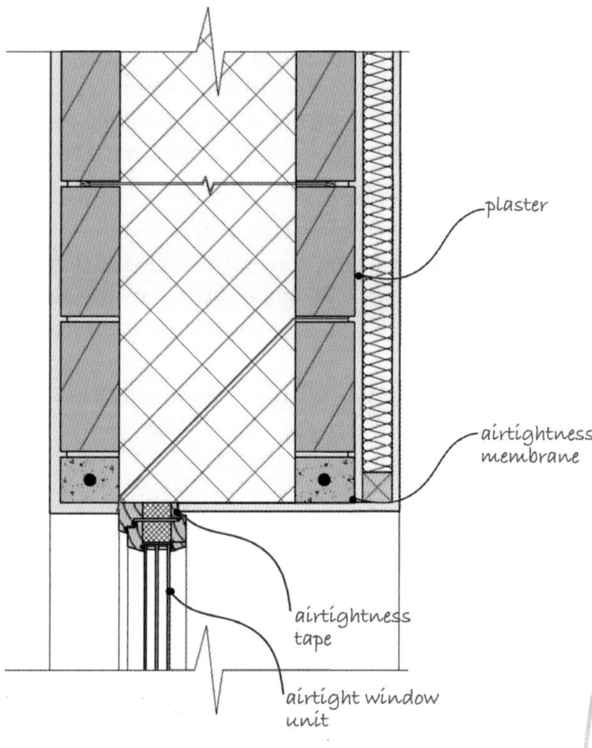

11.25 Airtightness: detailed drawings specify the materials used and show how connections are formed.

Airtightness materials

Airtightness can be achieved in many ways; the approach taken depends on the structural system involved. In masonry construction, ordinary gypsum plaster is used to make the surface of the masonry airtight. Joints between planar elements (i.e. floors, walls, ceilings) is achieved using tapes and/or membranes. In timber frame construction, airtightness membranes (AVCL) are used on walls. Ceilings are made airtight in the same way. The concrete slab of a typical floor provides airtightness with tapes/membranes used where the floor meets the walls. Proprietary grommets and collars are available to ensure an airtight seal around pipes or cables that penetrate the airtight layer.

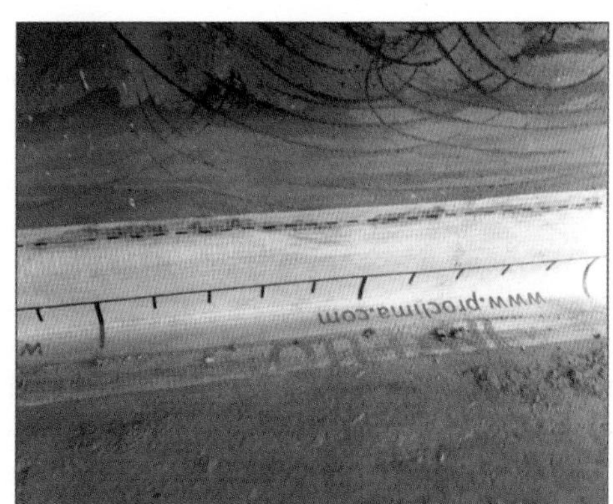

11.26 Airtightness – membrane sealed to floor slab and wall using flexible sealant.

11.27 Airtightness membrane (AVCL) installed to the inside of a timber frame wall.

11.28 Airtightness membrane (AVCL) installed to the inside of roof buildup and dressed down the face of masonry wall with plaster overlapping joint to ensure airtightness.

Service cavities

A service cavity is a zone created on the internal surface of the external envelope (i.e. inside the airtightness layer) that provides space for pipes, cables, ducting and other services. This is useful because it allows for services to be installed without compromising the airtightness layer. It is possible to build without a service cavity, but achieving airtightness is much more difficult; for example, in masonry construction conduit chases for cables must be plastered/parge coated before the conduit is installed.

The insulation installed in the service cavity is usually not included in the stated U-value of a Passivhaus wall. In other words, the real U-value is actually lower (i.e. better) than the stated U-value. This is because insulating the service cavity is usually considered a low-cost optional extra done on site to improve the energy efficiency of the building. U-values are examined in Chapter 23.

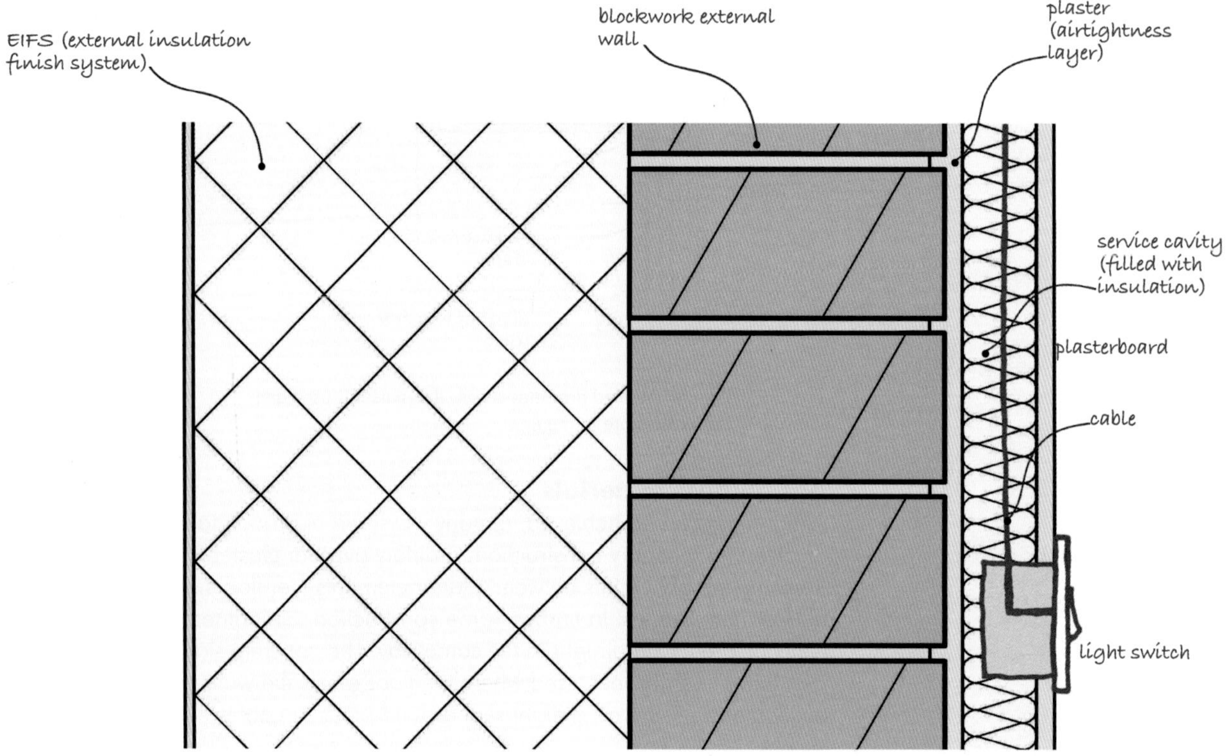

11.29 Airtightness: service cavity allows pipes, cables, etc. to be installed without penetrating the airtightness layer.

Fire resistance

The structural elements of a house must withstand fire for at least 30 minutes. For multiple unit buildings (e.g. flats/apartments) this time extends up to two hours, depending on building height. It is not possible to make a home fireproof; the temperatures reached during a house fire mean that any home, irrespective of structural system, will be destroyed by an uncontrolled fire. The goal is to resist the spread of fire within the dwelling to allow the occupants time to escape while the structure remains intact for 30 to 120 minutes. Unfortunately, anyone who does not escape quickly will likely succumb to the effects of smoke inhalation.

The spread of fire in a dwelling is typically resisted through the use of gypsum-based products: plaster and plasterboard. Gypsum is found in nature in mineral and rock form. Gypsum rock is mined in Ireland and used to manufacture plasterboard and other plaster products. The protective effect of plasterboard can be increased by increasing its thickness. Two layers is standard in the party walls of terraced or semi-detached houses built using timber frame systems.

landing
bedroom 3
plasterboard lining
terrace
plasterboard lining
bedroom 1
landing
bedroom 2
balcony
living room
kitchen/ dining room
WC
patio

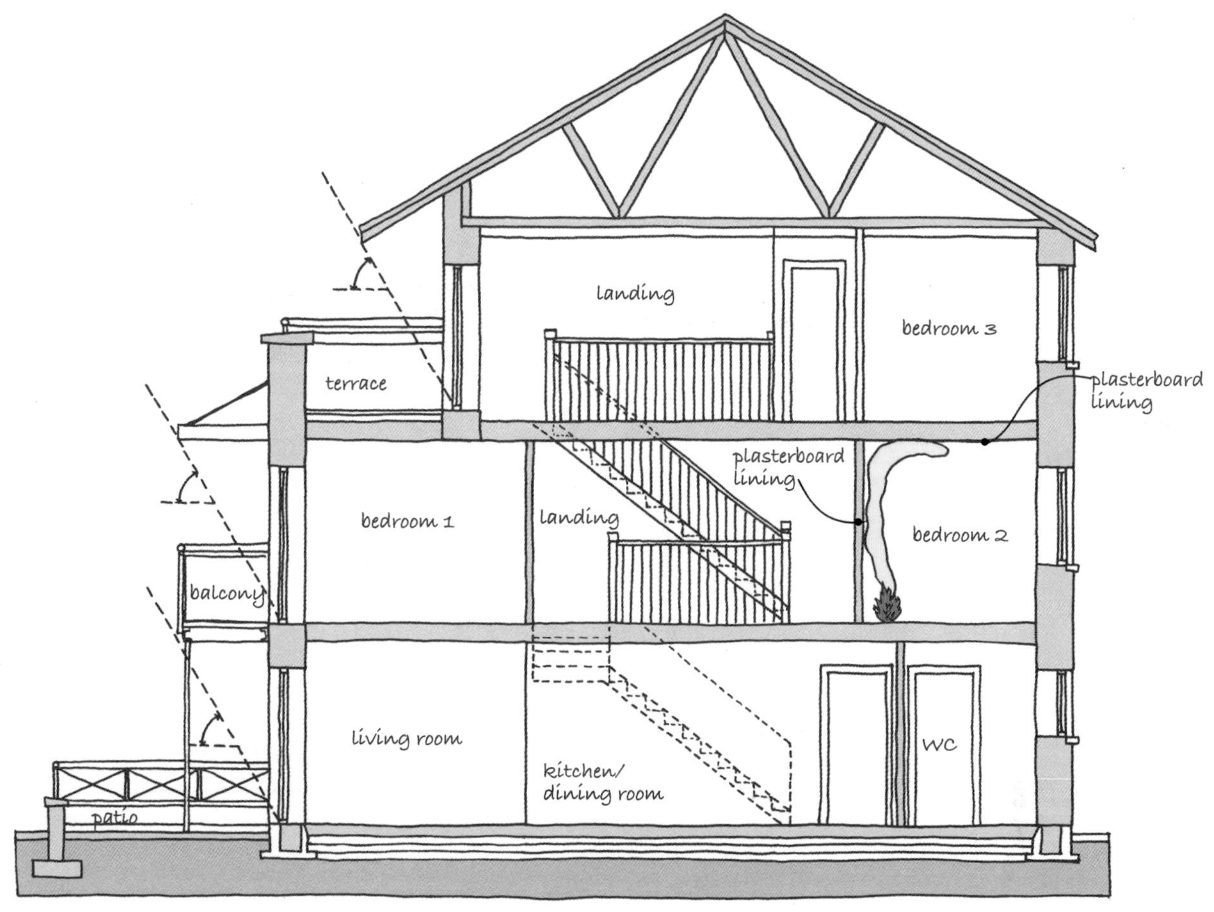

11.30 Fire resistance: compartmentation aims to prevent internal fire spread.

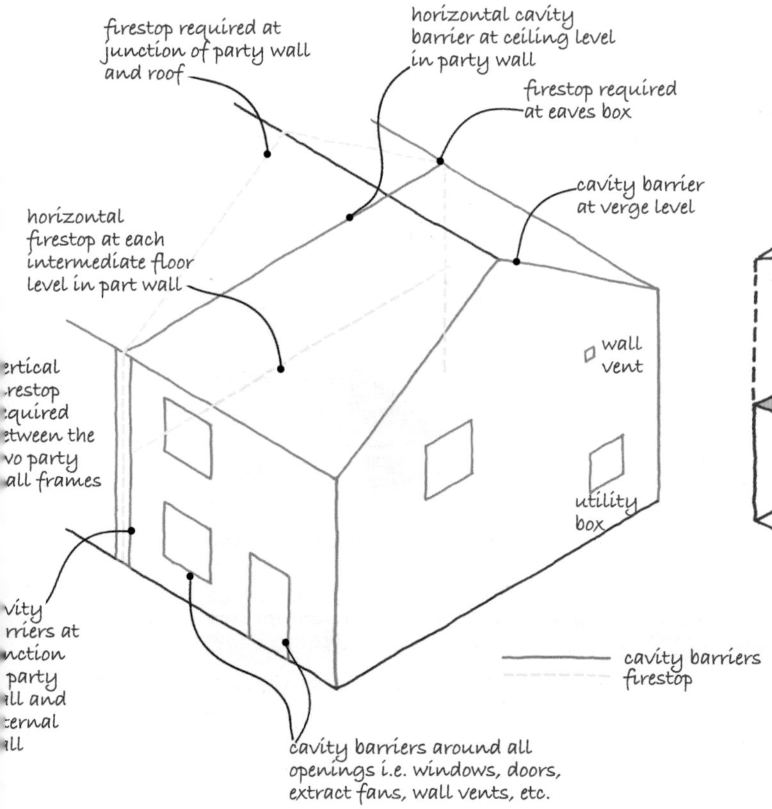

firestop required at junction of party wall and roof
horizontal cavity barrier at ceiling level in party wall
firestop required at eaves box
cavity barrier at verge level
horizontal firestop at each intermediate floor level in part wall
ertical ·restop :quired etween the vo party all frames
wall vent
utility box
vity rriers at ıction party ıll and :ernal ıll
cavity barriers
firestop
cavity barriers around all openings i.e. windows, doors, extract fans, wall vents, etc.

11.31 Fire resistance: in timber frame construction additional measures are required to prevent fire spread within the cavity–cavity barriers (e.g. wire-reinforced rock wool/mineral wool) and firestops (glass fibre).

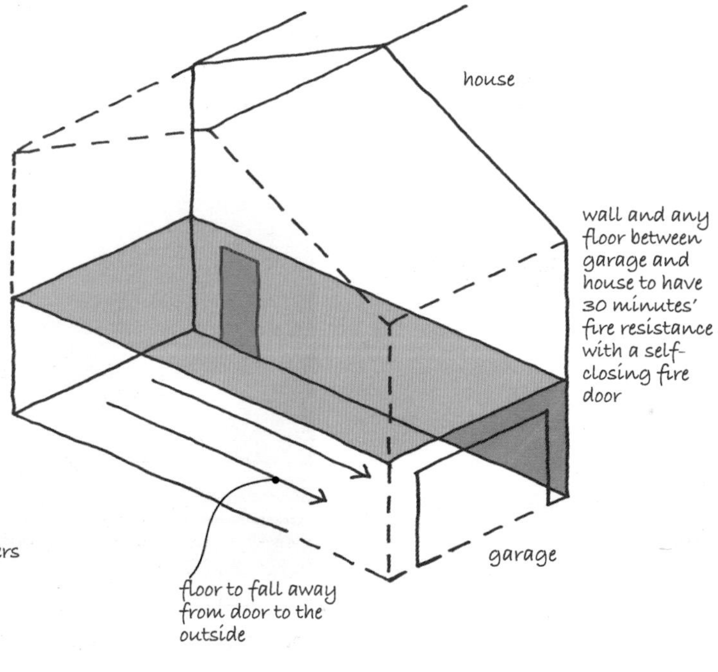

house
wall and any floor between garage and house to have 30 minutes' fire resistance with a self-closing fire door
garage
floor to fall away from door to the outside

11.32 Fire resistance: a garage must be separated from the rest of the home by 30 minutes' fire-resistant construction.

Sound resistance

The external envelope of a home should resist the passage of everyday sound from outside. Sound from outside a building travels through the air. A home that is designed and built to provide a high level of windtightness, thermal insulation and airtightness will be inherently resistant to the passage of airborne sound from outside.

Currently there is no stated requirement in the building regulations for sound resistance from externa sources – the focus is on sound resistance within and between homes. Sound insulation is examined in Chapter 30.

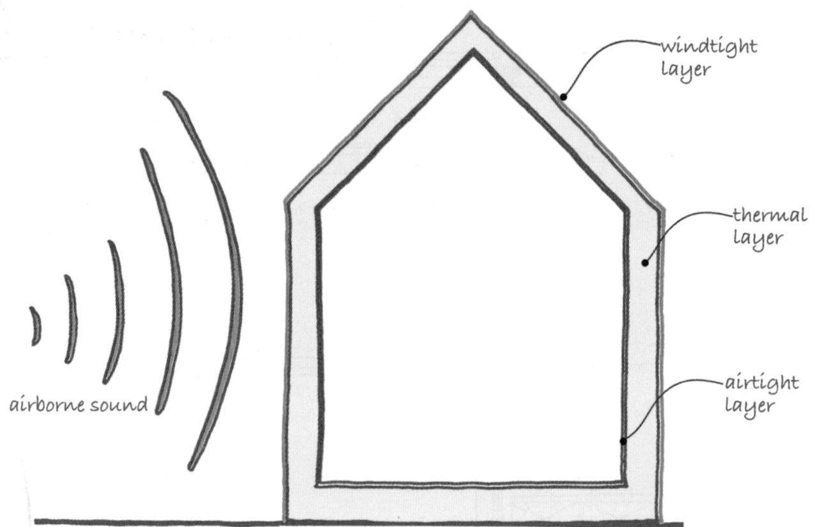

11.33 Sound resistance: a properly designed and built structure will resist external airborne sound

Aesthetics

Aesthetics is concerned with beauty or the appreciation of beauty. While most people may not wish their home to be 'beautiful', they would certainly want it to look nice. Of course, people have different tastes but whatever the style or look of a house, a high standard of quality should be evident. This is conveyed through the quality of materials (e.g. brick with a good colour, tone and texture) and the quality of the workmanship.

Form

Form is a general word used in architecture to describe the physical size, shape and mass of an object. While the word 'shape' is used in everyday life, it is more correctly used to describe a two-dimensional object (e.g. a square); the word 'form' is used to describe a three-dimensional object (e.g. a cube).

11.34 Form: a house in rural Fermanagh by Aughey O'Flaherty Architects. The form of the house is long and barrel-vaulted. The barrel encloses the maximum space with the least material and it recalls agricultural sheds in the landscape. At one end, the house splits into two levels: the lower is set into the ground and the upper within the vault. At the other end, a tall, bright open-plan kitchen/living/dining space is created.

Materials

The look and feel of materials can be used to great artistic effect. Ordinary construction materials used in thoughtful ways can bring a sense of wonder and delight to a building. The use of brick is a good example of this. Many colours and textures of brick are available. Coupled with the variety of bonding patterns that are possible, brick allows the designer to give the surface of a wall a rhythm or pattern that adds interest and enjoyment.

11.35 Materials: brick contrasts with plain render (painted grey) to make this contemporary extension to an existing red brick home stand out while blending in (Osborne Park, Belfast by Ciaran Mackel, Ard Architects). Notice how the two mono-pitched elements are brought together using a glazed 'tunnel' and also (in the right-hand photo) how the roof slope of the extension reflects the slope of the original building in ether background.

11.36 The aesthetic qualities of brick are emphasised through the use of 'separated' Flemish bond in the façade of this family home in Donnybrook, Dublin 4 ('House 1' by Taka Architects).

Craft

The work of a true craftsperson is readily recognised. The selection and use of materials, the attention to detail and the commitment to getting it just right create an impression that is pleasing and satisfying. In the pressure to build homes 'on time and in budget', craft can sometimes get pushed aside by expediency. This should not be allowed to happen; if for no other reason than that a well-built home will be more durable and functional than a speedily built one.

11.37 Craftsmanship: the high level of craftsmanship evident in the original house (on the left) has been matched in the contemporary extension (on the right). Clearly both buildings are of their time, yet the design of the new extension respects the character of the original in its use of materials and quality of workmanship.

REVISION EXERCISES

1 Describe, using a neat freehand sketch, the various actions that a typical home must withstand.
2 Describe, using neat freehand sketches, two examples of thermal bridging in a typical house.
3 Explain how wind can reduce the energy efficiency of a typical home.
4 Describe, using neat freehand sketches, how water vapour can be prevented from damaging a timber frame wall structure.
5 Explain, using a neat freehand sketch, how a service cavity can be used to improve the airtightness of a masonry wall.

CHAPTER 12

Site Assessment

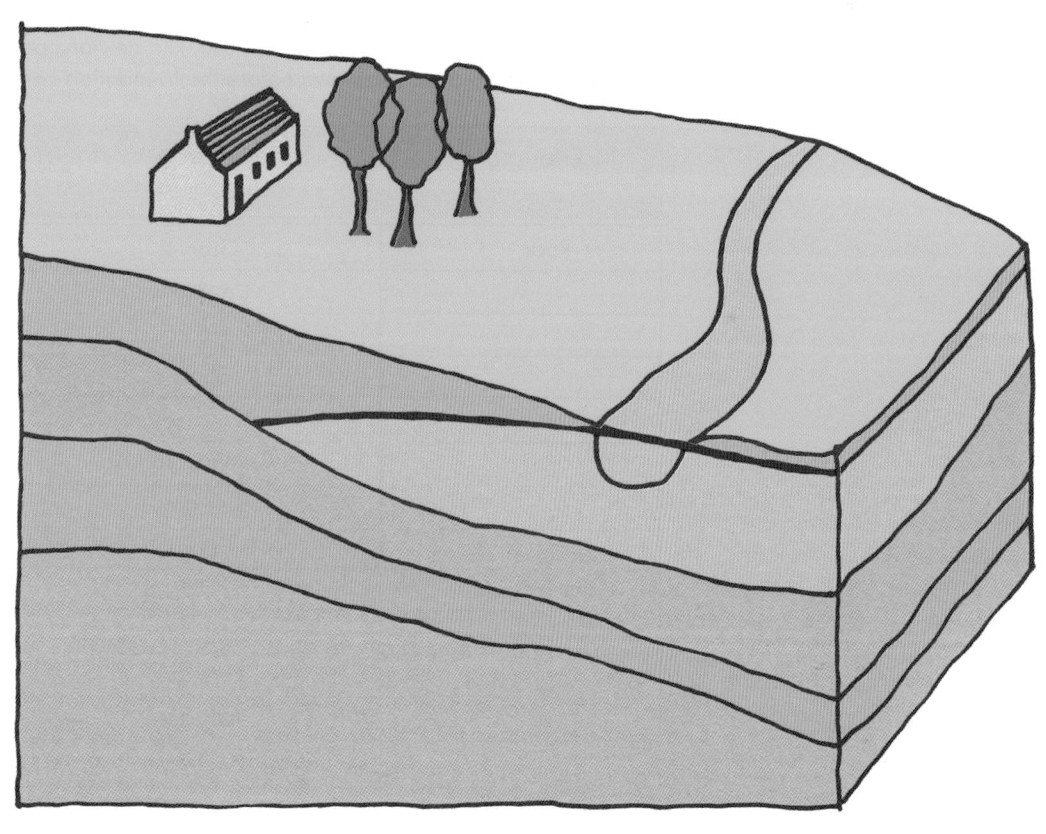

Not all land is suitable for building on. Before a house can be built, careful assessment of the site and the condition of the soil must be carried out.

Site selection

Before a site can be selected a number of simple checks have to be made. These include checking:

- the local authority development plan to see if residential development is permitted on the site
- the history of the site (e.g. previous uses, flooding)
- the location of existing drainage channels (drains and water courses)
- if there is safe access to the site from the existing road
- if there are services available (electricity, water, sewerage etc.)
- if there are any existing buildings, protected structures or protected trees on the site
- if there are overhead or underground services on the site (e.g. electricity power lines, sewers).

Once these basic checks have been carried out a more detailed analysis of the site can commence.

Soil investigation

Soil investigation involves detailed examination of the type and quality of the soil on a potential development site. This is necessary to ensure that the soil is suitable for house construction and to facilitate optimal foundation design.

Soil types

The most important thing to remember about soil is that it is made by nature. A single site can have many types of soil to various depths. A thorough soil investigation must be carried out to ensure that an accurate 'picture' of the soil is taken.

DEFINITION

Bearing capacity
The maximum applied pressure that the ground can support.

There are five categories of soil found in Ireland; gravels, sands, silts, clays and peats. These categories refer to the size of the soil particles. The size of the soil particles has an influence on the level of cohesion displayed by the ground. Smaller particles tend to be more cohesive (e.g. clays) whereas larger particles tend to be less cohesive (e.g. gravels).

The ability of a soil to carry a load is referred to as its bearing capacity. The bearing capacity is measured in force per unit area: in this case, kilo newtons per square metre (kN/m^2). The bearing capacity of the soil must be known before the foundation can be designed.

Group	Soil type	Safe bearing capacity kN/m^2
Rock	Granite	10,000
	Limestone	4,000
	Slate & schist	3,000
	Shale	2,000
Non-cohesive soils	Compact gravel	>600
	Compact sand	>300
	Loose gravel	<200
	Loose sand	<100
Cohesive soils	Very stiff clay	300 – 600
	Stiff clay	150 – 300
	Firm clay	75 – 150
	Soft clay	<75
	Very soft clay, silts, peat	nil

12.01 Guideline values for the safe bearing capacity of various soil types. It is possible to find more than one soil type on a site and various strata of different soils are sometimes revealed during excavations.

The uppermost layer of soil on most sites is called the topsoil. The topsoil is the upper 300–600mm of soil in which the vegetation (grass, plants, etc.) grows. Topsoil cannot support the load of a structure, so it is always removed and set aside for use in landscaping later. Once the topsoil has been removed the foundations are marked out and excavated. The remaining soil, usually called the subsoil, supports the foundation.

12.02 Site preparation: the outline of the house is marked on the grass and the topsoil is removed from this area.

12.03 Site preparation: after the topsoil has been removed the outline of the house is again marked out on the subsoil in preparation for marking out of the foundations.

12.04 Site preparation: an access route (later to become the driveway) to the site is also prepared.

12.05 Site preparation: crushed stone is placed on the access route to provide hard standing for site vehicles and delivery trucks.

The water table

Water occurs naturally below ground. This water, called groundwater, is located beneath the ground surface in the soil pore spaces (spaces between soil particles) and in the cracks and voids in rock formations. It is the source of water for wells drilled to supply water to homes in rural areas.

If the site is located in an area with a high water table this can lead to flooding, either during construction or once the dwelling is complete.

KEY PRINCIPLES

Soil investigation is carried out to:

- establish what type of soil is below ground level
- determine the suitability of the site for the proposed building
- ensure that the correct foundation design is chosen for the soil and for the type of building planned
- ensure that the building is constructed safely, efficiently and economically
- determine the level of the water table.

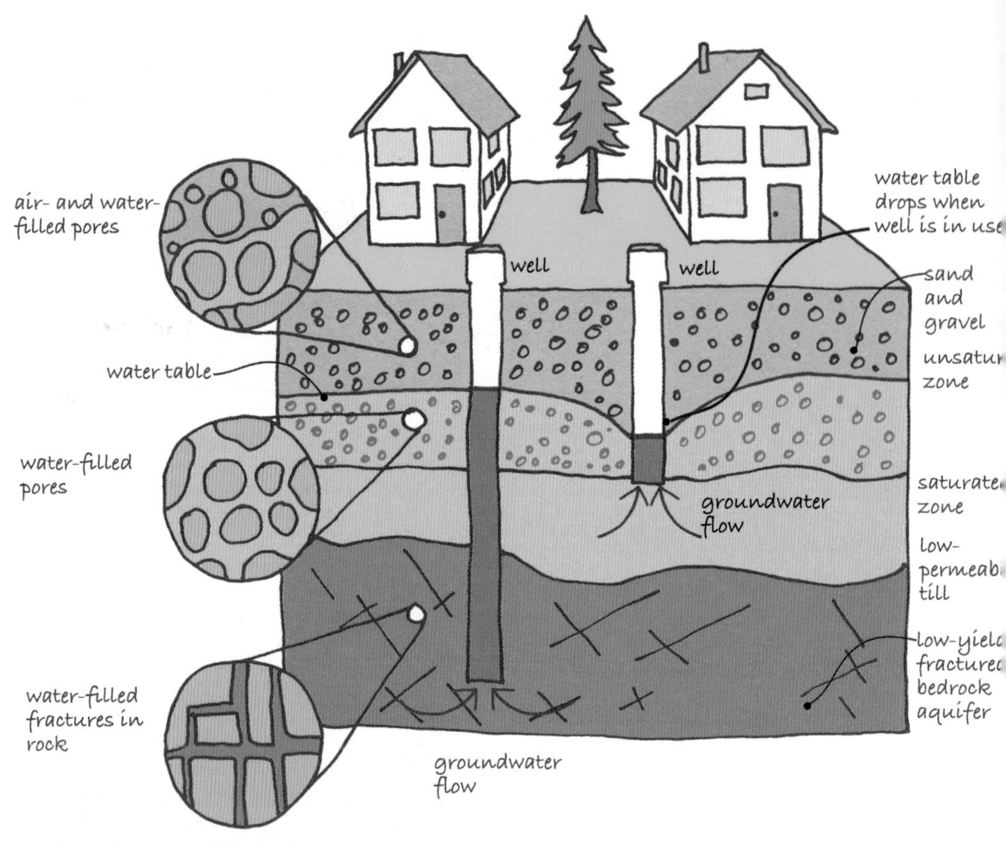

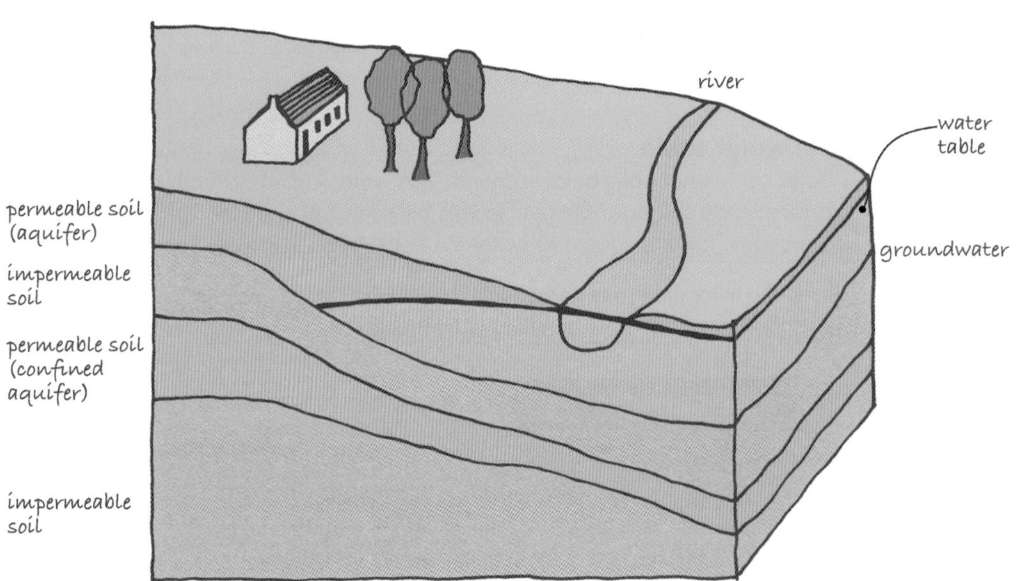

12.06 Water table: the 'top surface' of the groundwater. This level falls and rises throughout the year depending on the amount of rainfall.

Investigating the soil

When building houses, trial pits are usually used to examine the subsoil on a site. Trial pits are adequate where the foundation depth will be less than three metres and where the soil on site is firm and stable. Digging a trial hole involves excavating a rectangular pit approximately 1,200mm by 1,200m and at least 1,200mm in depth. This allows the designer to look into the hole to determine what type of soil is present. A number of trial pits should be dug around the site to ensure that the subsoil is consistent. If the site is for a single house in a rural setting a percolation test is also carried out at this stage (see Chapter 29).

ACTIVITIES

Talk to a builder who works in your locality. Ask about the type(s) of soil they have encountered when building houses in the area and how this has impacted on the building process.

12.07 Digging a trial hole sometimes reveals various soil types at different depths.

REVISION EXERCISES

1. Outline the checks to be made before a site can be considered for construction.
2. Describe three differences between a cohesive and a non-cohesive soil.
3. Why is it important to know the make-up of the subsoil on a site?
4. What could happen if a house is built on a site with a high water table?
5. Outline how a typical soil investigation is carried out.

CHAPTER 13

Foundations

The foundation is the part of the structure that transfers the actions (i.e. loads, forces) acting on the building to the soil. It is essential that these actions are carried safely and evenly to the supporting soil to ensure the stability of the building.

Functions

The primary function of a foundation is to connect a structure to the soil. It should:

- safely transmit all loads to the ground
- prevent subsidence
- limit settlement
- provide a level bed on which to build.

Performance criteria

When designing a new foundation system it is essential to consider all of the performance requirements expected of a modern foundation system, including:

- **sustainability** – foundations should be built using durable materials with a low embodied energy
- **structural stability** – the foundation should be able to safely transmit the actions imposed on it
- **durability** – the foundation should be designed to 'outlive' the building
- **thermal resistance** – the foundation should prevent thermal bridging and avoidable heat loss.

Factors influencing design

The structural design of a foundation depends on several elements:

- location and features of the site:
  - **gradients and ground level** – building on slopes or low-lying land
  - **nearby buildings** – building in a town or city centre
  - **proximity to streams, rivers, lakes** – performance during flooding
- type of soil:
  - **bearing capacity of the soil** – maximum load the soil can support
  - **depth of good strata** – where layers of different soils occur
  - **composition of the soil** – brownfield (reused) sites that have made-up ground
- possibility of ground movement:
  - **volume change** – seasonal shrinking/expansion of clay soils
  - **effect of trees** – volume change caused by large trees
  - **frost heave** – expansion of soil caused by freezing temperatures
  - **unstable ground** – caused by mining, fracking or other underground activity.

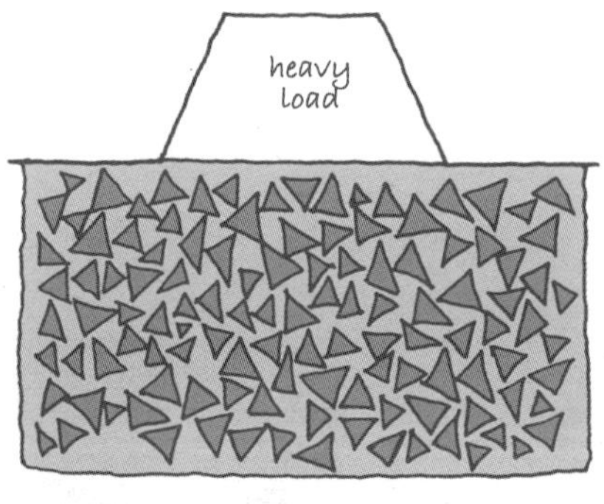

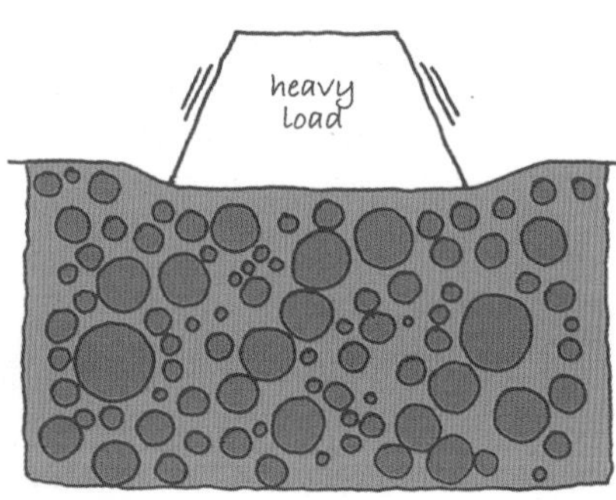

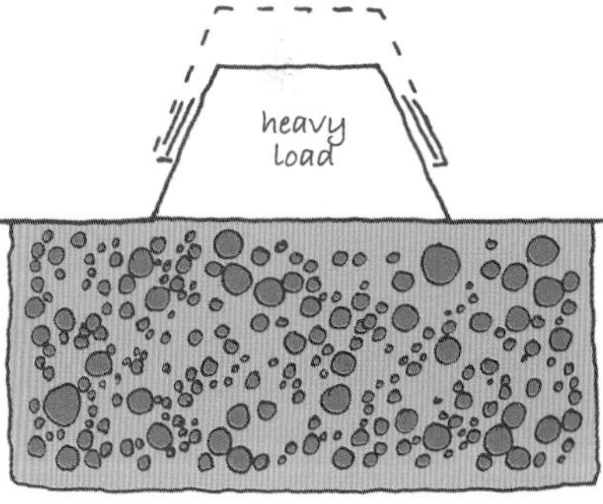

13.01 Bearing capacity of soils: coarse, rough, densely packed soils (e.g. gravel) perform better than fine, smooth, loosely packed soils (e.g. clay); waterlogged soils (e.g. sand) behave more like a liquid and lose most of their bearing capacity.

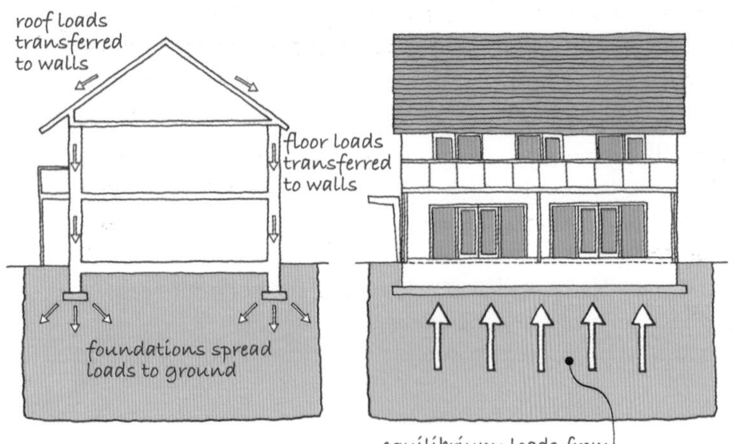

13.02 Foundation design: a well-designed foundation safely transfers the building loads to the soil to ensure the stability of the building.

13.05 Subsidence: a 'pocket' of weaker subsoil (that was not found when the soil investigation was carried out) causes subsidence and cracking of the structure.

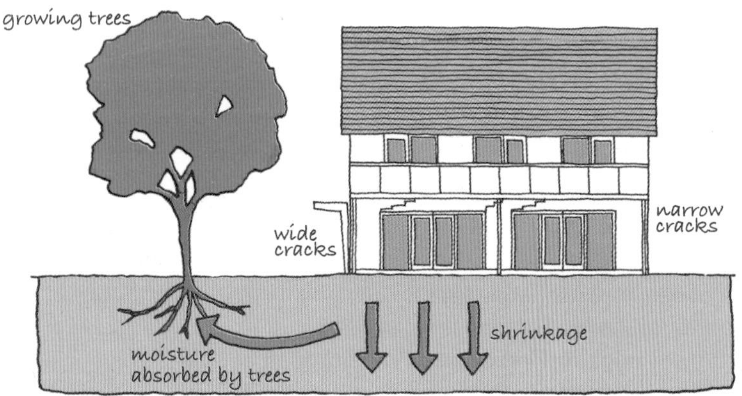

13.03 Effect of trees: large trees absorb huge volumes of water from the soil during the summer. This can cause shrinkage in clay soils. If the trees are felled, the soil might later heave during wet weather.

trees removed
surface heave
wide cracks
narrow cracks
moisture flow
swelling

13.06 Effect of trees: if the trees are felled, then the soil might later heave during wet weather.

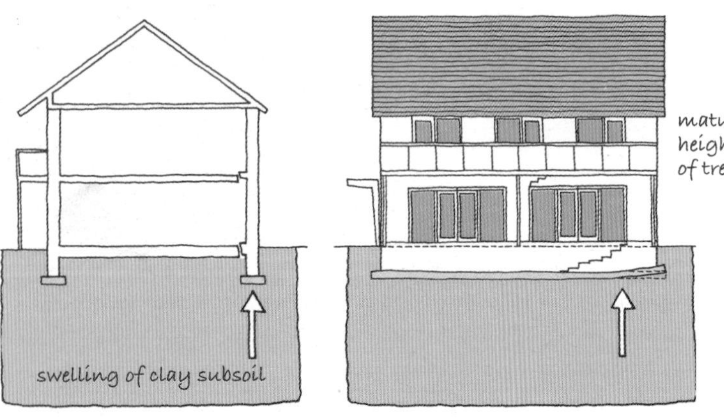

13.04 Ground movement: excessive water in clay soils or freezing of sandy soils can both cause heave (upward movement of the soil) and cracking of the structure.

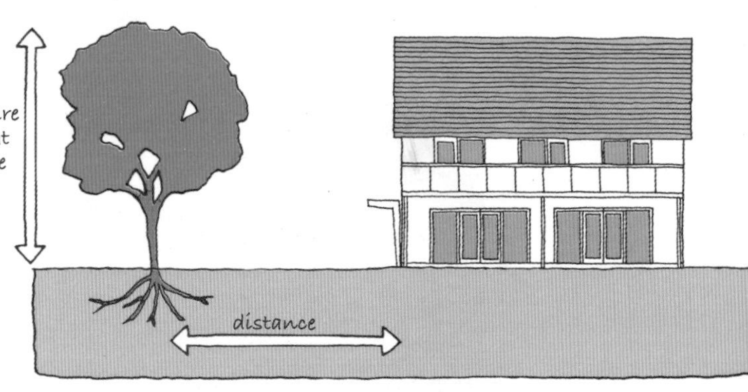

13.07 Effect of trees: new trees should be planted at a distance equal to their mature height from the house.

Foundation types

When building to meet the building regulations minimum standard, there are three main types of foundations used in the construction of houses: strip foundations, raft foundations and piled foundations. Traditionally the strip foundation is the normal foundation used when building a typical house because it is simple, quick and economical.

Compared to most structures, houses are actually quite light; the load exerted by a typical house would be in the range of 20–70 kN/linear metre. This means that for most soils a strip foundation is adequate. A raft or piled foundation is only used if a strip is not suitable because of the soil conditions on a particular site.

Each type of foundation is suited to particular soil types and conditions:

- **strip foundation** – most commonly used; used when soil is of good bearing capacity
- **raft foundation** – used when soil is of poor bearing capacity
- **piled foundation** – used when depth of good strata is shallow or when ground movement is a concern.

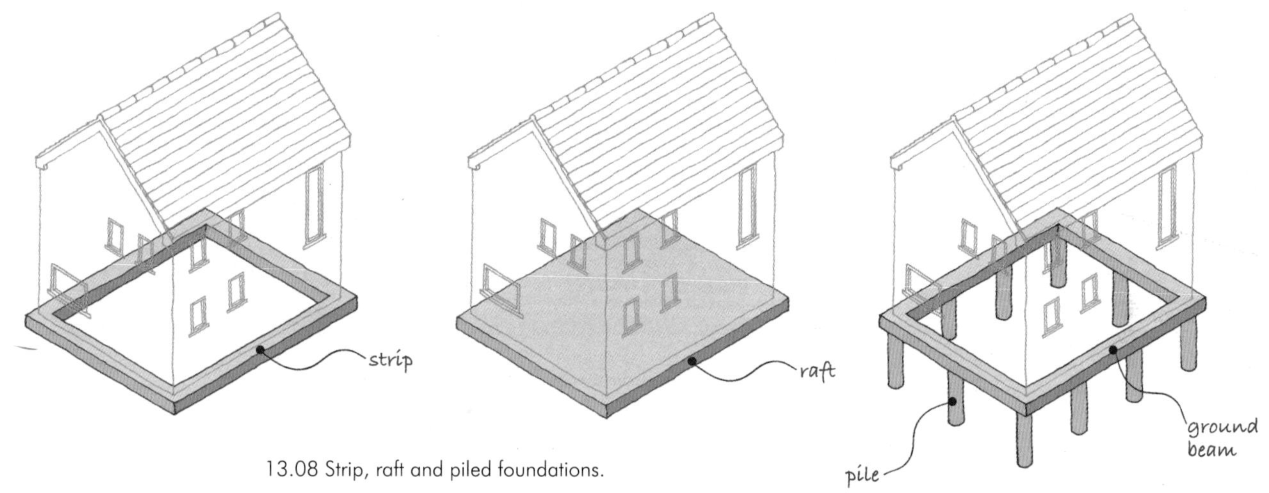

13.08 Strip, raft and piled foundations.

Strip foundations

A strip foundation consists of a wide trench of concrete that is poured on site to support the load-bearing walls of the house. The strip is typically three times wider than the wall so as to spread the load over a greater area.

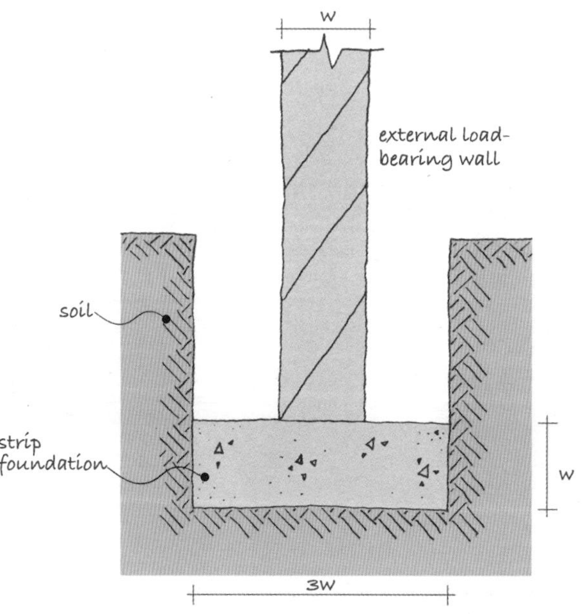

13.09 Strip foundation: the wall is centred on the foundation.

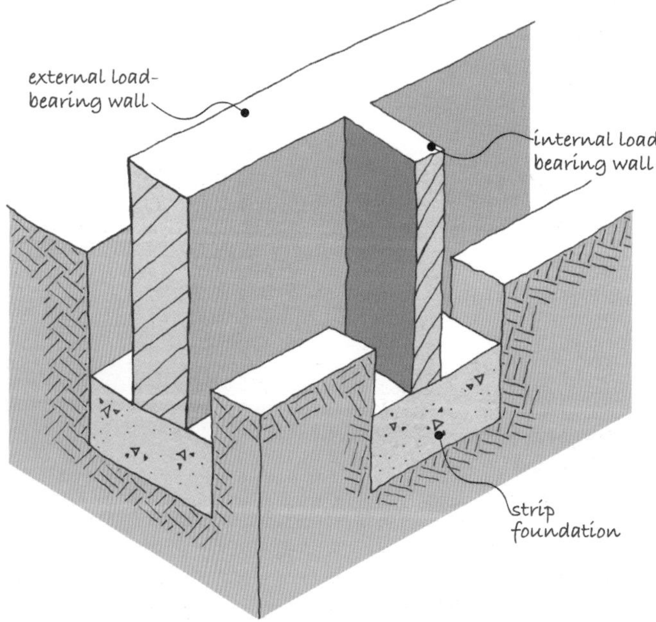

13.10 Strip foundations: each load-bearing wall must have its own foundation.

13.11 Strip foundation: trench being excavated (before steel reinforcement is placed into strip).

13.12 Strip foundation: the concrete being poured into a strip foundation (note the steel reinforcement is in place).

13.13 Strip foundation: top surface of strip after concrete has cured.

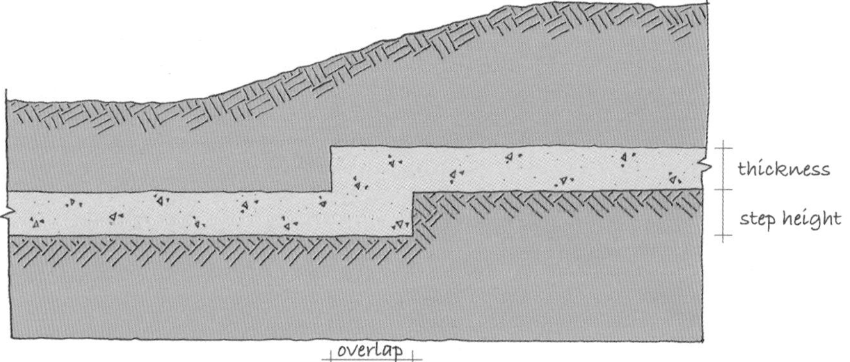

13.14 Stepped strip foundation: used when building on a sloped site.

When building on a slope it is safer, easier and more economical to step the foundation. This avoids having to excavate deep trenches. The strip is overlapped at the step to ensure strength and stability. The overlap should be at least twice the step height or equal to the thickness or a minimum of 300mm (whichever is greater). The step height should be less than or equal to twice the thickness.

1. Subsoil
2. Reinforced concrete foundation
3. Hardcore
4. Concrete fill
5. Sand blinding
6. Radon barrier or damp proof membrane (DPM)
7. Rigid insulation
8. Rigid insulation
9. Reinforced concrete slab
10. Airtightness layer
11. Floor covering
12. Skirting board
13. Damp proof course (DPC)
14. 12mm plaster
15. Inner leaf concrete blockwork
16. Cavity insulation
17. 50mm air cavity
19. Render
55. Concrete path
64. Aerated autoclaved concrete block

13.15 Strip foundation detail.

Raft foundations

A raft foundation is designed to 'float' on the ground, spreading the building's load over the widest possible area. It is used when the soil on site is too soft or loose to support a strip foundation. The raft is reinforced with steel to improve its tensile strength. It is usually thicker around the edge, where the external load-bearing walls exert most force, and also under internal load-bearing walls.

13.16 Raft foundation: a recently poured raft foundation for a pair of semi-detached houses. The timber formwork, hardcore and drainage pipes (for toilets) are shown.

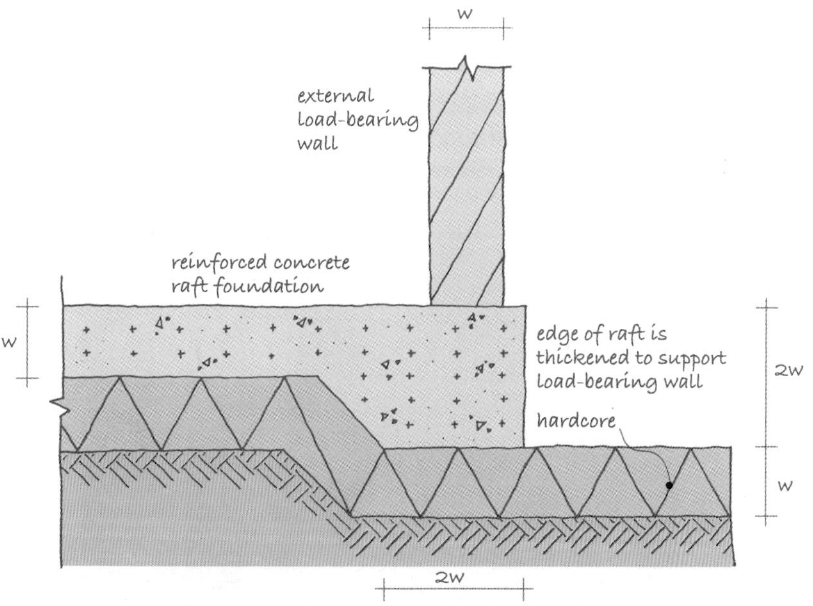

13.17 Raft foundation: the reinforced concrete foundation 'floats' on the site, supported on a bed of hardcore.

Piled foundations

A piled foundation is used to reach down to firmer ground or when ground movement might occur. Because the pile is supported at a greater depth, it is less prone to movement caused by surface heave. The top of the piles are connected together by a narrow concrete strip called a ground beam. The walls are built on the ground beam.

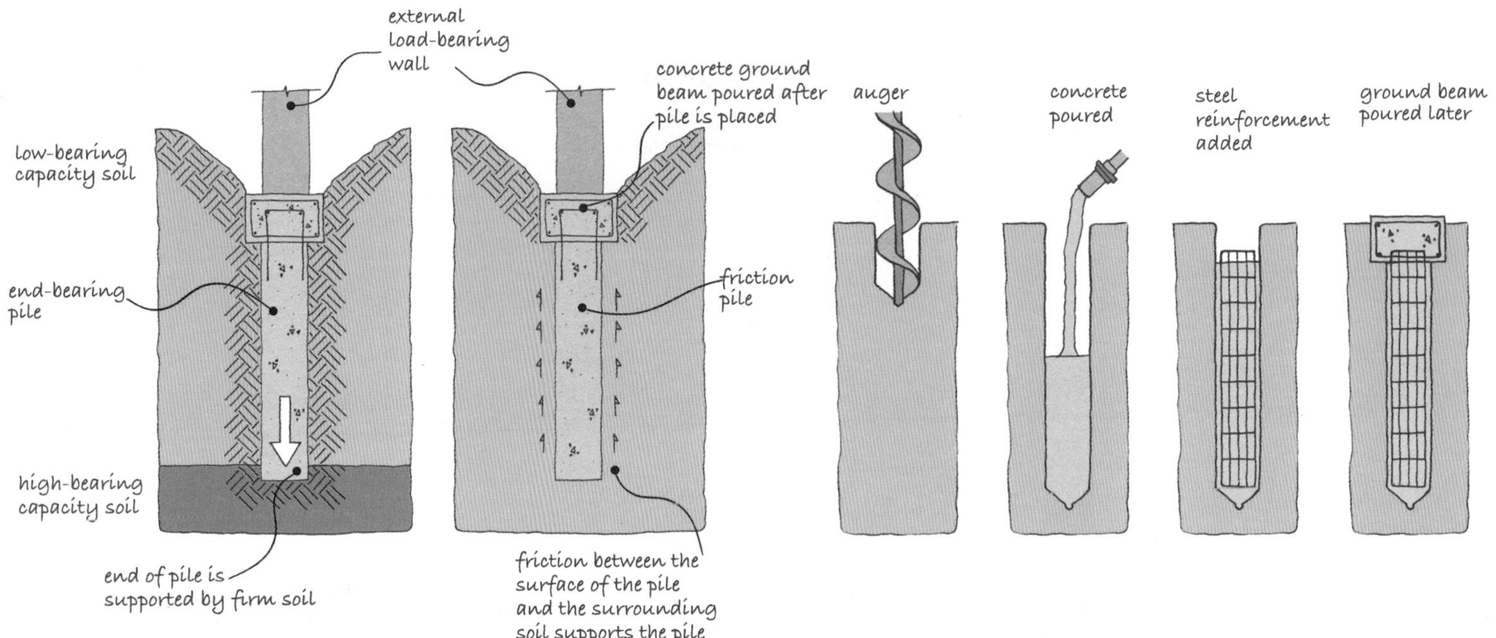

13.18 Piled foundation: end-bearing pile and friction pile.

13.19 Piled foundation: after the concrete has been poured, the steel reinforcement is added. Once the pile has cured, the ground beam is poured.

There are two methods of installing piles: displacement and replacement. Displacement piles are precast reinforced concrete piles that are driven into the ground until the correct level of resistance is achieved. Replacement piles are cast in situ; these are commonly called short bored piles.

13.20 Piled foundation: these displacement friction piles have been driven into place and will be cut down to the correct height later. Note the steel band around the top of the pile to protect it during driving.

Pad foundations

A pad foundation is used to support the load imposed by a column. Architects sometimes use pad foundations when the goal is to limit the impact of a building on the landscape. Instead of having a strip or raft of concrete, a series of pads are arranged in a pattern under the building provide support to load-bearing columns. The dimensions and spacing of the pads depend on the load to be supported.

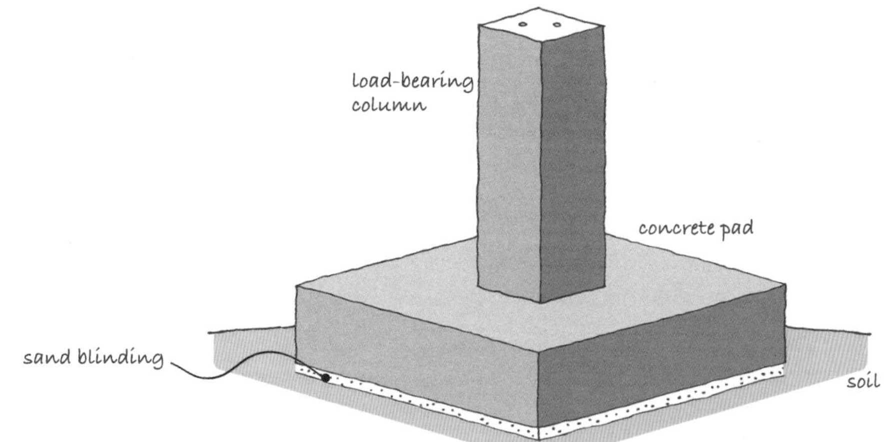

13.21 Pad foundation.

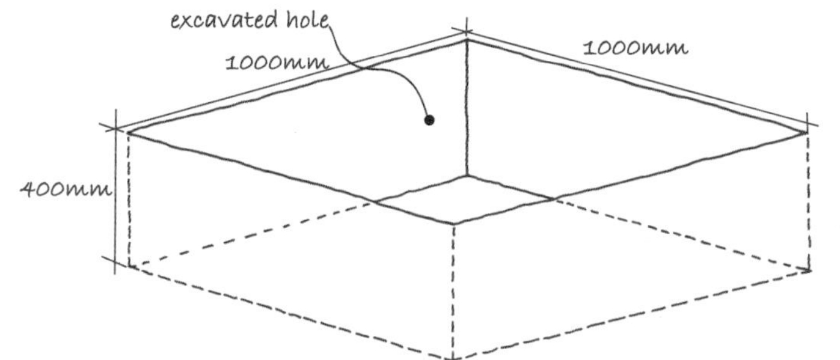

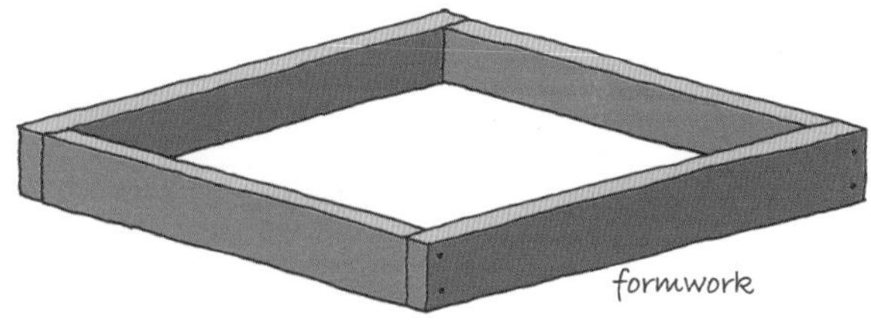

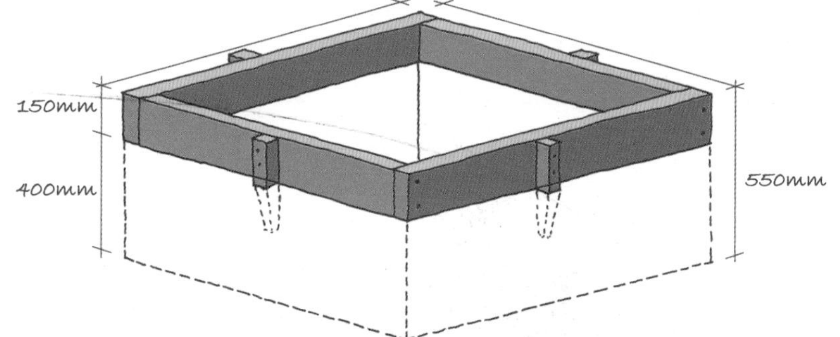

13.22 Pad foundation: these dimensions were calculated to support the house shown in the photos.

ACTIVITIES

Discuss this statement with your classmates:

Dominic Stevens used pad foundations for this house because:

(a) he wanted to use less concrete
(b) he wanted to minimise the impact of the house on the landscape
(c) pad foundations suited the structural design of the building.

Explore the website www.irishvernacular.com to learn more.

13.23 Pad foundation: this is the pad foundation used by Dominic Stevens for his vernacular home in Co. Leitrim (*see next photo*).

13.24 Pad foundation: a low-impact foundation system used when the building sits above the ground.

Insulated foundations

Energy-efficient houses (e.g. passive houses) require insulated foundations to prevent heat loss. This is particularly important at the joint between the external walls and the floor.

Traditional foundations rest directly on the soil. There is no thermal break between the inner leaf of a concrete cavity wall and the ground. This means that significant heat loss occurs at the wall–floor junction. Insulated foundation systems avoid this problem by creating a continuous layer of insulation from floor to wall. This insulation is much thicker than that used in traditional systems, ensuring much lower levels of thermal energy loss.

Insulated foundation systems have a number of advantages, including the following:

- they require minimal excavation, so there is less impact on the landscape
- they use much less concrete and have lower embodied energy than traditional strip foundations
- they prevent thermal bridging at the wall–floor junction, which reduces energy bills and CO_2 emissions
- they are quick to construct.

There are some disadvantages too:

- a high level of workmanship and attention to detail is required
- a specially trained team is needed for installation.

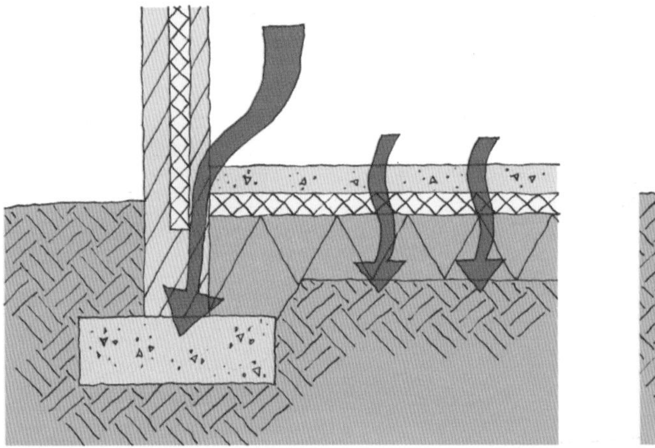

13.25a Insulated foundations: with an insulated foundation, heat loss is prevented by a continuous layer of insulation.

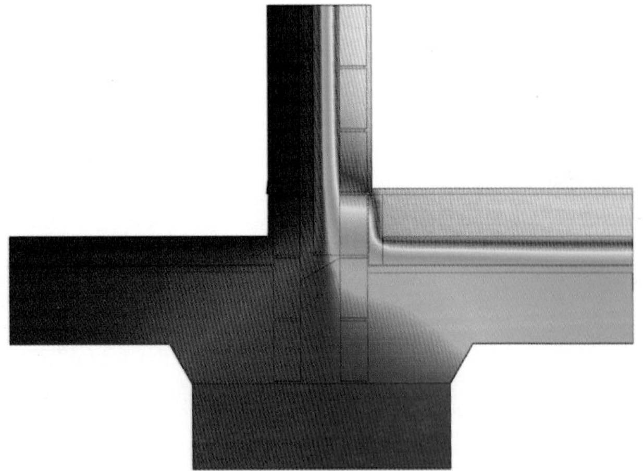

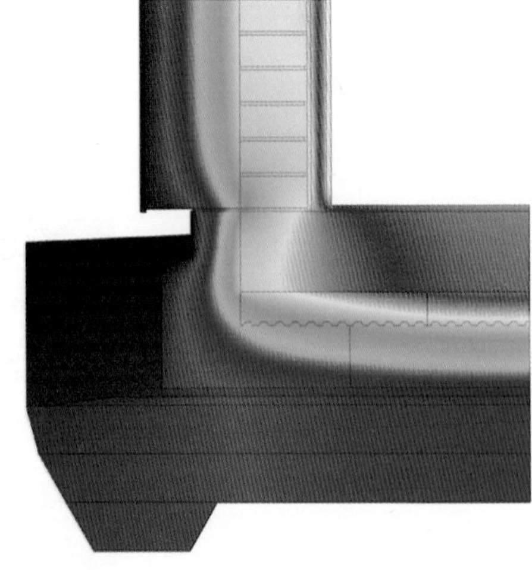

13.25b Insulated foundations: thermal transfer analysis highlights greater heat loss through the wall-floor junction of a traditional strip foundation (left) when compared to an insulated foundation (right).

SUPPLEMENTARY INFORMATION

Expanded polystyrene (EPS) is a rigid, non-biodegradable, recyclable plastic material. The EPS used in foundations is categorised by its compressive strength. Usually a high-strength expanded polystyrene (EPS300) insulation profile is used as permanent formwork when pouring the concrete for the ring beam and a lower strength insulation (EPS100) is used to support the floor slab where the loads are much lower.

Properties of EPS that make it suitable for use in foundations include:

- low thermal conductivity
- high compressive strength (e.g. EPS300 can support a short-term load of up to 300kN/m^2 and has a safe working load of 100kN/m^2)
- resistant to moisture
- non-biodegradable
- recyclable
- easy to use on site – lightweight, easy to cut and join.

Supergrund

This system was developed in Sweden and is manufactured in Co. Limerick by Aerobord Ltd. This system is comprised of two elements: a perimeter ring beam (to support the external load-bearing walls) and a floor slab. The ring beam and floor slab are connected by stainless steel ties to prevent rotation of the ring beam.

Various shapes and sizes of profiles are available for the ring beam. These are determined by the materials used and the structure of the external wall (e.g. single leaf, double leaf). The depth of insulation under the floor slab can also be adjusted to suit the design.

For internal load-bearing walls the slab is thickened and EPS300 is used instead of EPS100. The wall can then rest directly on the floor slab – this removes the thermal break traditionally found at this point.

SUPPLEMENTARY INFORMATION

The procedure for installing these systems varies, but the Supergrund system involves the following steps:

1 topsoil is removed and a geotextile is placed over the exposed subsoil
2 washed rounded stone (505 hardcore) is placed and compacted (150mm min.)
3 drainage pipes (for bathrooms, etc.) and a radon sump are also placed at this stage
4 radon membrane is placed over entire footprint of the house
5 30mm of blinding (3–8mm stone) is then placed
6 ring beam profiles and floor insulation are installed
7 steel reinforcement and ties are installed
8 concrete is poured.

ACTIVITIES

Search online for videos showing different insulated foundation systems being installed. Use the search terms 'Supergrund' and 'Isoquick' (in separate searches).

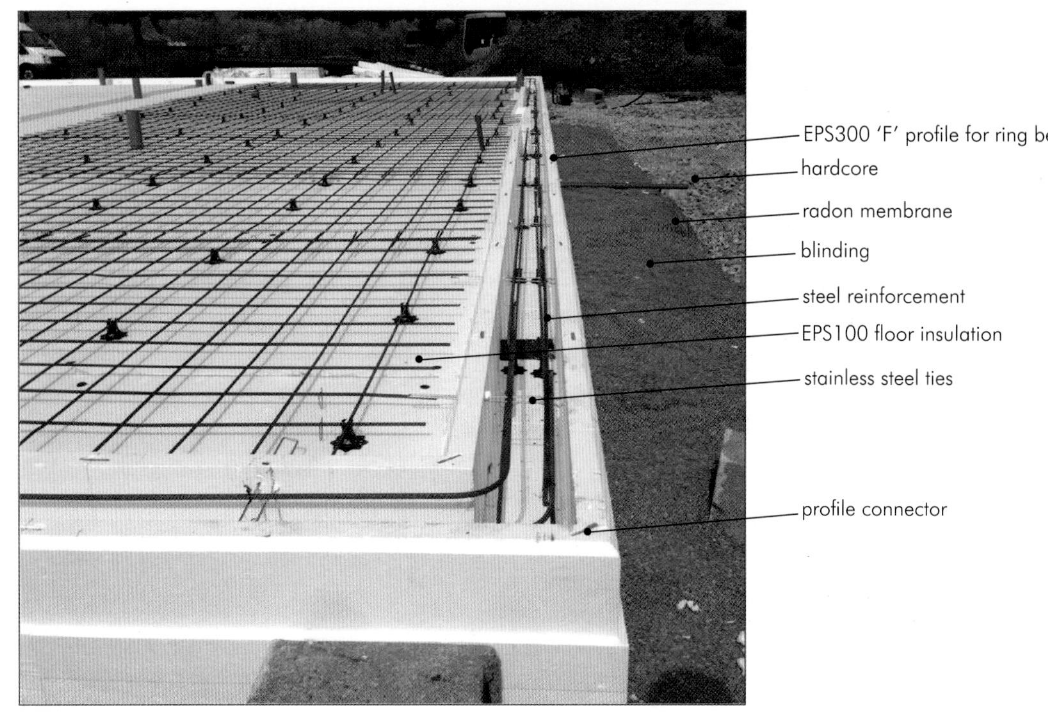

13.26 Supergrund insulated foundations: installed foundation prior to concrete being poured.

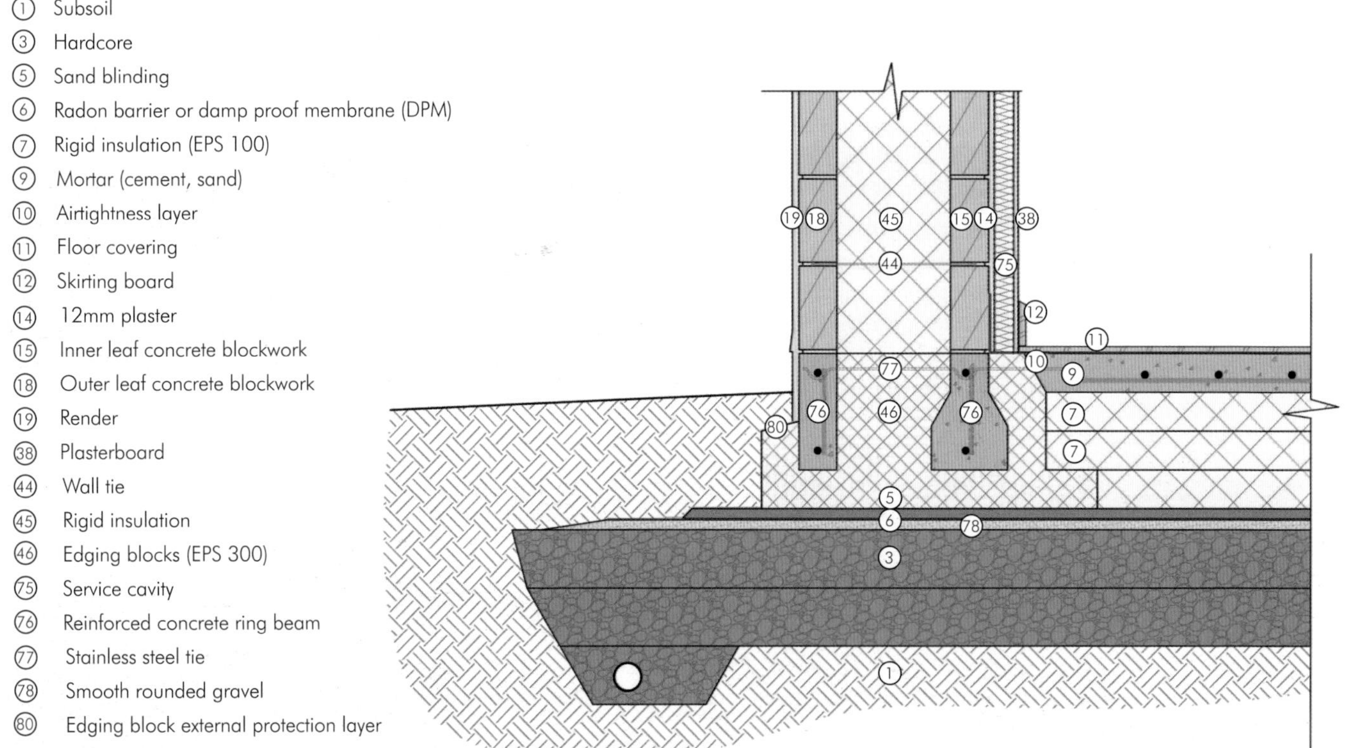

13.27 Supergrund insulated foundation and wide cavity concrete blockwork wall.

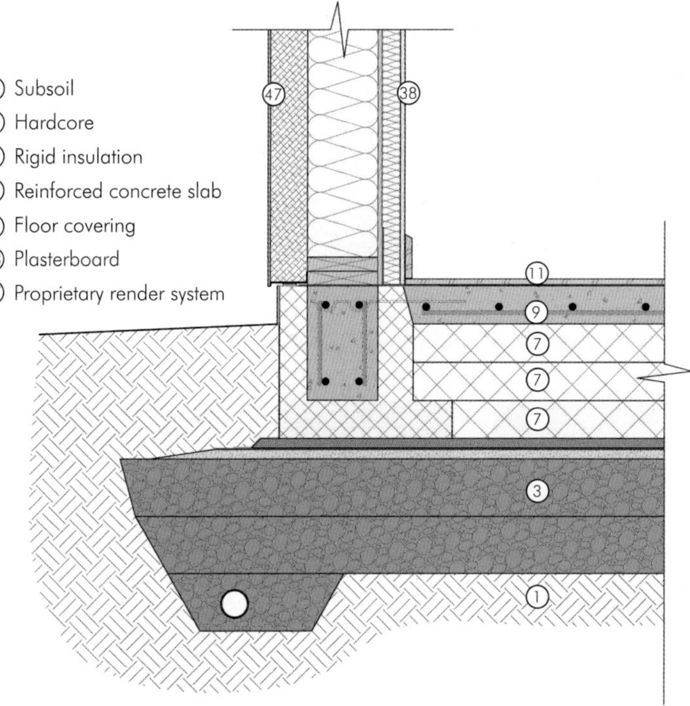

13.28 Supergrund insulated foundation and timber frame wall

③ Hardcore
⑤ Sand blinding
⑥ Radon barrier or damp proof membrane (DPM)
⑦ Rigid insulation
⑨ Reinforced concrete slab
⑪ Floor covering
⑫ Skirting board
⑭ 12mm plaster
⑮ Inner leaf concrete blockwork
㊻ Rigid insulation (EPS300)
76 Reinforced concrete beam
78 Smooth rounded gravel

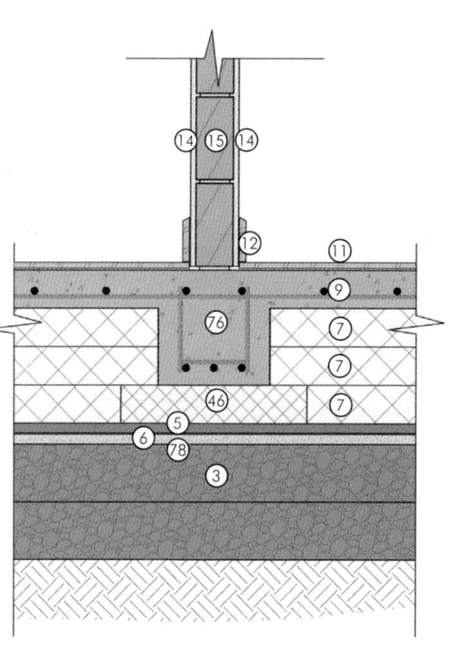

13.29 Supergrund insulated foundation: the floor slab is thickened and supported by EPS300 under internal load-bearing walls.

13.30 Supergrund insultated foundation: a passive house built by Eco Timber Frame in Co. Cork showing the steps involved in the installation of this system.

1 The topsoil has been removed, the geotextile and hardcore are being placed.

2 The hardcore is being compacted to create a solid, level base.

3 EPS ring beam and floor insulation going into place; note the grey drainage pipes and red electrical ducting; the insulation sits on fine stone blinding and the red radon membrane can be seen (at the edge) under the blinding.

4 The concrete has now been poured. The ring beam (light grey) was poured a day earlier; the floor slab is freshly poured (dark grey).

5 The completed timber frame house – this is a single leaf timber frame system with a rendered cement board cladding.

Isoquick

The Isoquick system was developed in Germany and has been used in the construction of many houses in Ireland. Unlike other systems, it does not have a perimeter ring beam – it relies entirely on a raft/floor slab.

The system consists of a number of expanded polystyrene modules that interlock to create a stable formwork that does not require any timber support when the concrete is being poured. The edge modules and base modules are available in various thicknesses to suit any design.

There are two significant differences between this system and the previous example: high-strength EPS330 is used throughout the system and the concrete floor slab is usually thicker (e.g. 250–300mm). This allows internal load-bearing walls to rest directly on the floor slab without any additional measures (e.g. thickening the floor slab/extra reinforcement) being required. This makes the Isoquick system the easiest and fastest to install.

13.31 Isoquick foundation: a passive house built in Co. Donegal showing the steps involved in the installation of this system.

1 Isoquick insulated foundation: the edge modules are connected by dovetail joints.

2 The floor insulation is laid in two layers: the bottom layer runs lengthways; the top layer runs across so the joints overlap. The top layer also overlaps the edge modules and bottom layer.

3 Once the edge modules are completed, the base modules can be installed.

4 The finished foundation/floor; the services (e.g. pipes, cables) can be clearly seen.

5 The completed 'perimeter base tub' – the setting-out boards used to ensure the correct alignment are also visible.

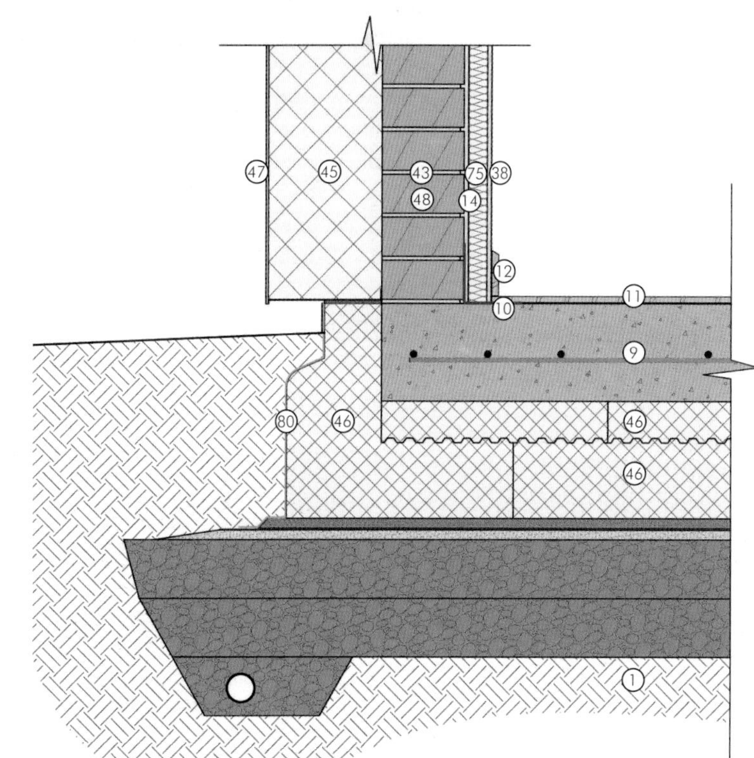

13.32 Isoquick insulated foundation: cross-section showing typical details for a single leaf external load-bearing wall with reinforced concrete floor slab.

ACTIVITIES

'The negative environmental impacts of using plastic-based insulants (e.g. expanded polystyrene) when building a home is offset by the increased energy efficiency of the home over its lifetime.'

Discuss this statement with your classmates.

Non-proprietary insulated foundations

It is entirely possible to achieve the high level of thermal and structural performance offered by proprietary solutions using off-the-shelf products. This example shows a wide cavity wall (with brick outer leaf) combined with a structural floor slab. The slab is thickened because it is supporting the load-bearing inner leaf of the wall; the exact thickness required would depend on the load to be supported.

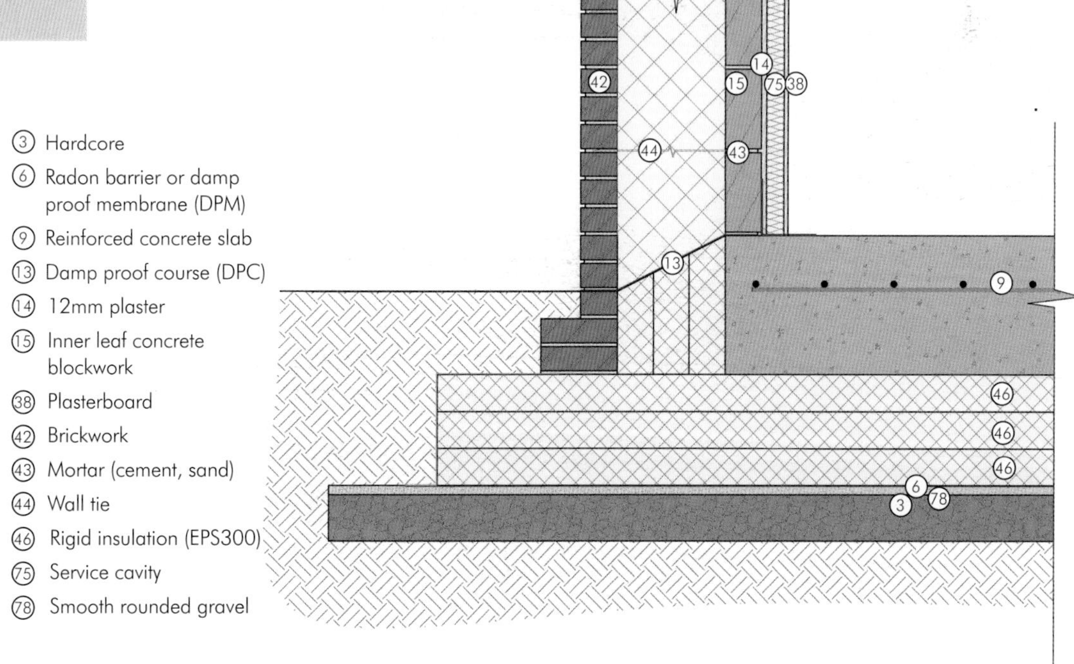

13.33 Non-proprietary insulated foundation: a raft foundation made up on site using 'off-the-shelf' construction products.

REVISION EXERCISES

1 How would the presence of a mature oak tree on a site influence the possible location of a house?
2 A house is to be built on a site with a subsoil that is a mixture of loose sand and gravel. Explain, using a neat freehand sketch, what type of foundation should be used.
3 Discuss the benefits of using a series of pad foundations instead of a strip foundation for a house.
4 Explain, using a neat freehand sketch, how an insulated foundation prevents thermal bridging at the wall–floor junction.
5 Describe, using a neat freehand sketch, an insulated foundation suitable for a single leaf timber frame wall.

CHAPTER 14

Floors

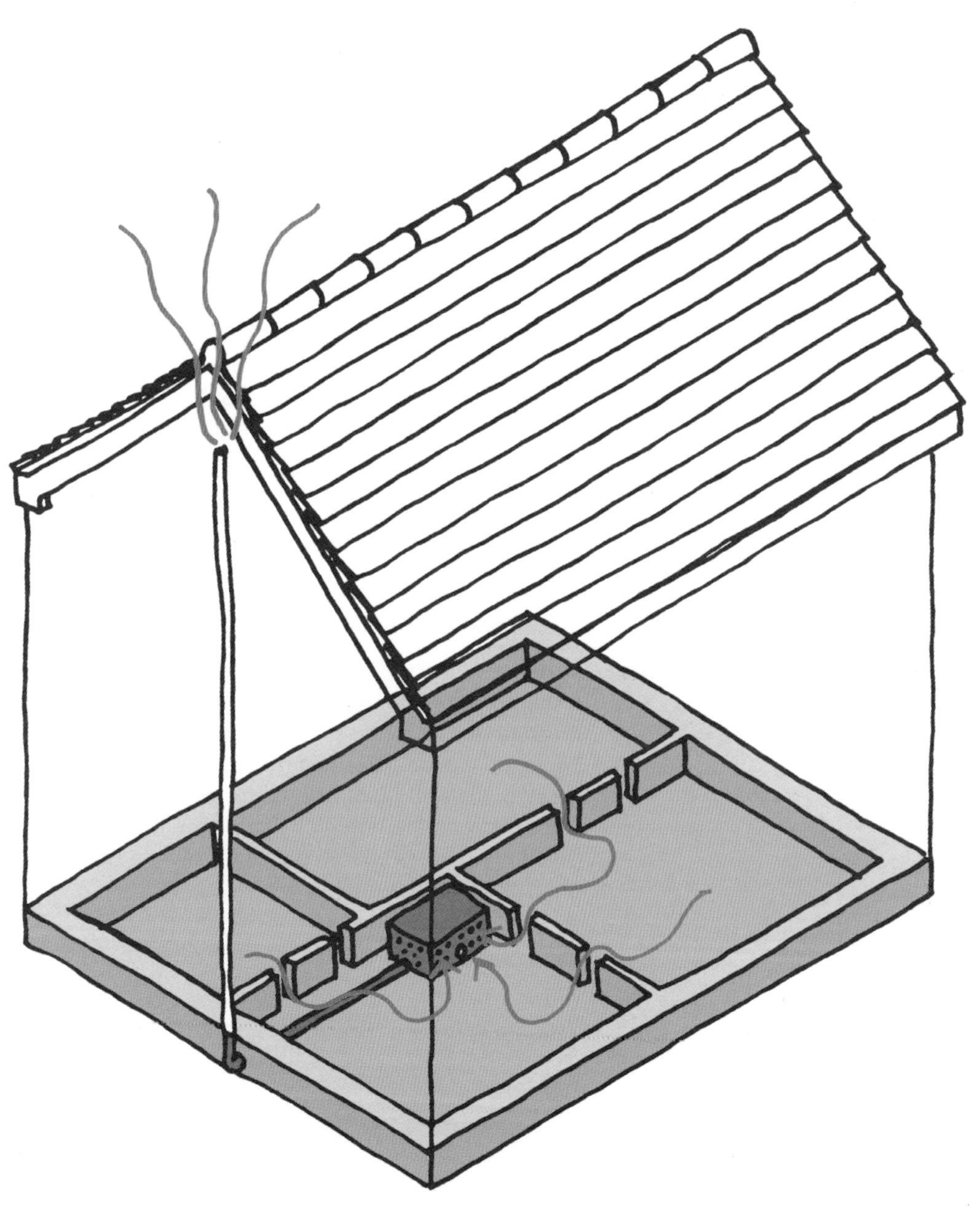

There are two types of floor in a typical house: ground floors and upper floors. While the type of floor structures used in a home are closely related to the foundation and external walls chosen, for now we will look at the different types of floors on their own – we'll see how they go together with the foundation and walls later.

Functions

The primary function of a ground floor is to provide a level indoor surface. It should:

- safely transmit permanent and variable actions
- prevent moisture penetration from the soil below
- prevent heat loss to the ground below.

Performance criteria

When designing a new floor (or assessing an existing floor) it is essential to consider all of the performance requirements expected of a floor, including:

- **sustainability** – floors should be built using durable natural materials with a low embodied energy
- **structural stability** – the floor should be able to safely transmit the permanent and variable actions imposed on it
- **durability** – the surface of the floor must be hard-wearing and the finish should be appropriate to the function of the room (e.g. kitchen floors should ideally be tiled)
- **moisture resistance** – the ground floor must resist the penetration of moisture from below by capillary action
- **radon protection** – the ground floor must keep out radioactive radon gas
- **airtightness** – the ground floor is part of the airtightness layer and must be well sealed
- **fire resistance** – suspended timber ground floors and upper floors should resist fire for at least 30 minutes to allow the occupants time to escape
- **thermal resistance** – the ground floor should be well insulated to prevent the loss of thermal energy and contribute to the overall energy efficiency of the home
- **aesthetics** – the materials (e.g. timber, carpet) used to finish floors should be pleasing to the occupants
- **sound resistance** – the floor should dampen noise to improve indoor sound comfort (particularly important for upper floors).

Factors influencing floor design

The structural design of a ground floor depends on several elements:

- type of foundation and external walls being used – in insulated foundations the foundation and floor are one unit
- type of soil:
  - soils with low bearing capacity may not be capable of supporting a floor
  - if more than 900mm of hardcore is used, a suspended ground floor will be required.

Floor types

Solid

A solid ground floor is supported by the subsoil. The actions are transmitted through the floor structure directly to the subsoil below. There are two variations of the solid ground floor: the insulation can be placed either below or above the concrete slab. If the insulation is placed below the slab, the slab usually serves as the finished floor surface. Floor finishes (e.g. tiles or carpet) are laid directly on the slab. If the insulation is placed above the slab, a thin layer of fine concrete, called a screed, is poured over the concrete to provide a hardwearing finished floor surface on which floor finishes are laid.

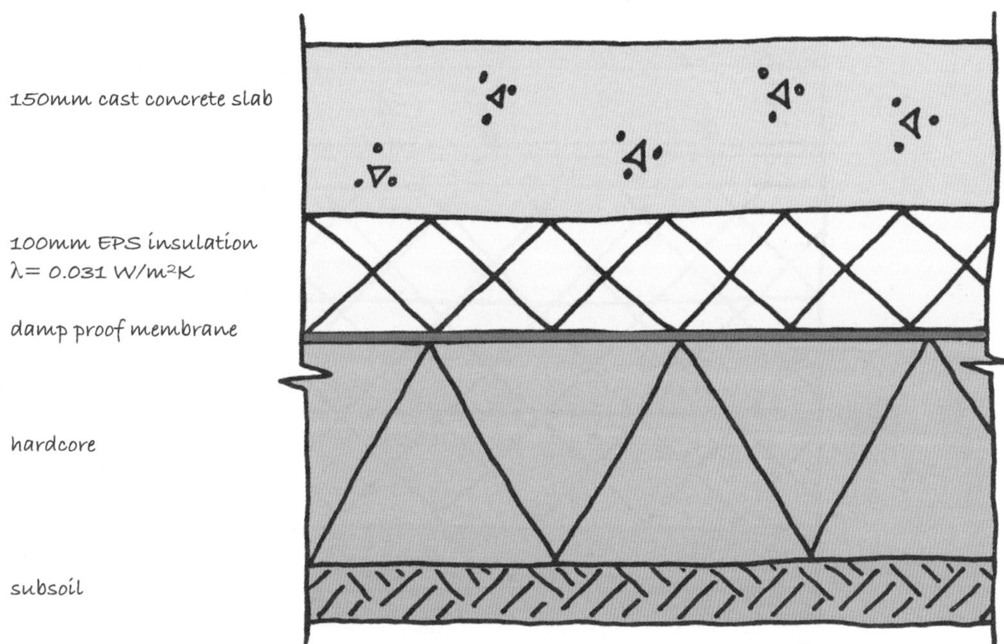

14.01 Solid concrete slab ground floor designed to comply with the 2011 building regulations ≤ 0.21W/m²K.

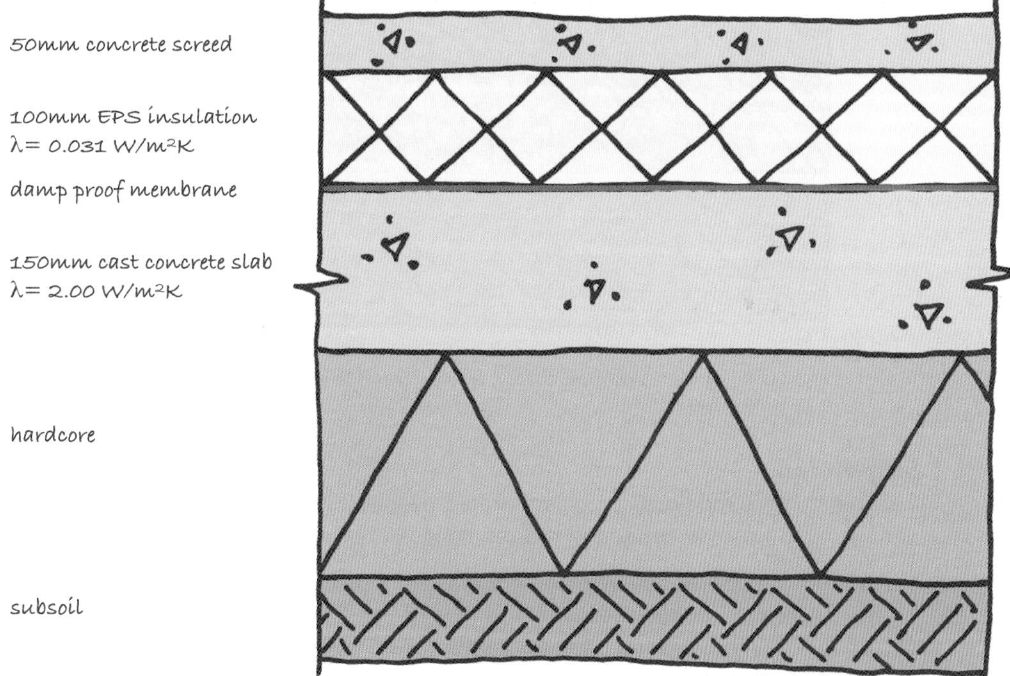

14.02 Solid concrete slab ground floor (insulation and damp proof membrane above the slab with 50mm screed) designed to comply with the 2011 building regulations ≤ 0.21W/m²K.

The floor design used to reach Passivhaus standard usually depends on the external wall and foundation used. This is because it is essential that the floor–wall junction is thermal bridge free. To achieve this there must be a significant overlap of insulation where the floor and wall connect. Each of the sample floors shown here would achieve a U-value of approximately 0.10 W/m²K.

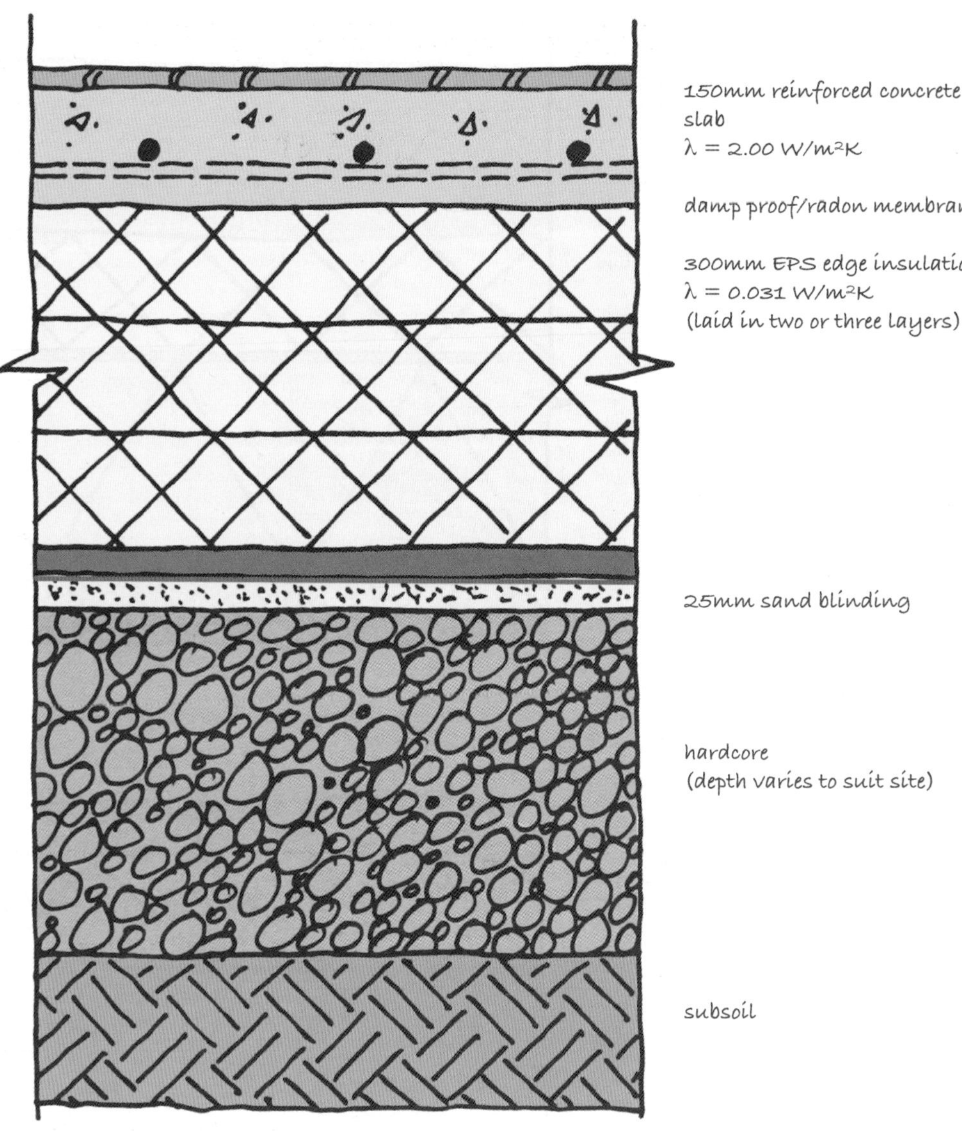

14.03 Solid concrete slab ground floor: 300mm graphite-enhanced EPS (e.g. Supergrund system).

Suspended

A suspended ground floor can be supported by the walls of the structure or by the ground. There are two main types of suspended ground floor: timber and concrete.

Suspended timber ground floors were popular in houses built in Ireland in the 1970s and 1980s. There are lots of houses with this type of floor all over the country. The major drawback of suspended timber ground floors is that they were poorly insulated. This type of floor must be ventilated to prevent dampness that would cause timber rot, and the ventilation makes these floors draughty and cold.

Suspended concrete ground floors became more common during the building boom because they are quick to construct. They are assembled on site using precast components.

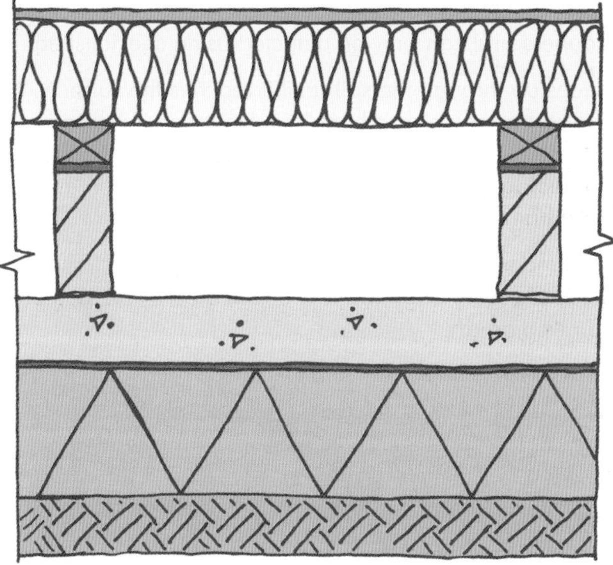

14.04 Suspended timber ground floor – 200mm mineral wool (or rigid insulation (e.g. EPS)) is placed between the joists – designed to comply with the 2011 building regulations ≤ 0.21W/m^{2}K.

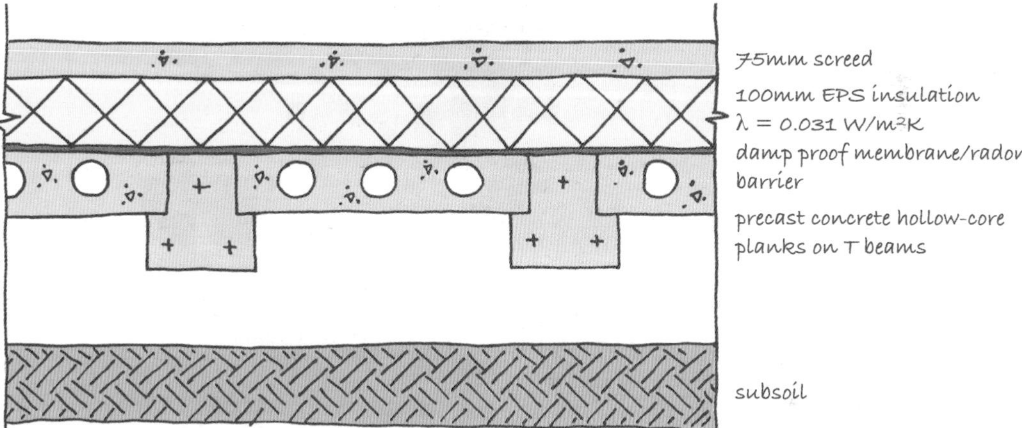

14.05 Suspended concrete ground floors – 100mm EPS insulation – designed to comply with the 2011 building regulations ≤ 0.21W/m^{2}K.

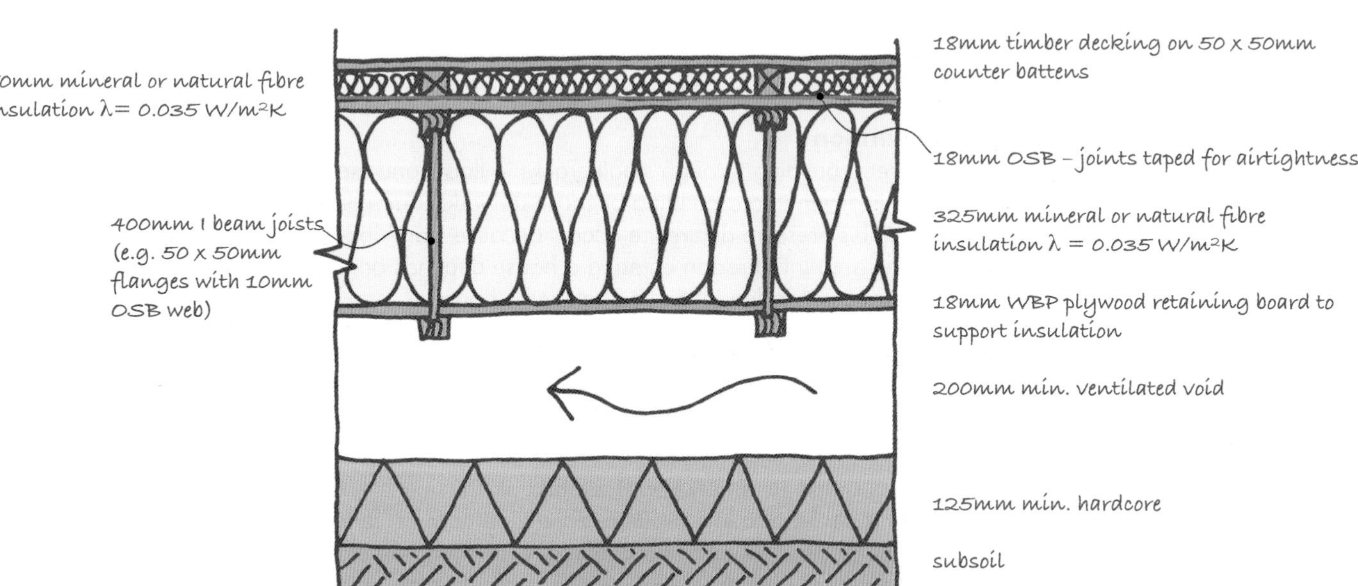

14.06 Suspended timber ground floor: 400mm deep engineered timber I joists are used to allow sufficient depth of insulation and longer floor spans.

Radon

Radon is a naturally occurring radioactive gas found in soils all over Ireland. It is colourless, tasteless, odourless and can only be detected using specialist equipment.

Radon gas seeps up through the soil until it reaches the surface. Where this occurs outdoors it is quickly diluted by fresh air and is harmless. However, if it emerges into an enclosed space, such as a house, it can build up to dangerous levels. Prolonged inhalation of radon gas causes lung cancer. The Radiological Protection Institute of Ireland (RPII) estimates that approximately 150–200 people die from radon-related lung cancer every year.

Radon is measured in becquerels per cubic metre (Bq/m^3). The national reference level for radon in Ireland is 200 Bq/m^3. Radon levels are indicated by the percentage of houses which are above this level in a given area.

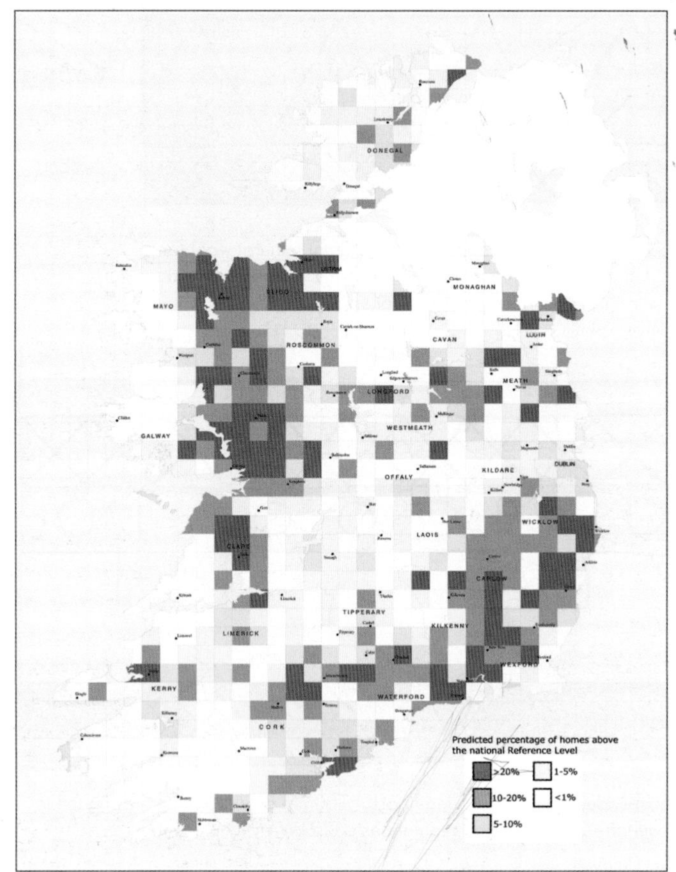

14.07 Radon in Irish dwellings – the darker areas have more houses above the 200 Bq/m^3 level. *Source*: RPII.

ACTIVITIES

Visit the website of the Irish Cancer Society www.cancer.ie to learn more about lung cancer.

Radon prevention

Radon can enter a building through small cracks in floors and through gaps around pipes or cables. Radon is driven into a building because the indoor air pressure is lower than the pressure below ground. This pressure difference occurs because warm indoor air is less dense than cool outdoor air. The amount of radon entering a house depends on:

- the concentration of radon in the soil below the house
- the density and porosity of the soil below the house
- the presence of entry points in the structure.

There are two elements to radon prevention: a radon sump; and a radon membrane.

Radon sump

A radon sump is simply an empty honeycombed plastic unit connected to a pipe. When buried under the floor it becomes a low-pressure zone that 'attracts' radon gas. The gas then flows through the pipe to the exterior of the building. Depending on the size of the building, two sumps may be required. Also, if the level of radon in the soil is high, a fan can be fitted to the pipe to maximise extraction of the gas.

14.08 Radon: a radon sump (installed in the hard core layer below the radon membrane) collects radon and allows it to flow to the outdoors.

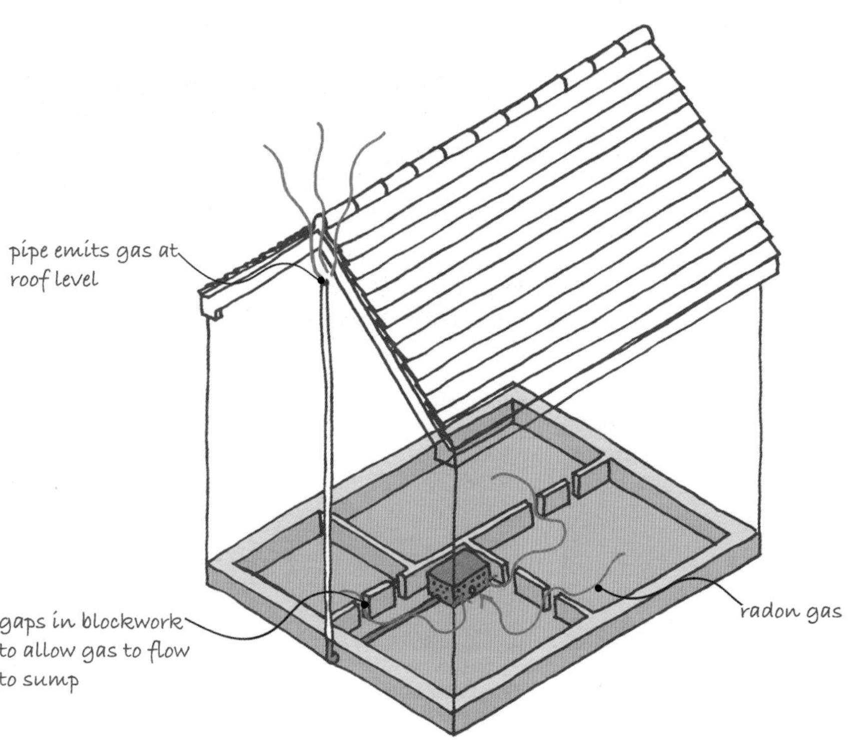

14.09 Radon: a radon sump (installed below the radon membrane) collects radon and allows it to flow to the outdoors.

Radon membrane

A radon membrane is similar to a damp proof course. The plastic used in radon membranes is resistant to the passage of radon gas. The membrane is usually installed by specialists because it requires a high level of workmanship to achieve reliable seals at junctions and around service pipes. The radon membrane must be continuous across the entire footprint of the building. Where precisely the membrane is installed will depend on the type of foundation and floor. Many of the insulated floor system manufacturers recommend installing the radon membrane below the foundation/floor so that it can be laid as a single flat sheet without penetrations for services (e.g. drainage pipes).

14.10 Radon: membrane installed above sump to prevent ingress of radon gas.

14.11 Hardcore: after the radon sump is installed the hardcore is laid and well compacted in preparartion for installation of the radon membrane.

14.12 Blinding: a thin layer (e.g. 25mm) of sand blinding may be laid on the hardcore to prevent any sharp stone edges puncturing the radon membrane.

14.13 Radon: the radon membrane must cover the entire footprint of the building. Note the use of proprietary blue tape to seal joints (e.g. at corners and around pipes).

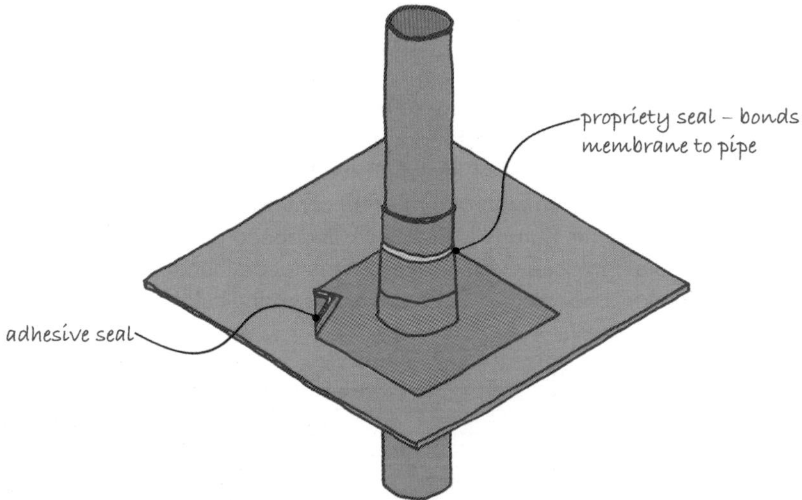

14.14 Any openings created to accommodate services (e.g. drainage pipes) must be carefully sealed.

REVISION EXERCISES

1 Discuss the benefits of a solid ground floor when compared to a suspended ground floor.
2 Discuss the risk posed by radon.
3 Look up the current RPII map of radon levels and note the percentage of homes in your area that are above the national reference level (*Hint*: visit www.rpii.ie and follow the link for radon maps).
4 Outline the factors that determine the potential amount of radon entering a home.
5 Describe, using neat freehand sketches, two strategies for preventing radon entering a home.

CHAPTER 15

Walls

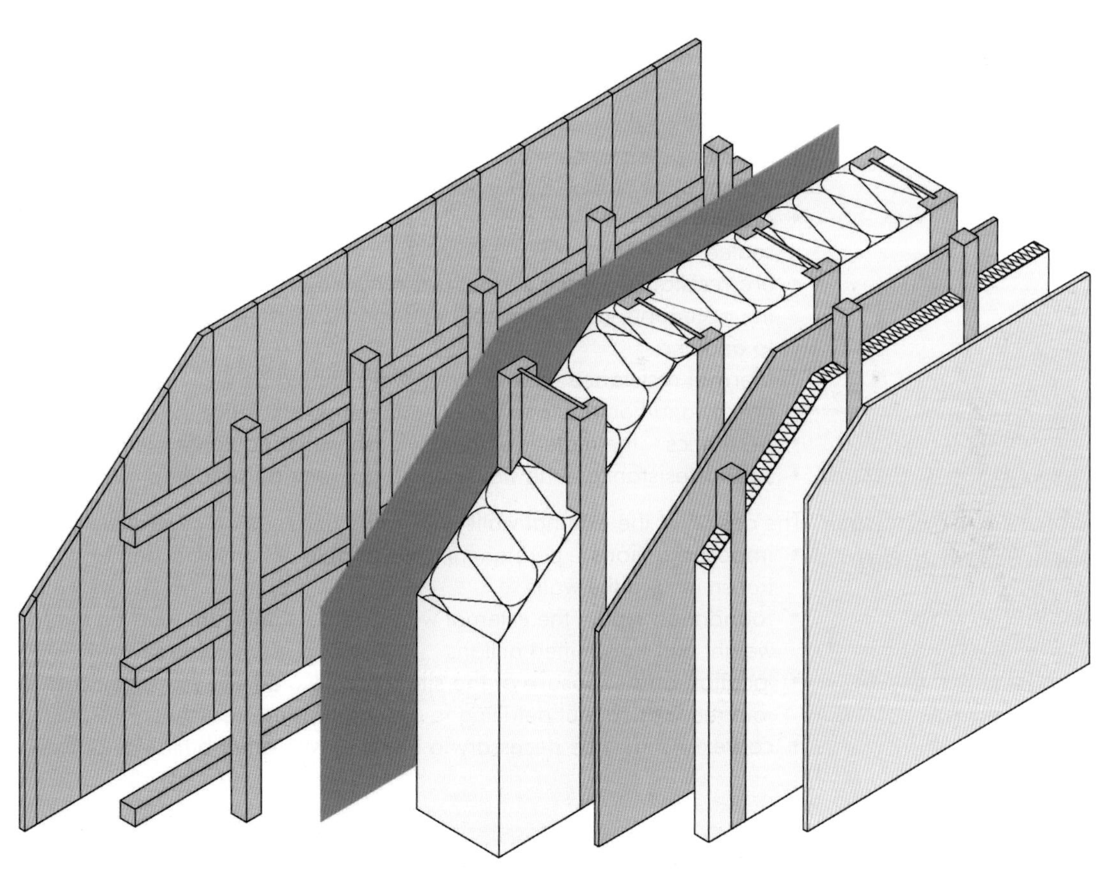

There are two types of wall in every home: external walls and internal walls. External walls have several important jobs to do, whereas internal walls are mainly used to divide up the internal space into separate rooms.

In the past, walls often merely consisted of solid masonry (e.g. stone and mortar) with a lime plaster finish on the inside. These walls relied on their thickness to provide a comfortable indoor environment. Of course, these houses would also have had a fire burning in almost every room. Nowadays, there is a much greater awareness of the impact homes have on the environment and walls are being designed to provide warm, healthy indoor spaces without the need for fossil fuel energy. For this reason, designing external walls has become increasingly complex and many factors have to be considered.

Functions

The primary functions of an external wall are to provide shelter from the weather and to support the roof. An external wall should:

- resist the actions of the weather (sun, wind, rain, etc.)
- prevent heat loss from inside to outside
- support the loads from the roof
- support the loads from upper floors.

Performance criteria

Most of the factors influencing external wall design are linked to energy efficiency or to structural integrity: how the wall retains heat energy; and ensuring that the wall remains stable and reliable over its lifetime.

When designing external walls (or assessing an existing wall) it is essential to consider all of the performance requirements expected of an external wall, including:

- **sustainability** – walls should be built using durable natural materials with a low embodied energy
- **structural stability** – they should be able to safely transmit the imposed permanent and variable actions
- **durability** – the wall should withstand the effects of weathering for the lifetime of the building
- **moisture resistance** – they must resist the penetration of moisture from below by capillary action, from outside by wind-driven rain and from within by water vapour pressure
- **airtightness** – the external walls are a significant part of the airtightness layer and must be well sealed
- **fire resistance** – walls should retain their load-bearing capacity for at least 30 minutes to allow the occupants time to escape, and should resist the spread of fire from one area of the building to another
- **thermal resistance** – the external walls should be well insulated to prevent the loss of thermal energy and contribute to the overall energy efficiency of the home
- **aesthetics** – the materials used to finish walls should be pleasing to the occupants
- **sound resistance** – the walls should dampen noise to improve indoor sound comfort.

Factors influencing external wall design

The design of the external walls of a home depends on several elements:

- **imposed actions** – permanent and variable actions imposed on the roof and upper floors are transmitted to the walls
- **foundation type** – the external walls exert a significant load on the foundation, including self weight and transmitted actions
- **location and exposure of the site** – an elevated site with significant exposure to wind-driven rain requires careful detailing to ensure moisture resistance
- **context** – it may be necessary to blend in with other buildings or the landscape.

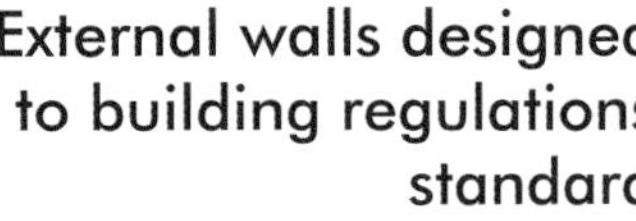

External walls designed to building regulations standard

Cavity walls built using masonry or timber frame are the most common wall types used to build houses in Ireland. The 2011 revision to TGD L reduced the allowable thermal transmittance of an external wall to U-value ≤ 0.21 W/m^{2}K. This update did not require a change in the design of traditional cavity walls. If a higher quality of insulant is used, the traditional systems can still be used.

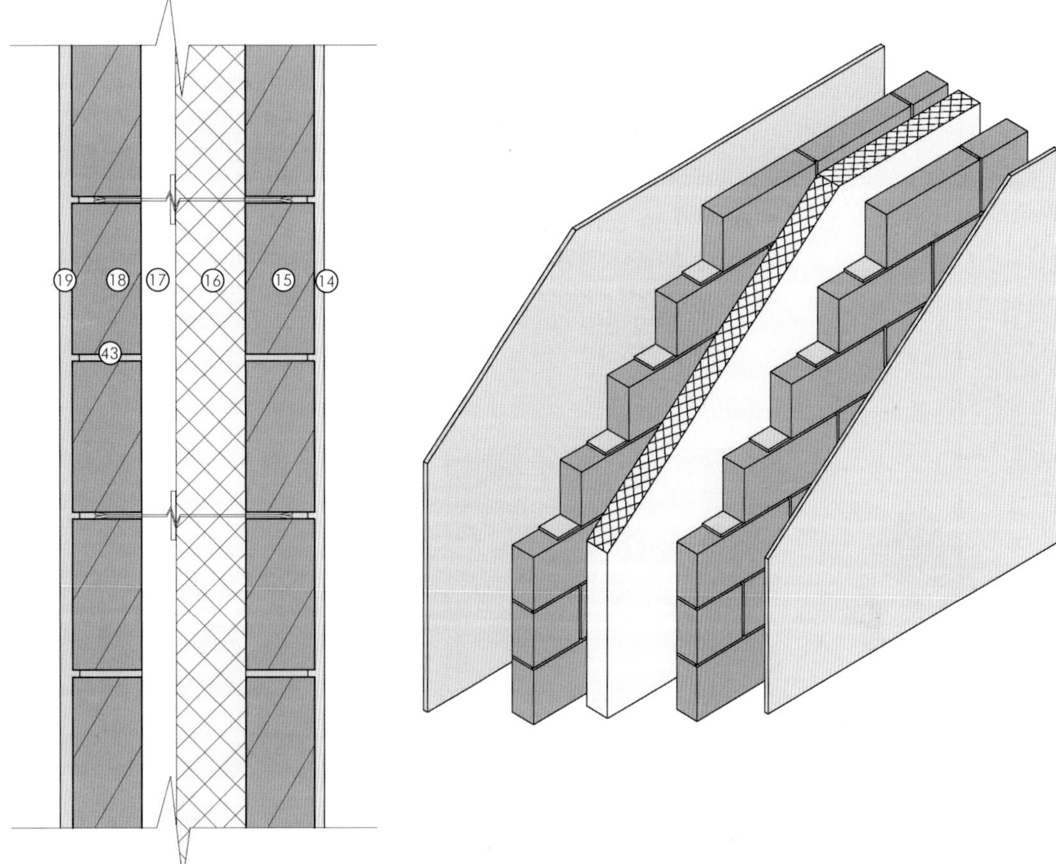

- (14) 12mm plaster
- (15) 100mm inner leaf cavity insulation
- (16) 100mm cavity insulation
- (17) 50mm air cavity
- (18) 100mm outer leaf
- (19) 20mm render
- (43) Mortar (cement, sand)

15.01 Concrete cavity wall designed to achieve a U-value ≤ 0.21 W/m^{2}K.

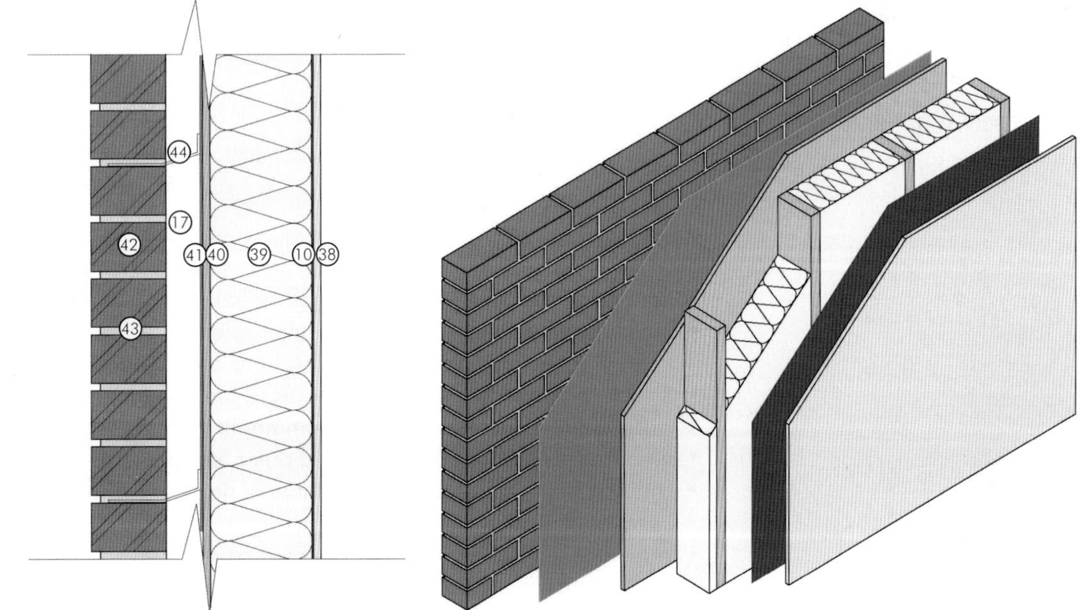

- (10) Airtightness layer
- (17) 50mm air cavity
- (38) 12.5mm plasterboard
- (39) Quilted insulation
- (40) Oriented strand board
- (41) Breather membrane
- (42) Brickwork
- (43) Mortar (cement, sand)
- (44) Wall tie

15.02 Timber frame wall designed to achieve a U-value ≤ 0.21 W/m^{2}K.

External walls designed to Passivhaus standard

The Passivhaus standard does not require the use of a particular structural system or wall design. In Ireland and around the world a wide variety of external walls have been used in houses built to the Passivhaus standard. The criterion is that a maximum U-value of 0.15W/m^{2}K is achieved. However, in practice most designers aim to achieve a lower value than this so as to minimise the energy consumption of the home.

Wide cavity masonry wall

This wall is commonly used by architects and builders who are new to the Passivhaus concept. It has the benefit of being familiar to those who have experience with traditional cavity walling. Modern water-repellent insulants make it possible to fill the cavity with insulation – if this had been done in the past, moisture would have bridged the cavity, defeating the purpose of the cavity. An internal service cavity is recommended to avoid disturbance of the plaster airtight layer.

Low conductivity wall ties

Low conductivity wall ties are an essential element of wide cavity walls built to meet the passive house standard. Manufactured from pultruded basalt fibres set in an epoxy resin, they avoid the point thermal bridging that would result if standard stainless steel ties were used.

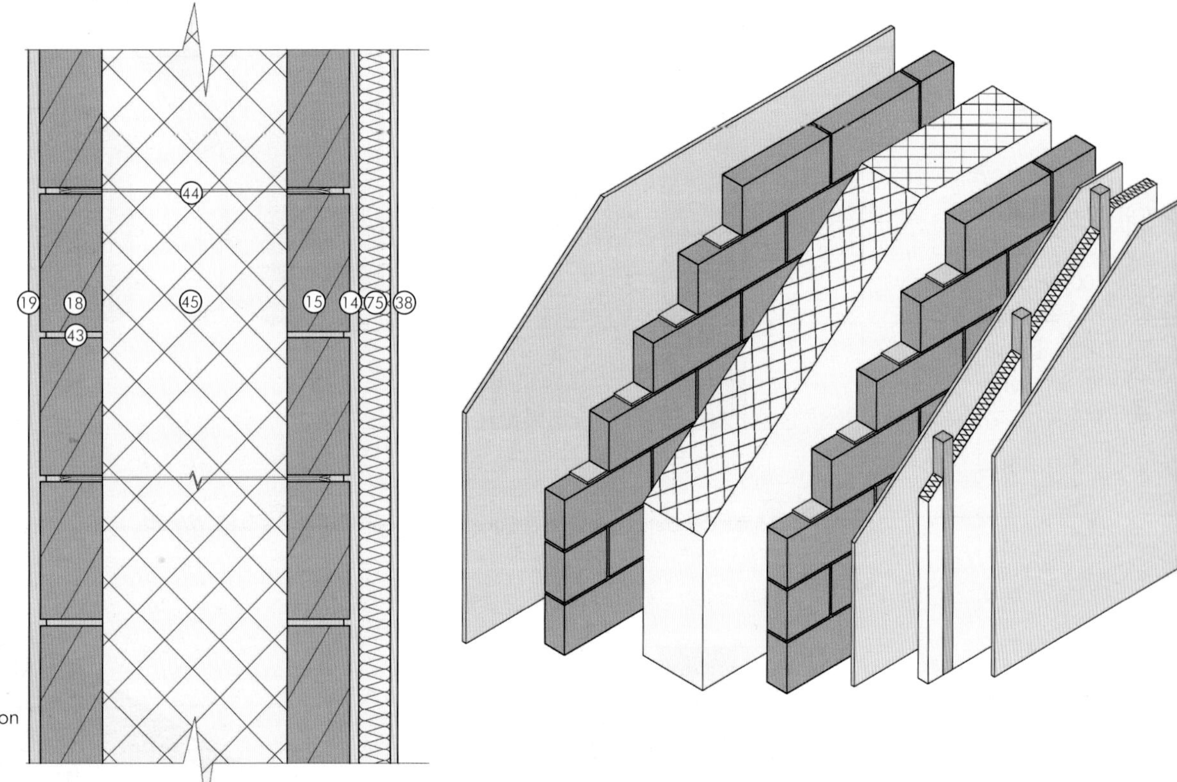

- (14) 12mm plaster
- (15) 100mm inner leaf
- (18) 100mm outer leaf
- (19) 20mm render
- (38) 12.5mm plasterboard
- (43) Mortar (cement, sand)
- (44) Wall tie
- (45) 250 or 300mm rigid insulation
- (75) 50mm service cavity

15.03 Full fill wide cavity masonry wall designed to meet the Passivhaus requirement: U-value ≤ 0.15 W/m^{2}K.

Performance characteristics of this wall include:

- sustainability – this wall is built using materials with a high level of embodied energy (e.g. cement, concrete, plastic-based insulants and mineral fibre insulants
- structural stability – the wall ties ensure that the inner and outer leaves act as one unit
- durability – concrete is a durable material
- weather resistance – the rendered outer leaf prevents the penetration of wind-driven rain
- airtightness – the plaster on the inner surface of the blockwork provides airtightness and vapour resistance
- moisture resistance – the damp proof course prevents rising damp
- fire resistance – concrete is non-combustible and will resist collapse in a fire
- thermal resistance – significant insulation layer provides a high level of heat retention
- aesthetics – render can be painted to give a pleasing finish
- acoustic resistance – dense masonry is a good sound insulator.

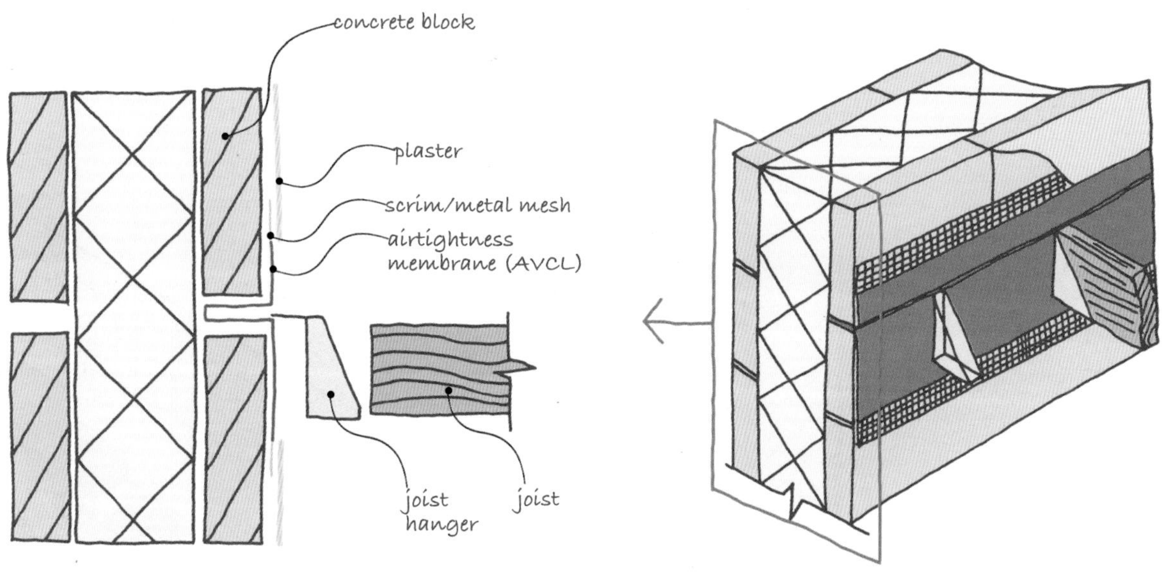

15.04 Wall – first-floor junction: airtightness and vapour control membrane dressed into masonry joint.

Where the joist hanger penetrates the plaster, a strip of airtightness and vapour control membrane is dressed along the face of the wall, into the joint and back out to the face of the wall to ensure airtightness. Proprietary scrim tape or expanding metal mesh is used to bond the membrane to the plaster.

15.05 Wall – first-floor junction: the solid timber joists are supported by galvanised steel joist hangers. The airtightness layer (AVCL) is dressed into the masonry joint to prevent air leakage.

Block 'on flat' masonry wall

This is the simplest wall buildup that can be used to meet the Passivhaus standard. A block 'on flat' wall with a proprietary external insulation and finish system (EIFS) is used to provide thermal insulation. A wide variety of insulants are available – polystyrene, polyurethane and mineral fibre products are commonly used. A service cavity is strongly recommended to avoid disturbance of the plaster airtight layer.

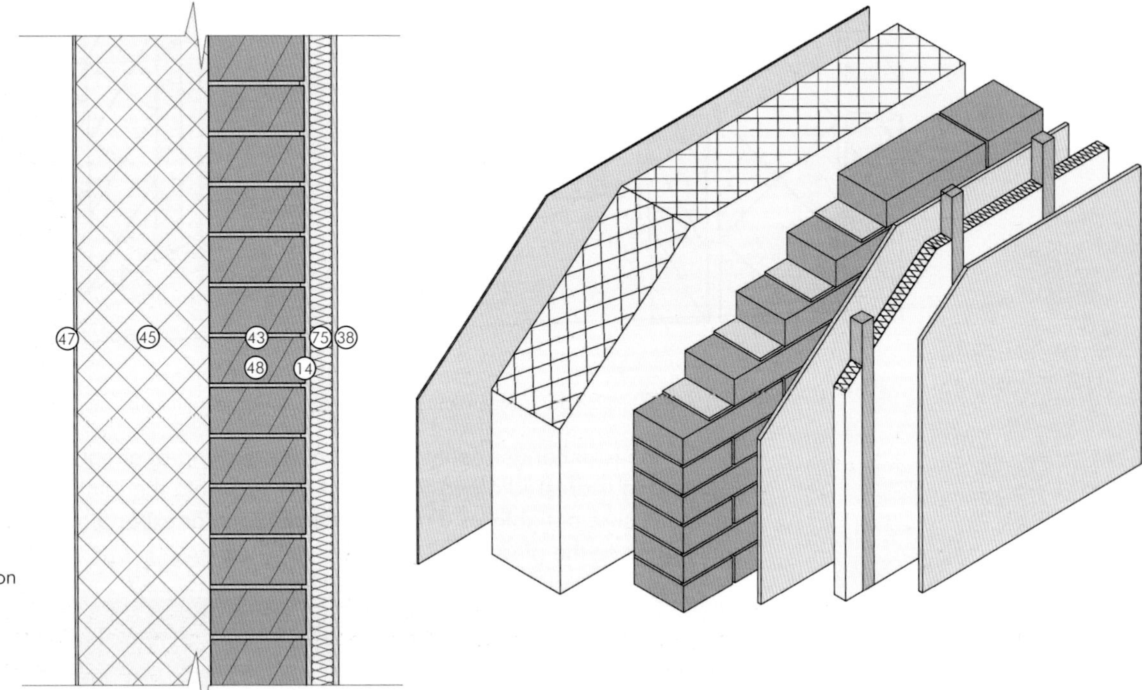

- (14) 12mm plaster
- (38) 12.5mm plasterboard
- (43) Mortar (cement, sand)
- (45) 250 or 300mm rigid insulation
- (47) Proprietary render system
- (48) 215mm block on flat
- (75) 50mm service cavity

15.06 Externally insulated block 'on flat' wall designed to meet the Passivhaus requirement: U-value ≤ 0.15 W/m^{2}K.

Performance characteristics of this wall include:

- sustainability – the wall is built using materials with a high level of embodied energy (e.g. cement, concrete, plastic-based insulants and mineral fibre insulants)
- structural stability – standard concrete blocks laid 'on flat' provide sufficient structural stability for low rise residential construction
- durability – concrete is a durable material; the long-term durability of the external render on external insulation is questionable, but is more than likely an aesthetic issue rather than a functional one
- weather resistance – breathable water-resistant render prevents the penetration of wind-driven rain
- airtightness – the plaster on the inner surface of the blockwork provides airtightness and vapour resistance
- moisture resistance – the damp proof course prevents rising damp
- fire resistance – concrete is non-combustible and will resist collapse in a fire
- thermal resistance – significant insulation layer provides a high level of heat retention
- aesthetics – render can be painted to give a pleasing finish
- acoustic resistance – dense masonry is a good sound insulator.

Timber frame wall with rainscreen

This wall consists of engineered I beam studs with solid timber sole and head plates. The studs are nailed to the sole/head plates to provide a structural frame into which the insulation can be placed. The OSB sheathing provides stiffness against racking (sideways movement) and also acts as the airtightness layer. The joints between OSB panels are taped to ensure an airtight seal. The timber cladding rainscreen is supported by battens and counter battens. This creates a ventilated cavity, which ensures the wall build-up remains dry when exposed to wind-driven rain. Timber panels (e.g. exterior plywood), cement fibre board and other materials can be used instead of timber cladding to provide an alternative aesthetic finish.

- (17) 50mm air cavity
- (36) 50x50mm timber batten
- (38) 12.5mm plasterboard
- (39) Quilted insulation
- (40) Oriented strand board
- (41) Breather membrane
- (52) Timber cladding
- (75) 50mm service cavity

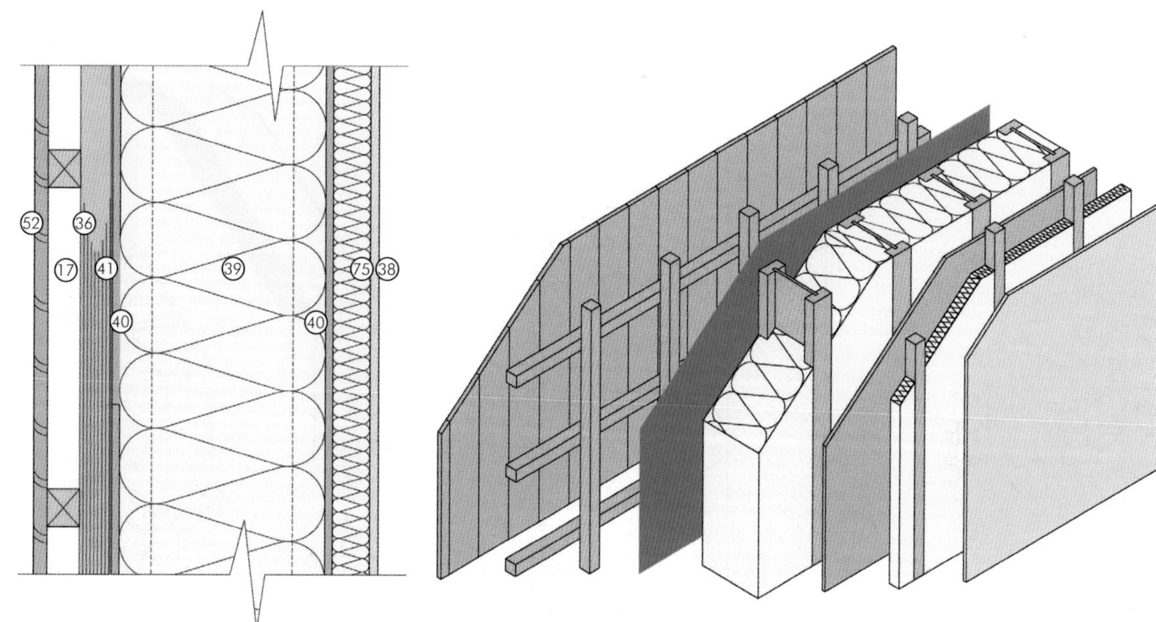

15.07 Timber frame wall with timber cladding rainscreen designed to meet the Passivhaus requirement: U-value ≤ 0.15 W/m^{2}K.

Performance characteristics of this wall include:

- sustainability – it is built using materials with a low level of embodied energy (e.g. timber, sheep's wool/cellulose/hemp insulation)
- structural stability – the primary timber frame panel (engineered timber I beams, solid timber sole/head plate/OSB sheathing) is stable and can safely withstand the imposed loads
- durability – timber cladding is durable, provided appropriate timber is used (e.g. larch) and it is properly maintained
- weather resistance – the ventilated rainscreen prevents the penetration of wind-driven rain
- airtightness – the OSB3 board is airtight and vapour resistant – all joints are taped
- moisture resistance –
  - damp proof course prevent rising damp
  - the vapour resistance of the buildup reduces from inside (OSB3) to outside (breather membrane on softboard)
- fire resistance – plasterboard is non-combustible and will protect the wall in the event of fire
- thermal resistance – significant insulation layer provides a high level of heat retention
- aesthetics – timber cladding finishes are very pleasing to the eye
- sound resistance – the thermal insulation and airtightness measures will resist noise from outside the building.

Timber frame wall with external insulation

This system comprises a simple solid timber stud wall with timber sole/head plates. OSB sheathing is used to prevent racking and provide airtightness. The outer layer is a breathable wood fibre insulation panel with a proprietary breathable render.

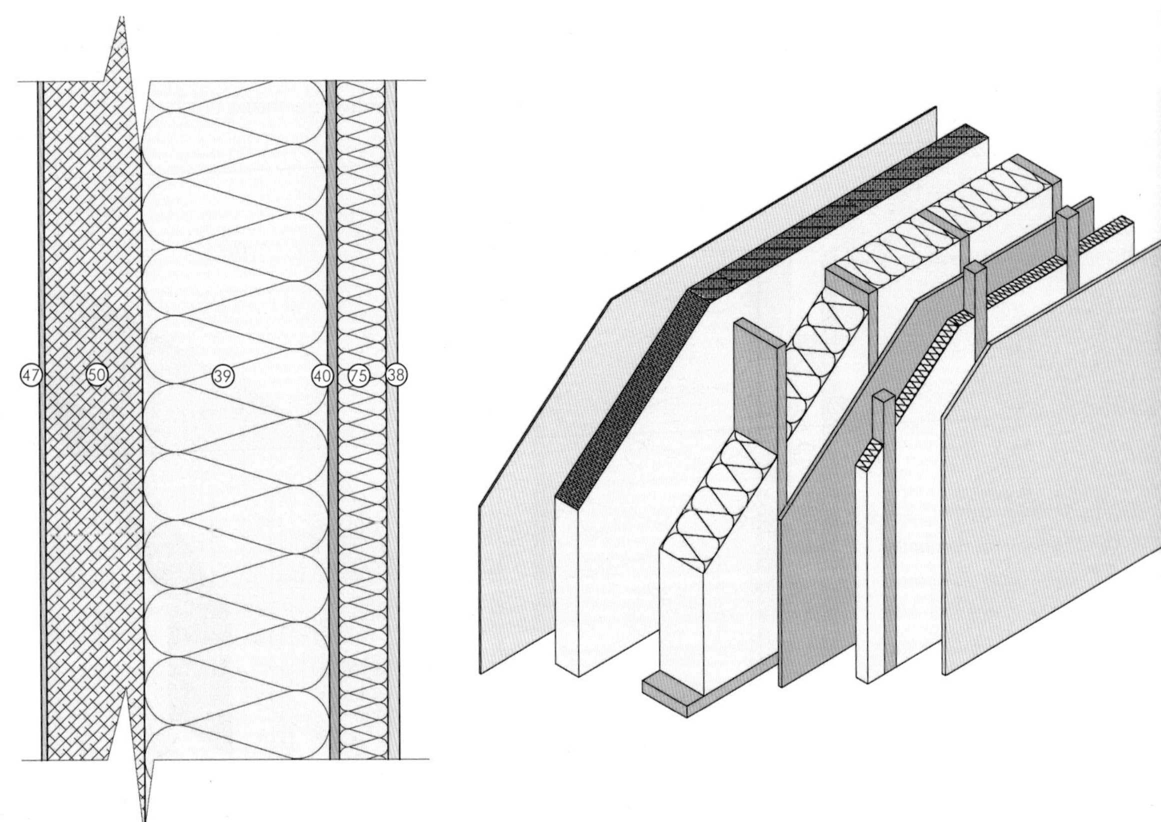

(38) 12.5mm plasterboard
(39) Quilted insulation
(40) Oriented strand board
(47) Proprietary render system
(50) Batt insulation
(75) 50mm service cavity

15.08 Timber frame wall with external insulation designed to meet the Passivhaus requirement: U-value ≤ 0.15 W/m^{2}K.

Performance characteristics of this wall include:

- **sustainability** – built using materials with a low level of embodied energy (e.g. timber, sheep's wool/cellulose/wood fibre/hemp insulation)
- **structural stability** – the primary timber frame panel (solid timber stud, solid timber sole/head plate, OSB sheathing) is stable and can safely withstand the imposed loads
- **durability** – the proprietary render on the wood fibre board is reinforced with mesh to ensure long-term durability
- **weather resistance** – the proprietary render is designed to prevent the penetration of wind-driven rain
- **airtightness** – the OSB3 board is airtight and vapour resistant – all joints are taped
- **moisture resistance** –
  - damp proof course prevent rising damp
  - the vapour resistance of the buildup reduces from inside (OSB3) to outside (rendered wood fibre panel)
- **fire resistance** – plasterboard is non-combustible and will protect the wall in the event of fire
- **thermal resistance** – two layers of insulation provide a high level of heat retention
- **aesthetics** – rendered finishes are very pleasing to the eye
- **sound resistance** – the thermal insulation and airtightness measures will resist noise from outside the building.

Wall finishes

Wall finishes comprise external rendering and internal plastering.

Rendering

Rendering is the term used to describe the application of a surface finish to an external wall. The render is the first line of defence against the weather.

Functions

The primary function of a render is to protect the wall. The render should:

- resist wind penetration
- resist moisture penetration from rain
- give an attractive surface finish.

ACTIVITIES

Conduct a telephone interview with a builder who has built a home to the Passivhaus standard. Compile a list of questions that you could ask about their experiences.

Performance criteria

Performance criteria for renders:

- wind resistance – it provides protection against heat loss caused by wind penetration of the building fabric
- moisture resistance – render provides protection to porous materials (e.g. concrete blocks), especially against wind-driven rain
- flexibility – it must be able to withstand the expansion and contraction caused by changes in temperature and moisture content (caused by changing weather)
- durability – it should last for the lifetime of the building – its longevity depends on the degree of exposure of the building, the proportions of the mix used, the bond between the rendering and the wall and the quality of the workmanship
- uniform weathering – render should weather or age uniformly to provide a pleasing appearance and avoid cracking
- aesthetics – workmanship should be of a high standard and the finished render should be appropriate to the style of house and the locality.

Cement render

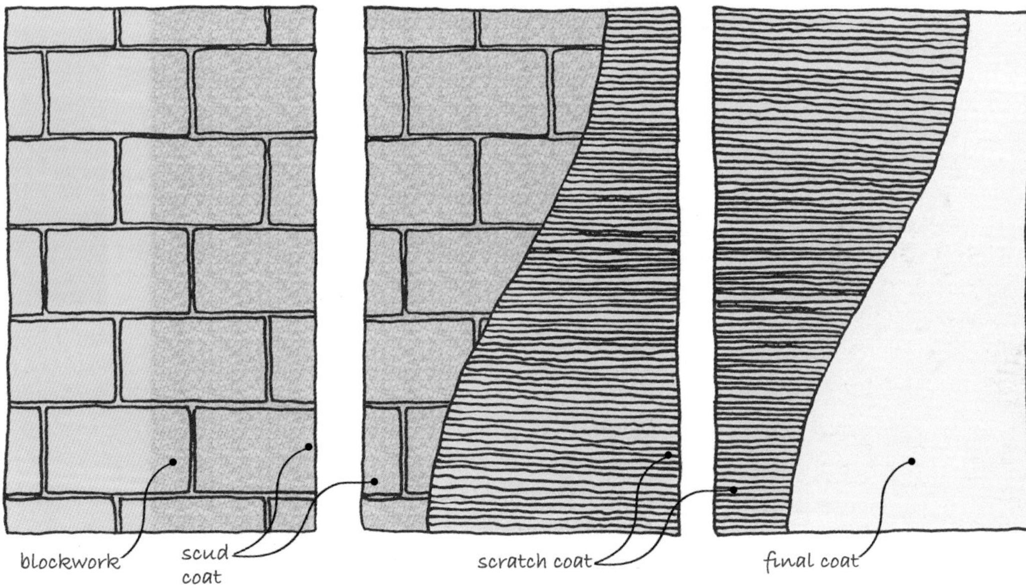

15.09 Rendering: a plain render applied to a concrete blockwork wall in three coats.

Method:

Scud coat:

Mix – 1 part cement : 1½ or 2 parts sharp sand

- mixed with just enough water to give the consistency of a thick slurry
- steel corner beads are installed to protect the corners and the edges of the reveals
- thrown onto the wall using a hand scoop to a thickness of 3mm
- surface should be dampened periodically until the coat has hardened and then allowed to dry
- the purpose of the scud coat is to provide a key or grip for the next coat of render.

Scratch coat:
Mix – 1 part cement : ½ part lime : 4 or 4½ parts sharp sand

- scratch coat is applied to a thickness of 8 to 10 mm and allowed to set firm
- when the scratch coat is set firm (but before it hardens) it should be combed or scratched to provide a key for the final coat.

Final coat:
Mix – 1 part cement : ½ part lime : 4 or 4½ parts sharp sand

- before the final coat is applied, the scratch coat should be fully hardened and sufficiently dry to provide adequate suction (absorption)
- if the scratch coat is bone dry it should be dampened to prevent excessive suction
- the final coat should be applied using a timber float because a steel float brings water and the finer particles of cement and lime to the surface, which, on drying out, shrink and cause surface cracks. A timber float leaves the surface with a coarse texture that is less likely to crack
- the final coat should be thinner than the scratch coat – usually about 6mm thick.

The overall thickness of the combined coats should not exceed 20mm.

Insulation render

Many proprietary rendering products are available to suit various insulation systems. While there are differences in the materials and techniques used the following method is typical.

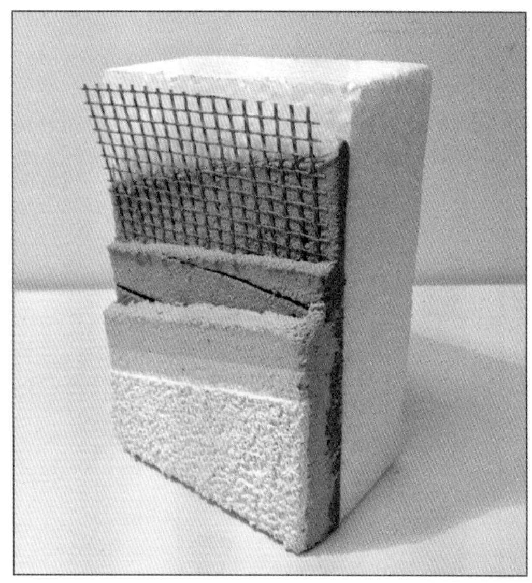

15.10 Proprietary render applied to EPS insulation.

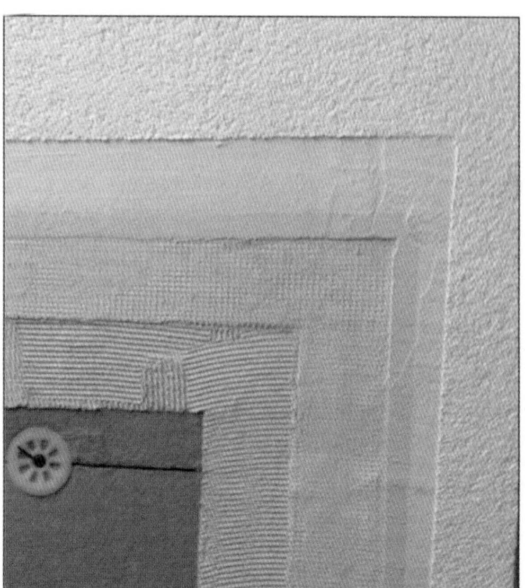

15.11 Proprietary render applied to wood fibre external insulation (Gutex). *Source*: taken by author at Ecological Building Systems.

Method

Base coat:

- a base coat is applied with a serrated trowel to provide a key for the following coat
- allowed to dry.

Undercoat with reinforcement mesh:

- uPVC corner beads are installed to protect the corners and the edges of the reveals
- a thin layer of undercoat is applied
- a reinforcement mesh (e.g. fibreglass mesh) is pressed into the undercoat
- another thin layer of undercoat is immediately applied (wet on wet) to achieve the appropriate thickness (e.g. 4–6mm)
- allowed to set.

Primer:

- some systems require a coat of primer paint to seal the undercoat and prevent rapid drying of the finish coat.

Finish coat:

- finish coat is applied to achieve the desired overall minimum thickness (e.g. 8–12mm).

Finish coats are usually available in various grain sizes (i.e. textures) and colours. They usually contain compounds that give them flexibility, breathability and water resistance.

Plastering

Plastering is the term used to describe the application of a surface finish to an internal wall. Plastering also functions as the airtightness layer in masonry external walls. Gypsum-based plaster is the most commonly used material for plastering.

Plastering blockwork

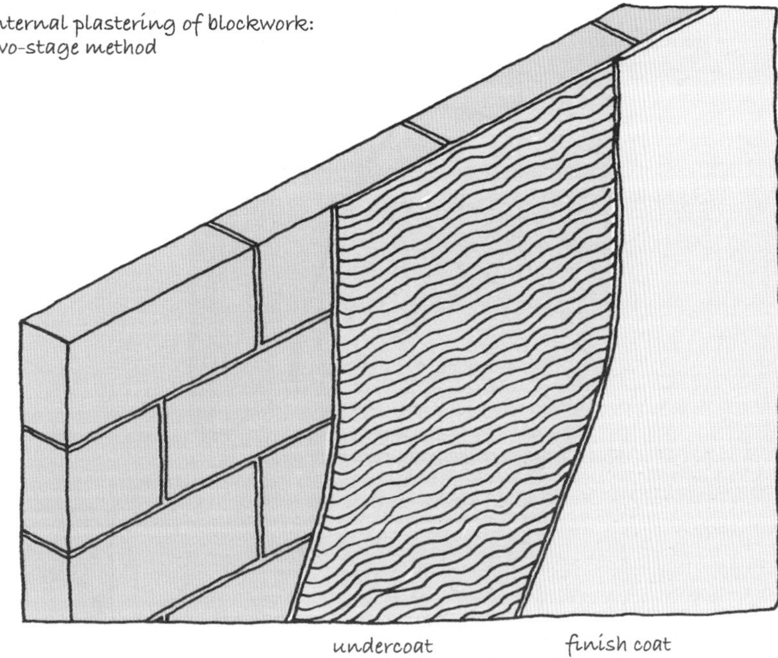

15.12 Plastering blockwork.

Method:

Base coat:

- a gypsum undercoat plaster 9mm thick is applied
- when the scratch coat is set firm (but before it hardens) it should be combed or scratched to provide a key for the final coat
- allowed to set.

Final coat:

- a finish coat of a gypsum plaster 2–3mm thick is applied and finished smooth with a steel float.

Plastering plasterboard

There are two methods that can be used to apply a finish to plasterboard:

- wet method – one or two coats of plaster are applied
- dry method – nail/screw heads are filled and joints are taped.

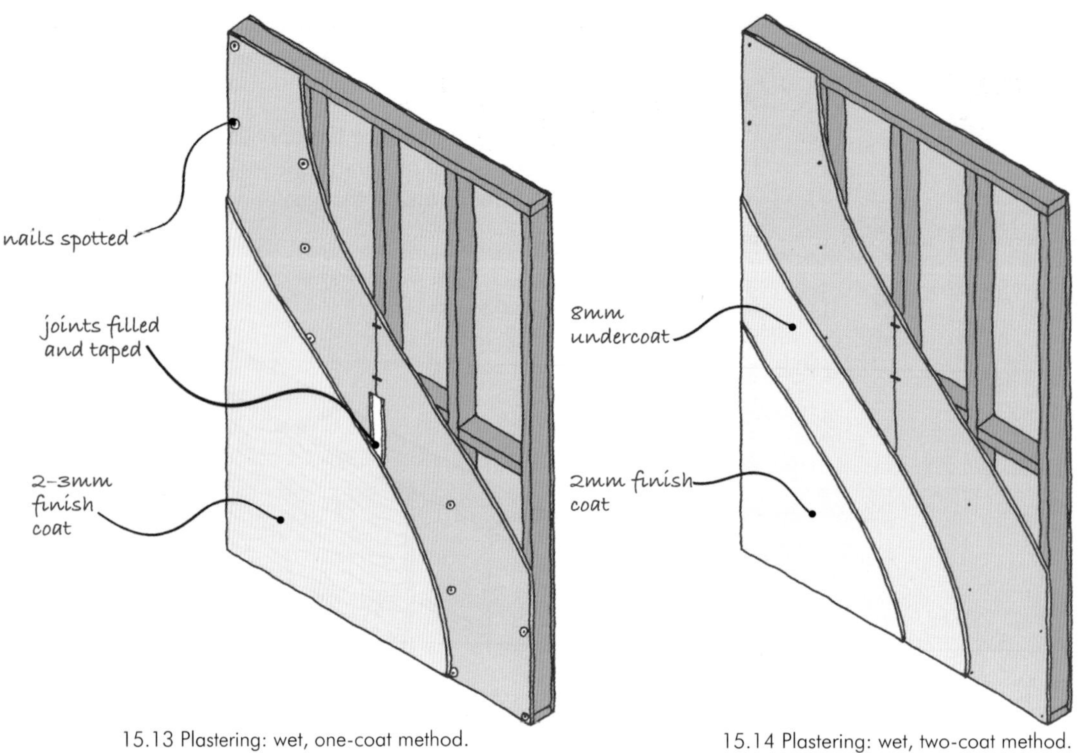

15.13 Plastering: wet, one-coat method.

15.14 Plastering: wet, two-coat method.

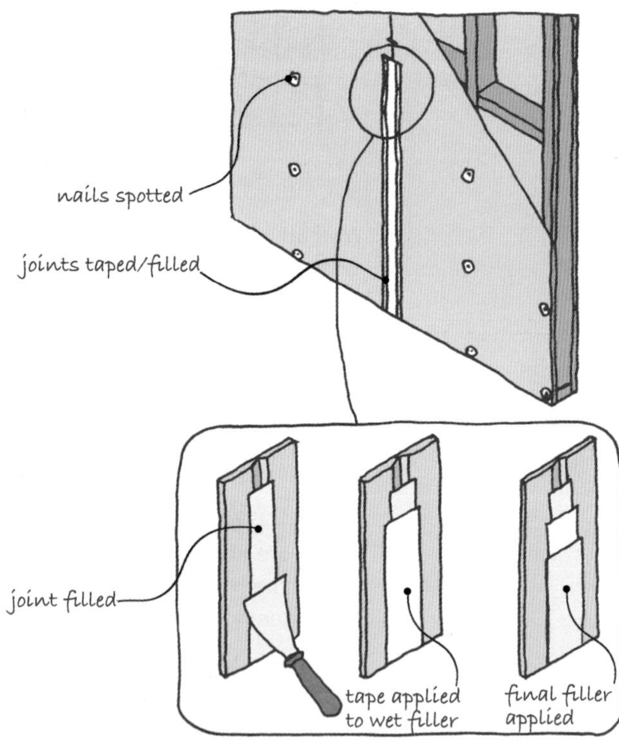

15.15 Plastering: dry method.

REVISION EXERCISES

1 Outline the factors that influence wall design.
2 Explain the functions of wall ties in masonry cavity walls.
3 Describe, using a neat freehand sketch, how the components of a timber frame wall with a rainscreen prevent moisture penetration by wind-driven rain.
4 Explain, using neat freehand sketches, how airtightness is achieved in a timber frame system designed to Passivhaus standard.
5 Describe the method used to apply a cement-based render to a blockwork wall.

CHAPTER 16

Roofs

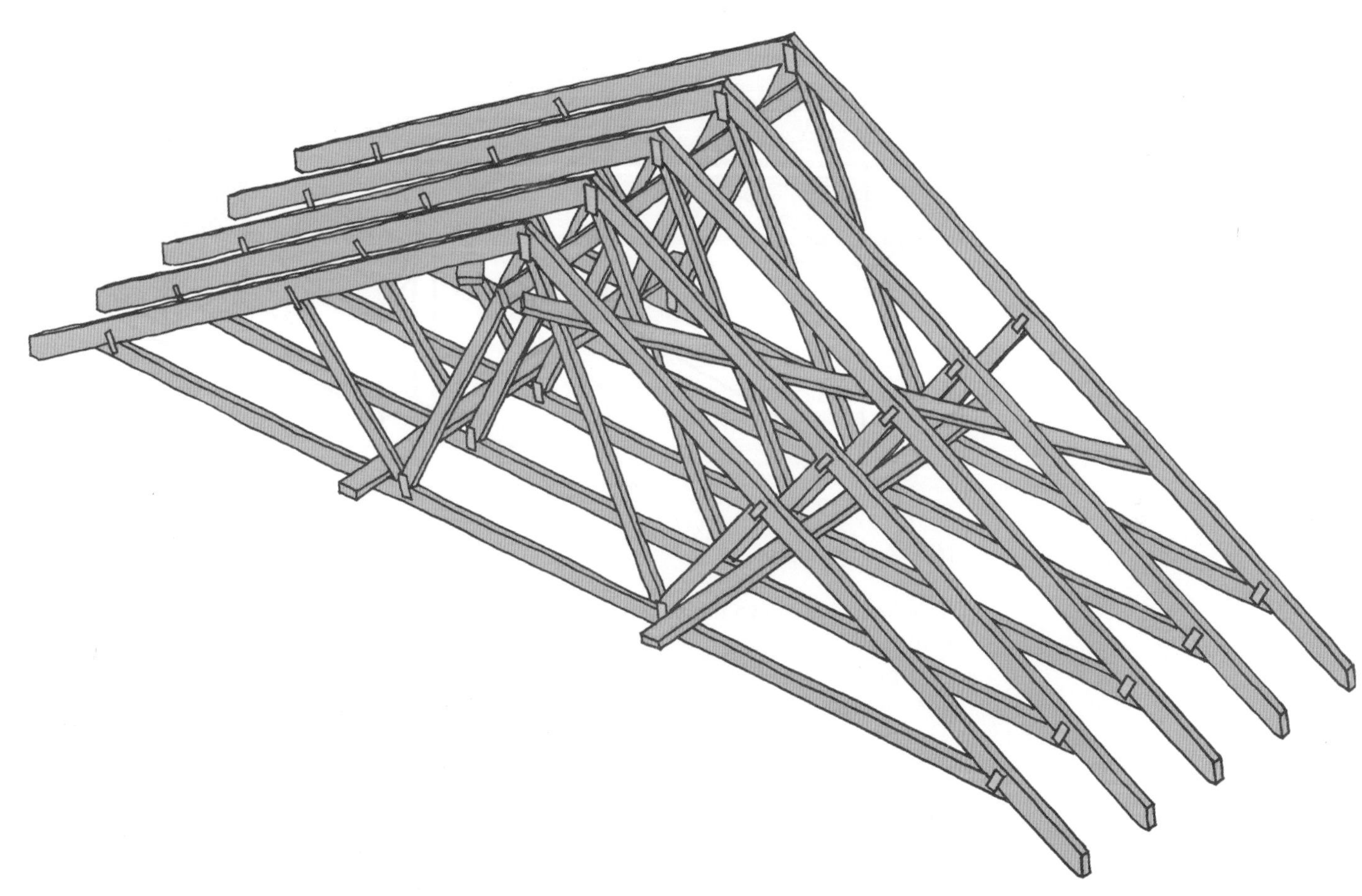

The first decision to be made when designing a roof is its pitch (i.e. slope). High-slope roofs are best suited to the Irish climate – pitch angles vary but most pitches are between 25° and 45°. A low-slope roof (also known as a flat roof) has a slope of up to 10°.

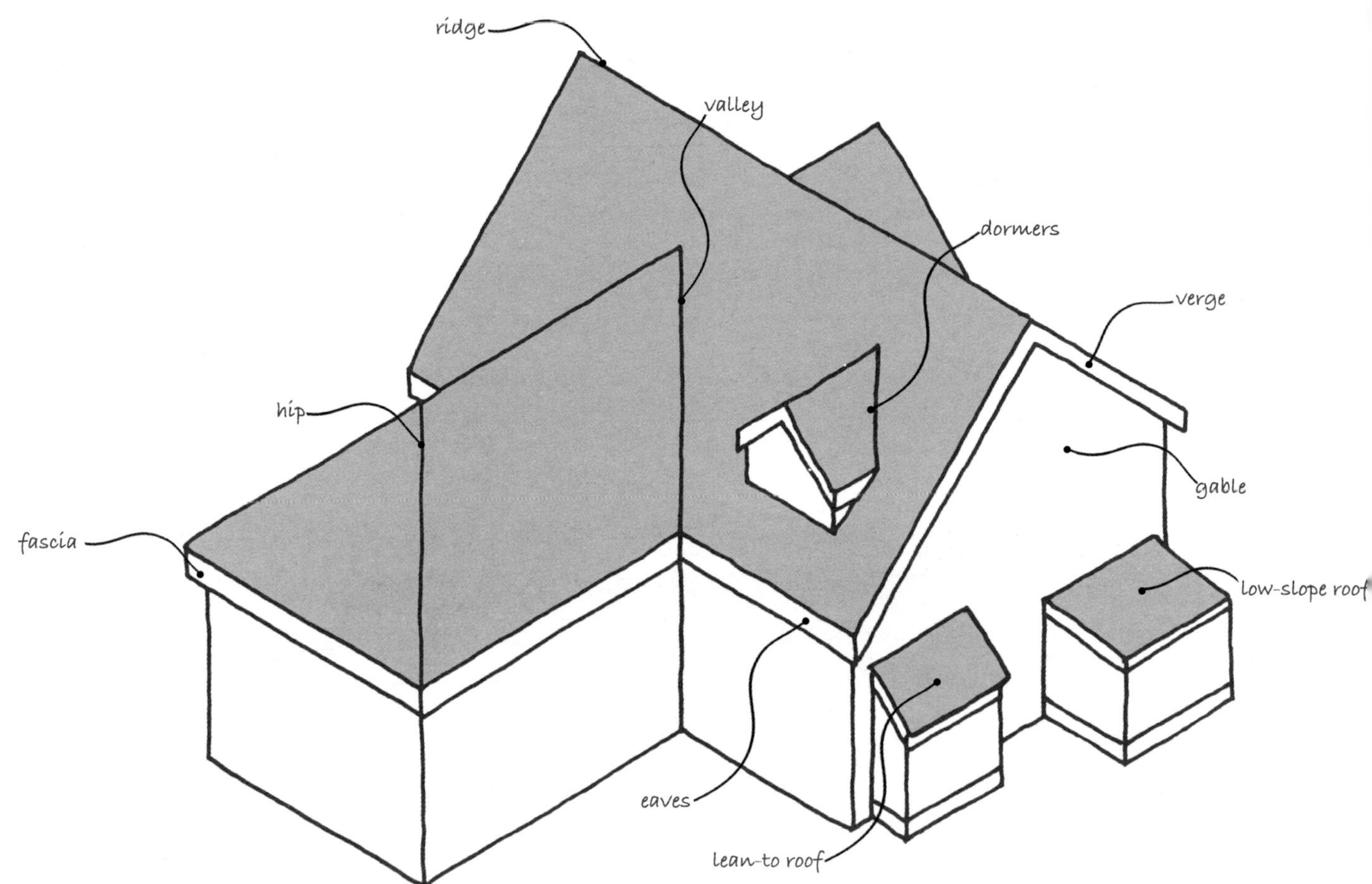

16.01 Roof terminology.

A roof consists of two main elements:

- roof structure:
  - purlin roof – traditional high-slope timber roof cut and assembled on site
  - trussed roof – engineered timber roof trusses designed and made in a factory and installed on site
  - flat roof – joists and decking cut and assembled on site.
- roof covering:
  - tile/slate – slate, clay, concrete, etc.
  - sheet – bitumen felt, waterproof membranes, zinc, etc.
  - green (living) – sedum, grass or other planting.

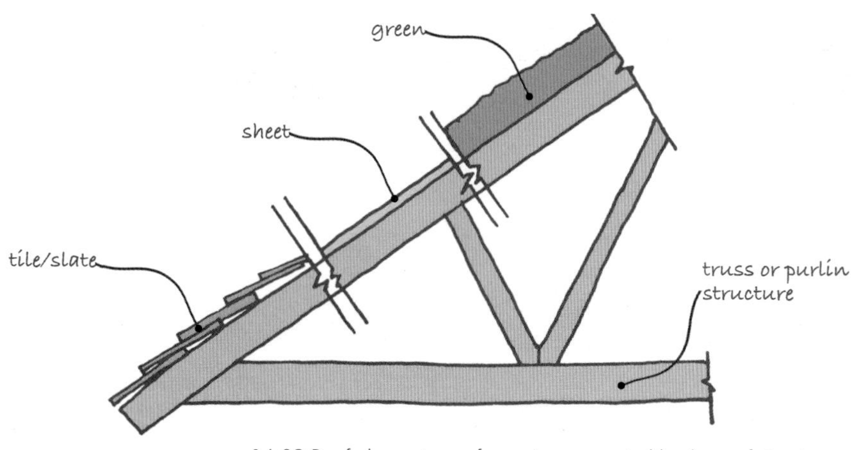

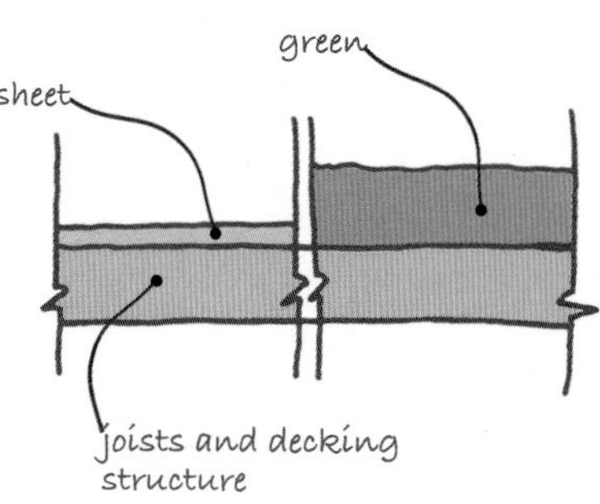

16.02 Roof elements: roof covering supported by the roof structure.

Functions

The primary function of the roof is to create a comfortable indoor environment by keeping the 'weather' out and maintaining a comfortable indoor temperature. Every climate brings particular challenges. In Ireland the main concern is rain, particularly wind-driven rain. For this reason, a pitched roof is the norm because the slope of a pitched roof is ideal for shedding rainwater. A well-designed and well-constructed roof should perform its functions and be maintenance free so as to avoid the hazards linked to carrying out maintenance work at height.

Factors influencing roof design

The structural design of a roof depends on several elements:

- climate – wind and snow load can be severe in certain climates
- one-off houses – it can be cheaper to manufacture the roof on site (purlin roof)
- span – roofs built for wide spans require careful engineering design
- living space – an 'attic' bedroom or other room requires space to be left clear
- floor plan – self-supporting roofs (e.g. truss) allow flexibility in room layout by avoiding the need for internal load-bearing walls
- form – the shape of the roof will influence the structural design.

Performance criteria for roofs

When designing a roof it is essential to consider all of the performance requirements expected of it, including:

- sustainability – roofs should be built using durable natural materials with a low embodied energy
- structural stability – the roof should be able to safely transmit the permanent actions (e.g. self weight) and variable actions (e.g. wind or snow load) imposed on it
- durability – a roof should be designed to be long-lasting and maintenance free
- weather resistance – it must withstand extremes of temperature and the actions of wind, rain and snow
- airtightness – some part of the roof structure (usually the ceiling) will be part of the airtightness layer and must be airtight
- fire resistance – it should resist the spread of fire (this is especially important in semi-detached or terraced dwellings)
- thermal resistance – the roof should be well insulated to prevent the loss of thermal energy and contribute to the overall energy efficiency of the home
- aesthetics – the form and finish (e.g. materials and eaves/verge treatments) of a roof should look appealing
- acoustic resistance – the roof should dampen noise to improve indoor acoustic comfort.

16.03 Sustainable roofing materials: the arched roof of this certified passive house built in southeast England is made from clay tiles. The clay was sourced from a nearby quarry and the tiles were manufactured in a local factory.

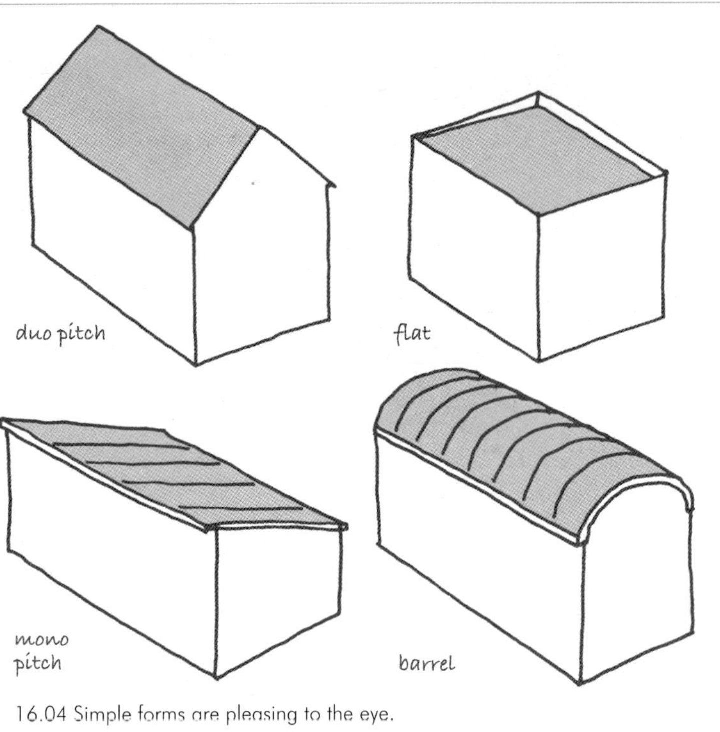

16.04 Simple forms are pleasing to the eye.

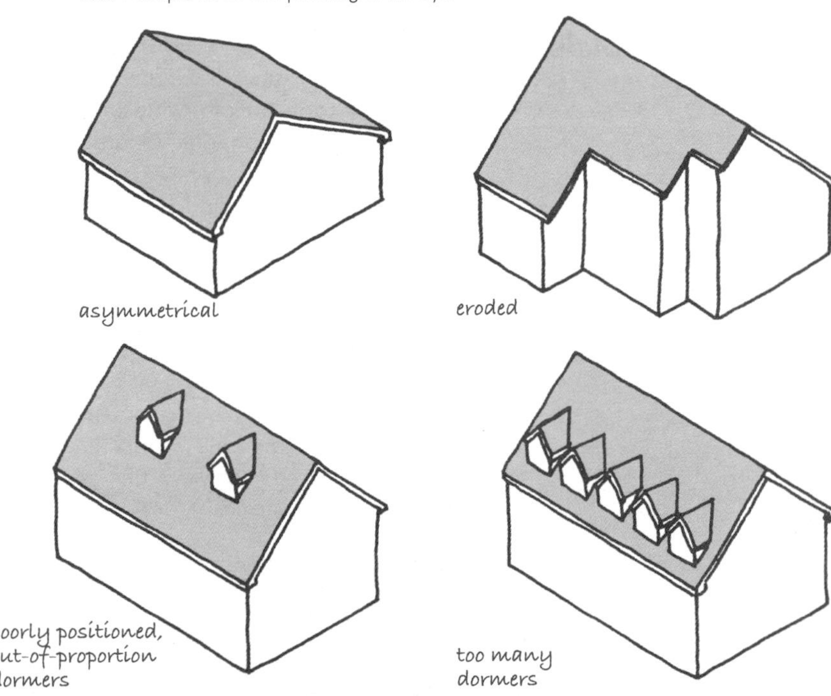

16.05 Form: the form of the roof has a significant impact on the overall appearance of a home. Common mistakes include asymmetric forms, eroded forms and roofs that include poorly designed dormer windows.

16.06 Roof finishes: natural slate.

16.07 Roof finishes: cement fibre slate.

16.08 Roof finishes: clay tile (smooth, flat 'terracotta' colour).

16.09 Roof finishes: concrete tile (flat, grey or navy colour).

16.10 Roof finishes: zinc.

16.11 Roof finishes: green (planted).

High-slope roof structures

There are two main types of high-slope roof structure: a traditional purlin roof and a truss roof.

Purlin roof

The traditional purlin roof is custom made on site to suit an individual house. This type of roof is less commonly used now because it is slow to construct and uses timber less efficiently. Purlin roofs tend to be 'over engineered', using more timber than a comparable truss roof.

The principle of triangulation is used to distribute the actions evenly through the members: this ensures the stability of the roof structure. The purlin runs along the length of the roof supporting the rafters at their midpoint. The purlin transfers the load from the rafters through the strut to the straining piece. The straining piece experiences equal but opposite loads from both sides of the roof structure. The central portion of the roof structure is supported by an internal load-bearing wall. Both the collar and the ceiling joist are in tension as they resist the tendency of the rafters to spread outwards. The hanger is also in tension as it 'pulls up' the ceiling joist at the midpoint of its span to prevent deflection (i.e. sagging) of the ceiling.

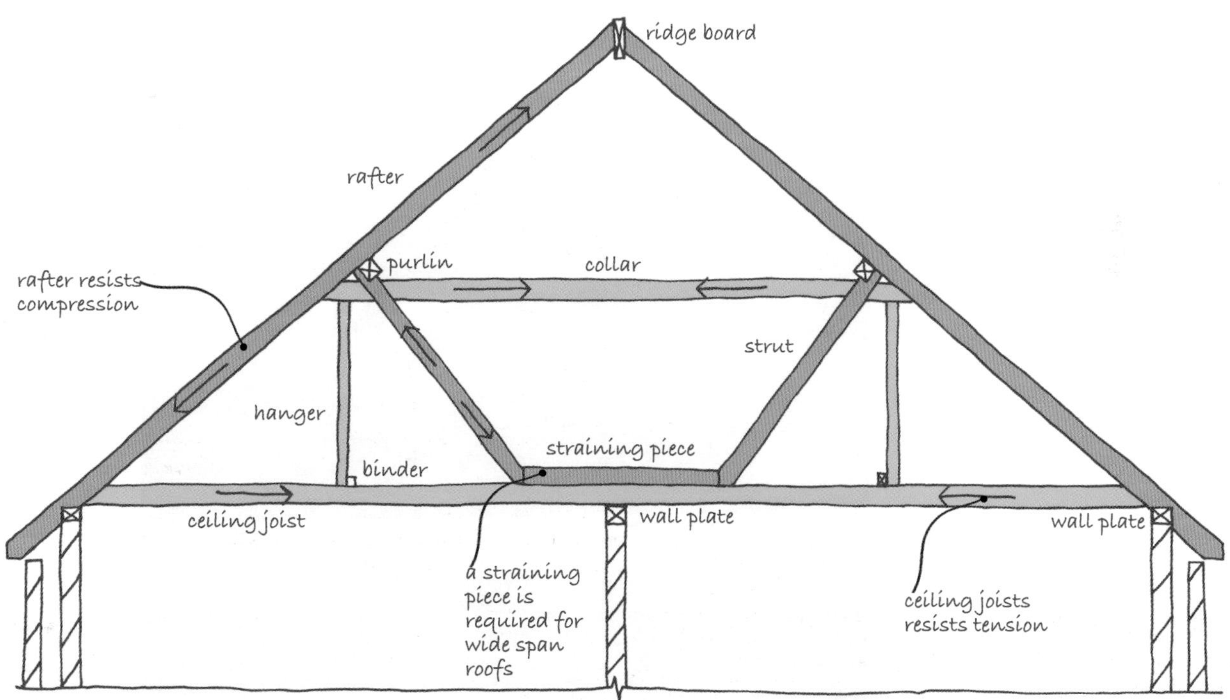

16.12 Traditional purlin roof: actions are transferred through the members to the load-bearing walls below. Some members are in tension (green) and some are in compression (blue).

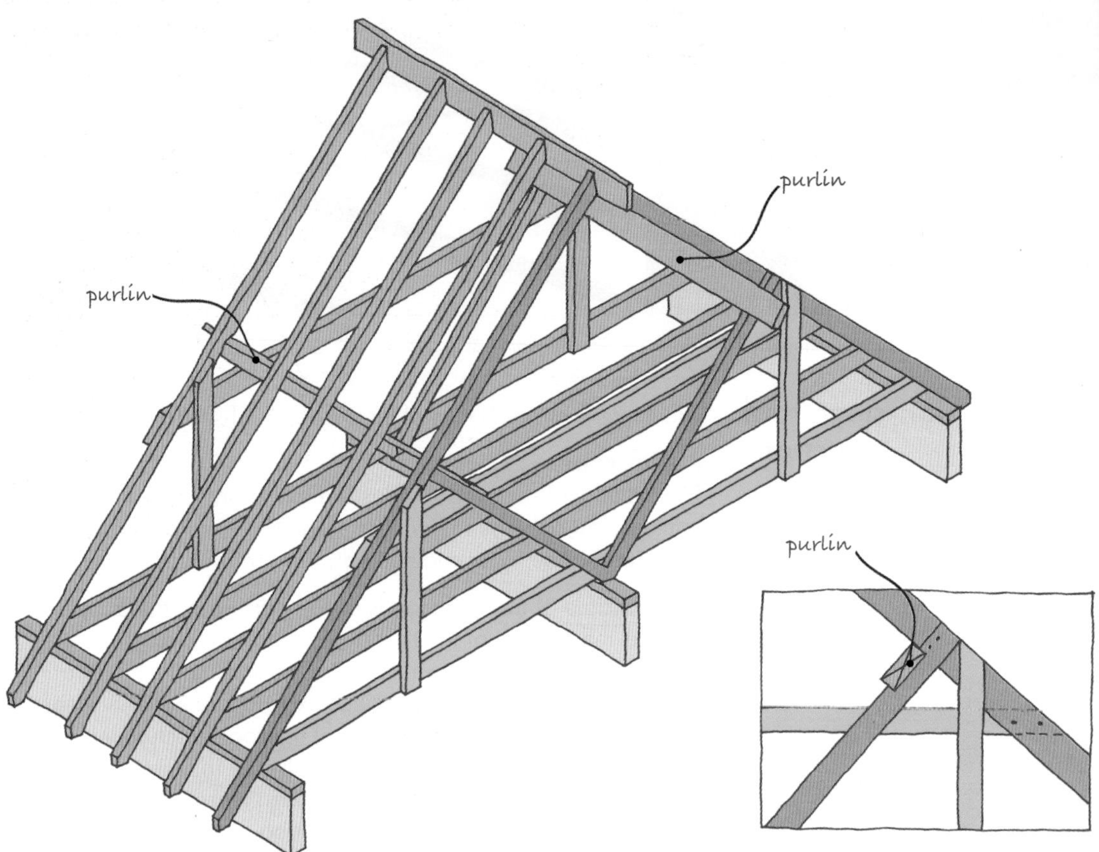

16.13 Purlin roof: the purlin supports the rafters midway along their length. The internal load-bearing wall is essential to this type of roof structure.

16.14 Purlin roof: in this roof under construction, the purlin can be seen here supported by two struts.

Where a living space is required in the roof the purlin is supported on a vertical strut. The strut is supported on a double joist (or engineered joist or rolled steel joist) which rests on the load-bearing walls.

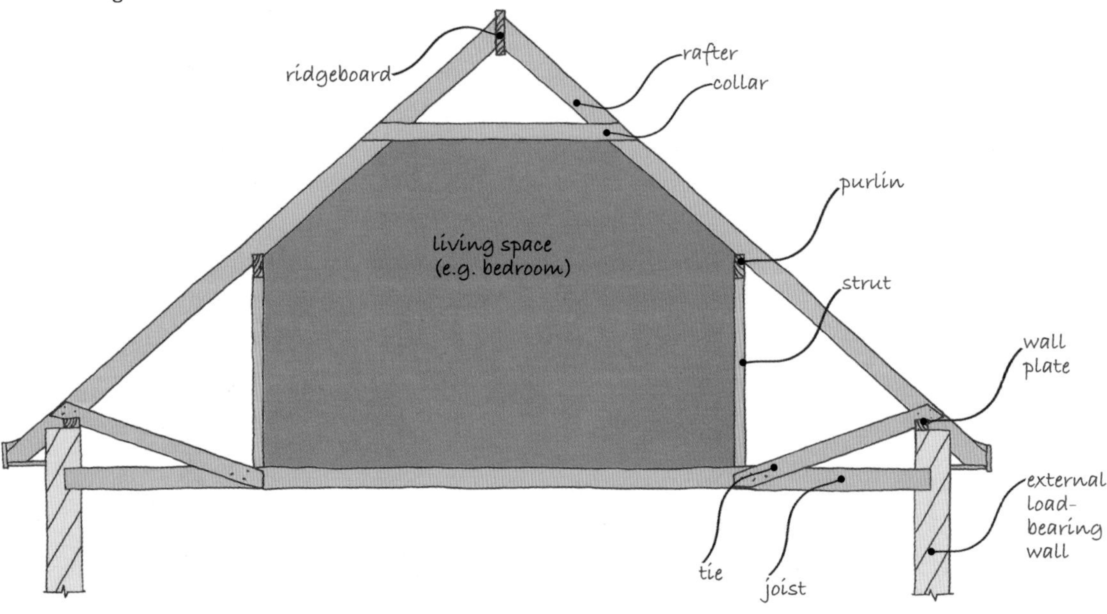

16.15 Purlin roof: living space – joist below wall plate.

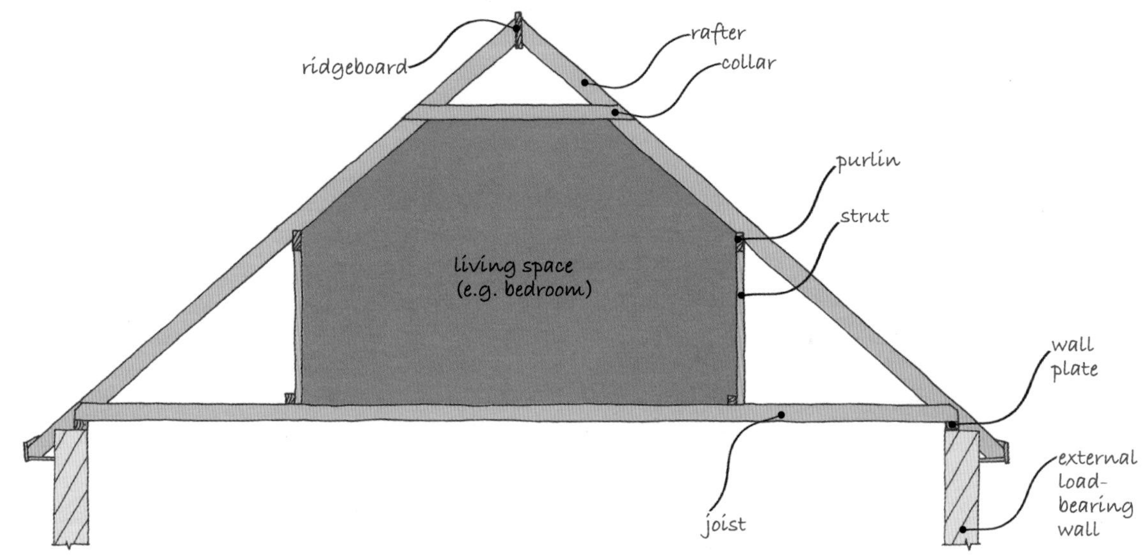

16.16 Purlin roof: living space – joist above wall plate.

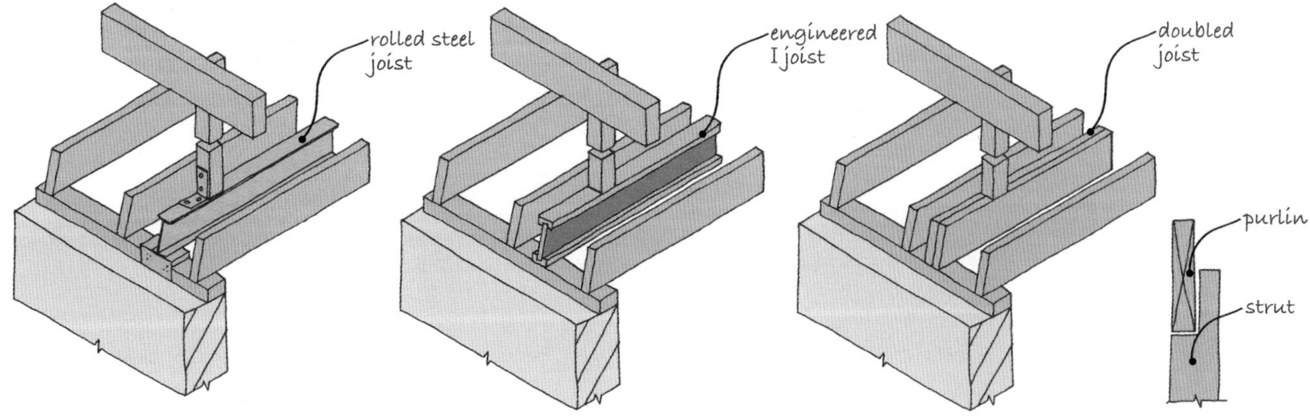

16.17 Purlin roof: living space – the load is transferred from the purlin to the strut, to a rolled steel joist or an engineered I joist or double joist.

Truss roof

A truss roof is designed and manufactured in a factory to meet the specific requirements of the roof design (e.g. span, pitch, spacing, exposure, loading (i.e. type of covering) etc.), so as to make the most efficient use of timber. Truss manufacturers must comply with strict standards governing the sizing of timbers to be used in roof trusses.

The chords and webs are butt jointed using galvanised steel nail plates. This engineered design does not require the use of ridge boards, collars, purlins and hangers.

When installed, the trusses are secured to the wall plate or head plate with truss clips. This is essential to prevent uplift of the roof by the wind. The trusses are linked to each other by diagonal bracing and longitudinal binders.

Truss roofs are capable of spanning from external wall to external wall without the need for internal support. This gives greater freedom for the initial design of the internal layout and allows for future redesign should the needs of the occupants change.

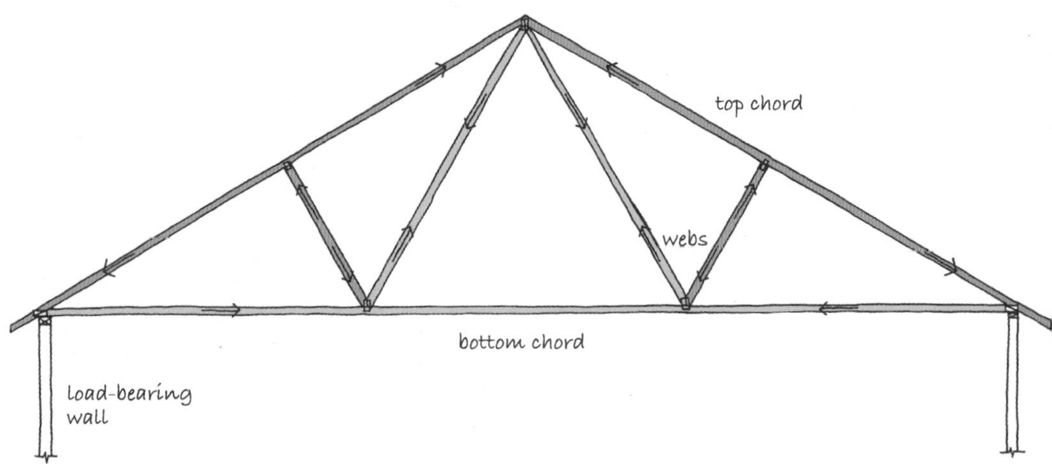

16.18 Trussed roof: a typical Fink truss suitable for spans up to 8m wide with a 30° pitch made using 35mm x 97mm components.

Where a living space is required in the roof a special attic truss is used. The top and bottom chords of an attic truss are approximately twice the width of a standard chord. This is to ensure that the truss can support the extra loads. In an attic truss all of the webs are in tension and all of the chords are in compression.

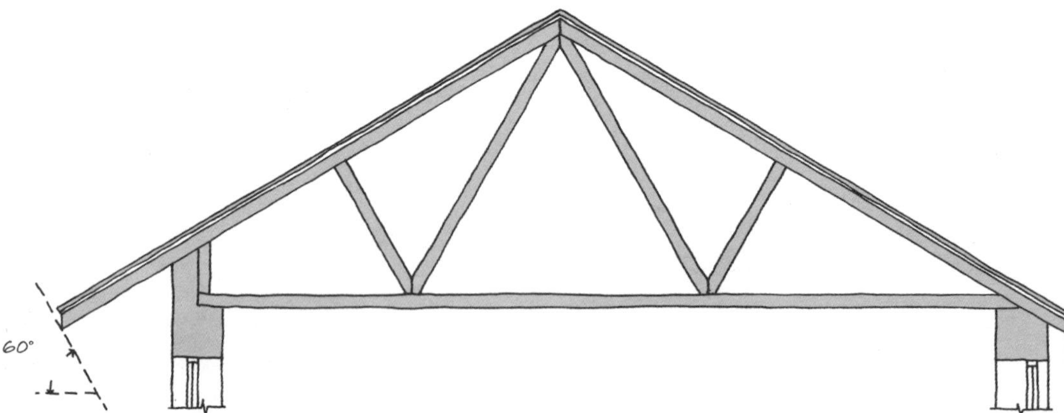

16.19 Bobtail truss: a specialist truss used where a deep overhang is required to provide shading to south-facing windows or to create more space for insulation at the eaves.

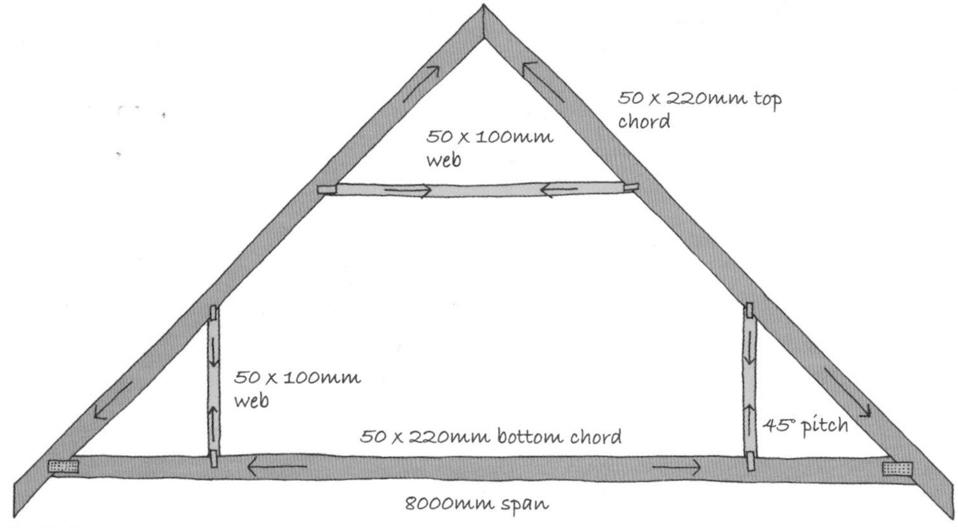

16.20 Attic truss: a typical attic truss for a 8m wide span with a 45° pitch will give a living space of approximately 5m wide with a full ceiling height (i.e. 2.4m) in the central area.

16.21 Trussed roof: a roof truss before fixing – note the nail plate connector.

16.22 Trussed roof: several Fink trusses before installation. Note the way the trusses span the full depth of the house without the need for internal support. Note also the hip truss at the back of the stack used to create the Dutch or barn hip end that can be seen on the roof in the background.

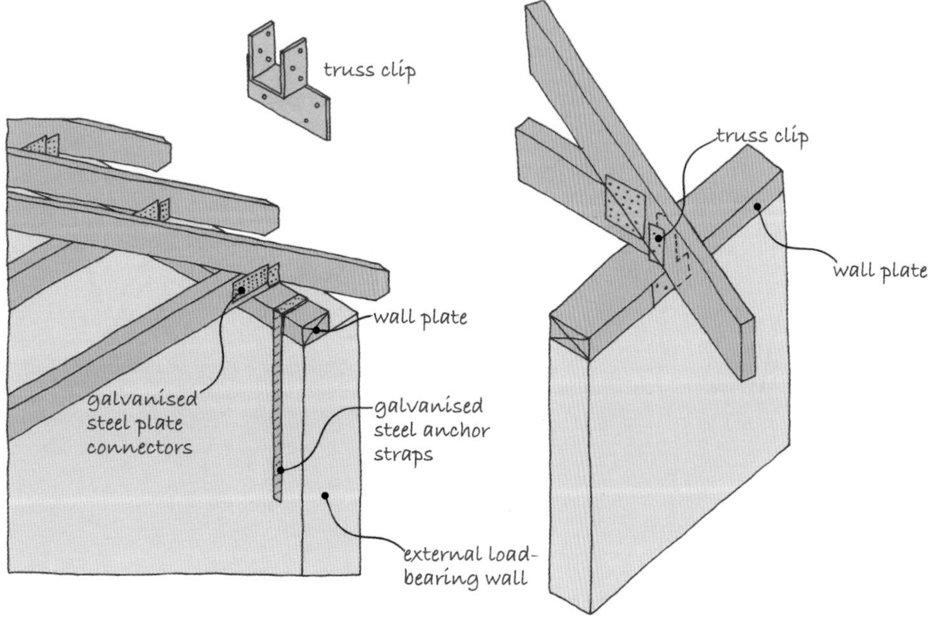

16.23 Truss fixing detail: the truss is secured to the outside face of the wall plate using galvanised steel truss clips; the wall plate is fixed to a concrete wall using galvanised steel straps.

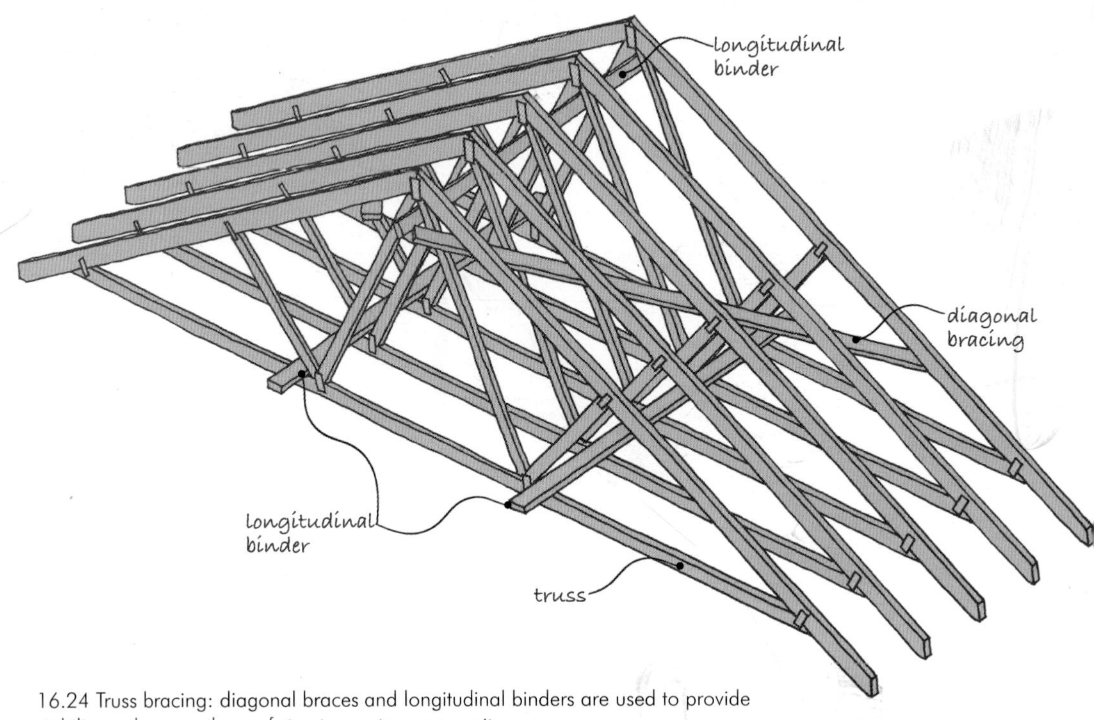

16.24 Truss bracing: diagonal braces and longitudinal binders are used to provide stability and ensure the roof structure acts as one unit.

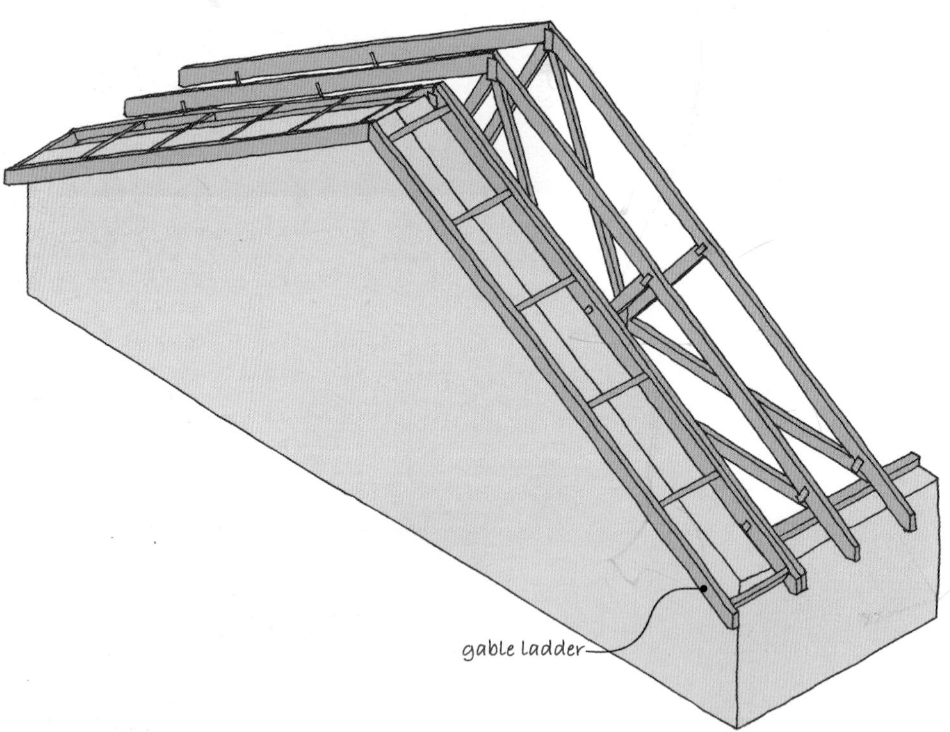

16.25 Verge detail: a gable ladder is used when a verge overhang is required.

Thermal resistance of high-slope roofs

While the building regulations standard and passive house standard for the thermal insulation of roofs are very similar, there is still a significant difference in relation to thermal bridging. This difference can be seen in the steps taken to prevent thermal bridging in the eaves details shown.

When insulating a typical pitched roof, there are two locations where the insulation can be installed: at ceiling joist level; or at rafter level. Insulating at the ceiling joists is the most common method. Insulating at rafter level is used when the roof space is needed as a living space (e.g. a bedroom).

In both cases the insulation is installed in two layers. The first layer is usually laid between the timbers (i.e. joist or rafters) and the second layer is laid perpendicularly across the first layer (either inside or outside). This prevents thermal bridging through the timber. It is essential that a vapour control layer is installed on the warm side of the insulation to prevent water vapour/moisture from entering the insulation.

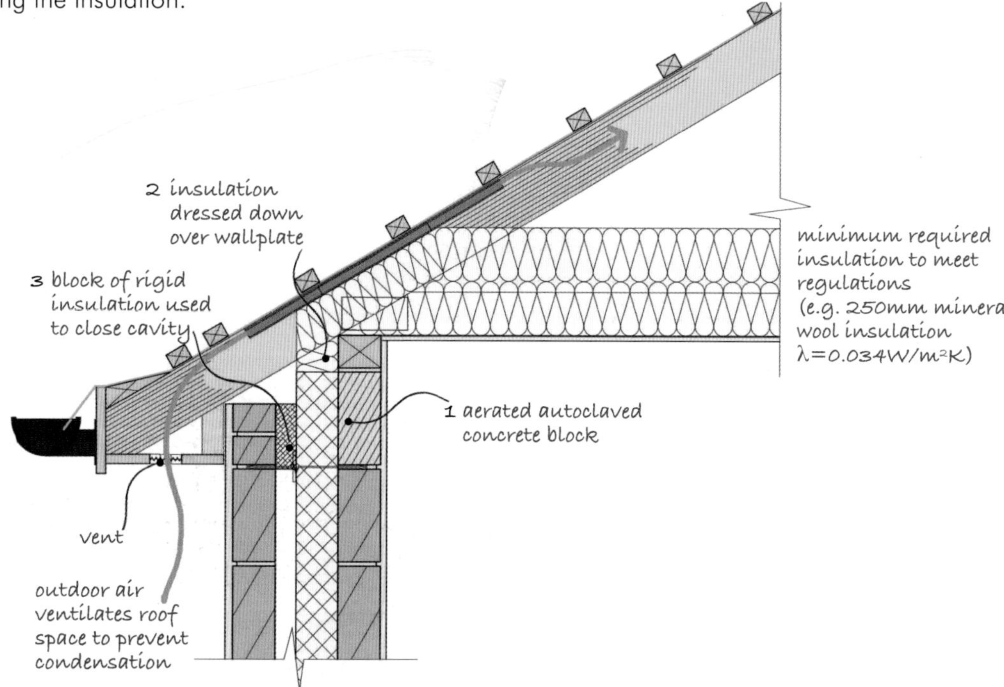

16.26 Thermal resistance (building regulations standard): three elements combine to prevent thermal bridging at the wall–roof junction. There is more insulation in the attic compared to the walls because the U-value requirement for the roof is lower (roof: 0.16W/m^{2}K, wall: 0.21W/m^{2}K).

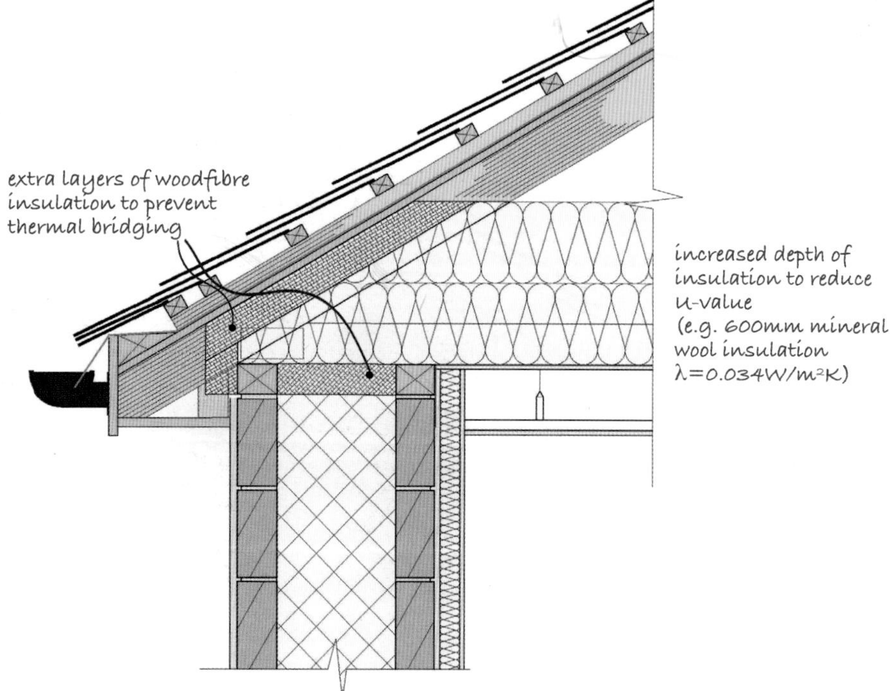

16.27 Thermal resistance (Passivhaus standard): extra layers of external insulation is installed to prevent thermal bridging at the wall–roof junction.

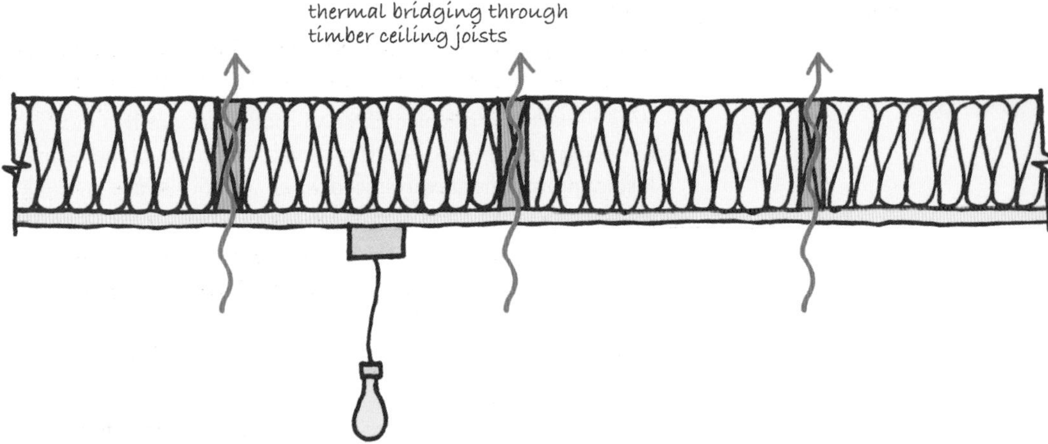

16.28 Thermal bridging through a typical ceiling.

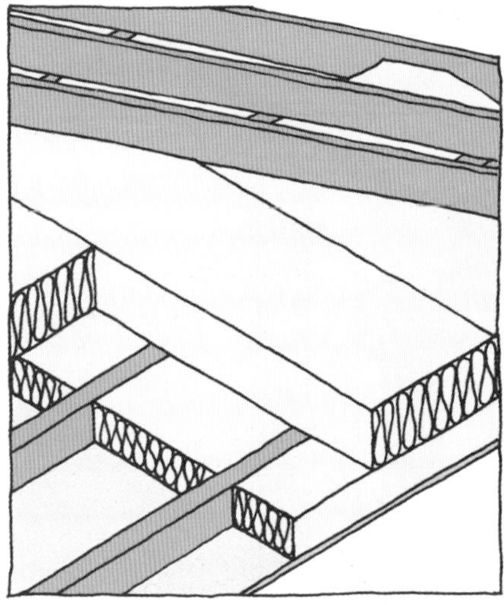

16.29 Thermal insulation of a roof: mineral or natural fibre insulation placed in two layers at ceiling joist level.

- (10) Airtightness layer
- (34) Rafter/top chord (truss)
- (35) Roofing underlay (breather membrane/ windtight layer)
- (36) 50x50mm timber batten
- (38) Plasterboard
- (39) Quilted insulation
- (40) Oriented strand board
- (50) Batt insulation
- (53) Slates
- (75) Service cavity

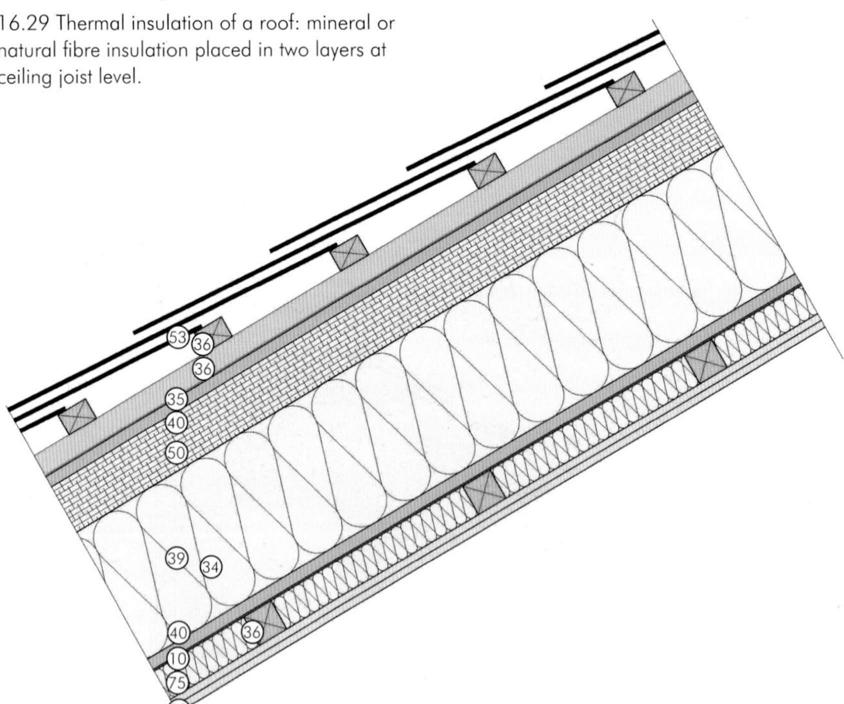

16.30 Insulation of a timber roof (i.e. traditional cut roof or trussed roof): insulation at rafter level. Approximately 250mm of a typical mineral or natural fibre insulant should meet the building regulations requirement.

Roof coverings

Slate

Natural slate is a traditional roof covering widely used in Ireland, where it blends well with the landscape and other houses. Fibre cement slates are a lightweight, cheaper alternative to natural slate that are manufactured in Ireland. Fibre cement slates are thin and smooth and are available in a variety of colours.

The slates must be securely installed to prevent the loss of slates in windy weather. The procedure for installing fibre cement and natural slates is quite similar. Slates are installed by nailing each slate through two holes provided approximately halfway up the slate. Nailing slates at their centre holds them more securely than head nailing, thereby reducing the likelihood of breakage (due to wind vibration) during severe weather.

While fibre cement and concrete slates are supplied with nail holes, nail holes are created in natural slates on-site. The holes are always made on the bed (underside) of the slate and positioned so that the thinner end of the slate is at the top when fixed. The holes are punched out so that a small countersunk depression in the face of the slate is created – this accommodates the head of the fixing nail. Two holes are created in each slate.

The battens are installed at a gauge (spacing) to suit the slates being used. The gauge length is calculated using the formula:

$$\text{gauge length} = \frac{\text{length of slate} - \text{headlap}}{2}$$

Slates are laid in courses beginning at the eaves. One (or two) courses of undereaves slates are laid first. An undereaves slate is a shortened slate laid to provide a lift to the tail of the first course. This is done to ensure that the slates sit at the correct angle and do not droop downward toward the gutter. The first course of slates is usually raised slightly (10–25mm, depending on slate used) above the plane of the battens. Slates usually have a 100mm double headlap. A typical slate is 500–600mm. The sidelap should occur at the midpoint of the slate immediately below. The ridge of a natural slate roof is commonly finished using a ridge slate bedded in mortar or a composite ridge that is secured using screws.

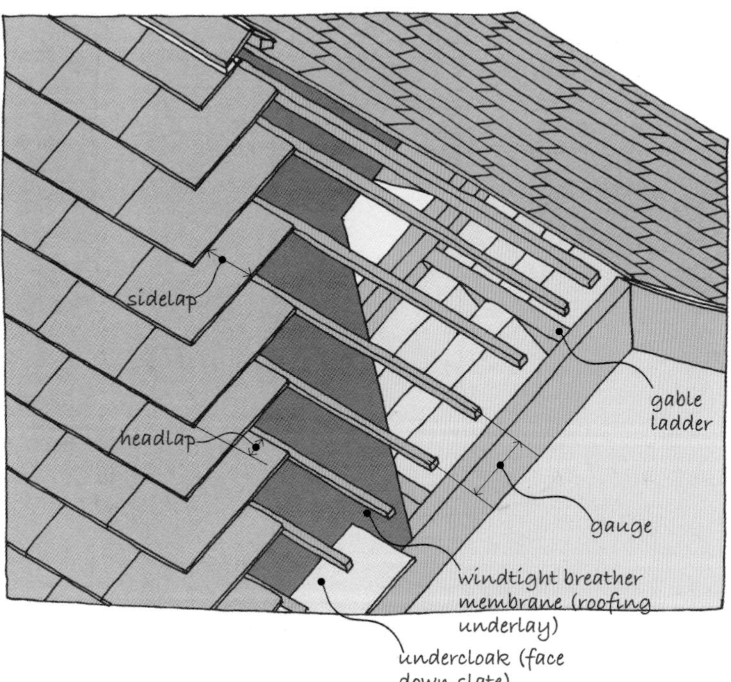

16.31 Slate roof covering: slates are laid in overlapping courses nailed to timber battens.

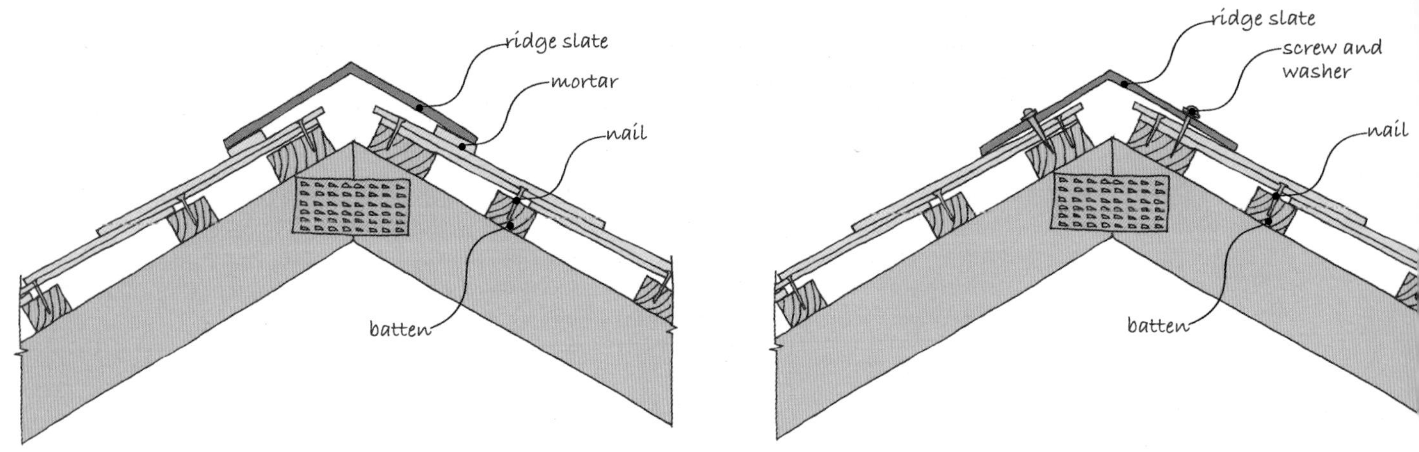

16.32 Ridge details: clay ridge slate secured using mortar.

16.33 Ridge details: clay ridge slate secured using stainless steel screws and washers.

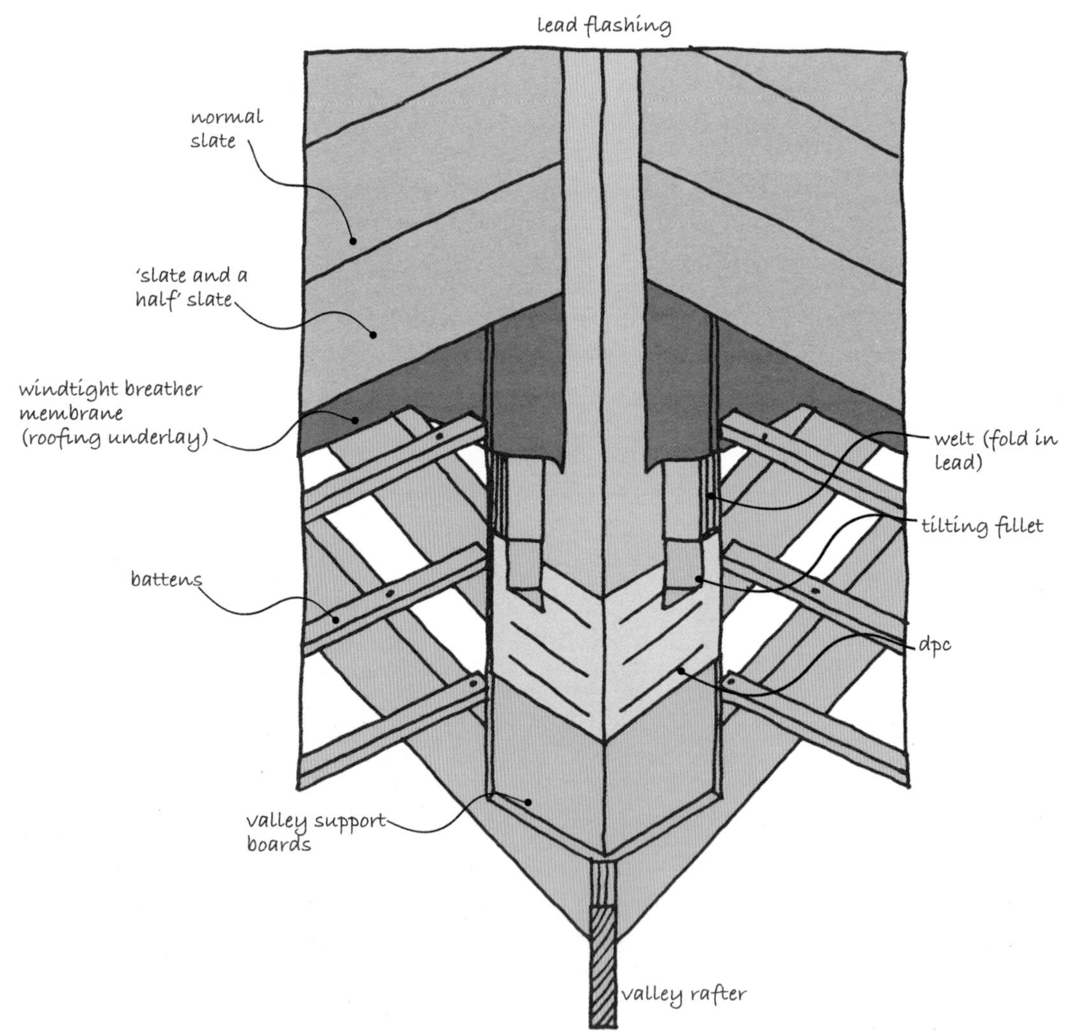

16.34 Valley detail: plastic damp proof course and lead lining combine to ensure that the valley remains watertight.

Sheet roof coverings

Sheet roof coverings include metals (e.g. zinc, copper, aluminium), synthetic elastomeric membranes (e.g. EPDM) and bituminous roofing felts and membranes. Each of these materials raises concerns about the source of raw materials (e.g. crude oil), production processes and embodied energy.

Traditionally, bituminous felt products were considered ahead of other sheet roofing products. However, there are a number of disadvantages to using bitumen products:

- bitumen is produced from crude oil and is not a sustainable construction material
- bitumen roofing felt becomes hard and brittle when exposed to sunlight (UV radiation)
- bitumen is highly flammable
- bitumen roofing products that are installed using heat may produce fumes that are harmful to health.

Zinc roofing

Zinc is a naturally occurring metal that is mined in Navan, Kilkenny and Tipperary. The mine at Lisheen, Co. Tipperary is the second largest zinc mine in Europe and approximately 40% of Europe's zinc supplies come from Ireland. The raw zinc concentrates are transported to Dublin and Cork, from where they are shipped to smelters around the world. Zinc is a recyclable product and more than 90% of the zinc used in the building industry is recycled. Zinc is naturally grey in colour and develops a patina over time, but colour-tinted versions are also available.

Zinc is commonly used as a coating to protect steel in a process called galvanisation. Galvanised steel corrugated roofing panels, gates and hardware (e.g. hinges, bolts) are commonly seen outdoor products. As well as its use as a coating, zinc can be used on its own as a roof covering. Sheet metal roof coverings are usually supplied in panels with preformed edges. These are installed down the slope of the roof and joined along their edges by folding the edges together to form a waterproof joint. This joint is called a standing seam. Proprietary clips are used to secure the sheets to the roof structure and these are hidden in the fold of the joints.

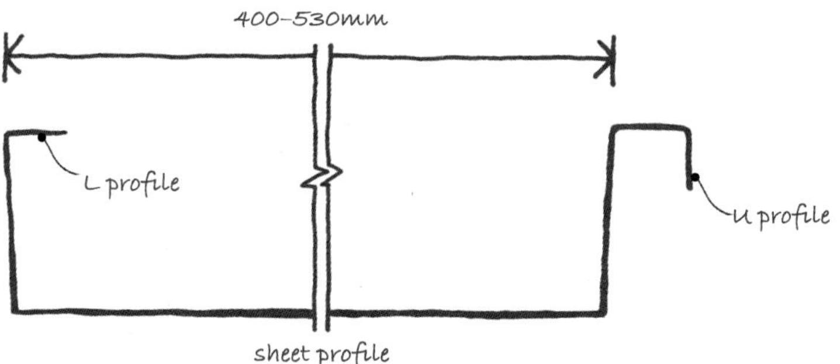

16.35 Zinc roofing: section through standing seam roof panel with preformed edges.

SUPPLEMENTARY INFORMATION

The clips used to secure the sheets are designed to allow the sheet to move along its length. It is important that the zinc is able to expand and contract freely. Typical zinc sheeting has a linear expansion of 0.022mm per metre and per degree centigrade.

In Ireland, the relevant temperature range is from –20°C in midwinter to +80°C on the surface of the zinc in the sun at the height of the summer. Assuming an ambient temperature of 20°C during installation, for a 10m length of material this means:

- summer:
  - plus 60°C (expansion)
  - 0.022mm x 10 x 60 = 13.2mm increase in length
- winter:
  - minus 40°C (contraction)
  - 0.022mm x 10 x 40 = 8.8mm decrease in length
- therefore, a 22mm change in length from summer to winter.

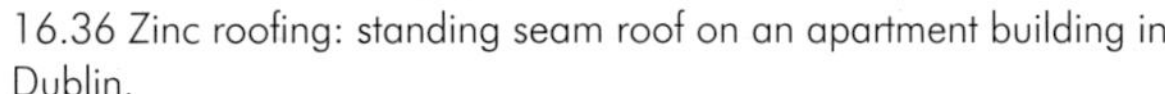

16.36 Zinc roofing: standing seam roof on an apartment building in Dublin.

16.37 Zinc roofing: standing seam roof on a house in rural Ireland.

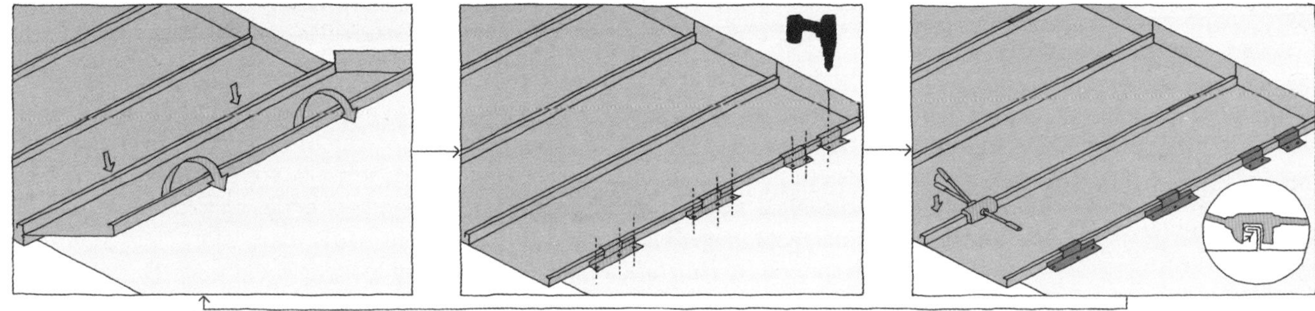

16.38 Zinc roofing: standing seam panel installation sequence.

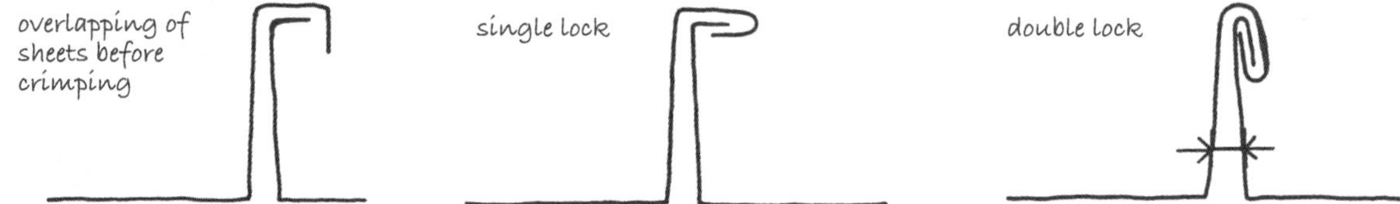

16.39 Zinc roofing: standing seam joint crimping sequence.

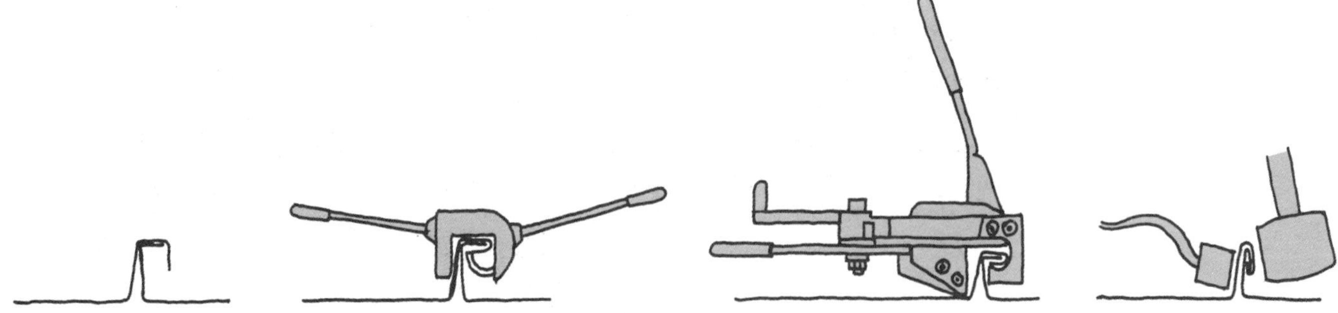

16.40 Zinc roofing: standing seam joint crimping tools and procedure.

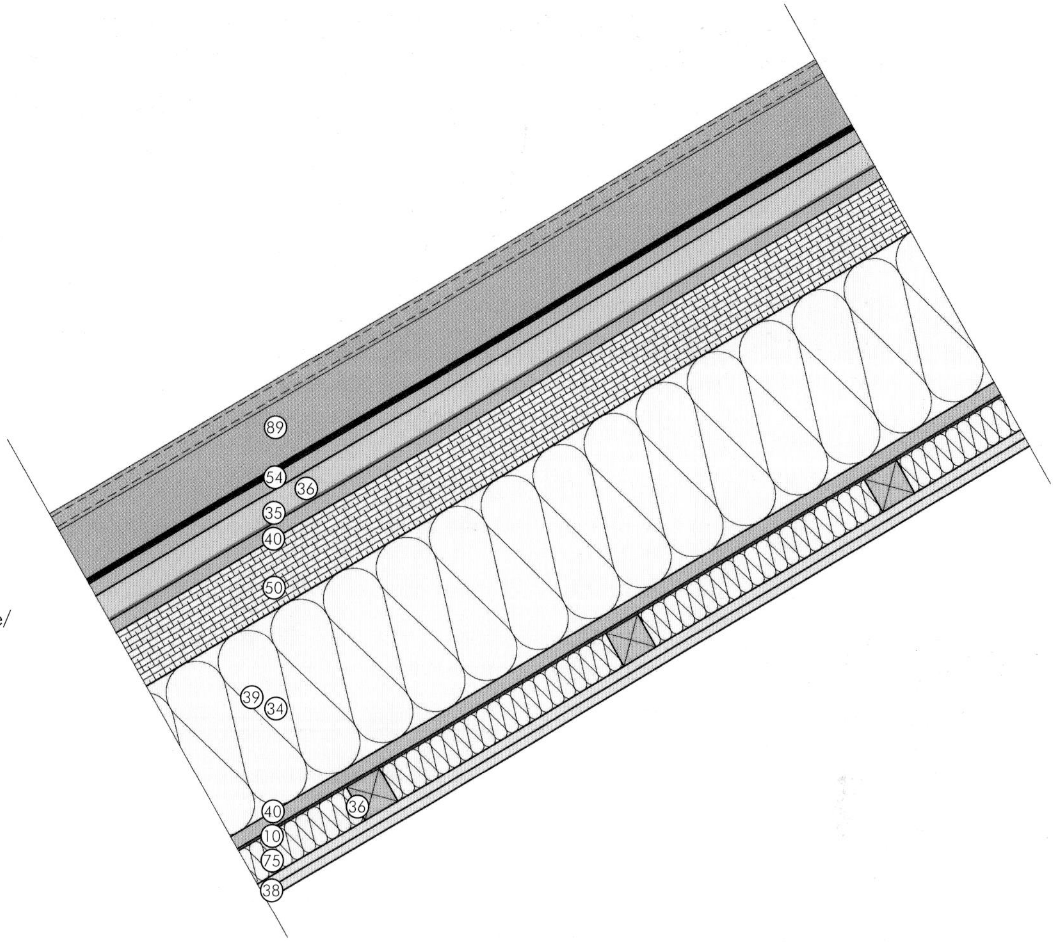

⑩ Airtightness layer
㉞ Rafter/top chord (truss)
㉟ Roofing underlay (breather membrane/ windtight layer)
㊱ 50x50mm timber batten
㊳ Plasterboard
㊴ Quilted insulation
㊵ Oriented strand board
㊿ Batt insulation
54 Sarking board
75 Service cavity
89 Sheet roof covering (e.g. zinc)

16.41 Zinc roofing: section through sloped roof with zinc covering.

Low-slope roof structures

Low-slope roofs are usually used for aesthetic reasons; to give a house a particular look that suits the style of the design. Low-slope roofs are an economical way of roofing a garage or a small extension to a house. The low pitch angle of this design makes it more susceptible to water penetration than other roofs.

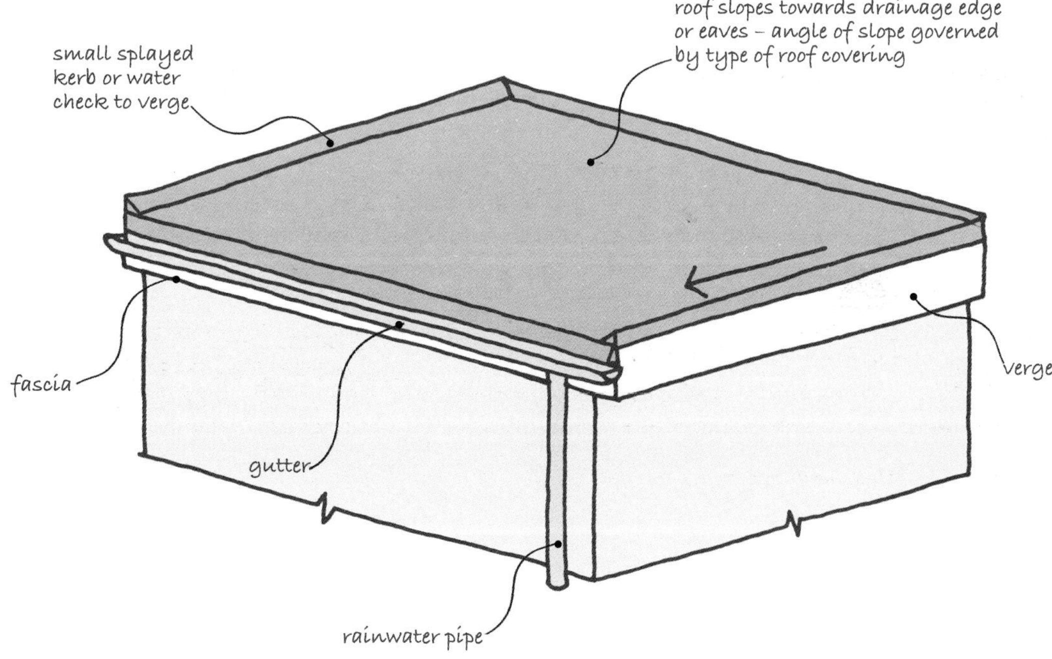

16.42 Low-slope (flat) roof terminology.

Components

A low-slope roof is a buildup of several layers of materials.

- **protection layer** – prevents damage to the waterproofing layer or insulation
- **waterproofing layer** – prevents water penetrating the structure
- **thermal insulation** – prevents heat loss and ensures the roof structure remains warm
- **decking** – provides a surface on to which the insulation and waterproofing layer are installed
- **load-bearing structure** – transmits the loads acting on the roof to the load-bearing walls
- **airtightness layer** – provides airtightness and vapour control to prevent interstitial condensation and reduce heat loss
- **ceiling** – provides an internal finish and protects the roof from fire.

Pitch

A low-slope roof is not flat, it is sloped. It must be sloped to ensure that rainwater doesn't sit on the roof. The term 'flat roof' is misleading and should be avoided.

A low-slope roof has a maximum pitch of 10°. The minimum required slope of the roof depends on the roof covering:

- metal covering (e.g. aluminium, copper or zinc) would typically require a minimum slope of 1:60
- built-up roof covering (e.g. asphalt or bitumen) would require a minimum slope of 1:80.

Both of these slopes (1:60 and 1:80) are less than 1°; in practice a minimum slope of 1:40 (1.5° approx.) is recommended.

16.43 Low-slope roof design: a minimum 1:40 pitch is recommended.

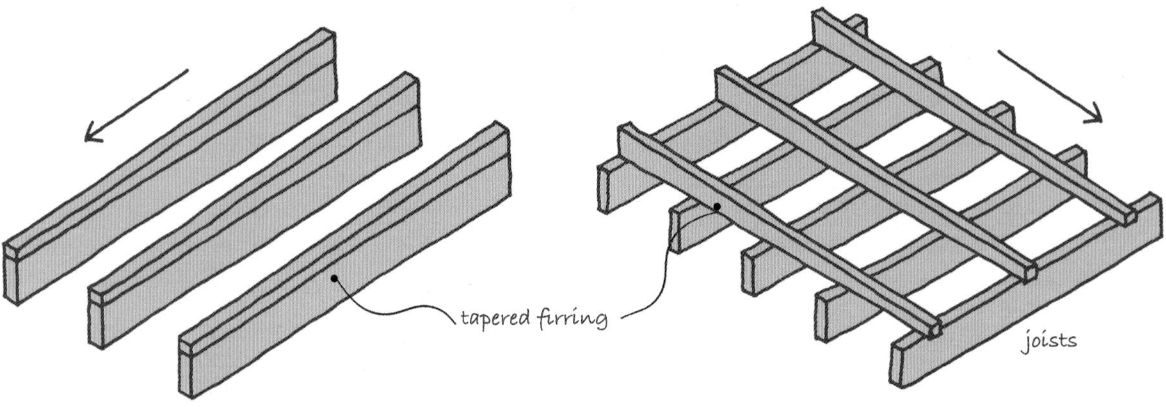

16.44 Low-slope roof construction: tapered firring pieces are used to provide a slope.

Low-slope roof coverings

The roof covering for a flat roof is usually made up of one or more layers of a sheet material. The material should be durable and weathertight. It should resist the action of wind, rain, snow and ice and should prevent water from entering the building. Several types of roof coverings are available:

- **bitumen membrane** – a polymer or glass fibre reinforced bitumen sheet material laid in two or three layers
- **mastic asphalt** – a hot liquid applied in two 10mm coats
- **single-ply membranes** – EPDM (rubber) sheet that is glued or screwed to the roof surface
- **metal sheet** – copper, zinc, lead or aluminium sheets
- **green roof** – a planted roof surface.

Vapour compensation layer

Many roof coverings are susceptible to blistering caused by the localised build-up of water vapour pressure under the roof covering. This can happen if water vapour penetrates the airtightness and vapour control layer. The vapour pressure works its way through the structure (e.g. through joints in the decking or insulation) until it emerges under the roof covering causing blisters. The impact of this localised build-up of pressure can be reduced by using a vapour compensation layer. A variety of products are available for this. A separate layer can be installed (e.g. perforated polymer felt sheet), or some roof covering products have a fleece or plastic raised mesh surface that performs as a vapour compensation layer. Irrespective of the product used, the goal is to allow the vapour to dissipate sideways instead of upwards. This will 'spread' the pressure over a wide area, thereby preventing blistering.

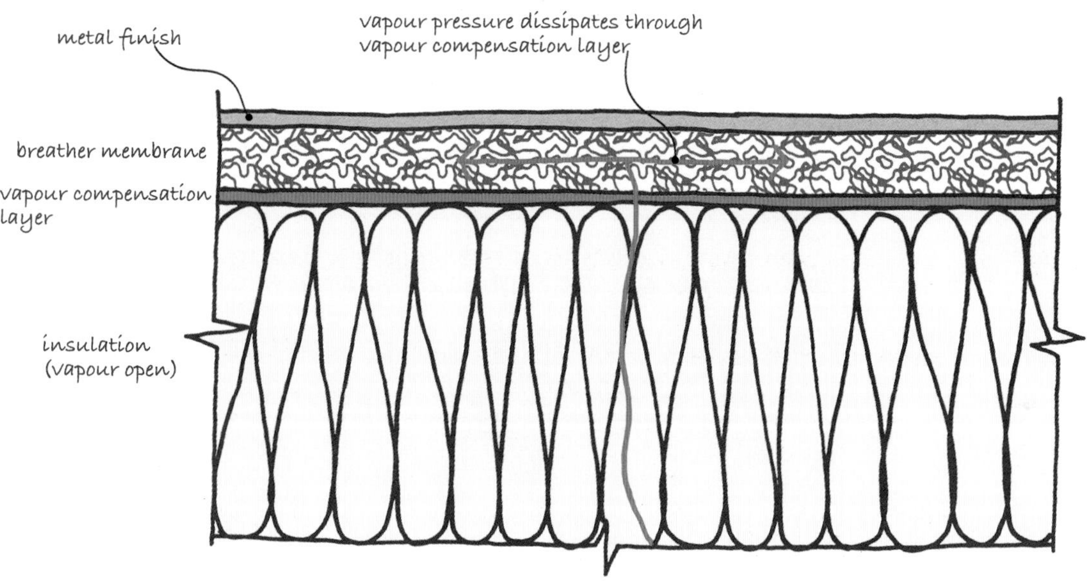

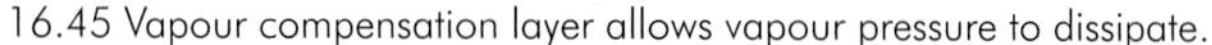

16.45 Vapour compensation layer allows vapour pressure to dissipate.

16.46 Breather membrane with inbuilt vapour compensation layer.

Decking

A number of wood-based panels may be used for the decking. The panel selected must be suitable for protected external applications, and should be capable of resisting weather exposure for short periods, e.g. when exposed during construction. It should also be resistant to decay caused by humid conditions.

Suitable panels include:

- **plywood** – marked S2 (400–700 kg/m^3)
- **particle board** – marked P5 (density: 600–680 kg/m^3)
- **oriented strand board** – marked OSB3 (density: 600–680 kg/m^3)
- **solid wood panels** – marked SWP2
- **cement bonded particle board** – marked S2 (1,200 kg/m^3).

SUPPLEMENTARY INFORMATION

Eurocode 5: Design of Timber Structures describes three 'service classes'.

- **Service class 1** – dry conditions. Characterised by a moisture content in the material corresponding to a temperature of 20°C and the relative humidity of the surrounding air only exceeding 65% for a few weeks per year.
- **Service class 2** – humid conditions. Characterised by a moisture content in the material corresponding to a temperature of 20°C and the relative humidity of the surrounding air only exceeding 85% for a few weeks per year.
- **Service class 3** – exterior conditions. characterised by climatic conditions leading to higher moisture contents than service class 2.

Wood-based panels used in low-slope roofs must be marked to indicate that it is suitable for service class 2.

Joist sizing

Softwood joists are sized in accordance with Eurocode 5: Design of Timber Structures. The size to be used depends on:

- strength class of the timber (e.g. C16, C24)
- length of the span
- spacing between the joists
- whether or not the roof will be accessible (e.g. a terrace).

Durability of traditional timber cold deck flat roofs

Traditional timber cold deck flat roofs are known to lack durability in the Irish climate and generally have a shorter life span than pitched roofs. This is because the traditional cold deck design is flawed. This design causes the materials to fail; the waterproofing layer fails and/or the timber joists and decking become damp and decay. A conventional cold deck design that relies on ventilation and vapour control has been developed; however, its use is not recommended – a warm deck design is better.

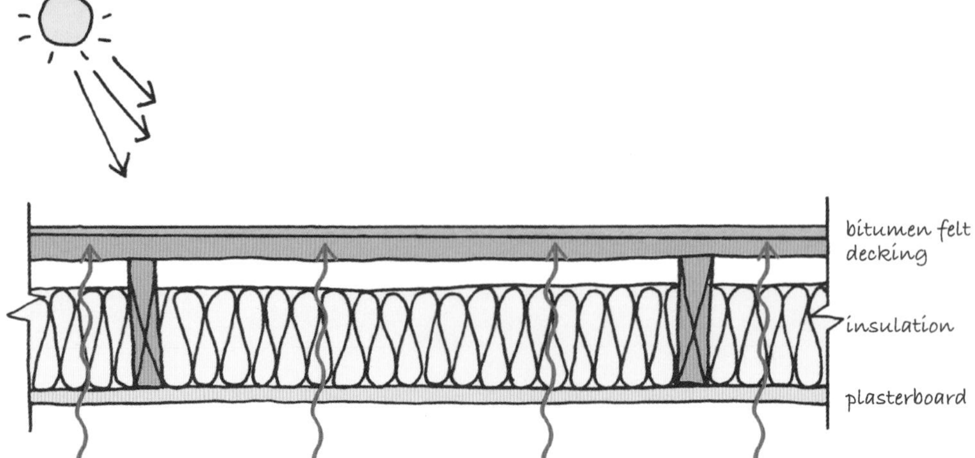

16.47 Traditional flat roof: failure mechanisms.

Failure mechanisms

- Weathering of the roof covering – the waterproofing layer typically consists of three layers of bitumen felt laid with staggered joints using hot bitumen. When a bitumen felt covering of this type is exposed to direct sunlight (ultraviolet light) over time it hardens and becomes brittle. Exposure to the weather also causes expansion and contraction of the felt as it heats and cools. This combination of factors causes the felt to crack and allows water to leak in.
- Ponding on the roof surface – if the roof is not laid to sufficient fall, puddles of rainwater will form on the roof surface. When the sun shines, the area of the roof under a pool of water is kept cool by the accumulated water (ponding) and does not heat up as quickly as the exposed areas of the roof. This leads to differential expansion and contraction of the roof covering and hence to cracking and leaks.
- Interstitial condensation – water vapour moves up through the roof, driven by the difference in vapour pressure from inside (high vapour pressure) to outside (low vapour pressure). When this water vapour gets to the cold space above the insulation, it cools, forming condensation on the roof joists and the underside of the decking. This wetting of the roof timbers eventually leads to fungal growth and decay.
- Checking failure – the temperature of the decking material will change when the outdoor temperature changes. This will lead to expansion and shrinkage of the decking, which will cause the waterproofing layer that has been laid on the decking to also expand and shrink: this will cause the waterproofing layer to crack and leak.
- Ventilation failure – it is difficult to provide adequate ventilation in a low-slope roof because (unlike a high-slope roof) there is no change in height across the ventilated space, so there is no natural convection to move the air. Unless it is windy outside, the air will tend to stagnate.

Building regulations: low-slope warm deck roof

The building regulations requirement for thermal insulation of low-slope roofs is a U-value of ≤ 0.20 W/m^{2}K. A warm deck design places the decking below (i.e. inside) the insulation. An airtightness and vapour control layer is used to prevent water vapour penetration from below. No ventilation of roof structure is required because the timber structure is warm. Rigid insulation must be used (e.g. expanded polystyrene or polyurethane board) to support the load of the gravel. The gravel protects the bitumen roof covering by absorbing solar radiation; it protects against UV damage and absorbs heat energy to reduce the effects of temperature changes. Alternatively, the insulation may be installed above the bitumen roof covering. This is called an 'inverted warm deck low-slope roof'. The inverted roof design provides greater protection to the roof covering.

(10) Airtightness layer
(28) Solid timber joist
(36) 50x50mm timber batten
(38) Plasterboard
(40) Oriented strand board
(45) Rigid insulation
(75) Service cavity
(78) Smooth rounded gravel
(86) Waterproofing layer

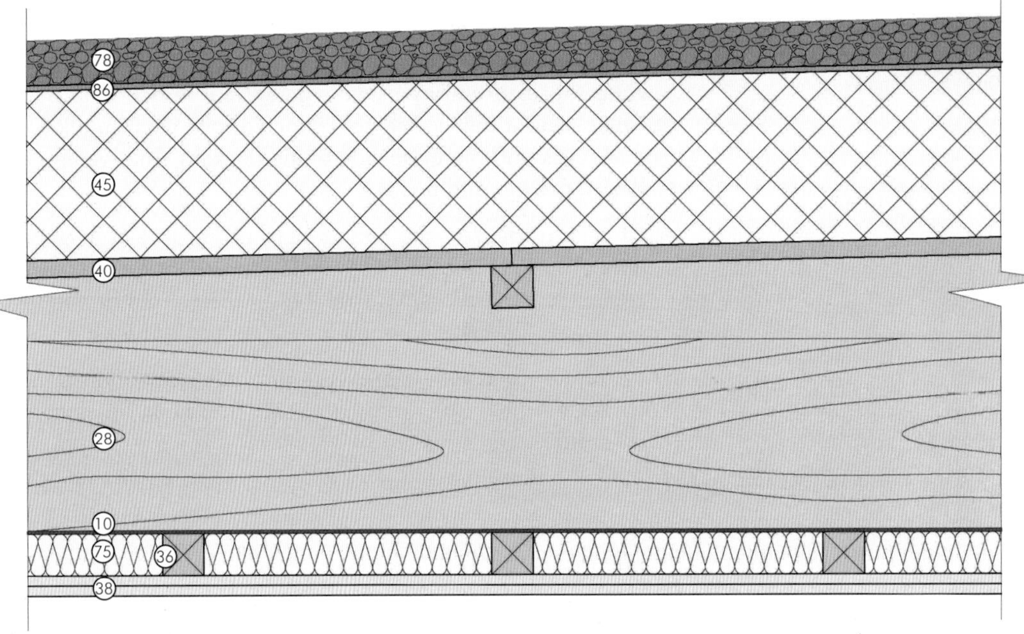

16.48 Timber low-slope roof – conventional warm deck – roof covering above insulation.

Layers:

- 50mm 16/32 washed round gravel (not pea gravel) on polyester/polypropylene filter fleece (i.e. geotextile)
- waterproofing layer (e.g. two or three-layer built-up polymer bitumen felt* with vapour compensating fleece layer or one layer of EPDM (rubber) or one layer PE or metal sheet or other proprietary covering
- 200mm rigid insulation (e.g. EPS, PIR, PUR)
- decking (18mm on joists at 600 c/c or 15mm on joists at 450 c/c OSB3, particle board P5, plywood S2, etc.) with 50 x 50mm noggins at joints
- 1:40 firring
- joist (44mm on joists at 600c/c or 38mm on joists at 450c/c x depth to suit span)
- airtightness and vapour control layer
- 12.5mm gypsum plasterboard x2 with staggered joints.

* 'Torch on' bitumen roof coverings should not be directly applied to insulation: an overlay board is required.

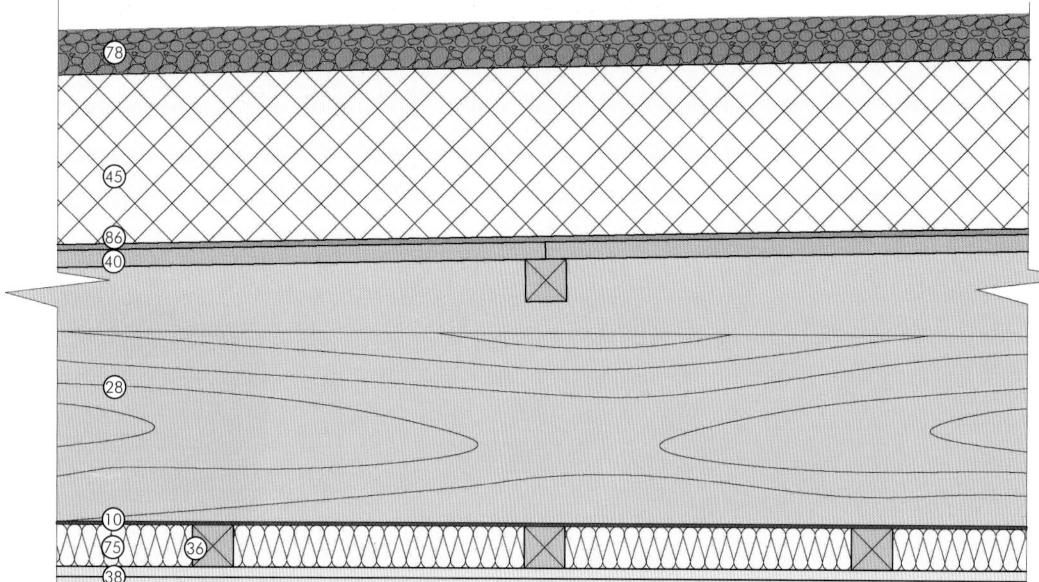

16.49 Timber low-slope roof – inverted warm deck – roof covering below insulation.

Passivhaus low-slope warm deck roof

The Passivhaus standard for the thermal insulation of flat roofs is the same as it is for all other parts of the external envelope: a U-value of ≤ 0.15 W/m^{2}K. There are many low slope roof buildups that can be used to achieve the required thermal performance. The timber warm deck detail shown here ensures the decking is protected and provides a 50mm service cavity. The airtightness membrane prevents interstitial condensation. The use of sheep's wool insulation or cellulose insulation between the joists would reduce the overall environmental impact of this roof.

16.50 Timber low-slope roof – to Passivhaus standard.

Layers:

- 50mm 16/32 washed round gravel (not pea gravel)
- polyester/polypropylene filter fleece (i.e. geotextile)
- 80mm XPS rigid insulation
- waterproofing layer, e.g. two- or three-layer built-up polymer bitumen felt* with vapour compensating fleece layer or one layer of EPDM (rubber) or one layer PE or metal sheet or other proprietary covering
- decking (18mm on joists at 600c/c or 15mm on joists at 450c/c OSB3, particle board P5, plywood S2 etc.) with 50 x 50mm noggins at joints
- 300mm quilted insulation (mineral wool/cellulose/sheep's wool/hemp) between engineered timber I joists.

- timber panel (18mm on joists at 600c/c or 15mm on joists at 450c/c OSB3, particle board P5, plywood S2 etc.) with 50 x 50mm noggins at joints
- airtightness and vapour control layer
- 50mm service cavity with quilted insulation (mineral wool/cellulose/sheep's wool/hemp) between 50 x 50mm timber counterbattens
- 12.5mm gypsum plasterboard x 2 with staggered joints.

  * 'torch on' bitumen roof coverings should not be directly applied to decking: a fire prevention layer/treatment is required.

Green roofs

Green roofs date back to the time of the Babylonians – the sixth century BC. The recent revival in the use of green roofs has been prompted by a growing awareness of the problems caused by the development of green field sites, including flooding and loss of habitats.

There are two types of green roof:

- intensive – a residential garden with a deep soil layer planted with lawn, shrubs, bushes and trees
- extensive – a low-maintenance shallow soil layer planted with grasses, moss, herbs, shrubs or bushes.

Benefits of green roofs

Green roofs have many benefits:

- insulation – the air trapped in soil, and microbial processes that generate heat reduce heat loss
- thermal mass – the soil provides thermal mass, storing heat energy and preventing overheating in the summer, and storing heat in the winter
- sound insulation – the plants and soil absorb sound energy
- air quality – the plants improve air quality by absorbing carbon dioxide and releasing oxygen and by capturing dust
- microclimate – the planted roof creates a positive microclimate around the building
- improve drainage – rainwater is absorbed and stored, which reduces flooding and assists the water cycle
- roof structure protection – the growing layer protects the underlying roof structure from UV light and extremes of temperature
- increased green areas – living roofs provide more green space in urban settings
- improved quality of life – green roofs can provide a pleasant private outdoor space for homeowners.

Construction layers

There are many green roof buildups possible. The arrangement of the layers is adjusted to suit the type of roof and the underlying roof structure.

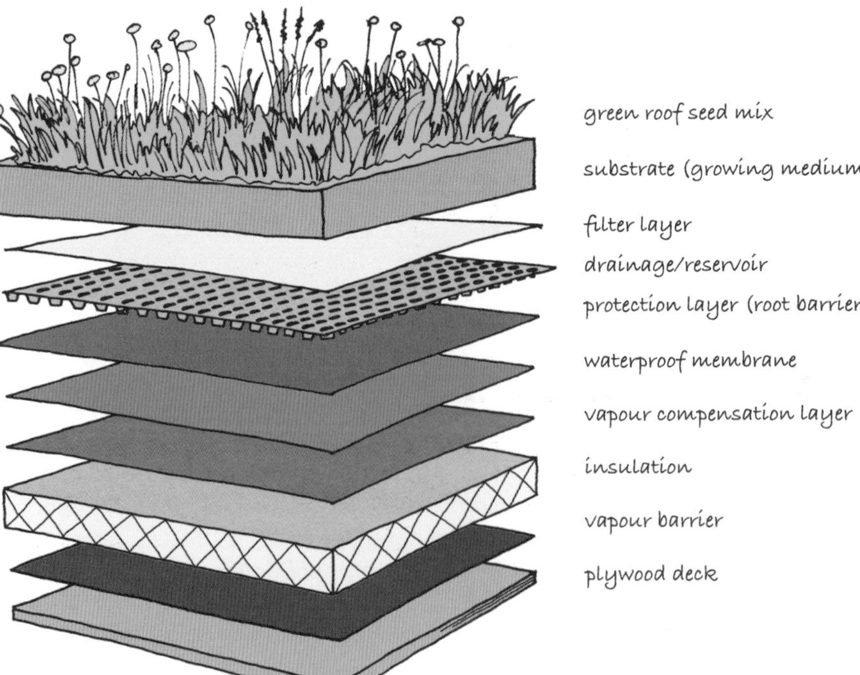

16.51 Green roof: typical roof build-up.

6.52 Lightweight expanded clay aggregate.

6.53 Extensive green roof planted with everal varieties of sedum.

A typical green roof comprises the following layers:

- growing medium – a special lightweight soil called LECA (lightweight expanded clay aggregate) is commonly used
- filter layer – a geotextile (e.g. filter fleece/landscaping fabric) that protects the drainage layer from becoming clogged with fine soil particles
- drainage layer – a honeycomb-type plastic structure that prevents the plants from becoming waterlogged
- root protection layer – prevents roots causing damage to the roof structure.
- protection layer – water-resistant breathable roofing membrane that protects the roof until the layers above are installed
- waterproofing layer – prevents the roof structure becoming wet
- vapour compensation layer – dissipates vapour pressure
- insulation layer – prevents heat loss
- airtightness and vapour control layer – ensures airtightness and resists water vapour
- roof structure – service class 3 timber decking on rafters/joists (or concrete).

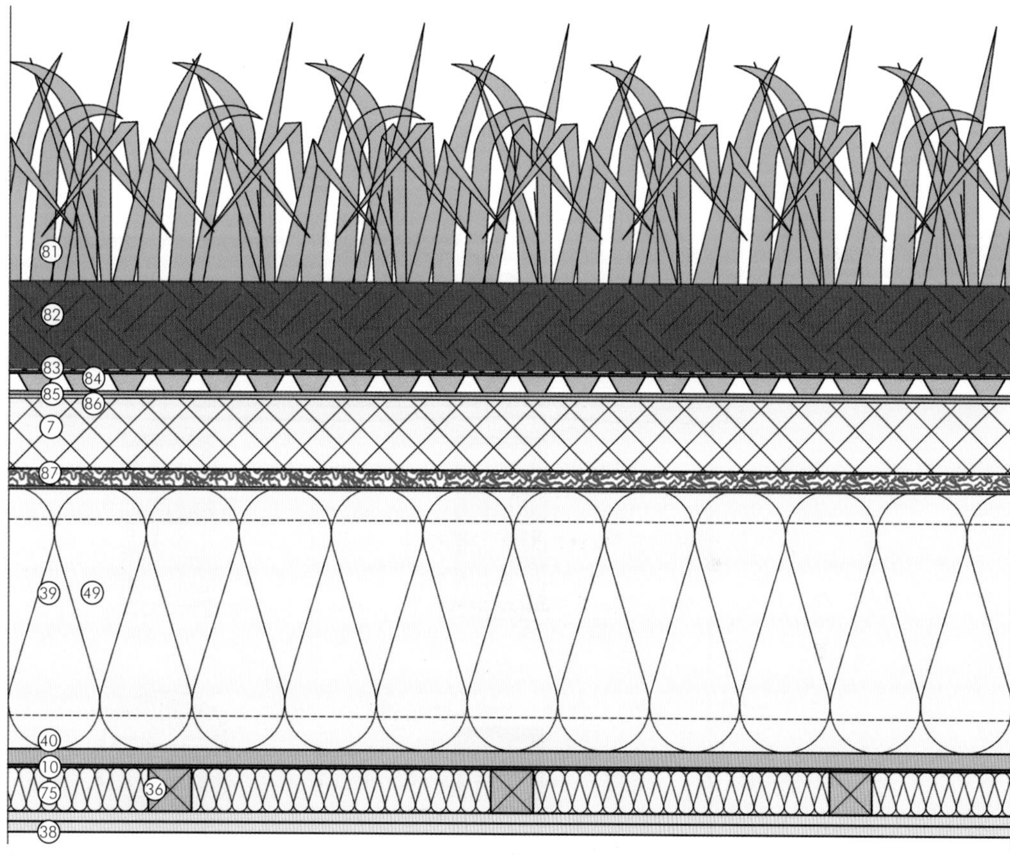

7) Rigid insulation
0) Airtightness layer
6) 50x50mm timber batten
8) Plasterboard
9) Quilted insulation
0) Oriented strand board
9) Engineered joist
5) Service cavity
1) Planting (e.g. sedum grass)
2) Growing medium
3) Filter layer
4) Drainage layer/ reservoir
5) Root barrier
7) Waterproofing layer

16.54 Low-slope green roof: sample green roof with Passivhaus standard roof structure.

ACTIVITIES

Green roofs are great way of reducing the environmental impact of homes. They should be compulsory for all houses built in a rural setting.

Discuss this statement with your classmates.

REVISION EXERCISES

1. Explain, using neat freehand sketches, how the principle of triangulation is used to strengthen roofs.
2. Discuss the advantages of a truss roof compared to a traditional purlin roof.
3. Explain how the forces acting in the members of a truss roof are resolved.
4. Describe, using neat freehand sketches, the problem of thermal bridging at the wall–roof junction.
5. What are the benefits of a green roof?

CHAPTER 17

Windows and Doors

While windows and doors connect our indoor world they are also the 'chink in the armour' of the external envelope of the building: the weak point where heat energy, air and moisture can penetrate the building envelope. In a typical house, a square metre of window will lose almost eight times more energy than the same area of wall. In a Passivhaus, the windows may lose up to double the energy of the walls during winter. It is essential that windows and doors are designed and installed to minimise this energy loss.

Functions

The primary function of a window is to provide light. It should:

- allow an appropriate amount of light into the interior space
- avoid overheating in summer
- resist the actions of the weather (sun, wind, rain, etc.)
- prevent heat loss
- prevent air movement (when closed)
- provide ventilation when required.

The primary function of a door is to provide access to the dwelling. It should:

- allow for universal access
- ensure security
- resist the actions of the weather (sun, wind, rain, etc.)
- prevent heat loss
- prevent air movement.

Performance criteria

Windows and doors must meet the same performance criteria for the external envelope as walls and roofs. There are additional performance criteria that are specific to windows and doors, for example allowing in light and providing security.

When designing windows and doors it is essential to consider all of the performance requirements, including the following:

- sustainability – they should be manufactured using durable natural materials with a low embodied energy. Timber from certified sources is the most sustainable material for window and door manufacture.
- durability – should withstand the effects of weathering
  - aluminium cladding is commonly used to improve durability and reduce maintenance
- moisture resistance – should resist the penetration of moisture from outside by wind-driven rain and from within by water vapour pressure
- airtightness – window and doors seals are an important part of the airtightness layer and must be airtight in both positive and negative pressure situations (i.e. on both the windward and leeward side of the building)
- thermal resistance – should be well insulated to prevent the loss of thermal energy and contribute to the overall energy efficiency of the home
  - the amount of heat loss depends on:
    - number of panes: double or triple glazing
    - gas fill between the panes: argon fill, an invisible insulating gas, improves performance
    - number of low-emissivity coatings: reflect heat into the interior
    - spacer bar between the panes: prevent heat loss around edge of glazing
    - frame: insulated frames reduce heat loss
    - window installation detail: frames wrapped in insulation reduce heat loss
- light – the size and type of glazing used should be designed to allow an appropriate amount of light inside
- solar gain – the glazing should allow heat energy from the sun to enter the home
  - solar energy transmittance value (g value) ranges from 0 to 1, a lower value representing less solar gain
    - for example, g value of 0.52 means that 52% of the solar energy that 'lands on' the glass gets through
- sound resistance – should resist noise to improve indoor sound comfort
- security – should be secure and prevent intrusion
- aesthetics – windows and doors have a significant impact on the appearance of the home.

Fenestration

Glazing is used by architects to bring light into interior spaces and to create a connection with the outdoors. In rural settings it is used to capture views of the landscape that illustrate the beauty of nature. In urban areas glazing is used to create a link to private outdoor spaces or other features.

17.01 Window elevation (height above floor level) and shape are influenced by the window's role.

Glazing also plays an important role in the overall appearance of a building. The relationship between the solid and void (i.e. wall and window), coupled with the size, shape and positioning of windows, significantly influences the sense of the scale and proportions of a building.

Fenestration is the term used to describe the arrangement of the windows on the façade of a building. Fenestration is a combination of:

- the pattern of windows on the façade of a building
- subdivisions of the window
- proportion of panes
- recessing and projection of the windows.

17.02 Fenestration: getting it wrong. A modern house (above) modelled on a Georgian house (below) but lacking the elegant windows and fenestration pattern of the original.

While the technical performance of windows (i.e. energy efficiency, etc.) is very important, it is also important not to lose sight of the aesthetic role of glazing in building design.

There are many window styles. Traditional sliding sash windows were the most common and these can be seen in heritage buildings everywhere. The side-hung casement window is the most common window type in use now. Casement windows can open inwards or outwards. In energy-efficient houses the casement usually swings inwards: this allows insulation to be wrapped around the window frame externally.

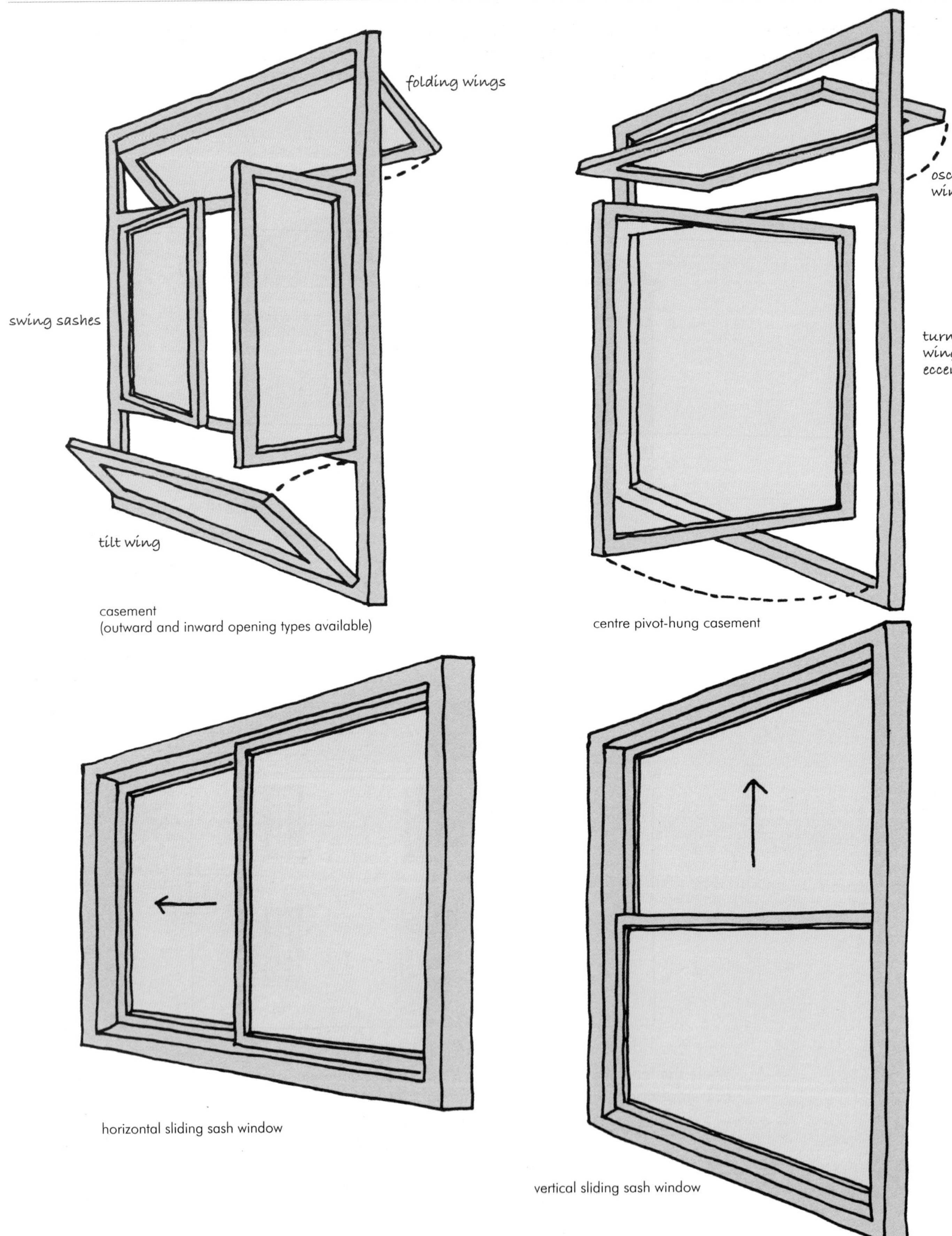

17.03 Window types.

Designing windows for maximum thermal performance

Heat is both lost and gained through windows over the course of a day/year. The goal is to design a window that achieves an overall gain. This means striking a balance between a window's ability to allow solar gain while preventing heat loss.

Single glazing	5.7W/m^{2}K
Double glazing (air fill)	2.7W/m^{2}K
Triple glazing (air fill)	1.9W/m^{2}K
Sealed double glazing unit (argon fill with one low-emissivity coating and insulated frame)	0.85 – 1.4W/m^{2}K
Sealed triple glazing unit (argon fill with two low-emissivity coatings and insulated frame)	0.5 – 0.85W/m^{2}K
Vacuum window (high vacuum)	<0.5 W/m^{2}K
Aerogel (20mm) window (low vacuum)	<0.3W/m^{2}K

17.04 Indicative U-values for various windows. A sealed triple glazing unit with two low-emission coatings and argon filling represent 'best practice': vacuum and aerogel windows are technically challenging to manufacture and prohibitively expensive.

There are four heat flow paths through a closed window. Heat can be lost through the glazing, the spacer bars, the frame and the window–wall junction. The design of the window unit and the installation detail should minimise the heat lost through each of these paths.

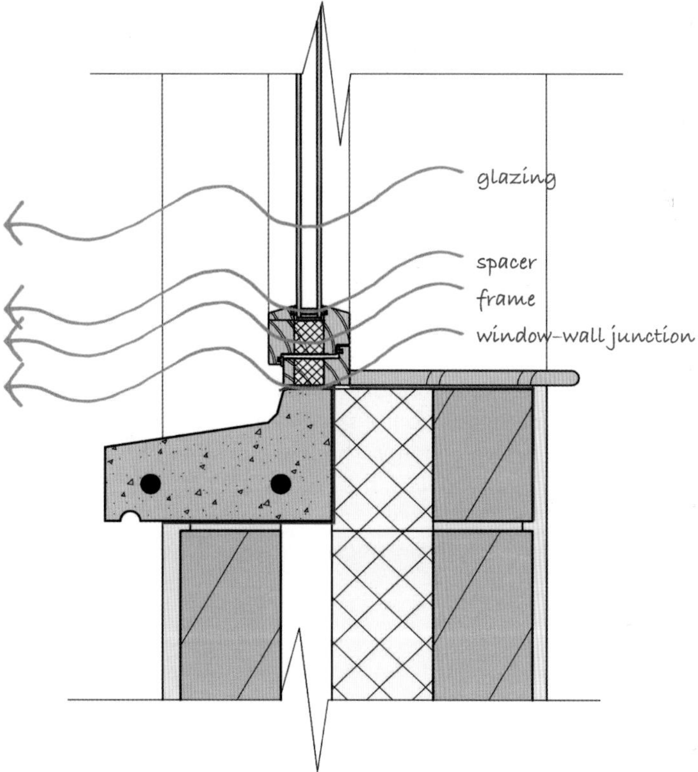

17.05 Windows' thermal resistance: four heat flow paths through a typical window installation.

Glazing units

A glazing unit comprises four elements: the glass, the low-e coating(s), the spacer bars and an insulating gas fill.

Glass

Glass reflects and absorbs light. A single-glazed window will maximise heat gain, but it will also maximise heat loss. Additional panes of glass allow insulating gas to be added between the panes and low-e coatings to be applied to the protected inner surfaces. The optimal number of panes depends on the climate: in Ireland triple glazing is optimal; in hot climates double-glazed units are sufficient; very cold climates require quadruple units.

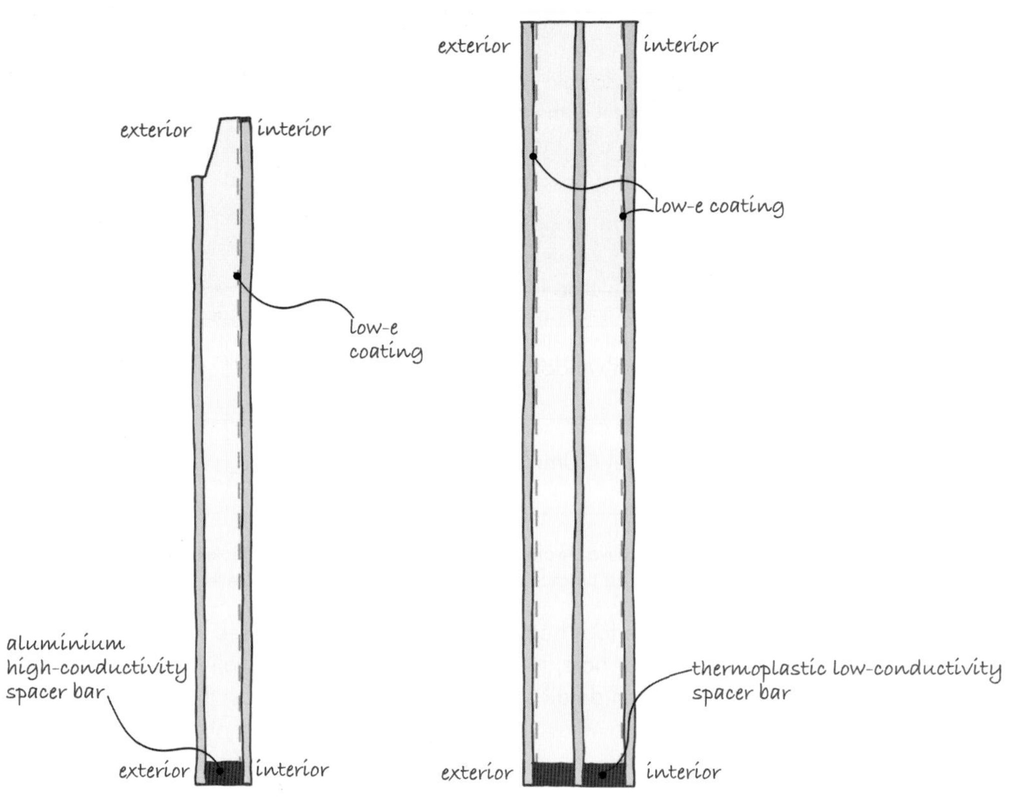

17.06 Window design: additional glazing absorbs solar energy but allows for more insulating gas to be used.

Low-e coatings

A low-emissivity coating (or low-e coating) is a very thin layer of metal that is applied to the surface of the glass to reflect infrared energy back to the side from which it originated. In winter this helps to keep heat inside the building. In summer it helps to prevent overheating. The low-e coating only reflects infrared light so it does not prevent visible light entering the building and providing light and heat.

In the winter, solar radiation passes through the glass, heating the indoor space and objects. These objects absorb the solar radiation and then re-radiate this heat energy in the form of invisible infrared energy. The low-e coating blocks this infrared energy from passing out through the glazing. In this way, the coating reflects heat from internal sources back into the home.

The spectrum of solar irradiation striking the Earth's atmosphere ranges from 100 nano metres ($1.0x10^{-7}$m) to 1millimetre ($1.0x10^{-3}$m). This includes some ultraviolet radiation, the visible spectrum and infrared radiation. Most of the sun's power output comes from the visible spectrum.

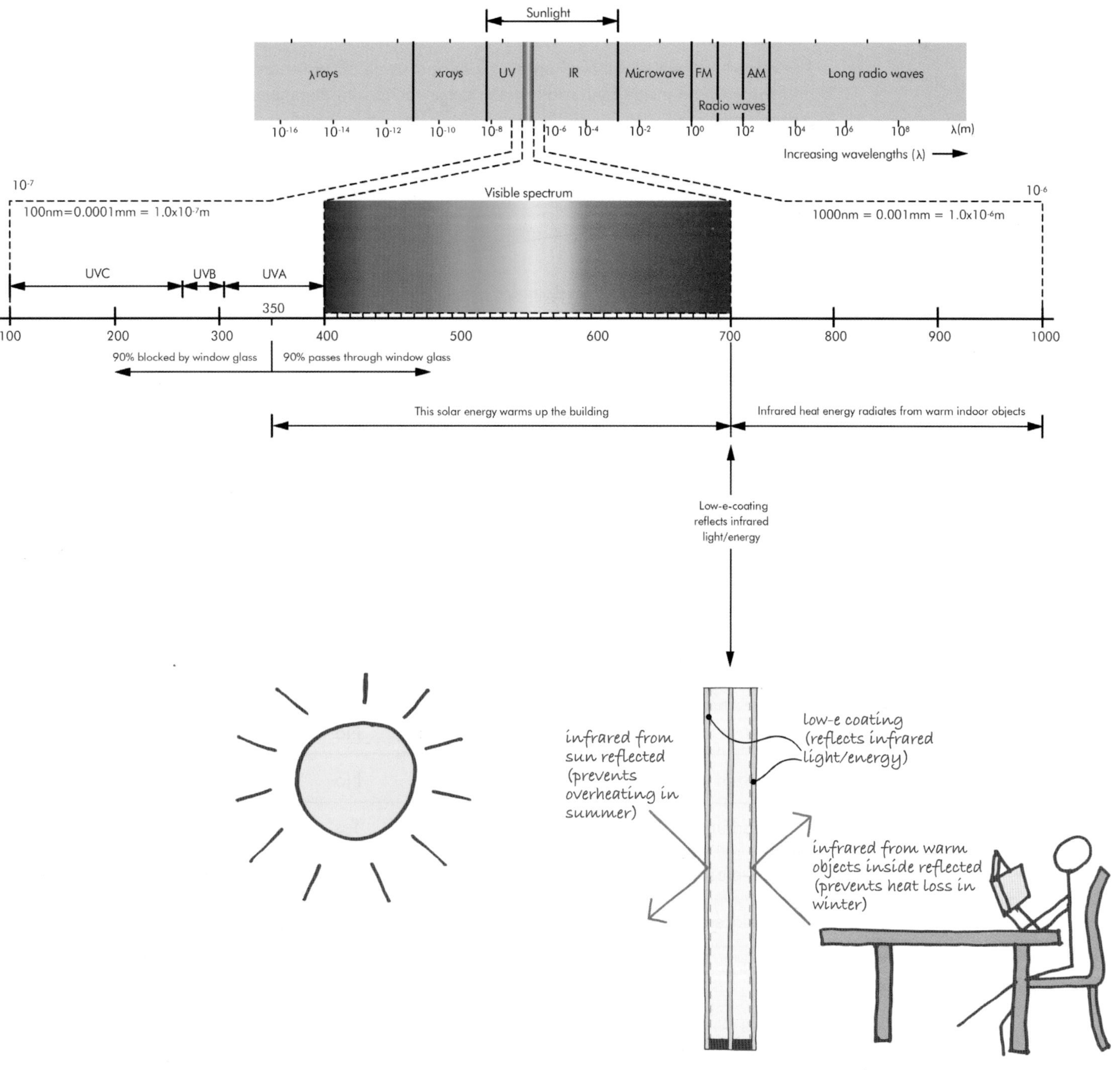

17.07 Low-e coating: infrared heat energy is reflected.

A standard double-glazed unit will have one low-e coating; a standard triple-glazed unit will have two – on the inside surface of the inner and outer panes. There is a variety of processes and materials used for coating glass. These are broadly described as soft or hard coatings. Soft coatings are more susceptible to damage (which is why they are applied on inner surfaces), but they generally provide higher thermal performance.

Solar energy transmittance value (g value)

The solar energy transmittance value (or g value) describes the proportion of the available solar radiant heat energy that can pass through the glass. Solar energy transmittance is not to be confused with light transmittance.

Some of the solar radiant heat energy is transmitted through the glazing (τ), some is reflected (ρ) and some is absorbed within the body of the glass (α) so that:

$\tau + \rho + \alpha - 1$

The absorbed energy will heat up the glass and some of this energy will be emitted to the outside and some to the inside by reradiation and convection (in the space between double and triple glazed units).

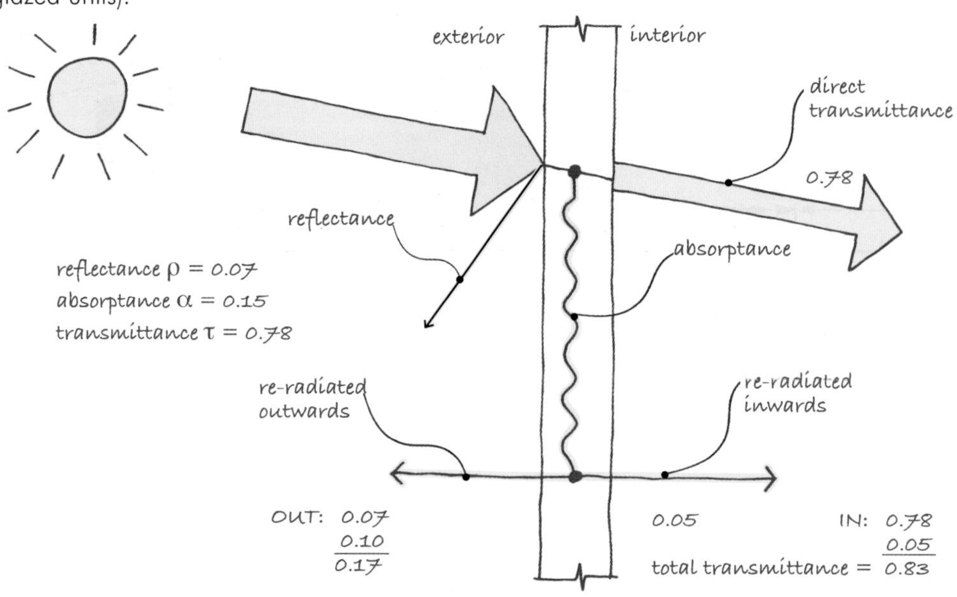

17.08 Solar energy transmittance: the portion of radiant heat that penetrates a glazing unit.

Glazing type	Suitable for Passivhaus	Typical g value
Single-glazed unit	No	0.87
Air-filled double-glazed units	No	0.77
Air-filled triple-glazed units	Yes*	0.70
Argon-filled double-glazed units	No†	0.56–0.64
Argon-filled triple-glazed units (standard float glass)	Yes	0.50
Argon-filled triple-glazed units (low-iron glass)	Yes	0.60

* if the Ug value is below 0.75W/m^{2}K

† but can be used in Passivhaus buildings in warmer climates.

17.09 Typical g values for various glazing units.

Spacers

The spacer is the thin edge element that can be seen between the panes of glass around the perimeter of a double or triple-glazed window. Its function is to bond the two panes of glass and create a tight seal that traps the air or gas between the panes of glass.

Aluminium and steel are commonly used for the manufacture of spacers. However, these metals have high thermal conductivity values and create a thermal bridge at the edge of the glazing unit. This is commonly seen in everyday life when condensation forms where the glazing meets the frame, when warm indoor air meets the cold glazing adjacent to the spacer bar.

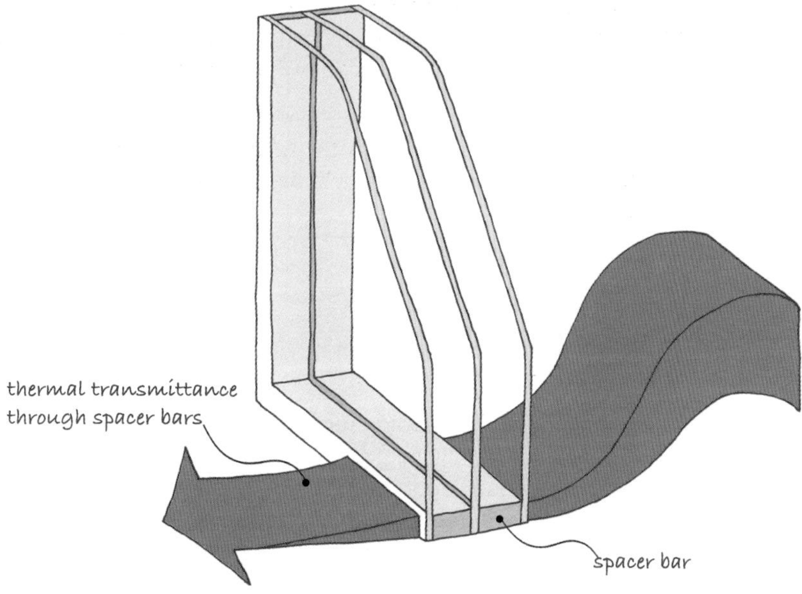

17.10 Triple glazing unit: the spacer bars are the 'weak link' in high performance windows.

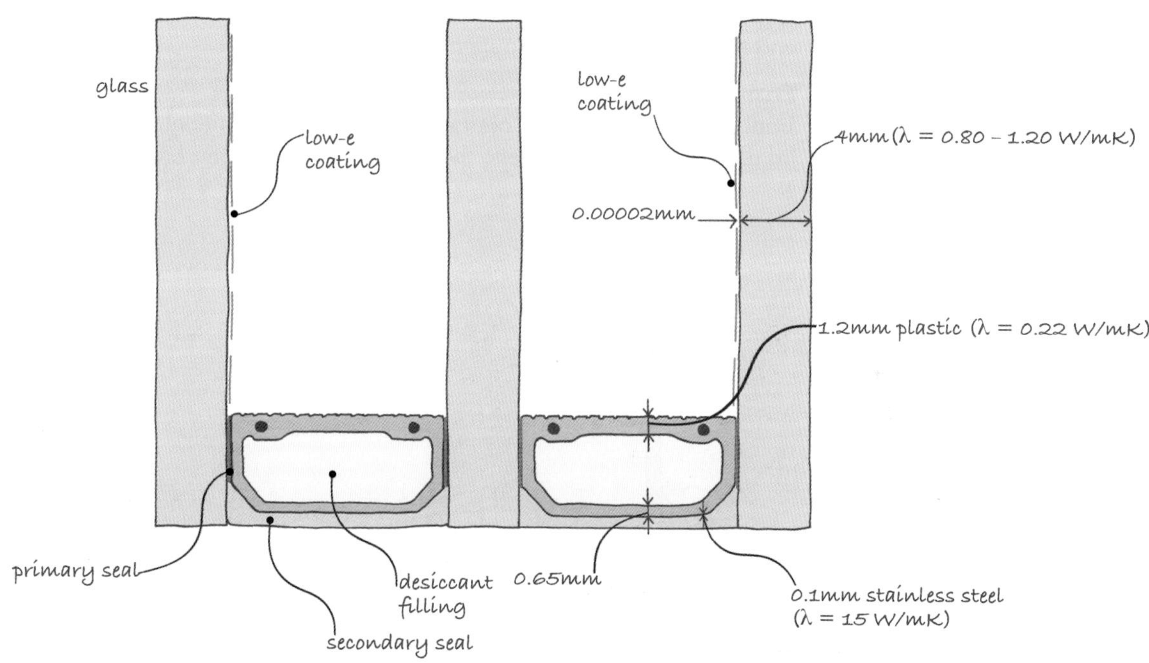

17.11 Warm edge spacer: section through generic glazing unit showing spacer (insulating plastic with stainless steel reinforcement).

'Warm edge' spacers comprise a thin plastic tube with a low thermal conductivity value (see 17.11). The plastic is only slightly thicker than an ATM card (spacer: 1.2mm, ATM card: 0.76mm). This plastic material is reinforced by an extremely thin layer of stainless steel.

The cavity in the spacer is filled with desiccant. This adsorbs any moisture that may be trapped between the panes of glass during manufacture, or that later finds its way into the sealed unit.

The spacer is bonded to the glazing using an adhesive primary seal (e.g. polyisobutylene) along the sides of the spacer and a heat curing or chemical curing secondary adhesive (e.g. polyurethane/ polysulphide) at the base of the spacer.

Material	λ values [W/(m-K)]
Plastic	0.22
Stainless steel	15
Steel	50
Aluminium	160

17.12 Thermal conductivity (lambda) values of spacer materials.

When building to the building regulations, the amount of heat lost through the spacer bar and window–wall junction is negligible compared to the overall heat loss through the building fabric. However, when building to the Passivhaus standard this heat loss is a very significant part of the overall heat loss and must be minimised.

Insulating gas: argon

An effective way to improve the insulation performance of a glazing unit is to replace the air in the space between the panes of glass with a gas of lower thermal conductivity. Argon is used because it is a poor convective conductor. Its thermal conductivity is about two-thirds that of air.

Krypton and xenon are alternative gases, but their use is discouraged because of their higher cost and their global warming potential.

Frames

Traditional window frames are made from a single material, most commonly uPVC or timber. These frames offer little resistance to thermal transmittance and are a significant cause of heat loss.

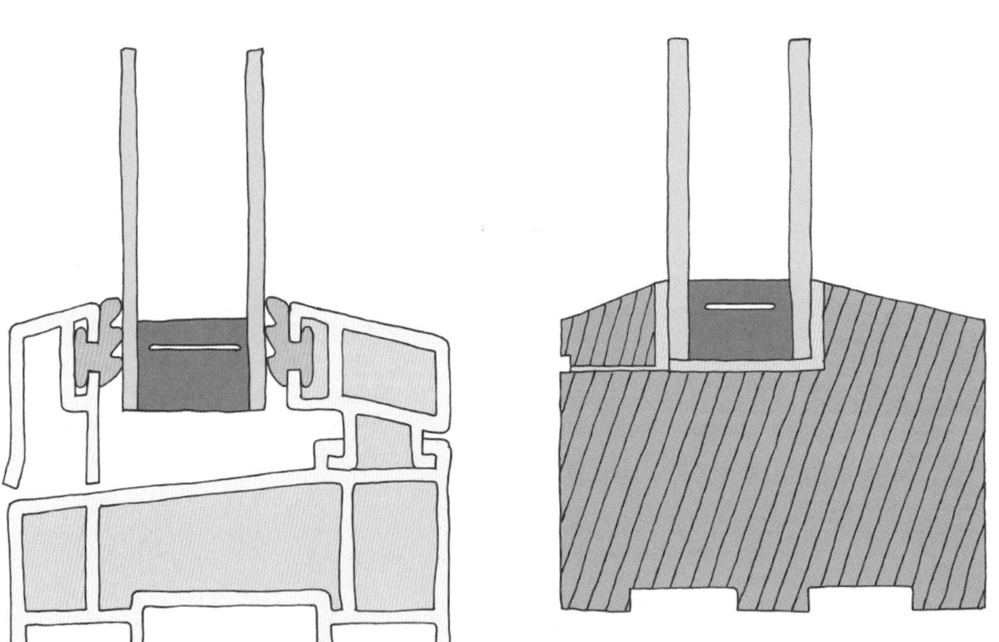

17.13 Traditional window frames.

Advances in the design of window frames have seen the use of multiple materials in a single frame, with each material making a different contribution to the overall performance of the window. Timber or uPVC are still the 'backbone' of most window frames but an insulant (e.g. cork low density fibreboard, extruded polystyrene, polyurethane foam) is built into the frame to prevent thermal bridging. Many manufacturers also use aluminium cladding as an external protective laye Aluminium is used because it doesn't rust like steel and can be easily painted in various colours.

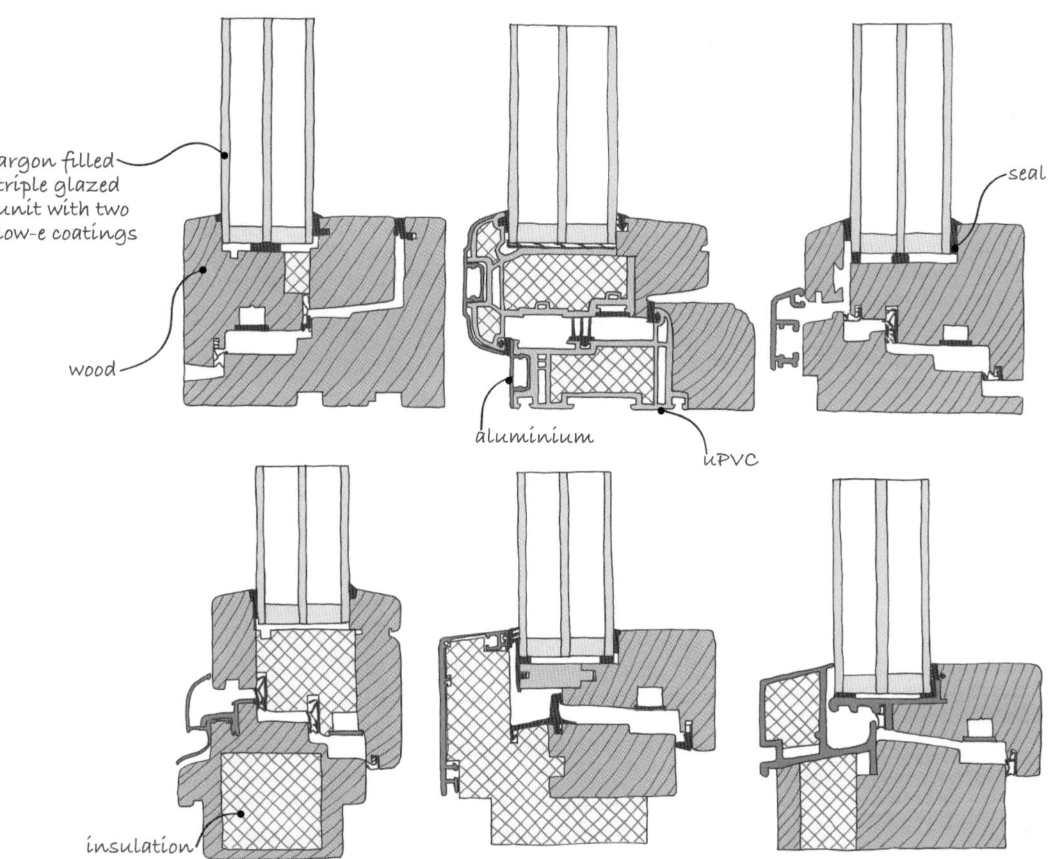

17.14 Passivhaus certified windows: a selection of A-rated windows showing the use of various materials.

Window–wall junction

Resistance to heat loss is typically lowest where the window frame meets the wall. Careful consideration needs to be given to the design of the installation detail because there is significant potential for thermal bridging at this point. When working to the Passivhaus standard, the overall U-value of the window as installed must be ≤ 0.85W/m^{2}K. To avoid thermal bridging these guidelines should be followed:

- windows should be installed in line with the insulation in the wall – staggering should be avoided
- insulation should wrap around the frame externally – this is why the windows usually open inwards.

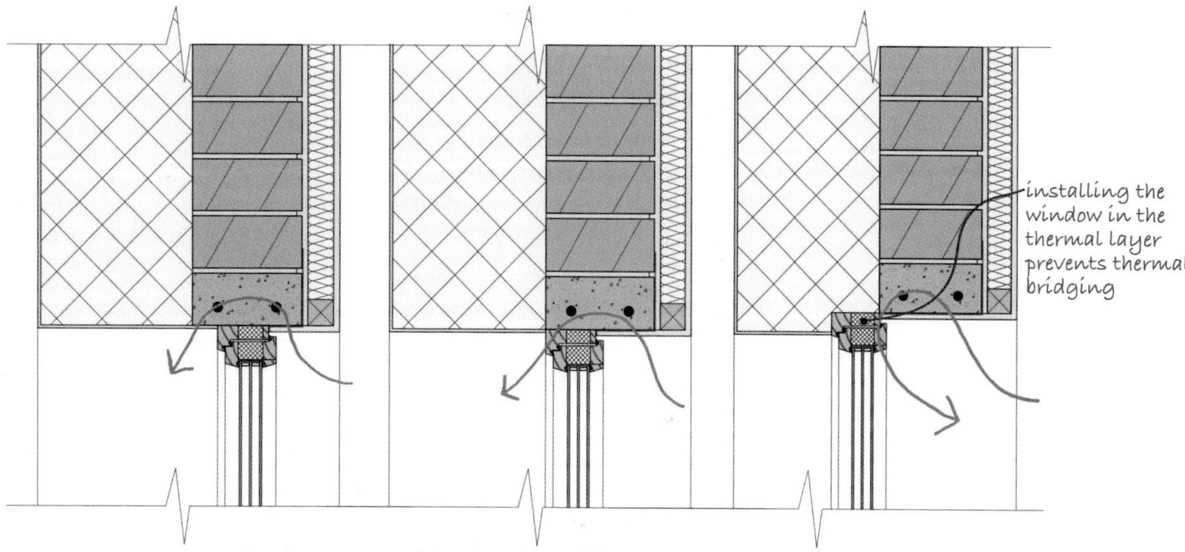

17.15 Window installation: an inward-opening Passivhaus window is installed within the insulation layer and the frame is wrapped in insulation to prevent thermal bridging at the window–wall junction.

Building regulations standard windows

A good-quality window designed to building regulations standard will comprise an insulated frame with a double-glazed unit that is filled with an insulating gas (e.g. argon) and one low-emissivity coating.

Note: There are hundreds of window products available: every manufacturer has their own details, materials and systems. The window details shown in this chapter were created to demonstrate the underlying concepts through a deliberately simplified design. They are not based on any particular product.

The building regulations standard for the thermal performance of windows is based on a sliding scale depending combined area of the windows and doors, expressed as a percentage of the floor area.

U-value:
- 0.80W/m^{2}K where combined window and door area is approximately 60% of floor area
- 1.60W/m^{2}K where combined window and door area is approximately 25% of floor area
- 2.60W/m^{2}K where combined window and door area is approximately 15% of floor area.

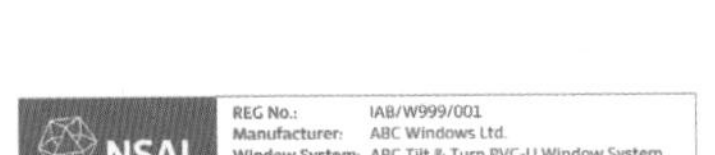

Window Energy Performance (WEP)

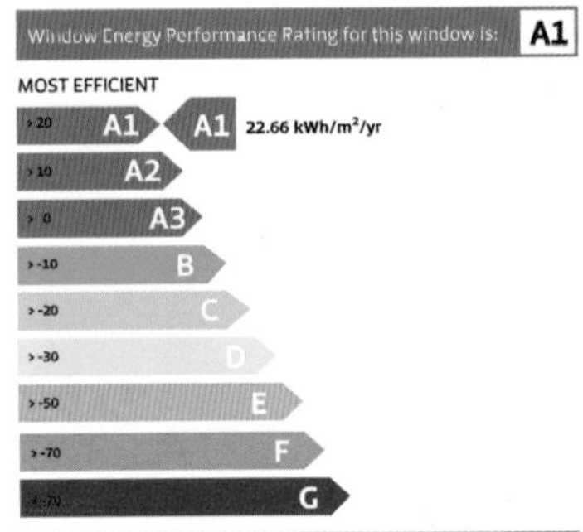

ENERGY INDEX (kWh/m²/year):		22.66

(Energy Index certified by NSAI Agrement and based on Irish standard window. The actual energy consumption for a specific application will depend on the building, the local climate and the indoor temperature)

CLIMATE ZONE		IRL
ENERGY PERFORMANCE CRITERIA		
Thermal Transmittance	U_{window}	= 0.85 W/m².K
Effective Air Leakage	L_{factor}	= 0.00 W/m².K
Solar Factor	g_{window}	= 0.37
ADDITIONAL INFORMATION		
Triple Glazed Unit	Ug	= 0.61 W/m².K
Frame Material		uPVC
Solar Energy Transmittance	$g_\perp$	= 0.61

This label is not a statutory requirement. It is a voluntary label provided as a customer service to allow consumers to make informed decisions on the energy performance of competing products.

17.16 Windows Energy Certificate Rating Scheme: sample certificate.

Window Energy Performance (WEP) Certification

The Window Energy Performance (WEP) Certification scheme is similar to the energy rating labels that are seen on domestic appliances such as fridges and washing machines. It allows consumers to compare the energy efficiency of different windows. The WEP rating is provided for a standard sample window size to allow comparison between different products. Each WEP rating label is specific to a unique window frame and glazing assembly from a single manufacturer.

The WEP Certificate Energy Rating Index combines the following elements to provide an overall rating:
- **thermal transmittance** – $U_{(window)}$ value for the combined window frame and glazing
- **solar factor $g_{(window)}$** – expressed as a number between 0 and 1: a higher solar factor means more heat gain
- **air leakage** $_{(L\ factor)}$ – a measure of the airtightness of the window assembly.

The rating for each window assembly is derived by combining these three values. For example:
- An A1-rated window has a rating index greater than +20 kWh/m^2/year
- An A3-rated window has a rating index in the range of 0 to +10 kWh/m^2/year
- A C-rated window has a rating index in the range of –30 to –20 kWh/m^2/year.

The WEP rating scheme is a useful tool that provides consumers with important information. Since its introduction it has encouraged window manufacturers to improve the energy efficiency of their products. Consumers can compare the ratings of windows on the NSAI website. However, it is important to note that some windows that have received a general A rating are actually not very good by international standards. For example, some A-rated windows have a $U_{(window)}$ value of over 1.40 W/m^{2}K: this is almost twice the energy loss permitted in the Passivhaus standard. Only windows with an A1 rating compare favourably with Passivhaus certified windows.

ACTIVITIES

Take photos of the windows in your home. Identify:
- frame material (e.g. timber, uPVC)
- glazing unit (e.g. single, double, triple glazed)
- any problems (e.g. condensation between the panes of glass at the perimeter of a double-glazed unit).

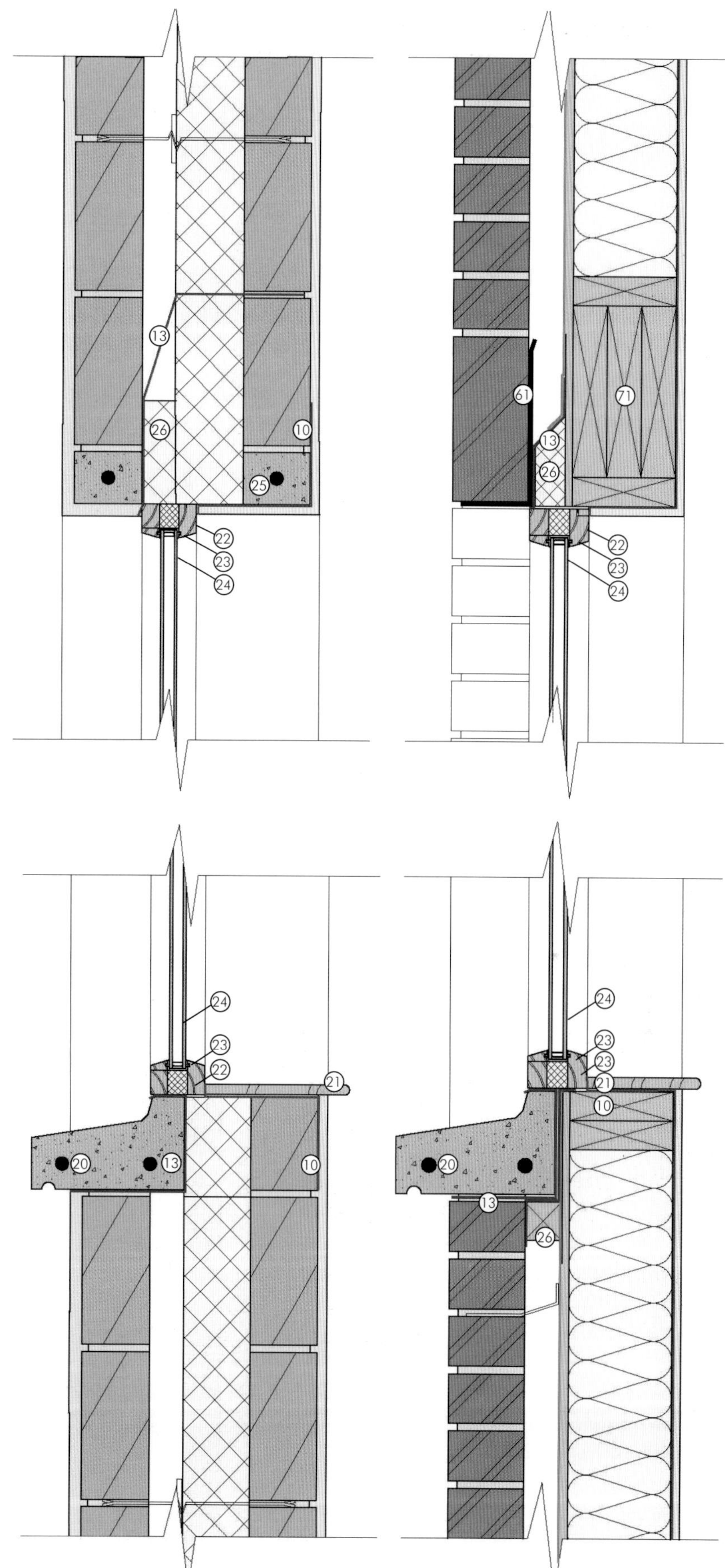

(10) Airtightness layer
(13) Damp proof course (DPC)
(20) Precast concrete sill (100x70mm)
(21) Window board
(22) Insulated window frame
(23) Insulated window casement
(24) Glazing unit (double or tripled glazed)
(25) Pre-cast concrete lintel
(26) Cavity closer/fire stop
(61) Steel lintel
(71) Timber lintel

17.17 Generic window: fixed – designed to building regulations standard.

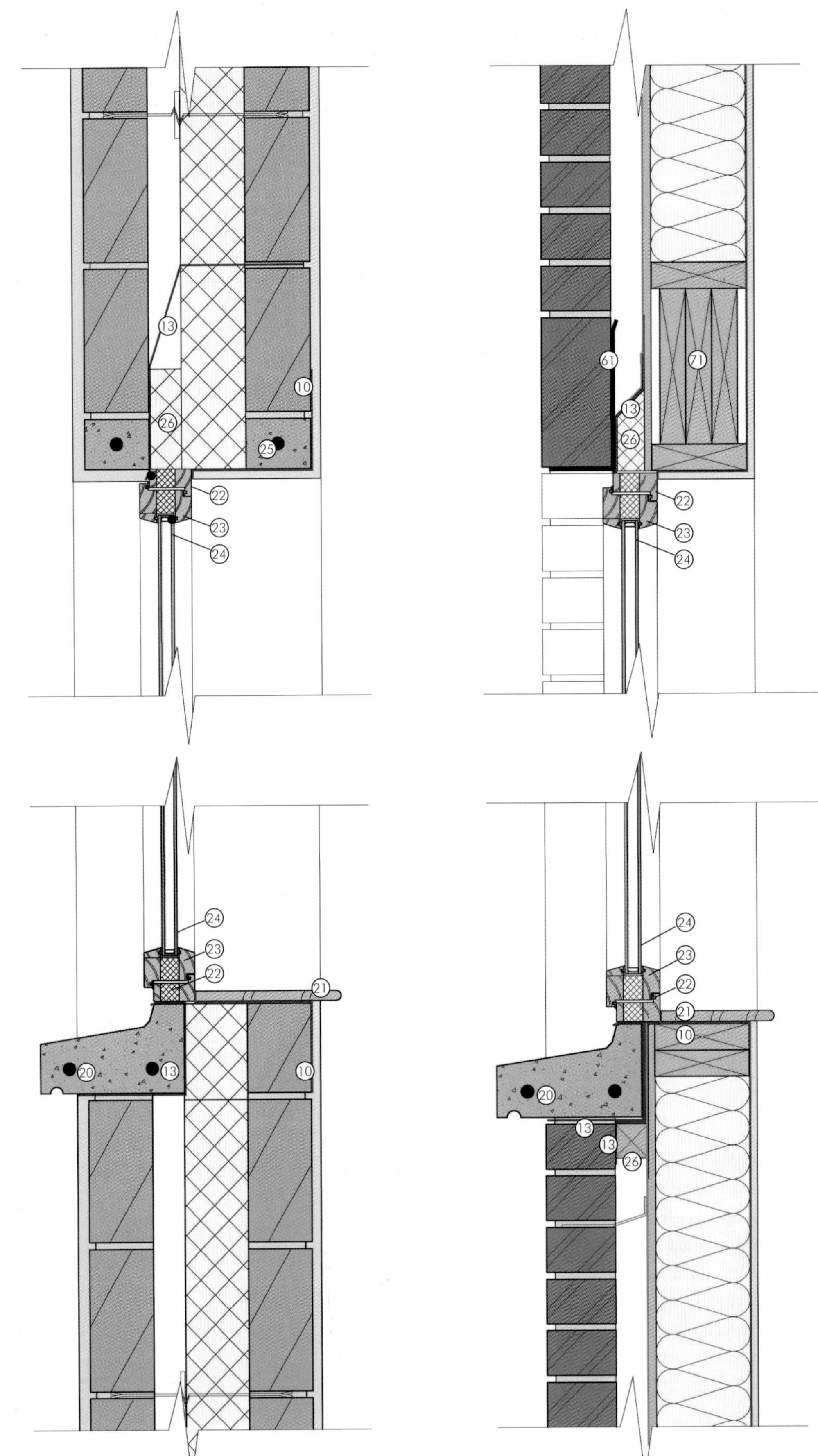

- ⑩ Airtightness layer
- ⑬ Damp proof course (DPC)
- ⑳ Precast concrete sill (100x70mm)
- ㉑ Window board
- ㉒ Insulated window frame
- ㉓ Insulated window casement
- ㉔ Glazing unit (double or tripled glazed)
- ㉕ Pre-cast concrete lintel
- ㉖ Cavity closer/fire stop
- 61 Steel lintel
- 71 Timber lintel

17.18 Generic window: outward opening – designed to building regulations standard.

Passivhaus standard windows

A good-quality window designed to Passivhaus standard will comprise an insulated frame with a triple-glazed unit with two low-emissivity coatings and filled with an insulating gas (e.g. argon). Passivhaus standard:

- U-value of glazing unit: $U_g \leq 0.75$ W/m²K
- U-value of windows (and doors): $U_w \leq 0.80$W/m²K
- U-value of windows (and doors) when installed: $U_{w(installed)} \leq 0.85$W/m²K.

Passivhaus certification

The Passivhaus Institute in Germany provides a certification process that is similar to the WEP scheme. Window manufacturers submit their products to the institute, where they are tested, and a certificate is issued. Certified products are then referred to as 'Passivhaus Certified Components'. A database of certified components is available online.

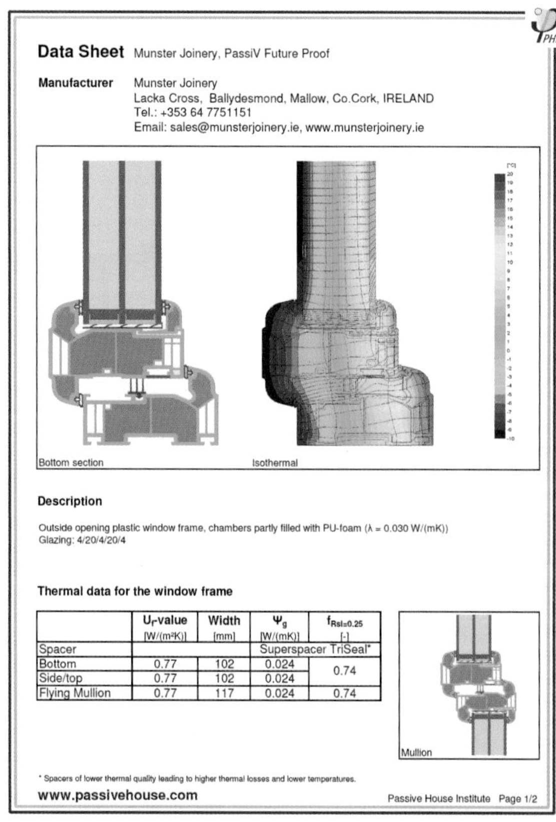

Data Sheet Munster Joinery, PassiV Future Proof

Manufacturer Munster Joinery
Lacka Cross, Ballydesmond, Mallow, Co.Cork, IRELAND
Tel.: +353 64 7751151
Email: sales@munsterjoinery.ie, www.munsterjoinery.ie

Description

Outside opening plastic window frame, chambers partly filled with PU-foam (λ = 0.030 W/(mK))
Glazing: 4/20/4/20/4

Thermal data for the window frame

	U_f-value [W/(m²K)]	Width [mm]	Ψ_g [W/(mK)]	$f_{Rsi=0.25}$ [-]
Spacer			Superspacer TriSeal*	
Bottom	0.77	102	0.024	0.74
Side/top	0.77	102	0.024	
Flying Mullion	0.77	117	0.024	0.74

* Spacers of lower thermal quality leading to higher thermal losses and lower temperatures.

www.passivehouse.com Passive House Institute Page 1/2

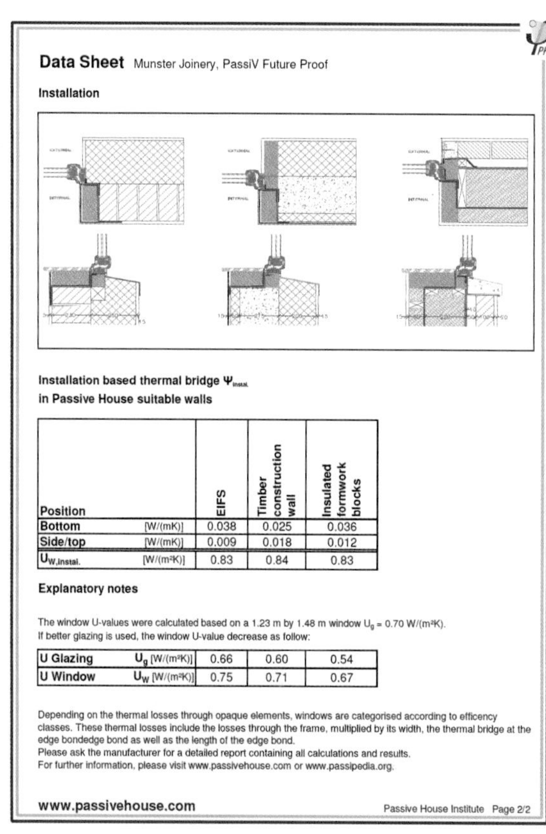

Data Sheet Munster Joinery, PassiV Future Proof

Installation

Installation based thermal bridge $\Psi_{instal.}$ in Passive House suitable walls

Position		EIFS	Timber construction wall	Insulated formwork blocks
Bottom	[W/(mK)]	0.038	0.025	0.036
Side/top	[W/(mK)]	0.009	0.018	0.012
$U_{W,instal.}$	[W/(m²K)]	0.83	0.84	0.83

Explanatory notes

The window U-values were calculated based on a 1.23 m by 1.48 m window U_g = 0.70 W/(m²K).
If better glazing is used, the window U-value decrease as follow:

U Glazing	U_g [W/(m²K)]	0.66	0.60	0.54
U Window	U_W [W/(m²K)]	0.75	0.71	0.67

Depending on the thermal losses through opaque elements, windows are categorised according to efficency classes. These thermal losses include the losses through the frame, multiplied by its width, the thermal bridge at the edge bondedge bond as well as the length of the edge bond.
Please ask the manufacturer for a detailed report containing all calculations and results.
For further information, please visit www.passivehouse.com or www.passipedia.org.

www.passivehouse.com Passive House Institute Page 2/2

17.19 Passivhaus certified component: certificate for an A-rated uPVC window showing detailed window performance data and various installation details.

Passivhaus criteria

A window designed to Passivhaus standard must meet the following criteria to ensure that a comfortable indoor environment is maintained and energy is not lost:

- comfort criterion: $U_w \leq 0.80$W/m²K
  - this is to ensure that the internal surface temperature of the glazing is always within 4°C of the indoor temperature
- any temperature difference above 4°C will make occupants feel uncomfortable
- energy criterion: $U_g - ((Sxg)) < 0$ where:
  - U_g = U-value glazing
  - S = radiation gain coefficient (represents the solar energy available)
    = 1.6 W/m²K for Europe
  - g = g value (solar energy transmittance value)
- for example, for a window with a g value of 0.52 (52%) and a U_g of 0.51 W/m²K:
  - energy criterion: 0.51 : (1.6 x 0.52) = – 0.33 W/m²K < 0
  - a minus U-value indicates a change in direction of the energy flow – from outside to inside; this calculation demonstrates that south-facing Passivhaus windows gain more energy than they lose over the course of a year – in other words, they are effectively 'radiators'.

ACTIVITIES

Visit the website of a company (e.g. Munster Joinery) that manufactures windows to the Passivhaus standard to learn more about how these windows are made.

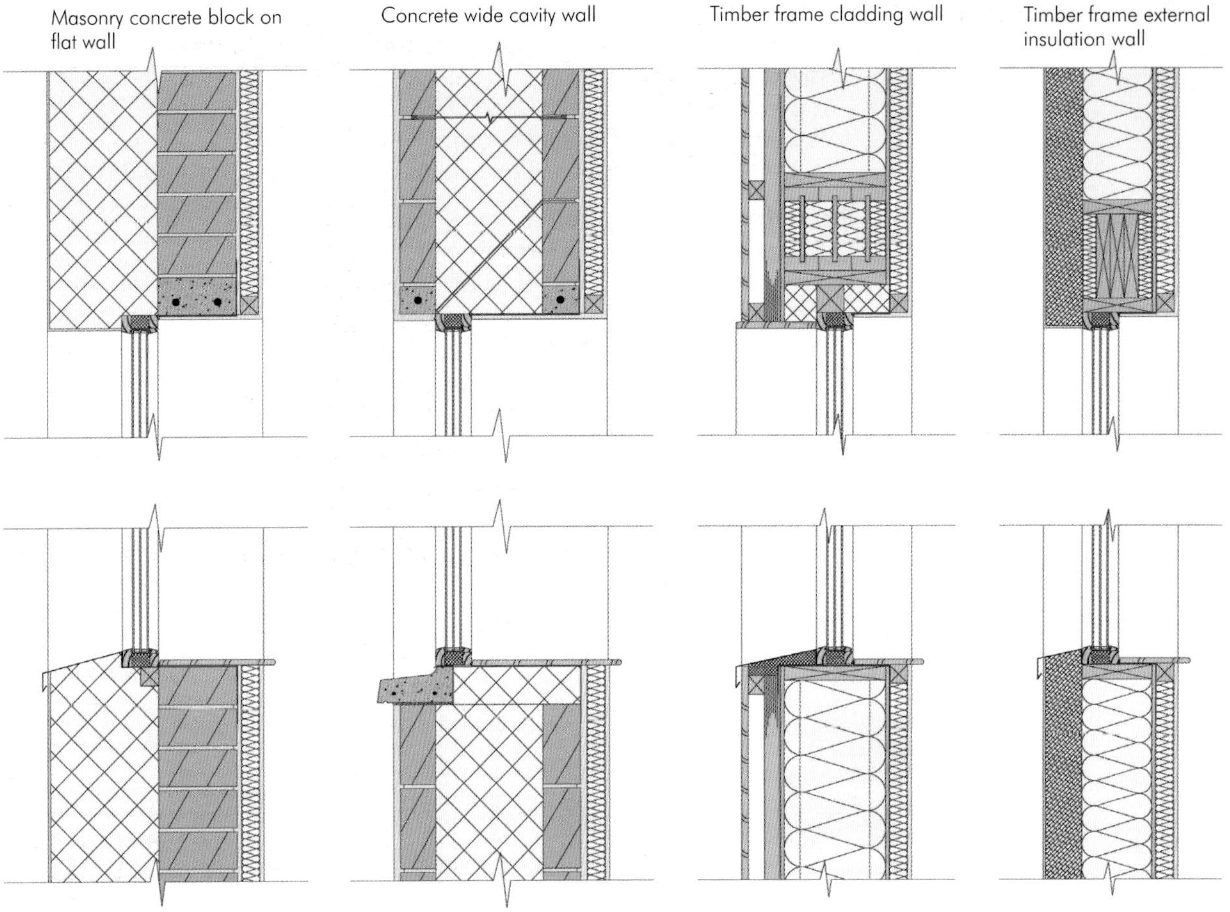

Masonry concrete block on flat wall

Concrete wide cavity wall

Timber frame cladding wall

Timber frame external insulation wall

17.20 Generic fixed window: triple-glazed thermal bridge free window – designed to Passivhaus standard. Please turn to Chapter 19 for more detail.

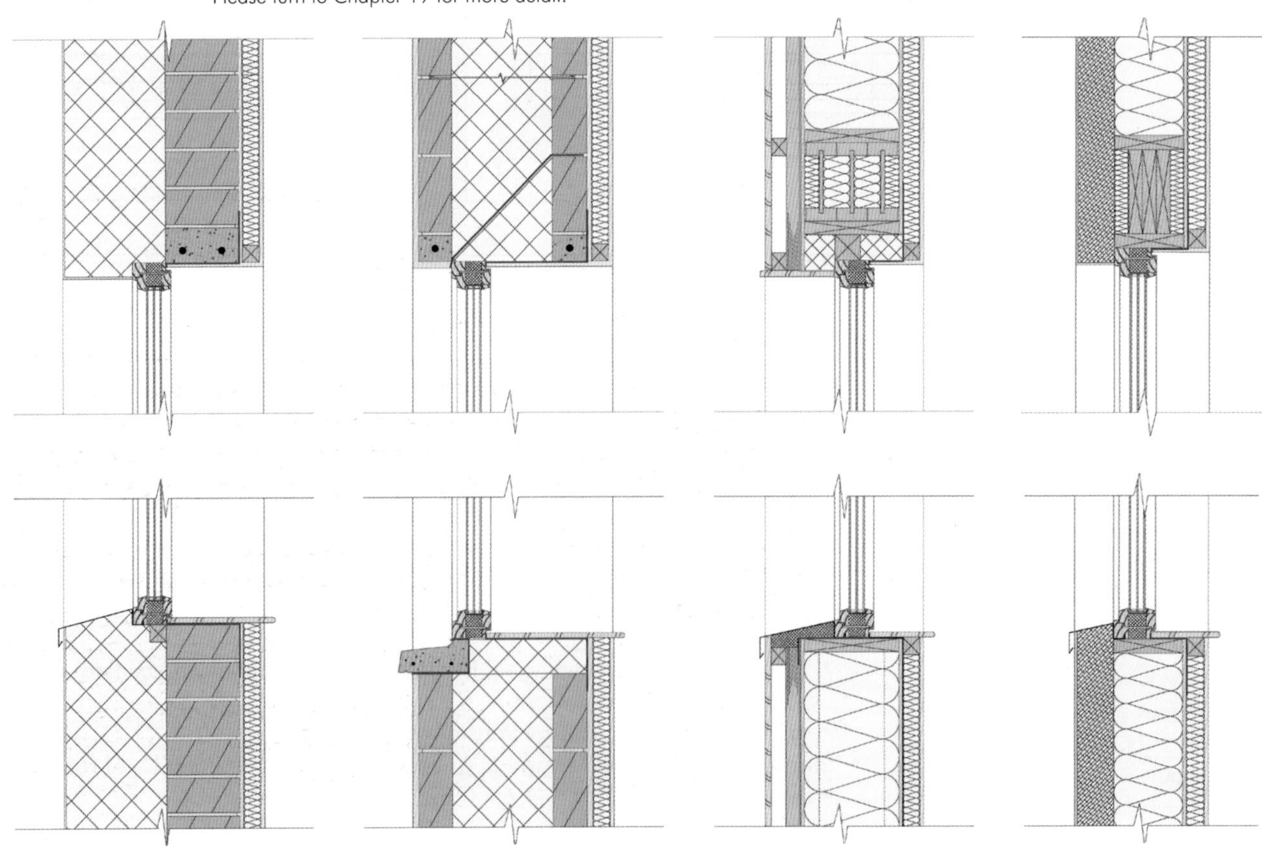

17.21 Generic inward opening window: triple-glazed, thermal bridge-free – designed to Passivhaus standard. Please turn to Chapter 19 for more detail.

Door design

17.22 Entrance door.

The front door of a home has an important aesthetic role and should make a good first impression. It should convey a sense of security and look solid and reliable. The proportion, colour and detail of the door contribute to making it an attractive feature of the house. Traditionally, panelled doors were very popular. Contemporary doors tend to be more plain in appearance, partly because the inclusion of insulation requires the door thickness to remain consistent. Fully glazed doors (which are effectively large windows) are also common, particularly at the rear of a dwelling.

17.23 Door design: a simple insulated matchboarded style door, a traditional solid timber panelled door and a fully glazed door.

Building regulations standard doors

The building regulations standard for the thermal performance of doors is the same as it is for windows. A good-quality door designed to building regulations standard will incorporate an insulated core and have double seals where the door meets the frame. The door threshold should be designed to ensure that rainwater is effectively collected. The requirements for accessibility should also be met (see Chapter 6).

(3) Hardcore
(4) Concrete fill
(5) Sand blinding
(6) Radon barrier or damp proof membrane (DPM)
(7) Rigid insulation
(9) Reinforced concrete slab
(10) Airtightness layer
(11) Floor covering
(13) Damp proof course (DPC)
(14) 12mm plaster
(15) Inner leaf concrete blockwork
(16) Cavity insulation
(17) 50mm air cavity
(18) Outer leaf concrete blockwork
(19) Render
(20) Precast concrete sill (100x70mm)
(25) Precast concrete lintel
(26) Cavity closer/fire stop
(43) Mortar (cement, sand)
(56) Threshold rainwater drain
(57) Door sill
(58) 100mm Insulated timber door leaf
(59) Door frame
(61) Steel lintel
(64) Aerated autoclaved concrete block
(71) Timber lintel

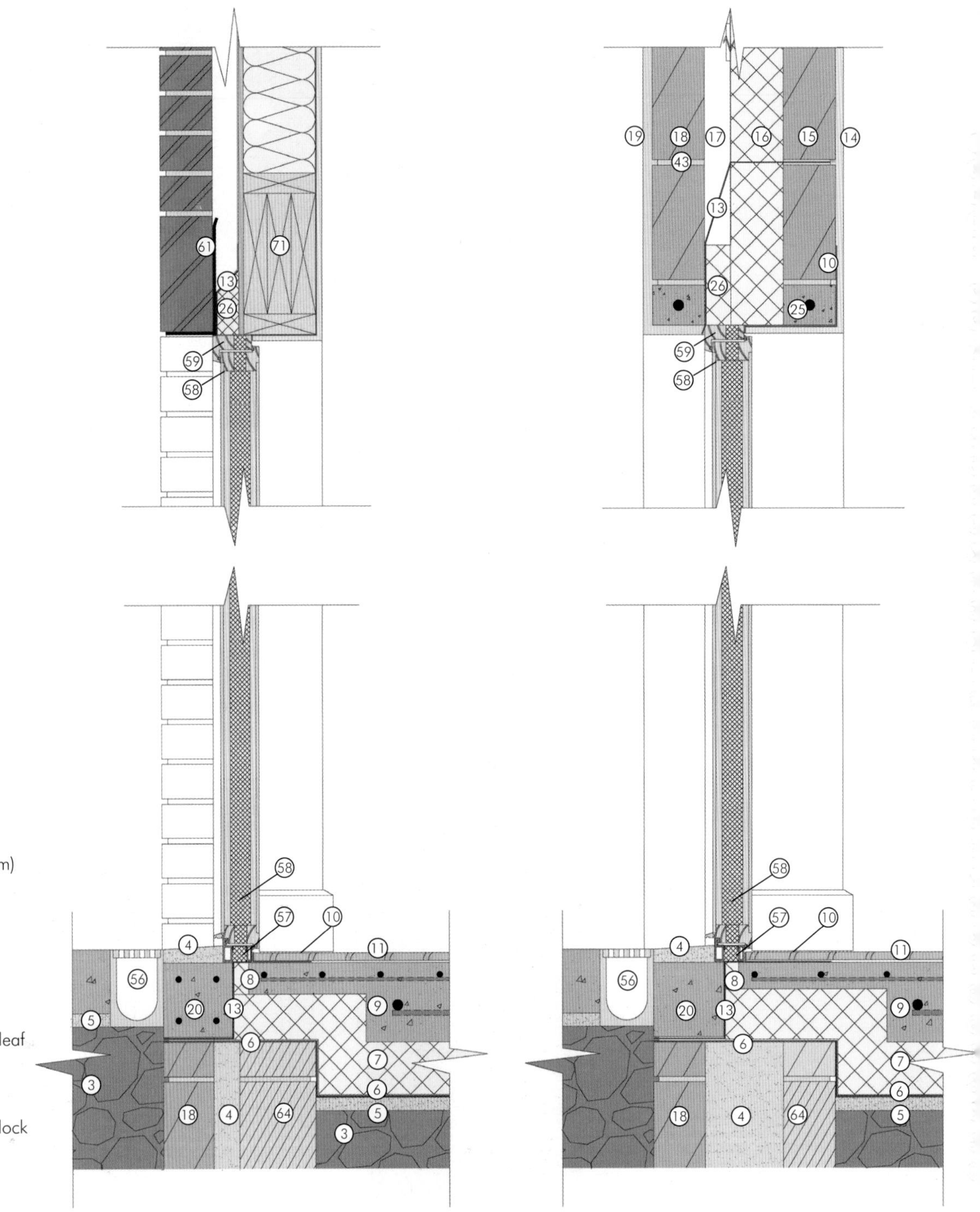

17.24 Generic door installed in a house designed to meet building regulations standard.

Passivhaus standard doors

The Passivhaus standard for doors is the same as it is for windows: U-value ≤ 0.80W/m^{2}K. All of the principles that apply to the design and installation of windows also apply to doors. Fully glazed doors are very commonly used as entrance doors in houses built to the Passivhaus standard.

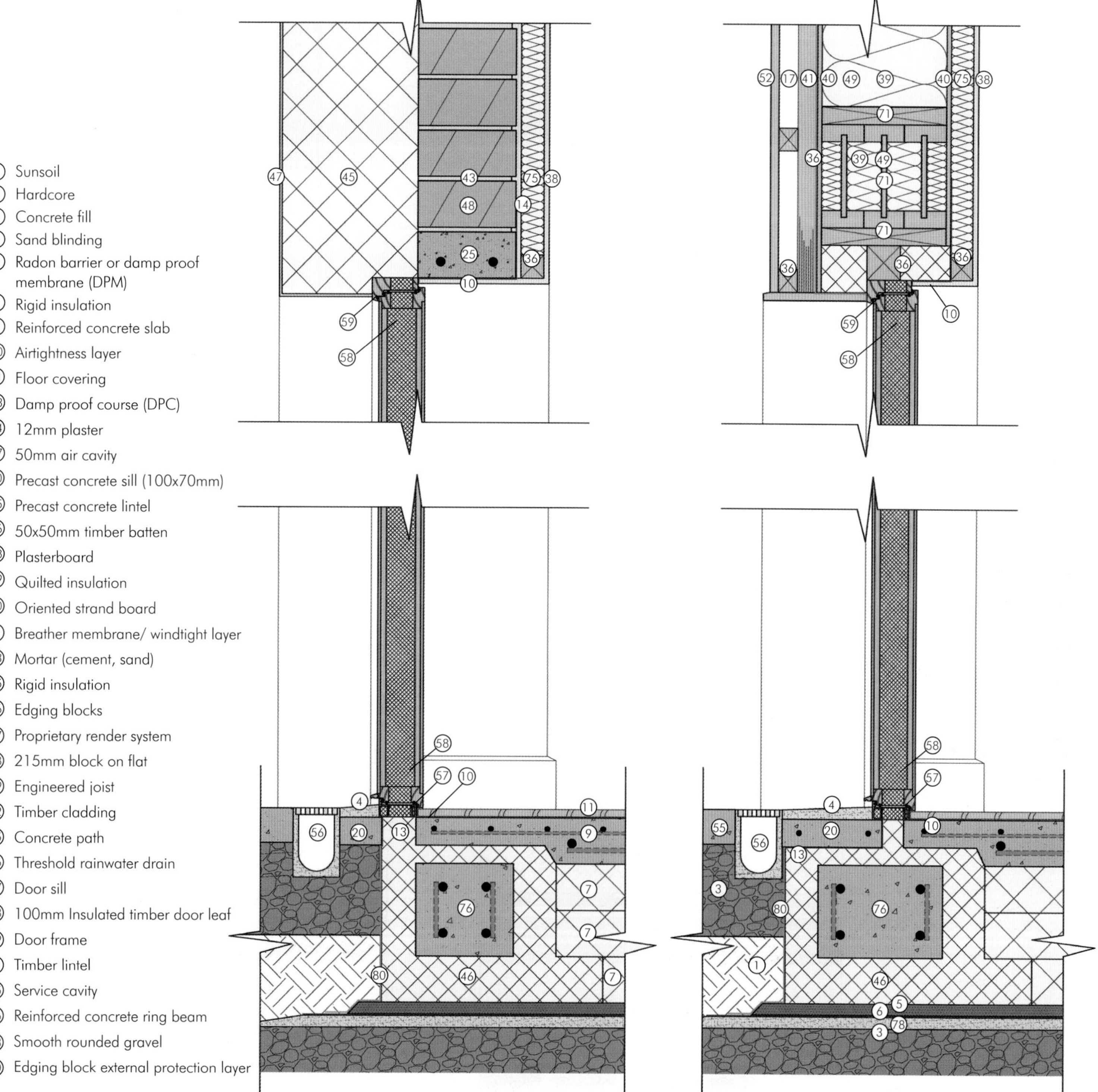

17.25 Generic solid door designed to meet Passivhaus standard.

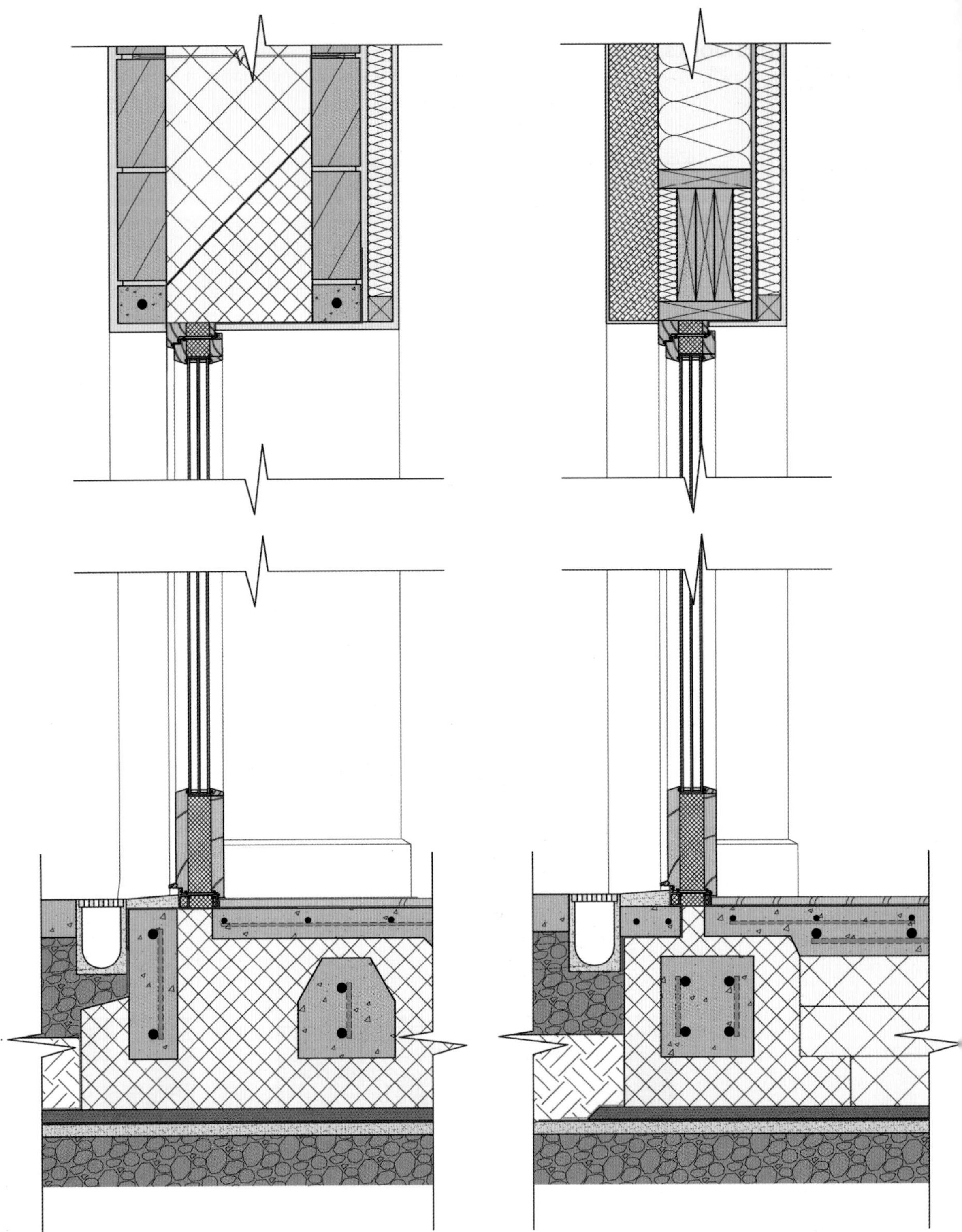

17.26 Generic fully glazed door designed to Passivhaus standard.

REVISION EXERCISES

1. Explain, using neat freehand sketches, the role of fenestration in building design.
2. Describe, using a neat freehand sketch, how heat is lost through a typical window.
3. Explain, using a neat freehand sketch, how low-e coatings contribute to the energy efficiency of windows.
4. Explain, using a neat freehand sketch, the importance of window position in the reduction of thermal bridging at the wall–window junction.
5. Outline how moisture penetration is prevented at a typical door threshold.

CHAPTER 18 Internal Elements

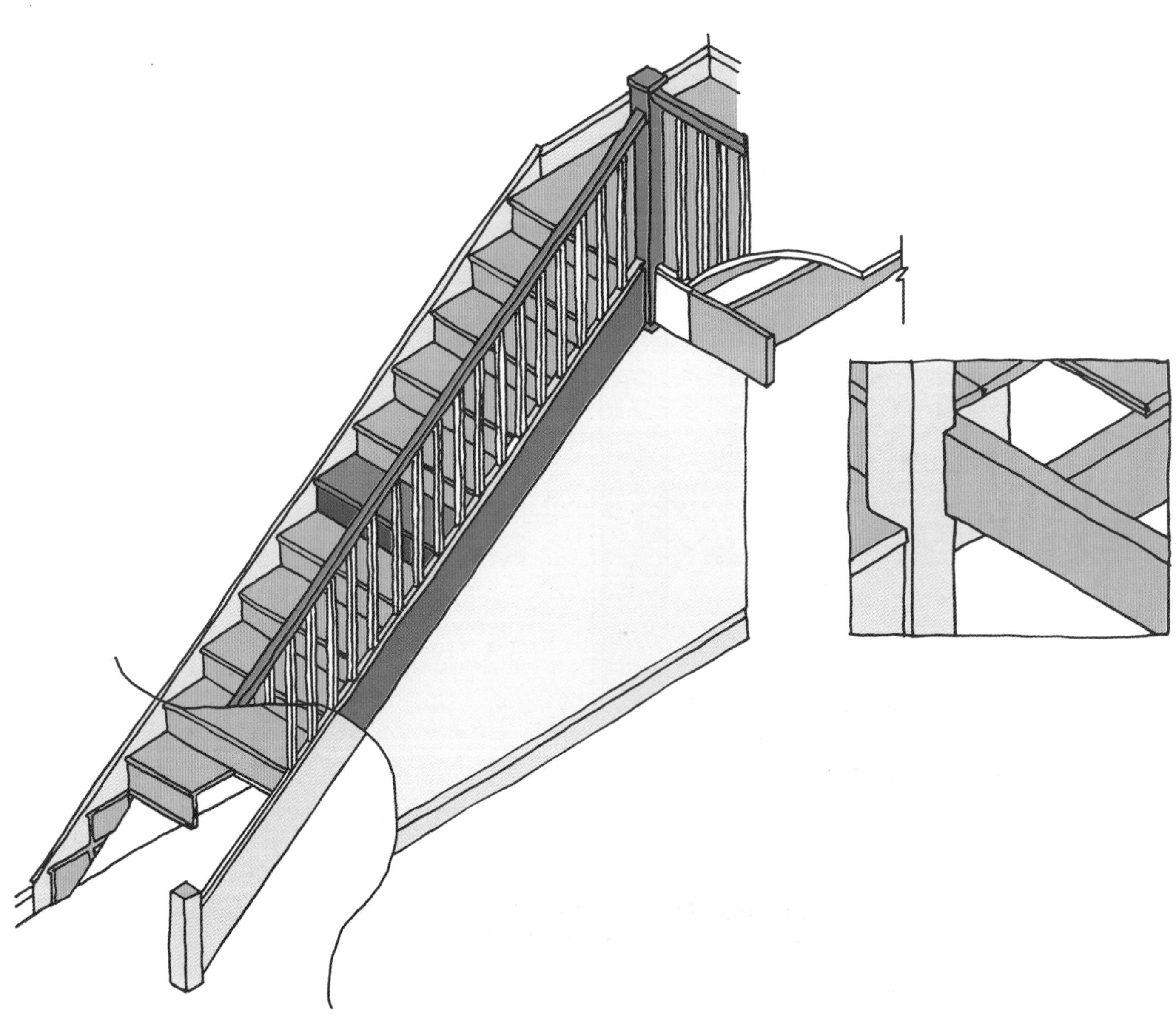

Upper floors

Like suspended ground floors, upper floors can be constructed in concrete or timber. Concrete suspended floors are very heavy, so they require concrete walls to support them. Timber suspended floors are used with both concrete and timber walls. Traditionally timber floors were constructed using solid timber joists. Engineered joists are in increasing use because they can carry greater loads and can accommodate services (e.g. pipes, cables, ducts).

Timber upper floors

Timber suspended floors are easy to install and are useful for accommodating services (e.g. electrical wiring, plumbing pipes or air ducting). There are three main types of joist used in the construction of upper floors: solid timber joists, I beam joists and metal open web joists.

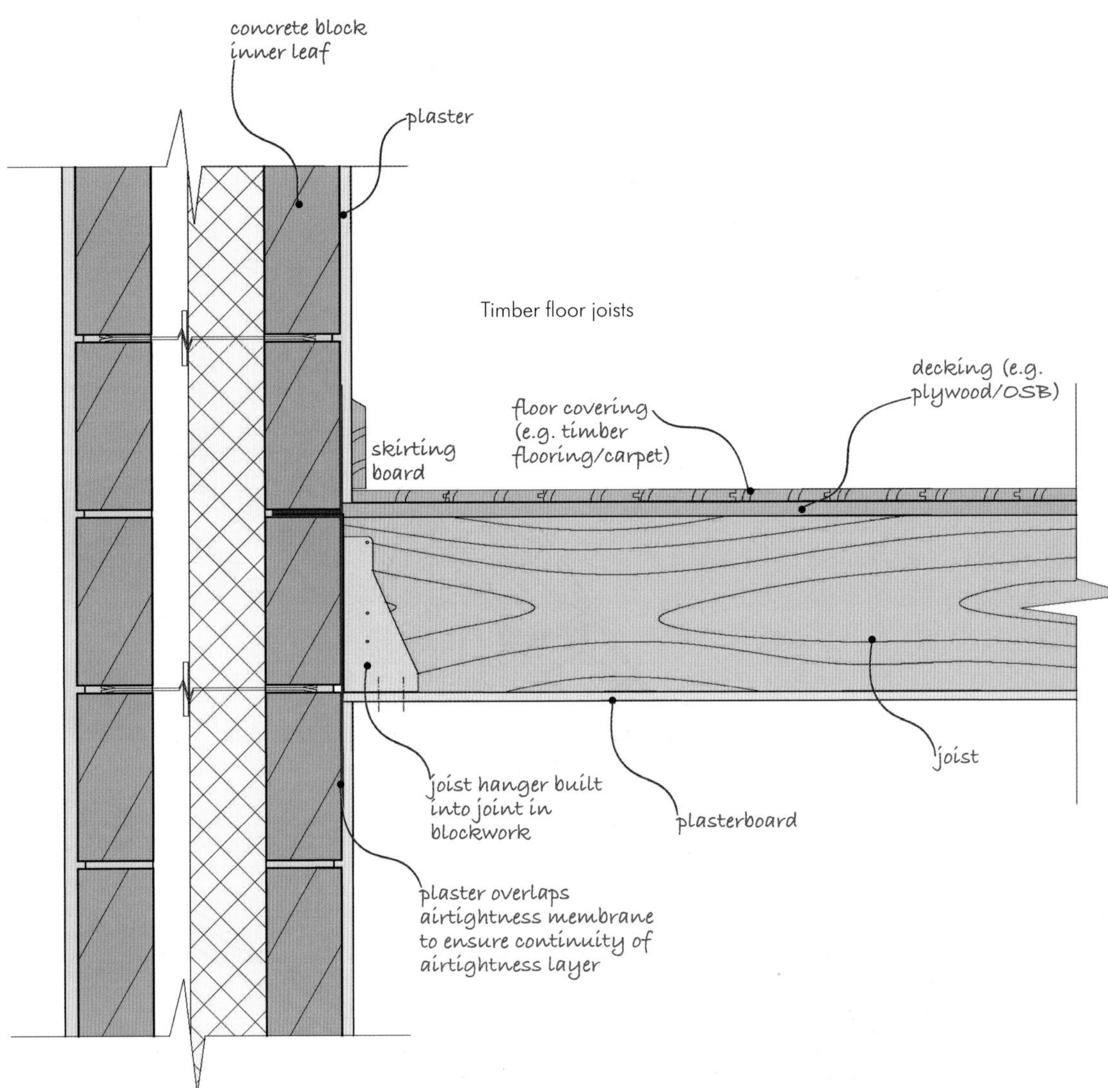

18.01 Suspended timber upper floor: solid timber joists are the most common type of upper floor.

Drilling/notching

It is essential that the joists are not weakened by notching or drilling when pipes and cables are being installed. The bottom portion of the joist is in tension – any damage in this area could cause the joist to fail. The centre line of the joist is the best place for drilling, while notches should be made in the upper edge only.

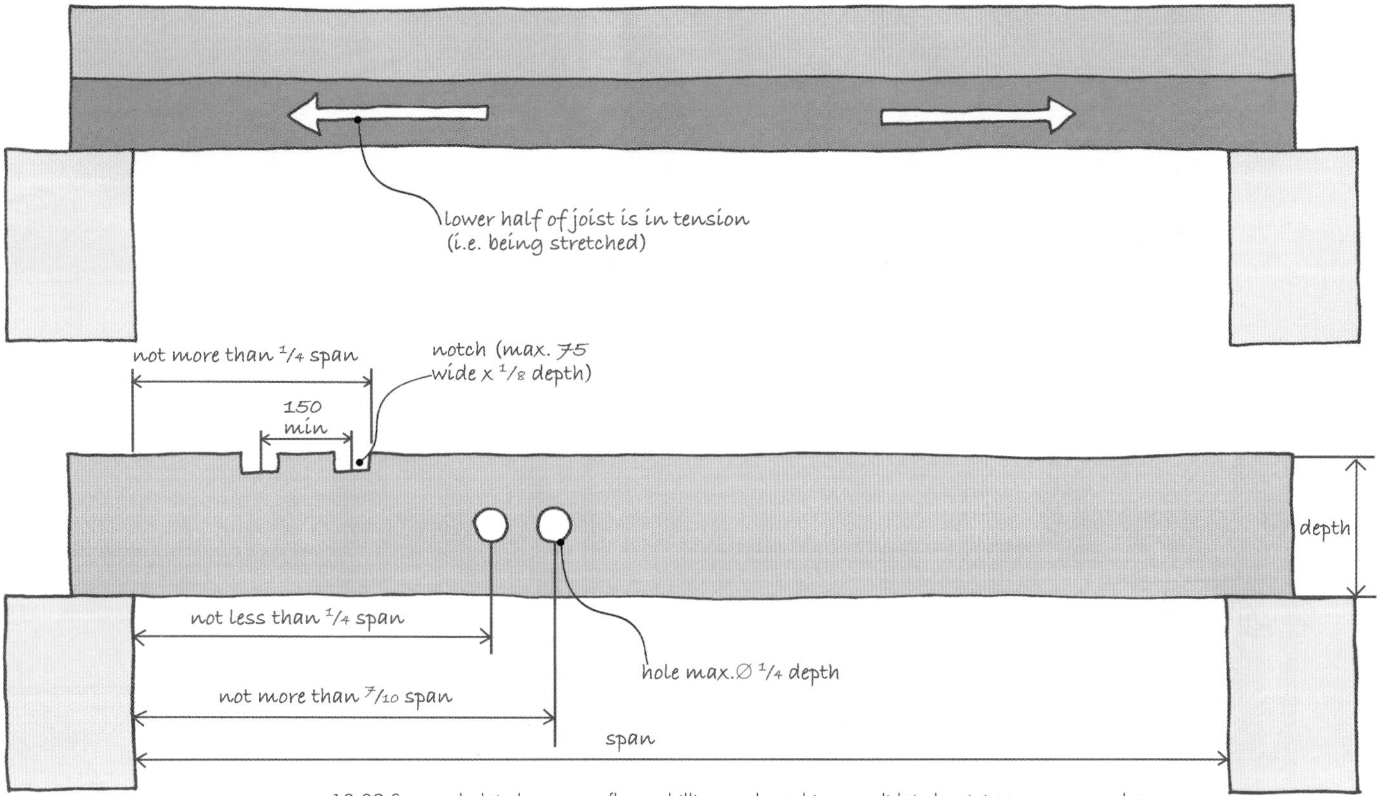

18.02 Suspended timber upper floor: drilling and notching a solid timber joist to accommodate services must be done carefully to avoid weakening the joist.

Stairs ope

The joists used to create the opening for the stair are usually thicker than the regular joists because of the increased loading they have to carry.

18.03 Upper floor: solid timber joists with ope for stairs.

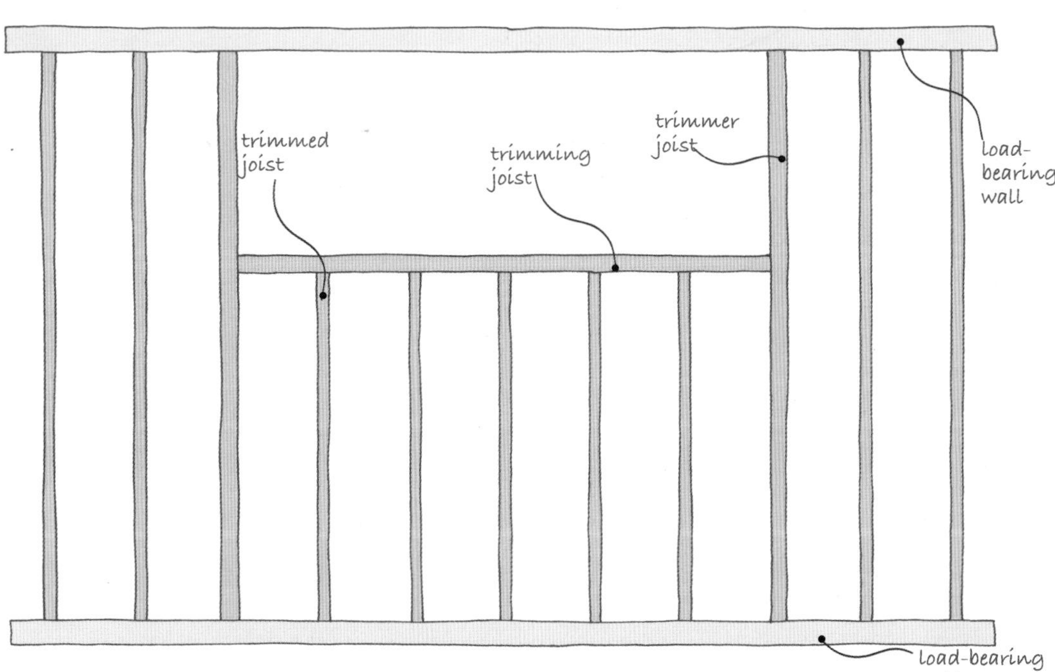

18.04 Upper floor: plan view of stair ope. Note the increased thickness of trimming joist and trimmer joists (joist sizes depend on load and span).

18.05 Upper floor: solid timber joists with herringbone bridging.

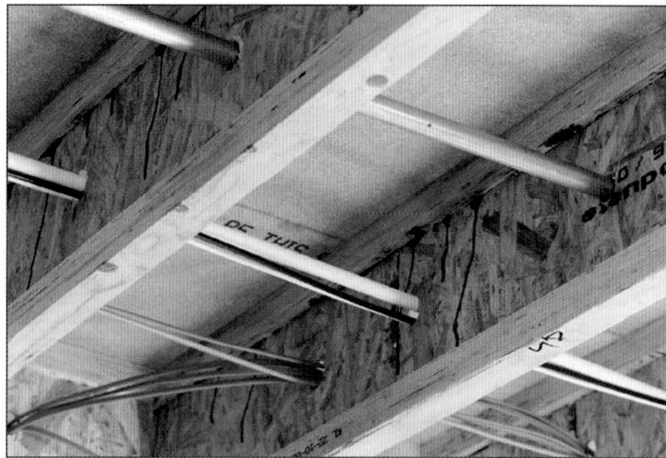

18.06 Upper floor: engineered I beam timber joists.

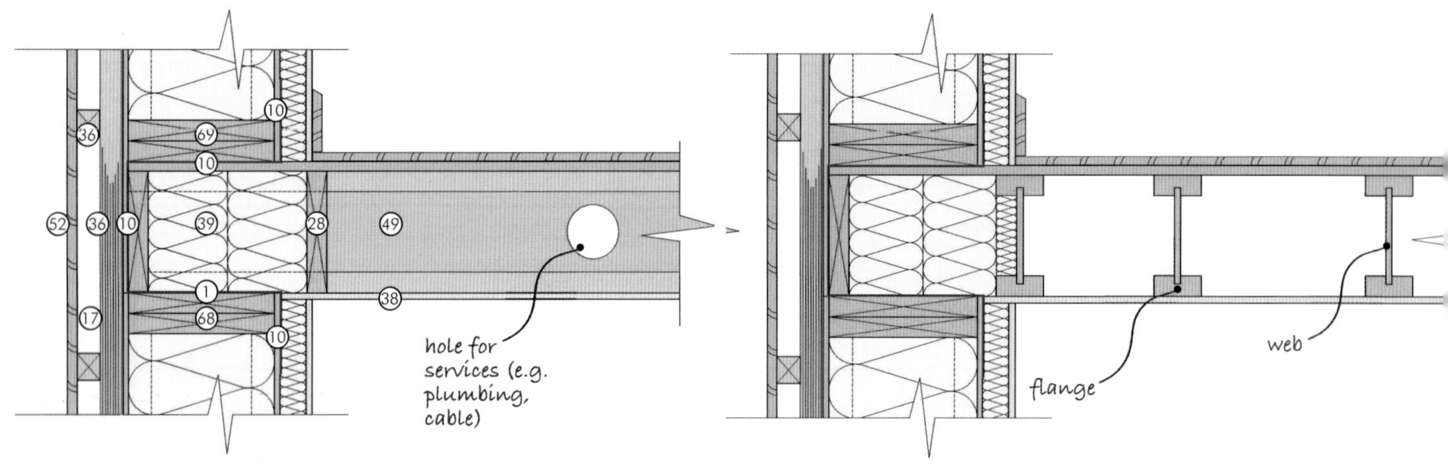

⑩ Airtightness layer
⑰ Breather membrane/ windtight layer
㉘ Solid timber joist
㊱ 50x50mm timber batten
㊴ Quilted insulation
㊾ Engineered joist
52 Timber cladding
68 Head plate
69 Sole plate

18.07 Suspended timber upper floor: 200mm engineered I beam joist (softwood flange with OSB web).

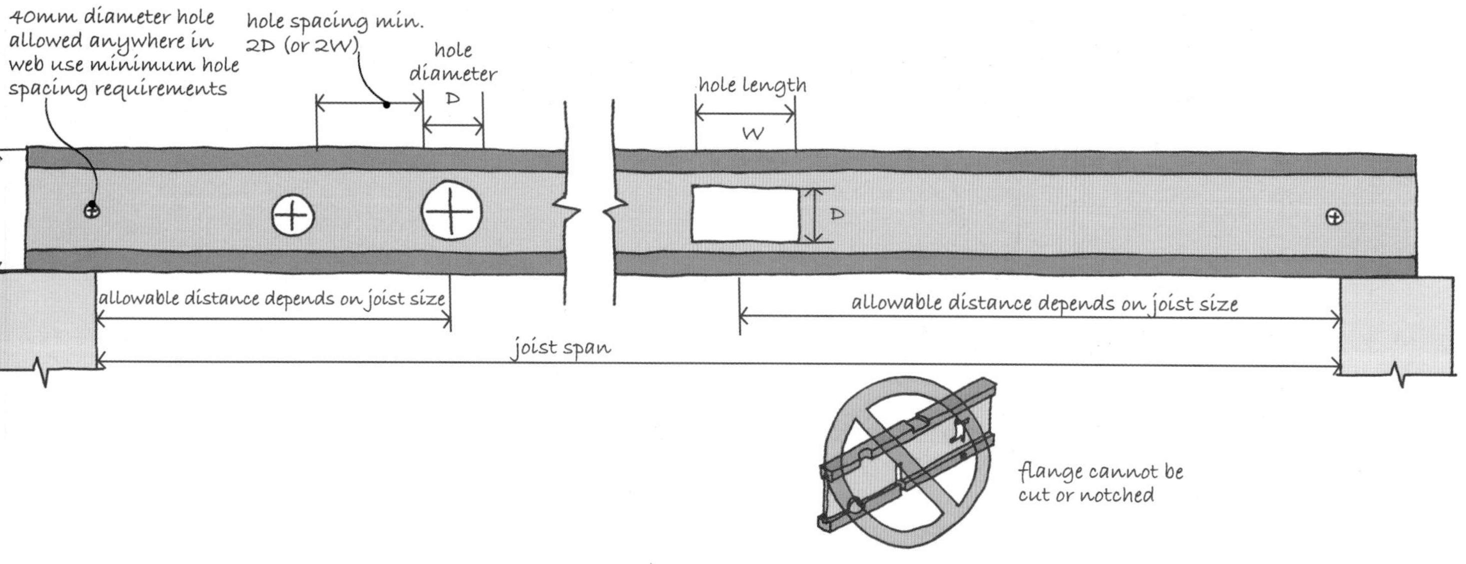

18.08 Suspended timber upper floor: engineered I beam joists have pre-cut 'knock-outs' that can be removed to allow services to be installed.

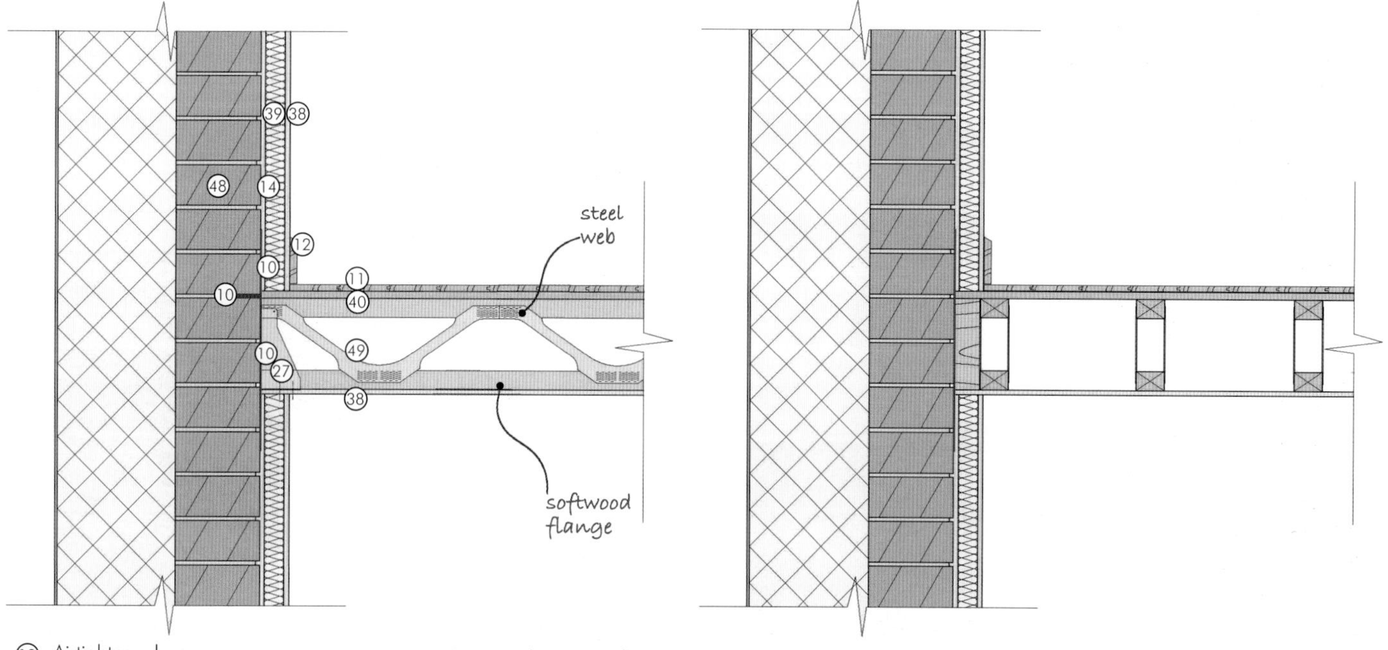

⑩ Airtightness layer
⑪ Floor covering
⑫ Skirting board
⑭ 12mm plaster
㉗ Joist hanger
㊳ Plasterboard
㊴ Quilted insulation
㊵ Oriented strand board
㊽ 215mm block on flat
㊾ Engineered joist

18.09 Timber upper floors: steel open web joists.

18.10 Suspended timber upper floors: steel open web joists allow for easy installation of services.

Concrete upper floors

Concrete suspended floors are heavy and require carefully designed walls to support their load. Precast units are manufactured off site and craned into place on site. They have the benefit of providing good sound insulation.

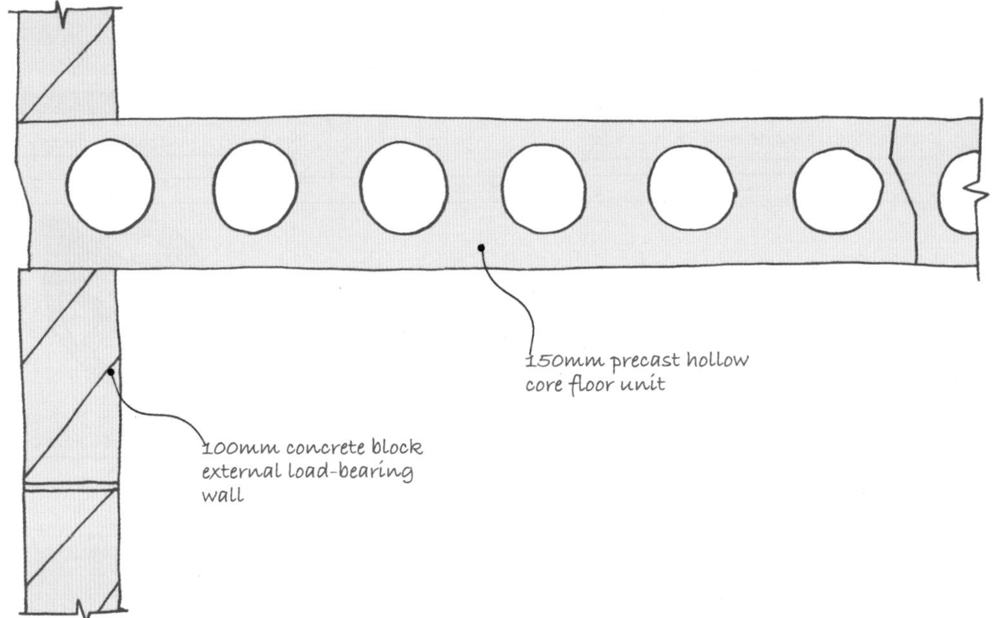

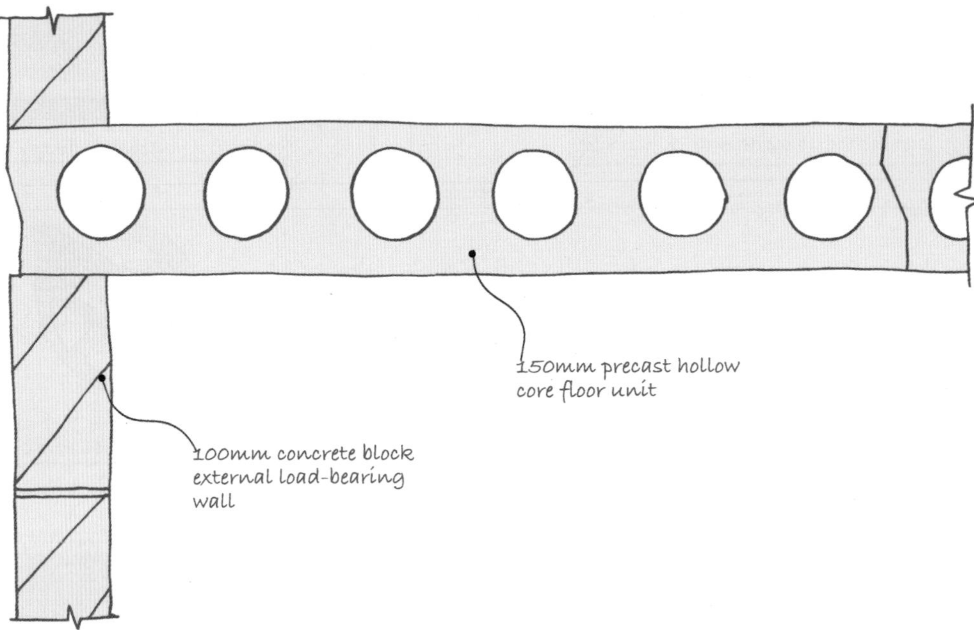

ACTIVITIES

The sound insulation benefits of concrete upper floors is outweighed by the environmental and economic costs of using concrete floor panels instead of timber joists. Discuss this statement with your classmates.

18.11 Suspended concrete upper floor: 150mm hollow core floor units are supported by external and internal blockwork walls.

18.12 Suspended concrete upper floor: hollow core precast floor panels used with a traditional cavity wall structure.

18.13 Suspended concrete upper floor: the inner leaf of these walls is built 'block on flat' to support the weight of these hollow core precast floor panels.

Stairs

A stairs (also known as a stair, stairway, staircase or flight of stairs) is a set of steps combined with a railing. The function of a stairs is to provide safe, comfortable walking access between floor levels in a building.

Performance criteria

Stairs must meet the following performance criteria:

- safety – the stairs should be safe to use
- durability – they should resist the wear and tear of everyday use
- fire – the stairs should be enclosed with fire-resisting storey-height construction
- aesthetics – the stairs should add to the appearance of the space.

Stair forms

Deciding on the form and location of a stairs is surprisingly tricky. If you sketch out the floor plans of a two-storey home and then try to fit in a stairs afterwards, you'll see the problem. Not only must the 'footprint' of the stairs be taken into account, but the space required for landings on both levels must also be considered. For this reason, many forms of stairs have evolved. The straight flight is the simplest; the spiral is the most compact.

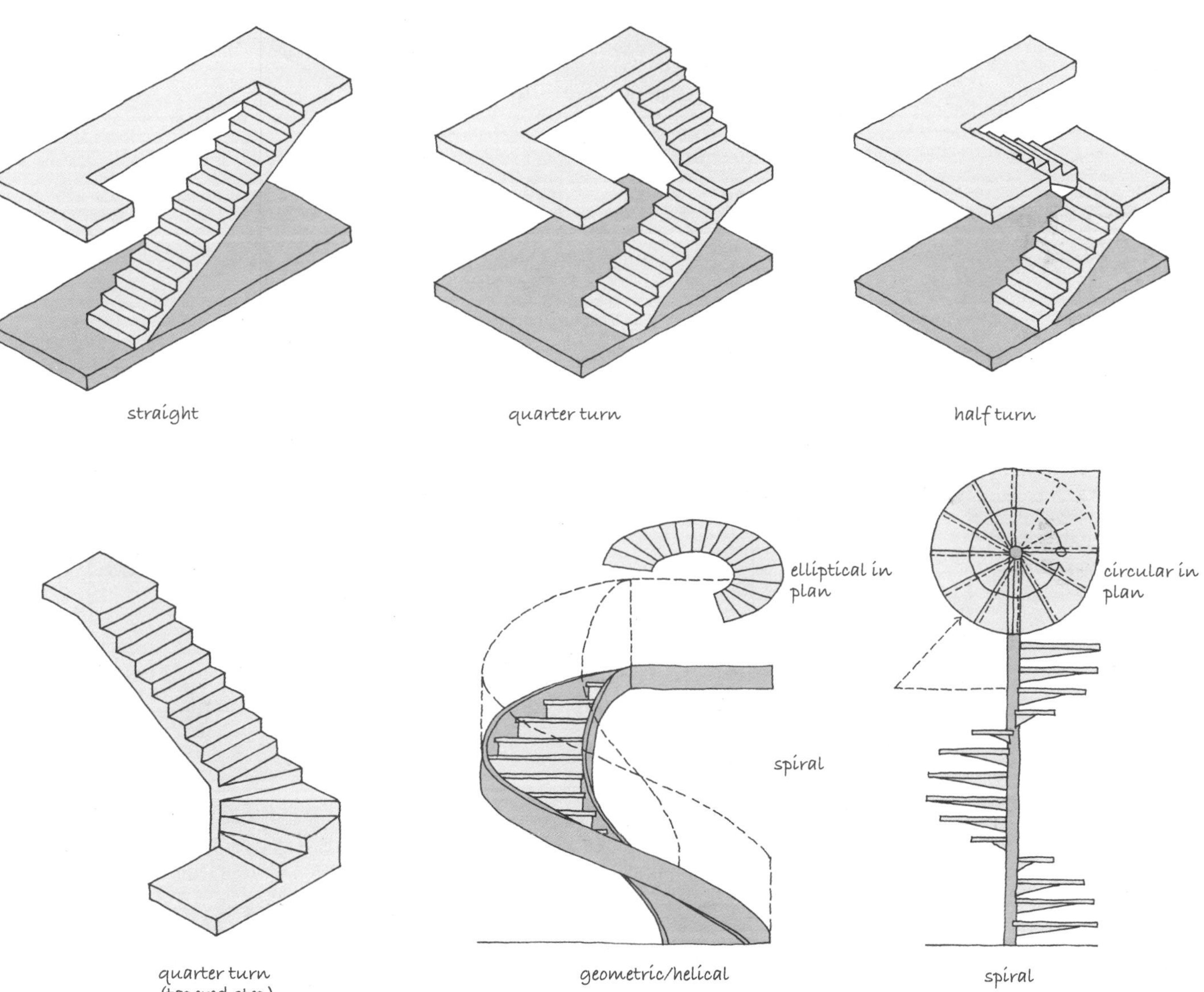

18.14 stairs: various forms can be used to suit the interior layout of a dwelling.

Stairs terminology

A timber stairs comprises treads and risers housed into the strings. The step is wedged and supported with glue blocks to provide durability. The handrail is supported by the newel posts and vertical balusters. The staircase is supported by the ground floor. The wall string and upper newel post are notched over the trimmer joist.

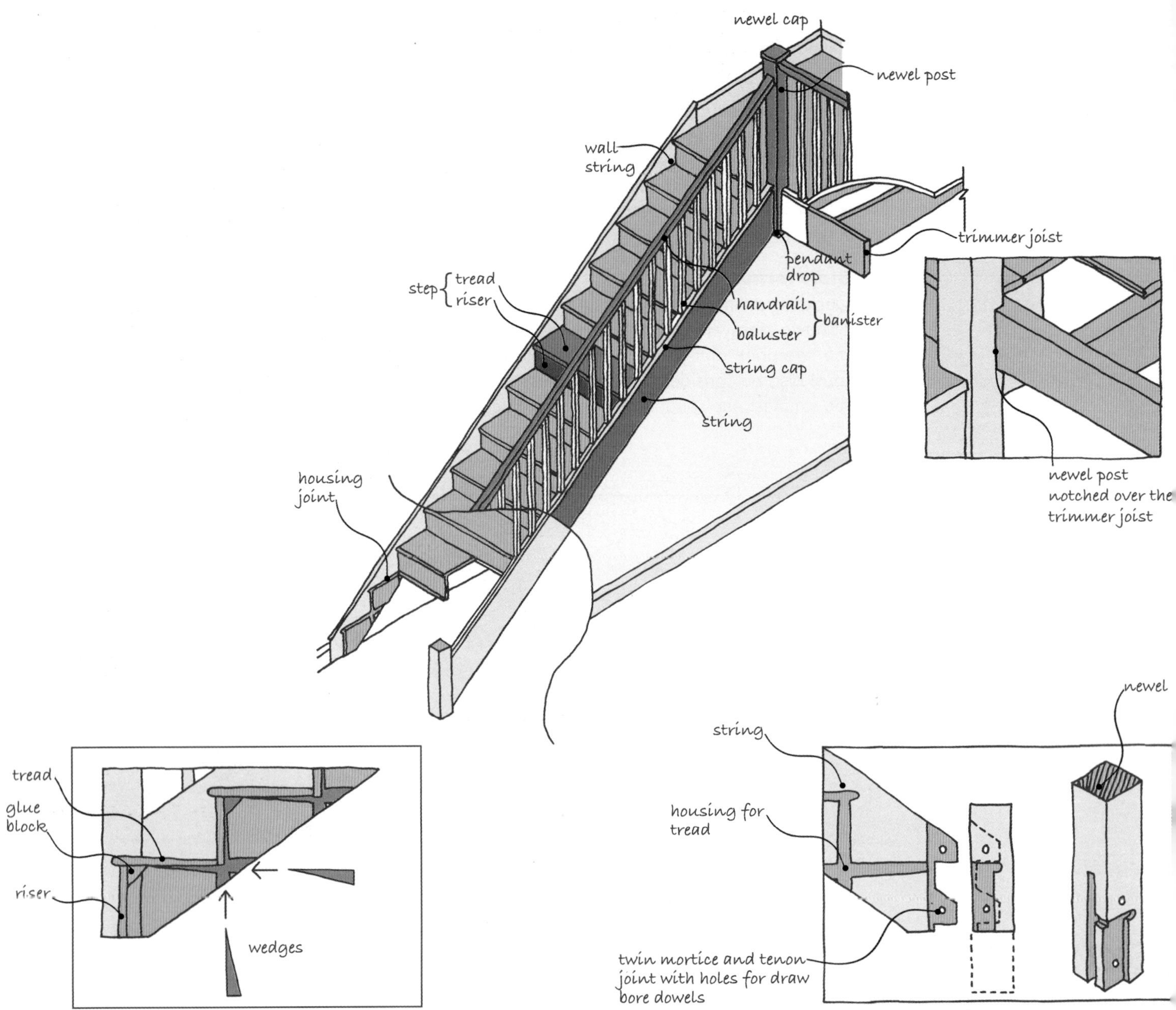

18.15 Stairs: terminology and construction.

Design for safety

While the designer has control over the form, materials and details that create the appearance of a stairs, most of the practical features of a stairs are driven by safety considerations and the requirements of the building regulations. This is to ensure uniformity and consistency from one stairs to another. It is because all stairs are designed within these tight constraints that walking on a stairs comes naturally: they all feel the same. This consistency, from one stairs to the next, makes stairs safer to use and so people are less likely to fall.

The design of the banister needs careful consideration (particularly if children under the age of five are likely to use the stairs). The balusters should be vertical so as to deter climbing and a 100mm diameter sphere should not pass between any openings in the railing.

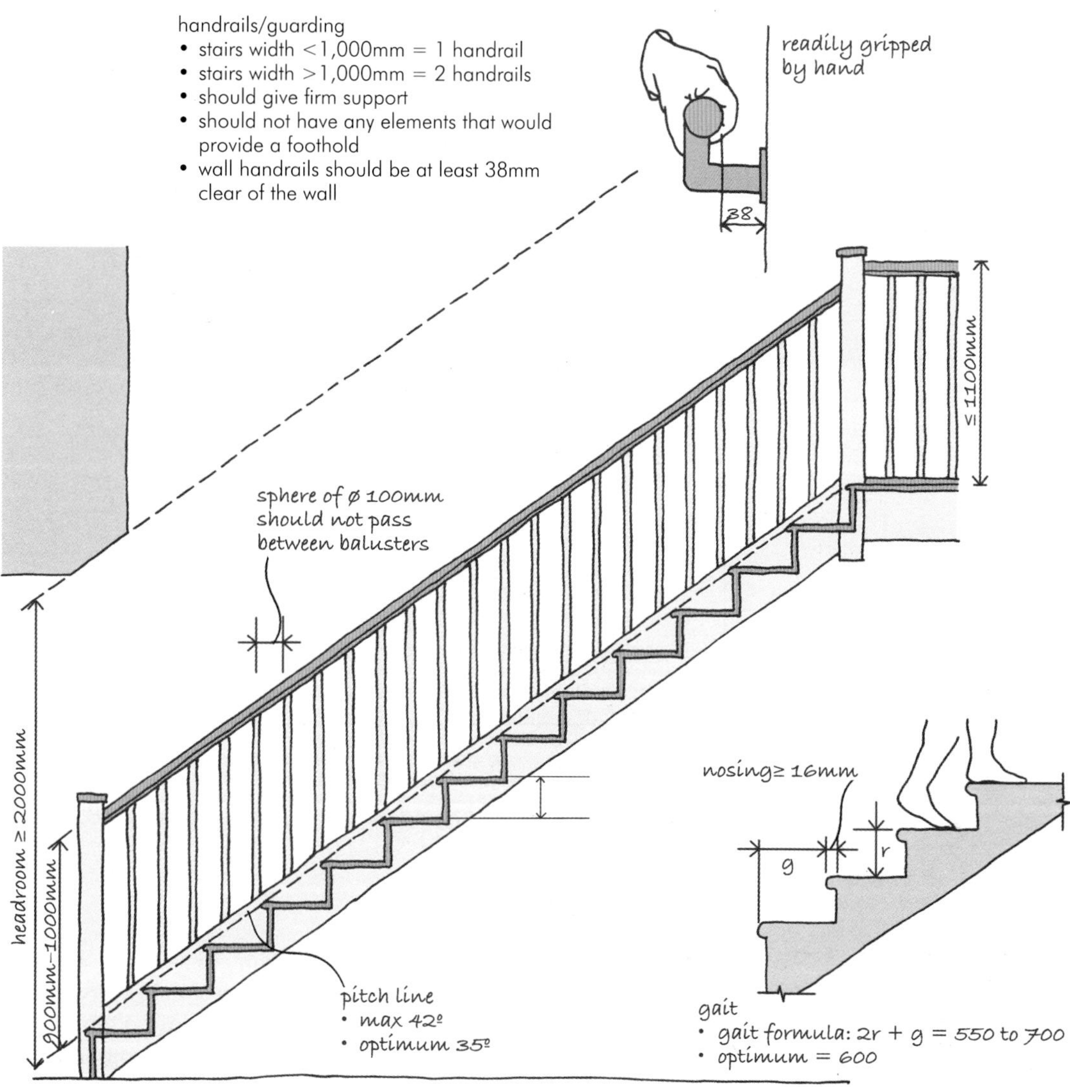

rise (r)
vertical distance from the surface of tread to the surface of tread
- max rise 200mm
- optimum rise 175mm
- 16 max risers in any one flight

going (g)
- horizontal distance from nosing to nosing
- min 220mm
- optimum 250mm

18.16 Stairs: building regulations requirements for safety.

ACTIVITIES

Take a photo of a stairs you use regularly. Make a note of the safety features designed into the stairs and discuss any issues that you think should be addressed. (Many older stairs do not meet current building regulations.)

Stairs calculations

The height between floors varies from building to building. The building regulations state that the floor-to-floor heights should not exceed 2.7m. It is important to calculate the rise and going of a stair, to suit the specific building in which the stair is to be installed to ensure that every rise is exactly equal.

For a straight flight of stairs without an intermediate landing, stair dimensions are calculated in three steps.

1 Divide total rise by 16 or less
  - maximum allowable number of rises is 16
  - rise must be less than 200mm
  - aim for a round number.
2 Optimum going is 250mm.
3 Input these values into the gait formula to check if twice the rise plus the going is between 550mm and 700mm:
  - if necessary adjust number of risers and/or going length until gait formula is satisfied.

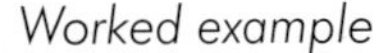

Worked example

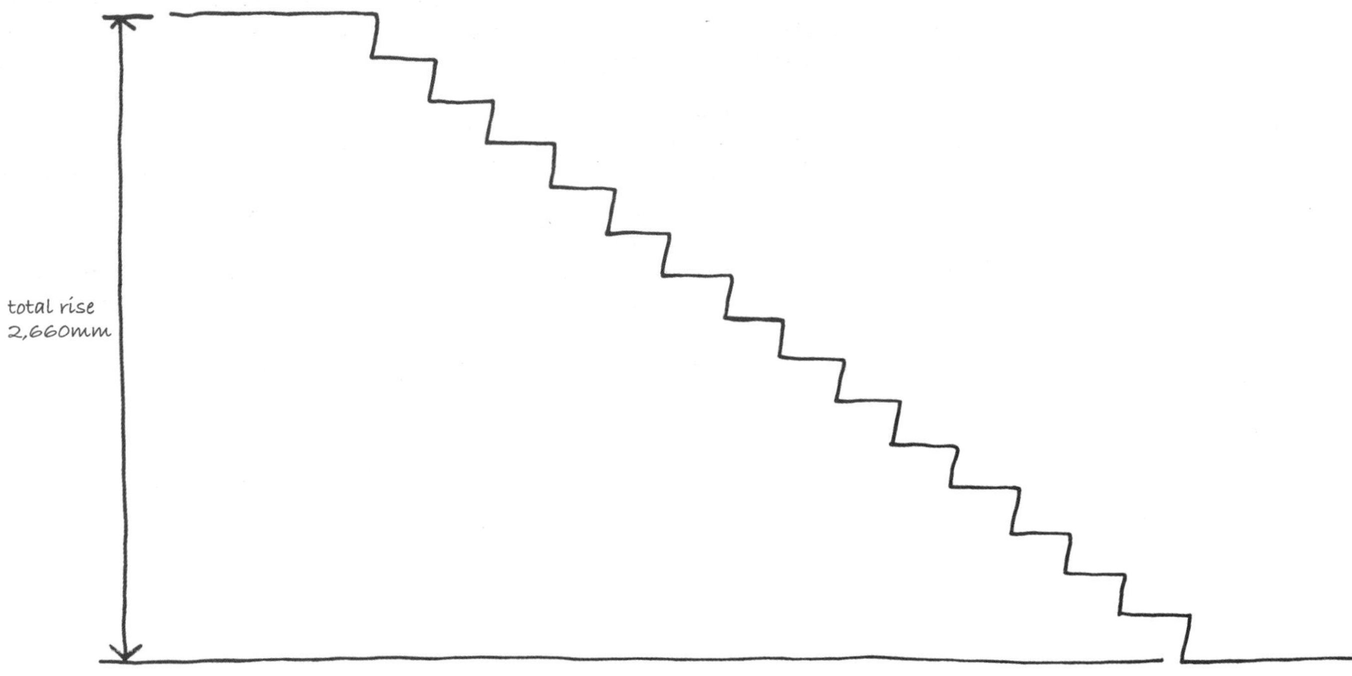

18.17 Stairs: calculation of gait (i.e. rise and going).

Calculate the rise and going of a straight flight of stairs to span between two floors of a house which are 2,660mm apart.

Step 1
Maximum number of rises = 16.
Rise must be between 150mm and 200mm.

- 2,660 ÷ 16 = 166.25 mm (difficult dimension to work with when cutting timber)
- 2,660 ÷ 15 = 177.33 mm (again, too awkward a dimension)
- 2,660 ÷ 14 = 190mm (perfect – a nice round number and it's between 150mm and 200mm)

Step 2
Choose the optimum going of 250mm.

Step 3
Gait formula: twice rise plus going must be between 550mm and 700 mm.

- $550 \leq (2(R) + G) \leq 700$
- $550 \leq (2(190) + 250) \leq 700$
- $550 \leq (630) \leq 700$

630 is between 550 and 700mm, so a rise of 190mm and a going of 250mm would suit this house and meet building regulations requirements.

Total rise 2,660mm; total going 3,250mm.

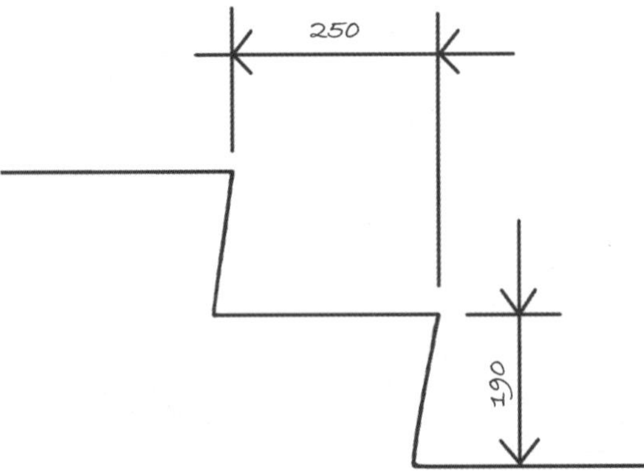

18.18 Stairs solution to worked example.

Internal walls

The primary function of internal walls is to divide the overall space within the house into smaller spaces. Internal walls also have a number of secondary functions, including the accommodation of services, acoustic insulation and fire resistance. Some internal walls are load-bearing: they provide structural support to other building elements.

Performance criteria

Internal walls must meet the following performance criteria:

- load-bearing – load-bearing walls must be capable of supporting the load imposed by the upper floor or roof
- fire resistance – resist the spread of hot gases, smoke and fire in the house
- sound insulation – provide a reasonable degree of acoustic insulation so that activities in one room (e.g. watching television) do not interfere with those occurring in another (e.g. reading a book)
- services – provide secure fixing for light switches and sockets and accommodate electrical cables and plumbing pipes
- finishing – provide a suitable surface for painting or wallpapering.

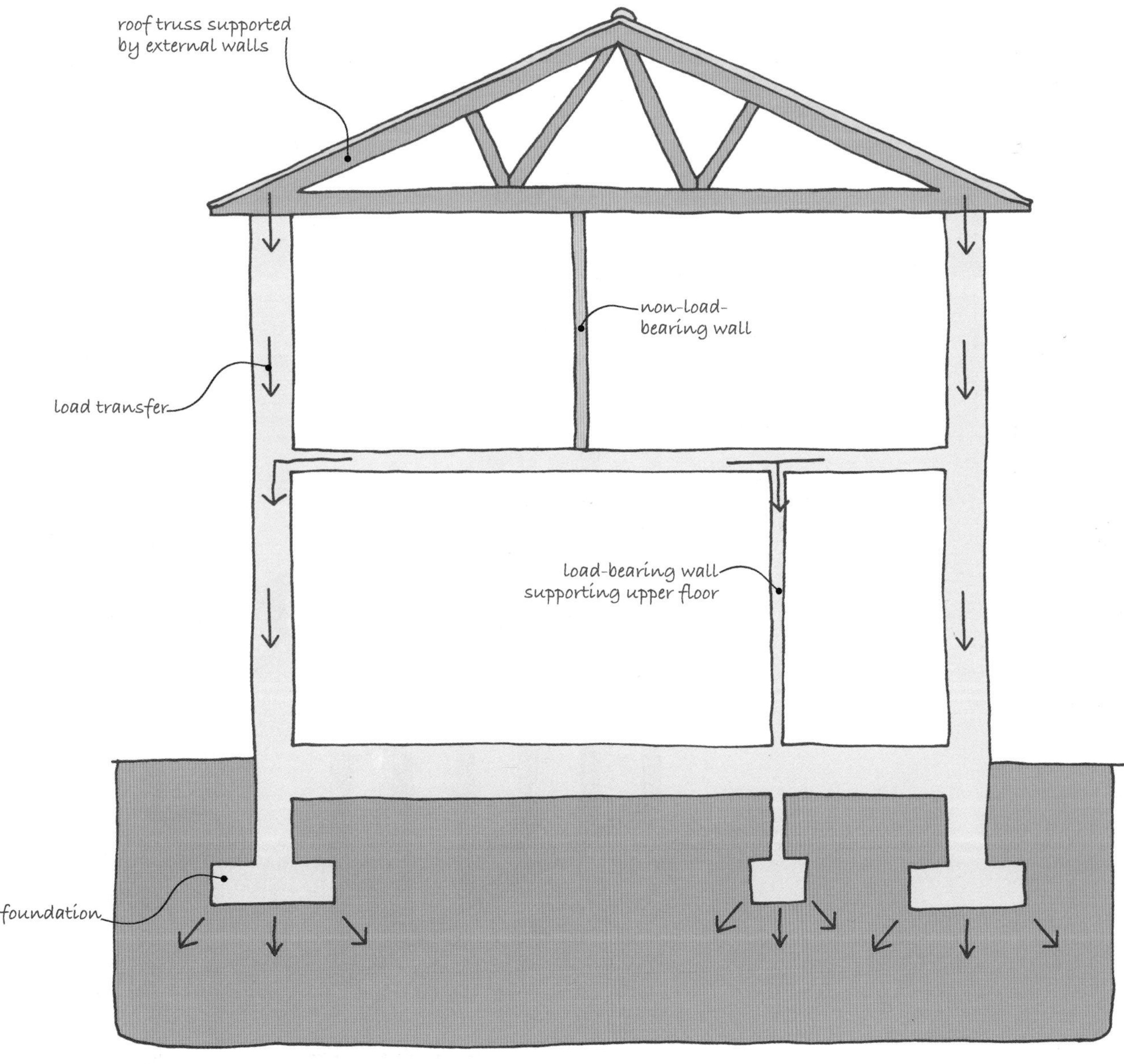

18.19 Internal walls: load-bearing and non-load-bearing walls.

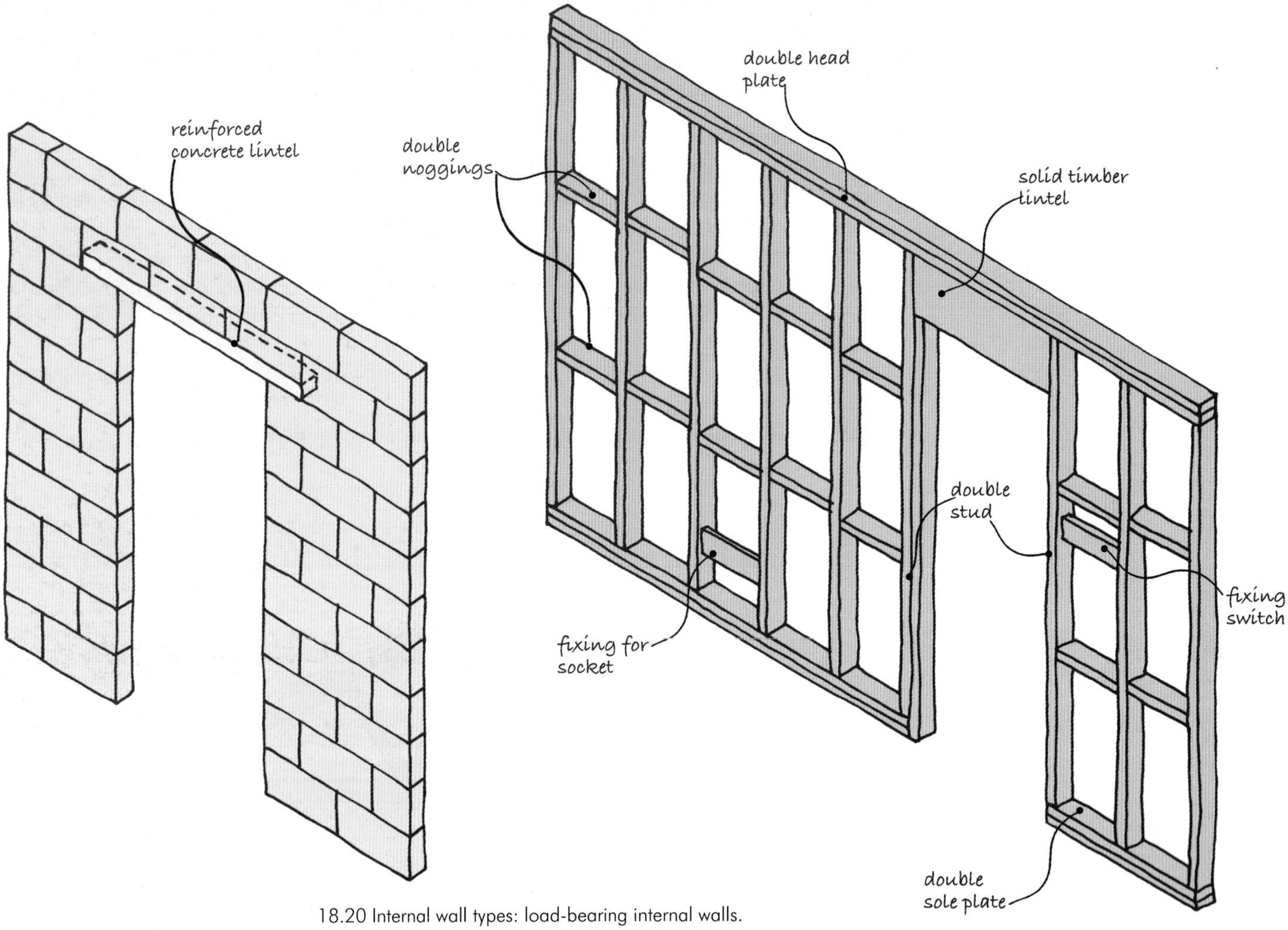

reinforced concrete lintel
double head plate
double noggings
solid timber lintel
double stud
fixing switch
fixing for socket
double sole plate

18.20 Internal wall types: load-bearing internal walls.

single headplate
framed ope
single noggings
single soleplate
fixing for switch
fixing for socket

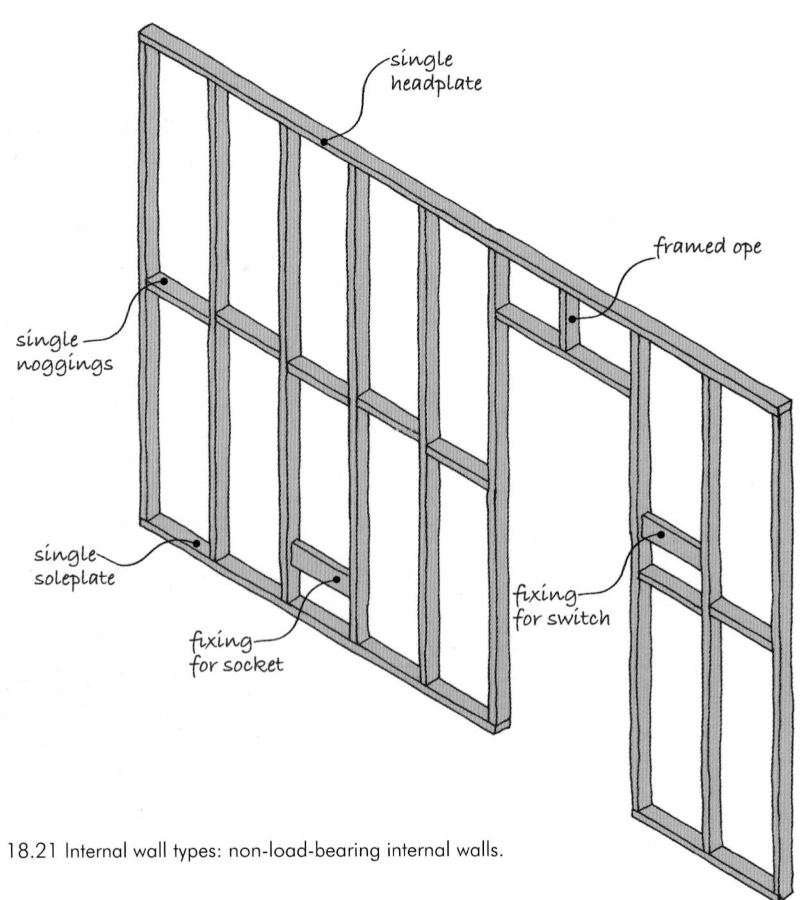

18.21 Internal wall types: non-load-bearing internal walls.

Where services are to be accommodated through the studs of a timber partition, it is important that the strength and stability of the studs is not reduced. To ensure this, holes should only be drilled along the centre line of the stud. The edges of the studs should not be notched.

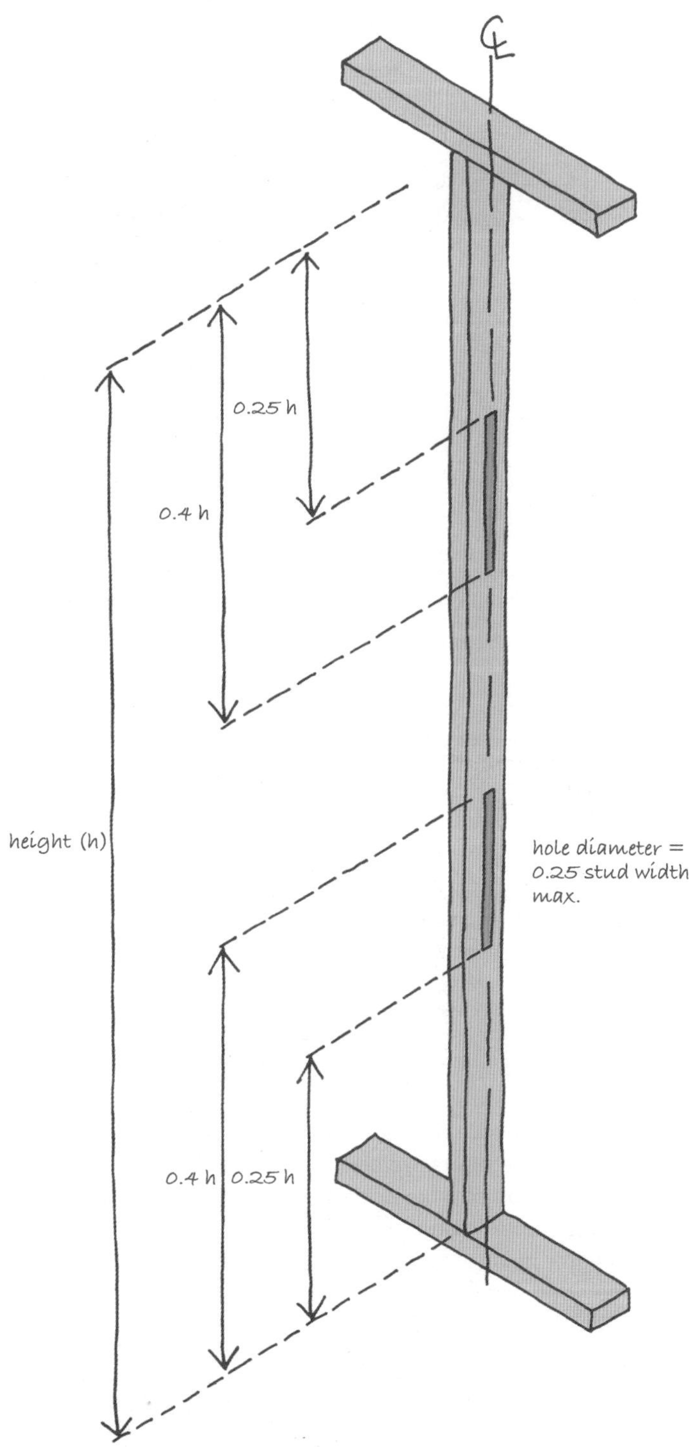

18.22 Accommodating services: holes for pipes and cables can be made in the green zone only to avoid weakening stud.

Internal doors

Flush doors usually have either a hardwood veneer facing or a fibreboard surface which has been press-manufactured to look like a panelled door. These doors often have a wood grain effect and are supplied pre-finished. Solid timber panel doors are usually supplied in softwood (e.g. red deal).

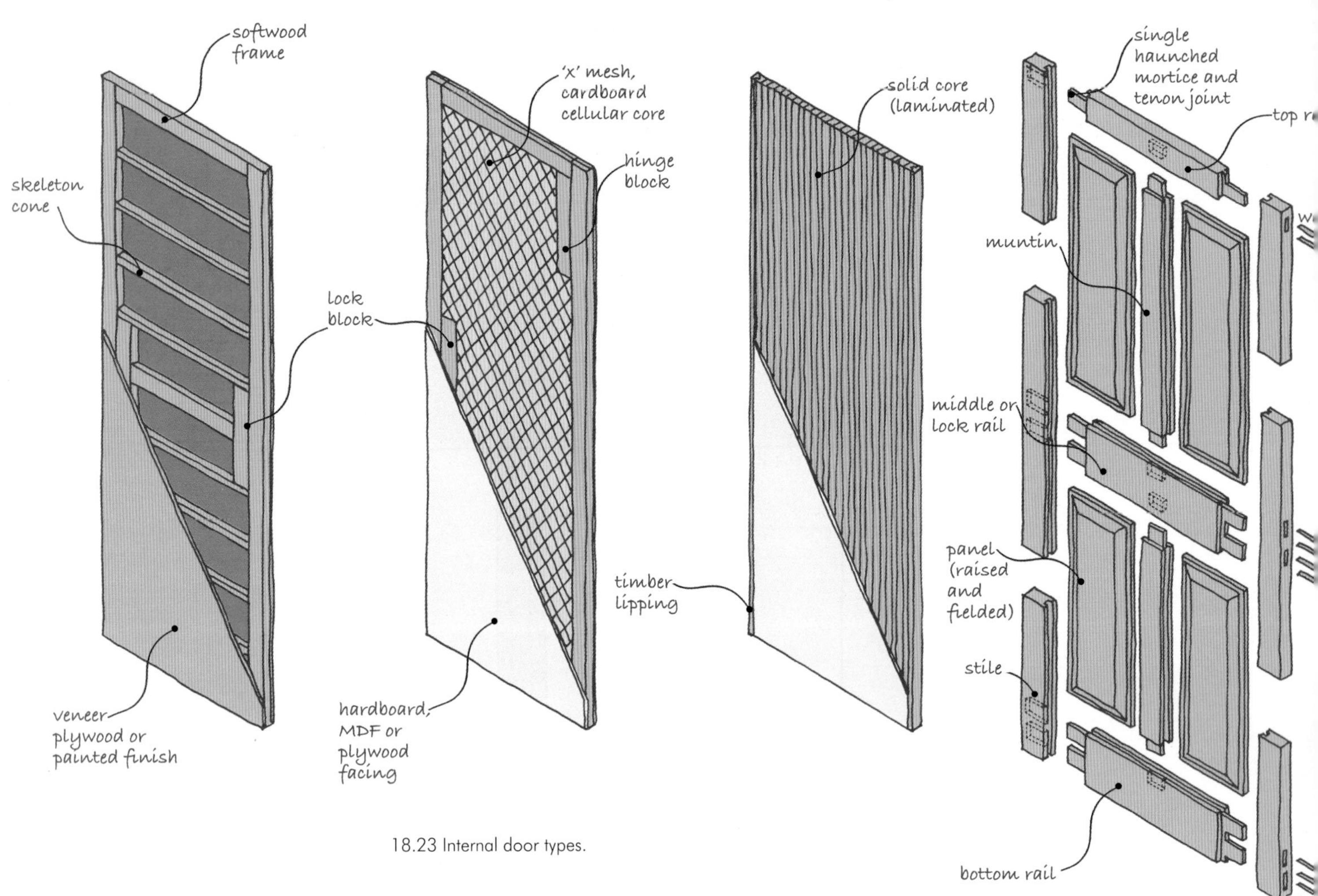

18.23 Internal door types.

Fire doors

A fire door is a special type of internal door which is designed to resist the spread of flames and hot gases. A fire door is fitted in a house where access to the house is possible from an adjoining garage. Fire doors are classed by the length of time they provide protection. The precise classification of a fire door provides two pieces of information: insulation and integrity. Insulation in this context means the resistance to thermal transmittance between the surfaces of the door. Integrity means resistance to the penetration of flame and hot gases. The performance standard of the door is measured in minutes and denoted by FD (fire door) and a number. For example, FD30 is a 30-minute fire door. Common materials used in the manufacture of fire doors include plasterboard, compressed mineral wool and high-density (fire-resistant) particle board.

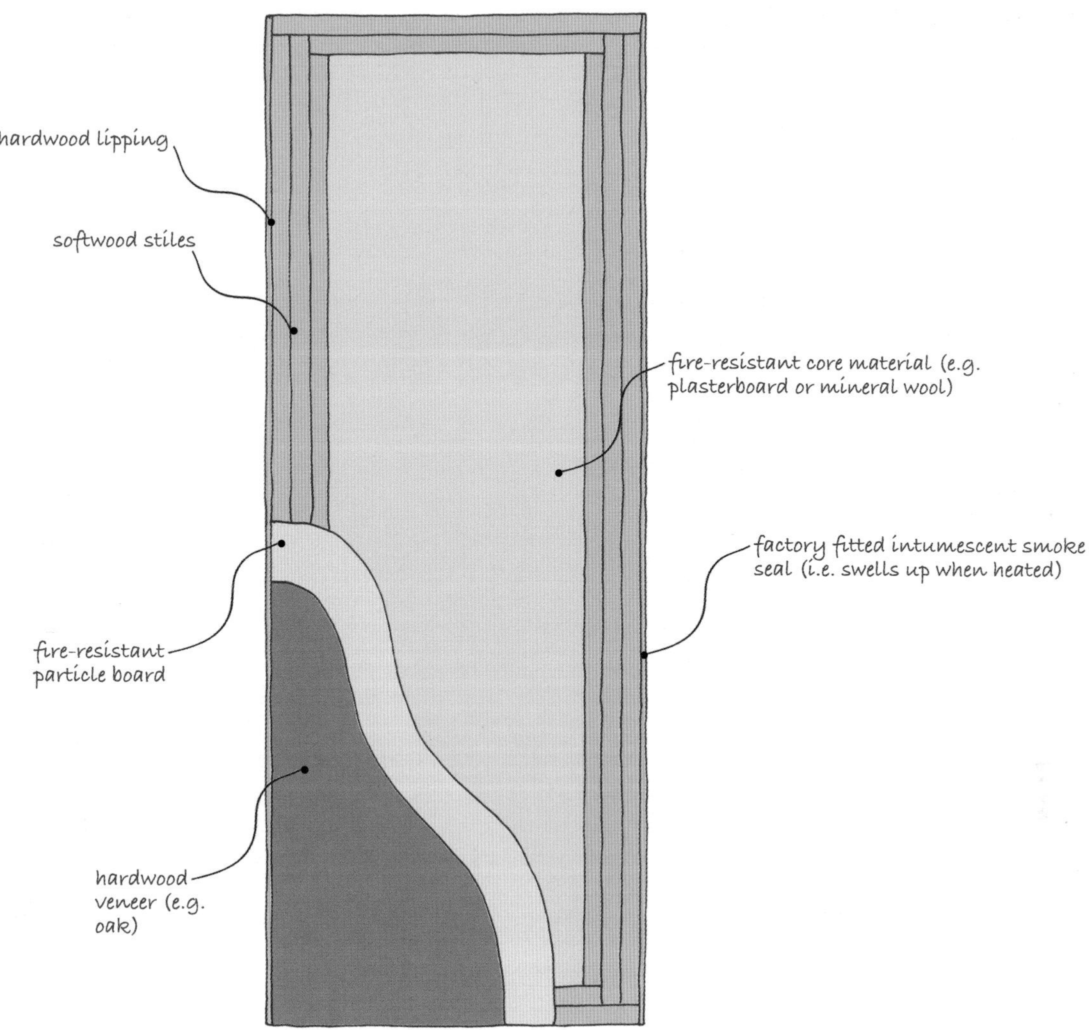

18.24 Fire door: conceptual design for a fire door showing typical components.

REVISION EXERCISES

1 Explain, using a neat freehand sketch, the guidelines for drilling and notching solid timber floor joists.
2 Describe the advantages of engineered timber joists compared to solid timber joists.
3 Discuss the advantages and disadvantages of concrete upper floors.
4 Summarise, using a neat freehand sketch, the safety requirements for a typical stairs.
5 Calculate the rise and going for a straight flight of stairs to span between two floors of a house which are 2,590 mm apart.

CHAPTER 19

Structural Systems – Drawings and Details

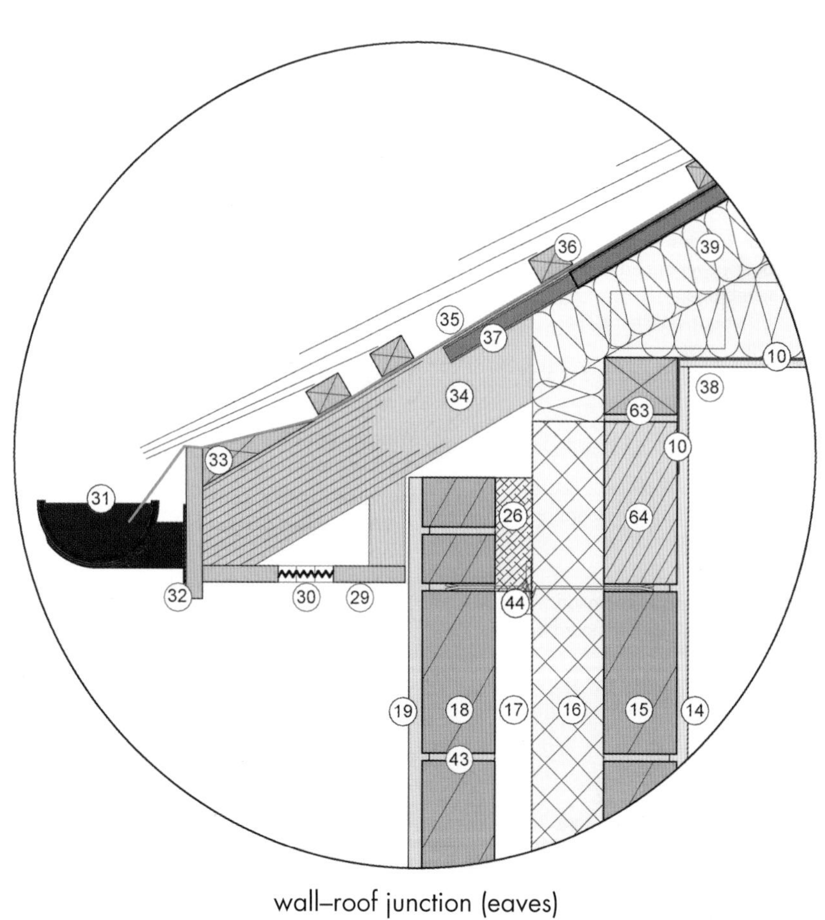

wall–roof junction (eaves)

List of Elements

(1) Subsoil
- min. loadbearing capacity 100kN/m^2

(2) Reinforced concrete foundation
- C25/30 concrete (i.e. cube strength 30N/mm^2)
- 12mm rebars, 100mm c/c, min. cover 50mm
- max. water cement ratio 0.55
- design to comply with TGD A Structure
- design to comply with IS EN 1992 Design of Concrete Structures
- concrete to comply with IS EN 206

(3) Hardcore
- unbound granular fill
- only natural material
- washed graded coarse aggregate (e.g 0/31 crushed rock or 0/40 gravel)
- to comply with IS EN 12620
- to comply with SR21:2013 Annex E (i.e. to contain no pyrite)
- no recycled or manufactured materials
- embedded radon sump & drainage pipes (where necessary)

(4) Concrete fill
- well compacted
- to comply with TGD A: Structure

(5) Sand blinding
- 50mm depth
- 0/2 washed graded fine aggregate
- to comply with IS EN 12620

(6) Radon barrier or damp proof membrane (DPM)
- NSAI certified radon membrane:
  - radon measures to comply with TGD C: site preparation and resistance to moisture
  - all joints properly overlapped and sealed
- Damp proof membrane:
  - certified 1200 gauge polythene film
  - 300μm min. thickness
  - all joints properly overlapped and sealed

(7) Rigid insulation
- 150mm – single layer in building regulations floors
- 100mm – three layers in Passivhaus floors
- EPS100 – expanded polystyrene board or similar

(8) Rigid insulation
- 60mm vertical upstand edge insulation
- EPS 100 – expanded polystyrene board or similar

(9) Reinforced concrete slab
- C25/30 concrete
- ø10mm rebars min. 500mm c/c
- max. water cement ratio 0.55
- concrete to comply with IS EN 206
- design to comply with TGD A Structure
- design to comply with IS EN 1992 Design of Concrete Structures

(10) Airtightness layer
- airtightness membrane or
- panel (e.g. OSB3) or
- 12mm gypsum plaster (on blockwork)
- all connections and joints taped with appropriate airtightness tape

(11) Floor covering
- timber flooring
- tiles
- carpet etc.

(12) Skirting board
- timber selection and finish to suit client

(13) Damp proof course (DPC)
- to comply with EN 14909

(14) 12mm plaster
- gypsum based plaster applied in two coats
- 10mm base coat
- 2mm finish coat
- λ: 0.18W/mK

(15) Inner leaf concrete blockwork
- 440x215x100mm standard concrete blocks
- compressive strength 5N/mm^2
- λ: 1.33W/mK
- blocks to comply with IS EN 771-3
- design to comply with IS EN 1996 Design of Masonry Structures

(16) Cavity insulation
- 100mm PIR (polyisocyanurate board)
- λ: 0.023W/mK

(17) 50mm air cavity
- thermal resistance: 0.180 m^{2}K/W

(18) Outer leaf concrete blockwork
- 440x215x100mm standard concrete blocks
- compressive strength 5N/mm^2
- λ:1.33W/mK
- blocks to comply with IS EN 771-3
- design to comply with IS EN 1996 Design of Masonry Structures

(19) Render
- 20mm cement, lime, sand based render
- applied in 3 coats to total thickness 20mm
- : 1.00W/mK
- to comply with IS EN13914-1

(20) Precast concrete sill (100x70mm)
- pre-stressed steel (double cord)
- to comply with BS 5642-1

(21) Window board
- timber selection and finish to suit client

(22) Insulated window frame
- WEP certified or Passivhaus certified (as appropriate)

(23) Insulated window casement
- WEP certified or Passivhaus certified (as appropriate)

(24) Glazing unit (double or triple glazed)
- WEP certified or Passivhaus certified (as appropriate)

(25) Precast concrete lintel
- prestressed steel (double cord)
- lintel to comply with IS EN 845-2
- design to comply with IS EN 1996 Design of Masonry Structures

(26) Cavity closer/fire stop
- rigid insulation in masonry wall (e.g. EPS 100 or similar)
- proprietary fire stop in timber frame wall

(27) Joist hanger
- galvanised steel hanger & nails
- to comply with EN 845-1

(28) Solid timber joist
- C16 or C24 timber joist to suit span and spacing
- design to comply with IS EN 1995 Design of Timber Structures

(29) Timber soffit

(30) Air gap for ventilation
- proprietary vent cover

(31) Rainwater gutter
- connected to rainwater pipe and drain

(32) Timber fascia

(33) Tilting fillet

(34) Rafter/top chord (truss)
- roof truss to comply with IS 193 and IS EN14250
- design to comply with IS EN 1995 Design of Timber Structures

(35) Roofing underlay (breather membrane/windtight layer)
- all joints properly overlapped and sealed
- NSAI certified roofing membrane
- to comply with EN 13859-1

(36) 50x50mm timber batten
- to comply with IS EN 1995 Design of Timber Structures

(37) Proprietary eaves ventilator
- installed along continuous length of eaves

(38) Plasterboard
- 12.5mm thick board
- joints taped and filled or
- 2mm gypsum plaster finish coat

(39) Quilted insulation
- depth/thickness varies – scale from drawing
- mineral fibre, sheep's wool, hemp, cellulose etc.
- λ:0.034W/mK – 0.039W/mK

(40) Oriented strand board
- OSB3 – airtight board
- design to comply with IS EN 1995 Design of Timber Structures

(41) Breather membrane/windtight layer
- all joints properly overlapped and sealed
- to comply with EN 13859-1

(42) Brickwork
- design to comply with IS EN 1996 Design of Masonry Structures

(43) Mortar (cement, sand)
- design to comply with IS EN 1996 Design of Masonry Structures

(44) Wall tie
- to comply with with EN 845-1
- stainless steel ties in building regulations walls
- low thermal conductivity ties (e.g. Teplo) in Passivhaus walls

(45) Rigid insulation
- 250 or 300mm – scale from drawing
- EPS 100 – expanded polystyrene board
- λ: 0.034W/mK
- or suitable alternative that provides equal performance
- NSAI certified insulation system

(46) Edging blocks
- high-density rigid insulation EPS 300 Fprofile
- to comply with EN 13163

(47) Proprietary render system
- to suit NSAI certified external insulation system

(48) 215mm block on flat
- concrete block 440x215x100mm
- compressive strength 5N/mm^2
- blocks to comply with IS EN 771-3
- design to comply with IS EN 1996 Design of Masonry Structures

(49) Engineered joist
- 220mm deep metal web joist or
- 220mm deep timber I joist (e.g. 45x45mm flange, 8mm web thickness)
- NSAI certified joists (e.g. Ecojoist)
- design to comply with IS EN 1995 Design of Timber Structures

(50) Batt insulation
- woodfibre insulation, mineral wool or similar
- λ: 0.034W/mK – 0.039W/mK

(51) Anchor strap
- galvanised steel strap
- fixed to stud of timber frame wall
- built into joint of masonry
- to comply with EN 845-1

(52) Timber cladding
- from FSC certified timber supplier
- design to comply with IS EN 1995 Design of Timber Structures

(53) Slates
- natural or fibre cement slate
- 600x300mm
- copper nails/crampions, stainless steel hooks
- installation to comply with Irish Code of Practice for Slating and Tiling ICP2: 2002

(54) Sarking board
- 25mm breathable woodfibre board or similar

(55) Concrete path
- to comply with IS EN 206

(56) Threshold rainwater drain
- recycled plastic U channel with stainless steel grate
- connected to main drain/soakage pit

(57) Door sill
- thermally insulated door sill
- Passivhaus certified (as appropriate)

(58) 100mm Insulated timber door leaf
- e.g. 88mm PUR insulation bonded to
- 6mm timber surface layers with
- solid timber lipping
- Passivhaus certified (as appropriate)

(59) Door frame
- thermally insulated door frame
- Passivhaus certified (as appropriate)

(60) Noggins/bridging
- design to comply with IS EN 1995 Design of Timber Structures

(61) Steel lintel
- galvanised steel lintel to comply with EN 845-1.
- design to comply with IS EN 1996 Design of Masonry Structures

(62) Timber stud
- design to comply with IS EN 1995 Design of Timber Structures

(63) Wall plate
- 100x75mm
- design to comply with IS EN 1995 Design of Timber Structures

(64) Aerated autoclaved concrete block
- 440x215x100mm AAC concrete blocks
- compressive strength 5N/mm^2
- λ: 0.17W/mK
- NSAI certified blocks
- blocks to comply with IS EN 771-3
- design to comply with IS EN 1996 Design of Masonry Structures

(65) Suspended plasterboard ceiling
- 12.5mm plasterboard fixed to proprietary suspended metal framework
- plasterboard joints taped and filled or
- 2mm gypsum plaster finish coat

(66) Roof truss (bottom chord)
- manufactured by NSAI certified manufacturer
- roof truss to comply with IS 193 and IS EN 14250
- design to comply with IS EN 1995 Design of Timber Structures

(67) Roof truss (top chord)
- manufactured by NSAI certified manufacturer
- roof truss to comply with IS 193 and IS EN 14250.
- design to comply with IS EN 1995 Design of Timber Structures

(68) Head plate
- 44mm solid timber – width to suit design – scale from drawing
- design to comply with IS EN 1995 Design of Timber Structures

(69) Sole plate
- 44mm solid timber – width to suit design – scale from drawing
- design to comply with IS EN 1995 Design of Timber Structures

(70) Timber decking
- 18mm OSB, plywood or similar
- design to comply with IS EN 1995 Design of Timber Structures

(71) Timber lintel
- design to comply with IS EN 1995 Design of Timber Structures

(72) Spandrel panel
- manufactured by NSAI certified manufacturer
- roof truss to comply with IS 193 and IS EN 14250
- design to comply with IS EN 1995 Design of Timber Structures

(73) Gable ladder
- manufactured by NSAI certified manufacturer
- roof truss to comply with IS 193 and IS EN 14250
- design to comply with IS EN 1995 Design of Timber Structures

(75) Service cavity
- 50x50mm timber batten with mineral fibre, sheep's wool, hemp or similar insulation
- λ: 0.034W/mK – 0.039W/mK

(76) Reinforced concrete ring beam
- C25/30 concrete
- λ12mm rebars –100mm wide: 2 bars, 215mm wide: 4 bars, min. cover 50mm
- max. water:cement ratio 0.55
- concrete to comply with IS EN 206
- design to comply with TGD A Structure
- design to comply with IS EN 1992 Design of Concrete Structures

(77) Stainless steel tie
- λ5mm, length 350mm
- s500 stainless steel U-sinus tie

(78) Smooth rounded gravel
- 5mm to 8mm washed graded stone

(79) Proprietary sill
- powder coated aluminium sill

(80) Edging block external protection layer
- proprietary external render or similar
- to prevent mechanical damage by plant roots or vermin

(81) Planting (e.g. sedum grass)

(82) Growing medium
- lightweight expanded clay aggregate (LECA)

(83) Filter layer
- geotextile – filter fleece/landscaping fabric
- protects the drainage layer from becoming clogged with fine soil particles

(84) Drainage layer/reservoir
- honeycombed plastic structure that prevents plants becoming waterlogged or from drying out

(85) Root barrier
- prevents roots causing damage to the roof structure
- non-woven polypropylene geotextile

(86) Waterproofing layer
- single ply membrane (e.g. PVC, EPDM)
- NSAI certified waterproofing membrane
- to comply with EN 13956/13583/1928

(87) Vapour compensation layer

(88) Firring piece
- min. thickness 50mm (at thin end of taper)
- to comply with IS EN 1995 Design of Timber Structures

(89) Sheet roof covering (e.g. zinc)
- NSAI certified roof covering
- to comply with EN 501

Masonry cavity wall: building regulations standard (transverse section)
238–239

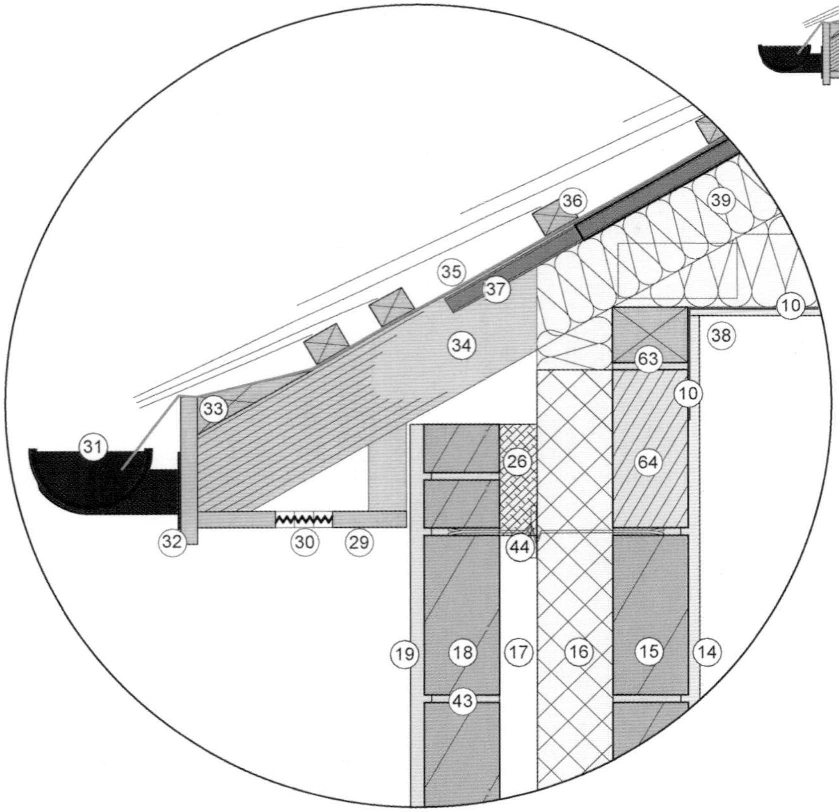

wall–roof junction (eaves)

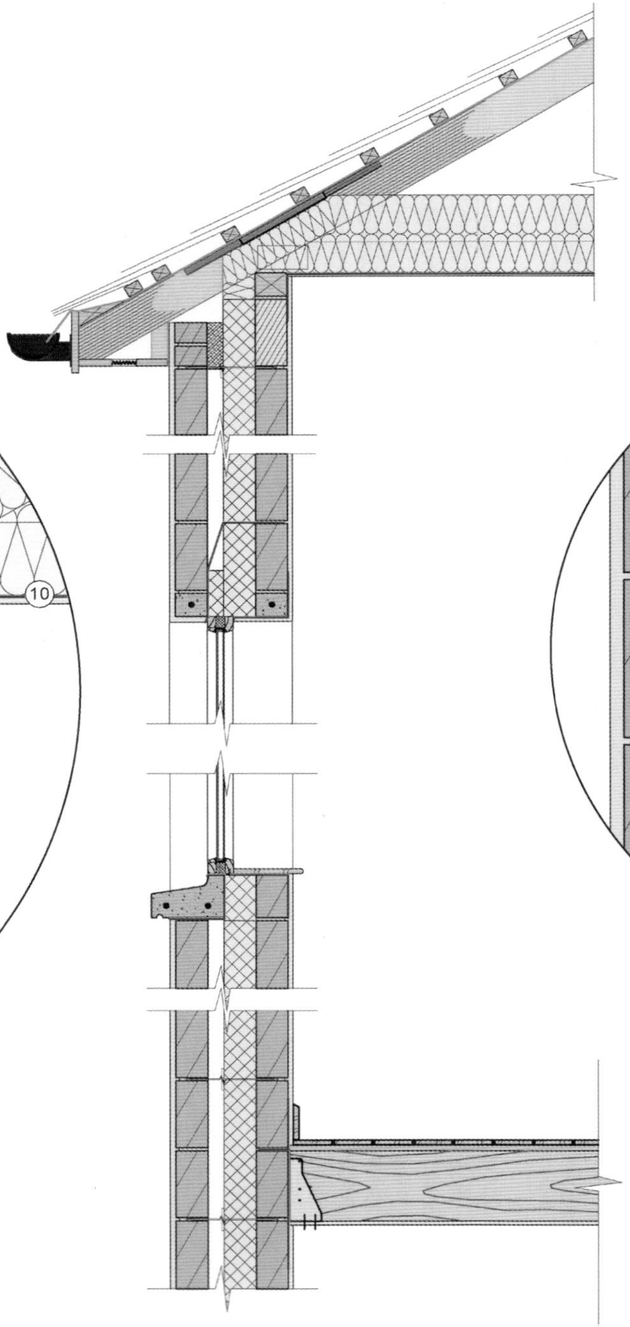

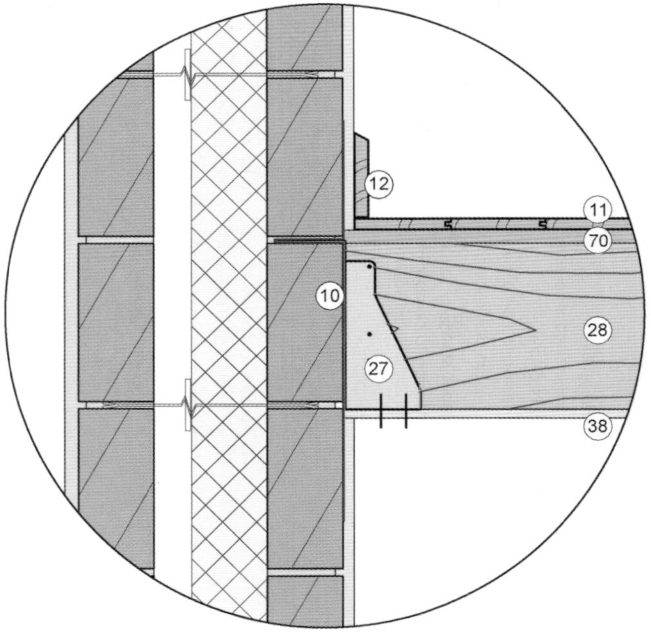

wall–first floor junction

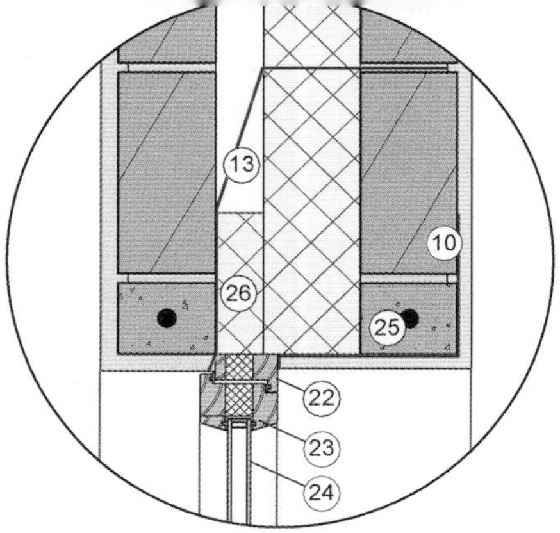

window head

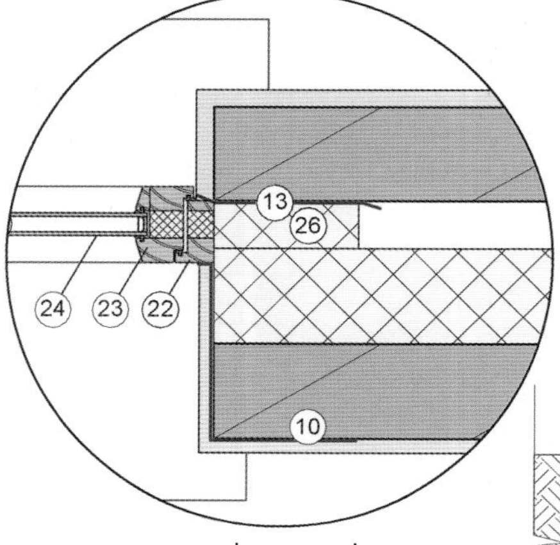

window jamb

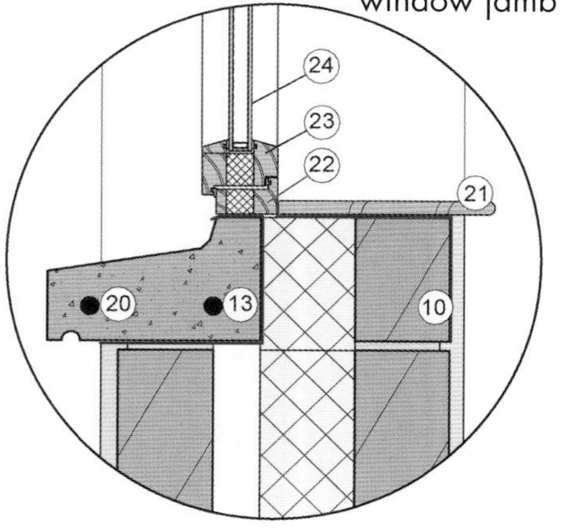

window sill

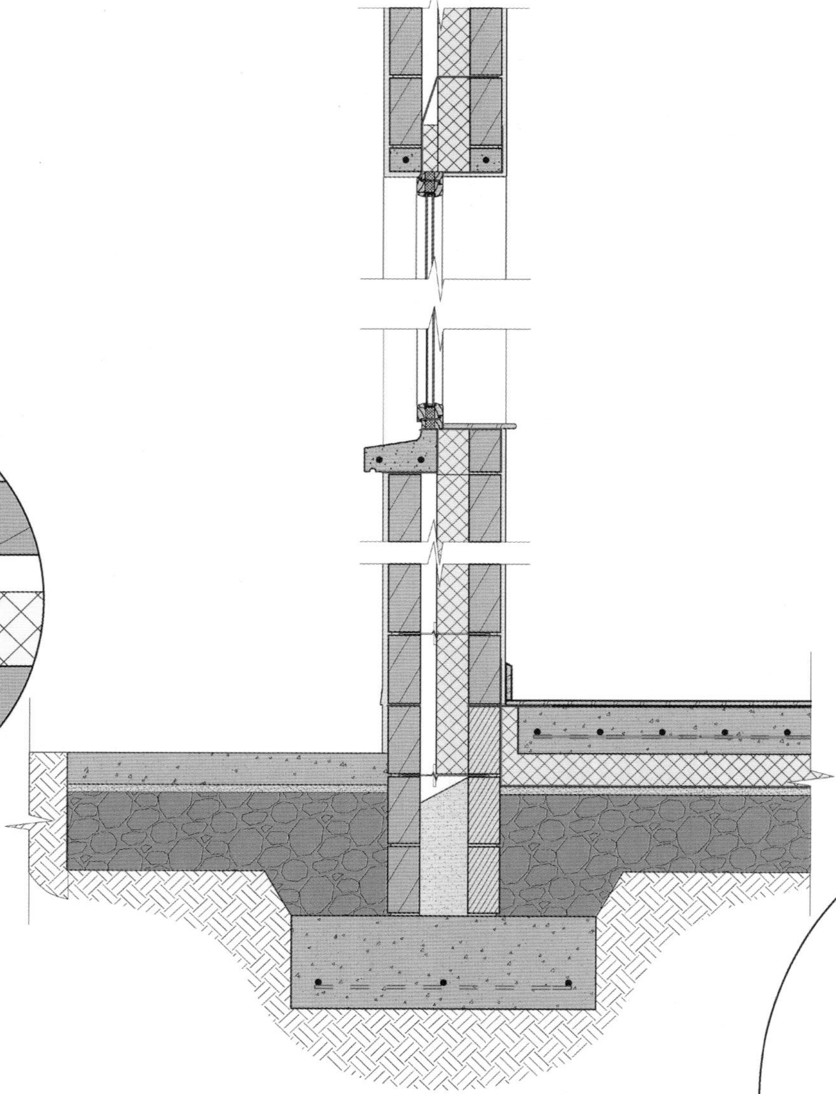

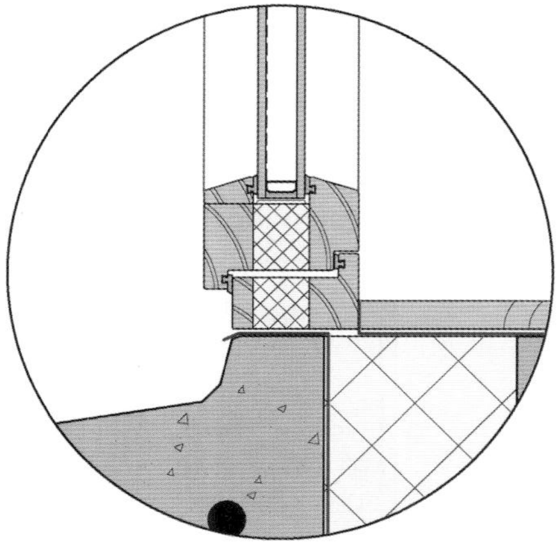

window frame (1:5)

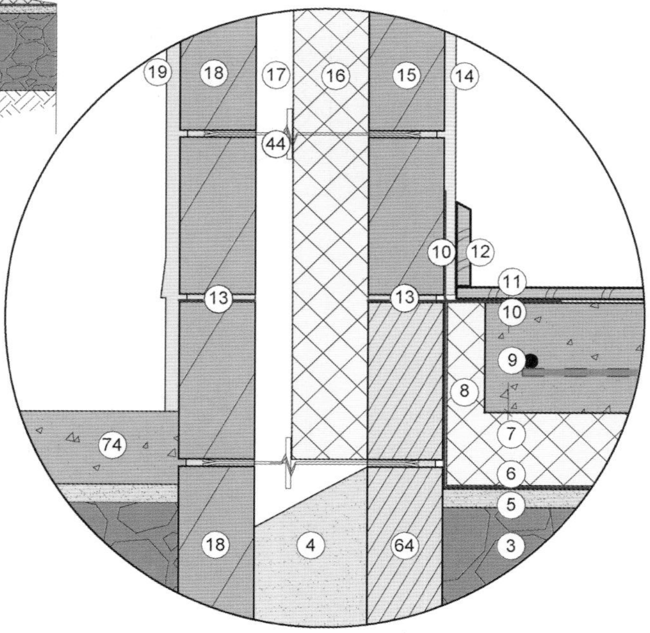

wall–ground floor junction

Circled details are at scale 1:10. Main detail is NOT TO SCALE.

Masonry cavity wall: building regulations standard (longitudinal section) 240–241

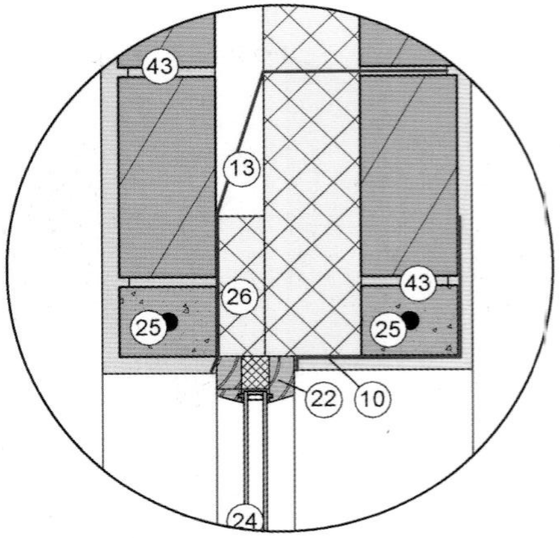

43
13
26
43
25
25
22
10
24
window head

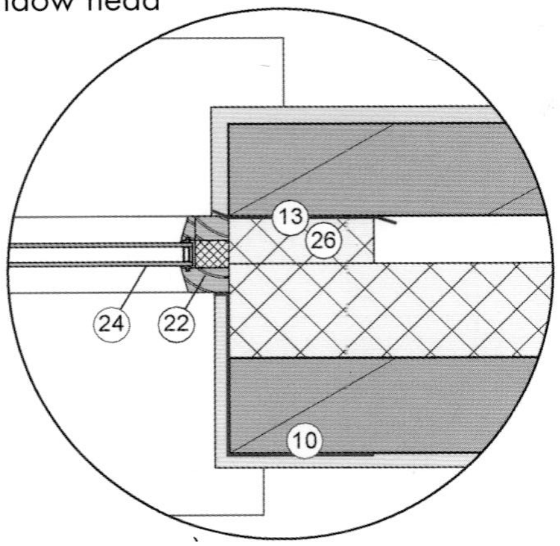

13
26
24
22
10
window jamb

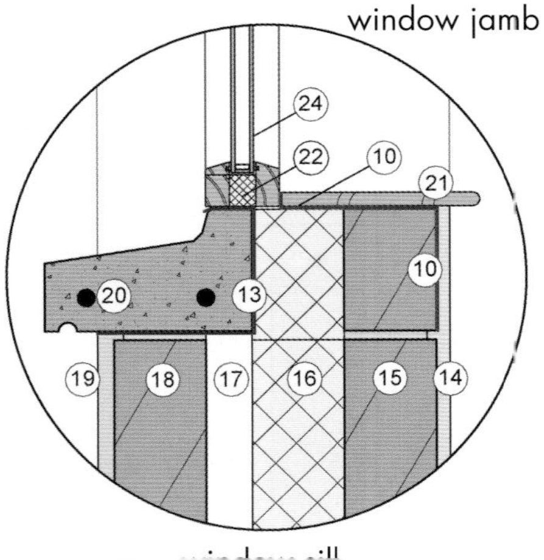

24
22
10
21
10
20
13
19
18
17
16
15
14

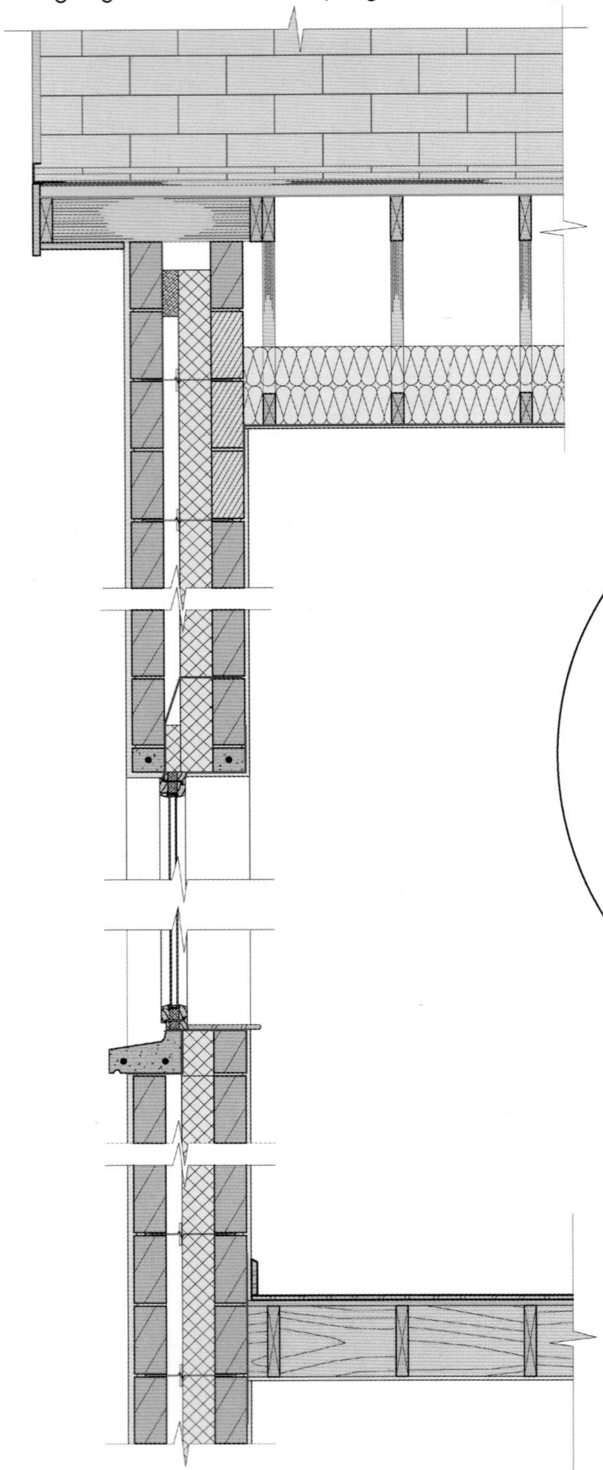

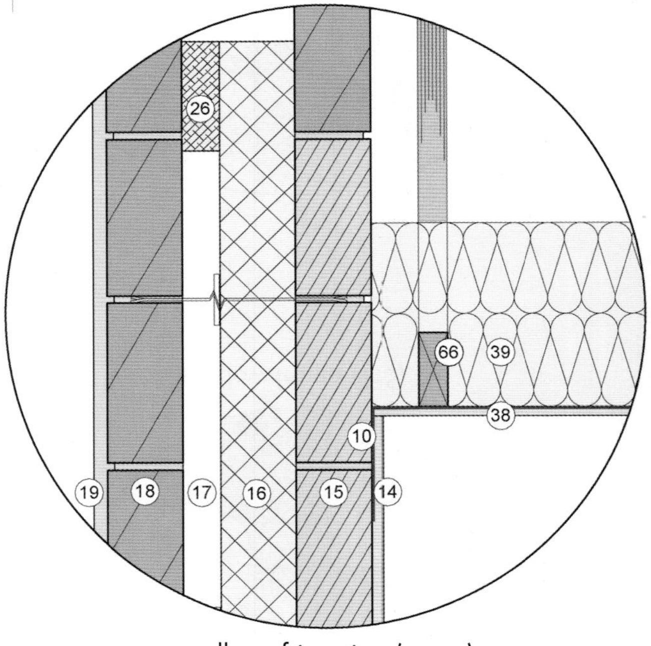

26
66
39
38
10
19
18
17
16
15
14
wall–roof junction (verge)

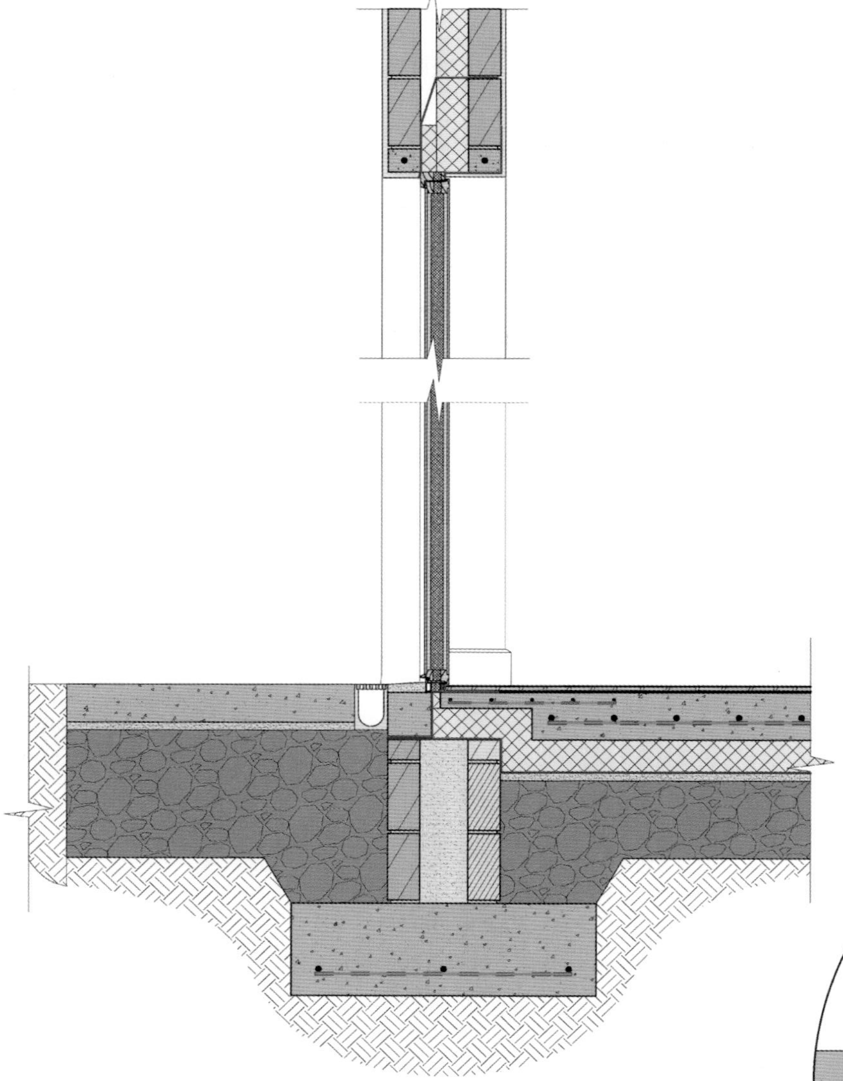

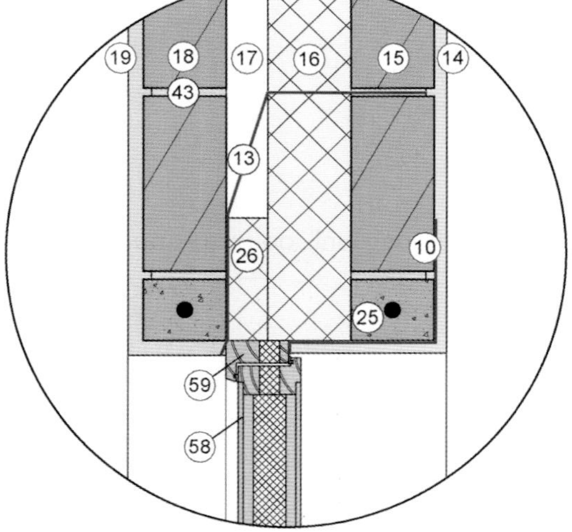

door head

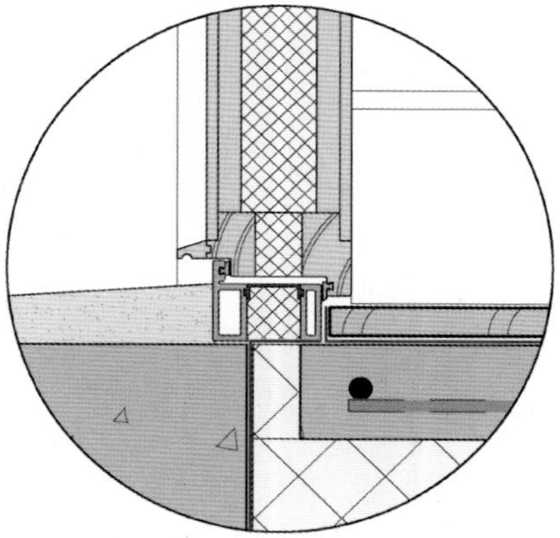

door sill (threshold)

door threshold (1:5)

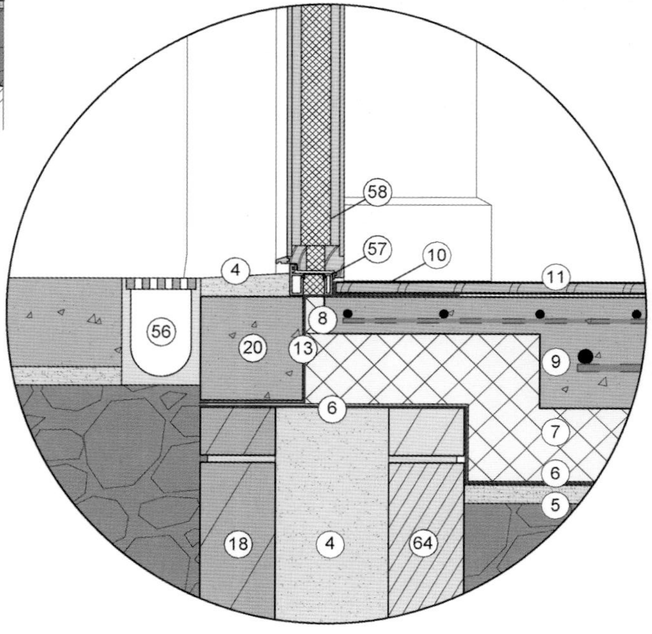

Circled details are at scale 1:10. Main detail is NOT TO SCALE.

Timber frame cavity wall: building regulations standard (transverse section)

242–243

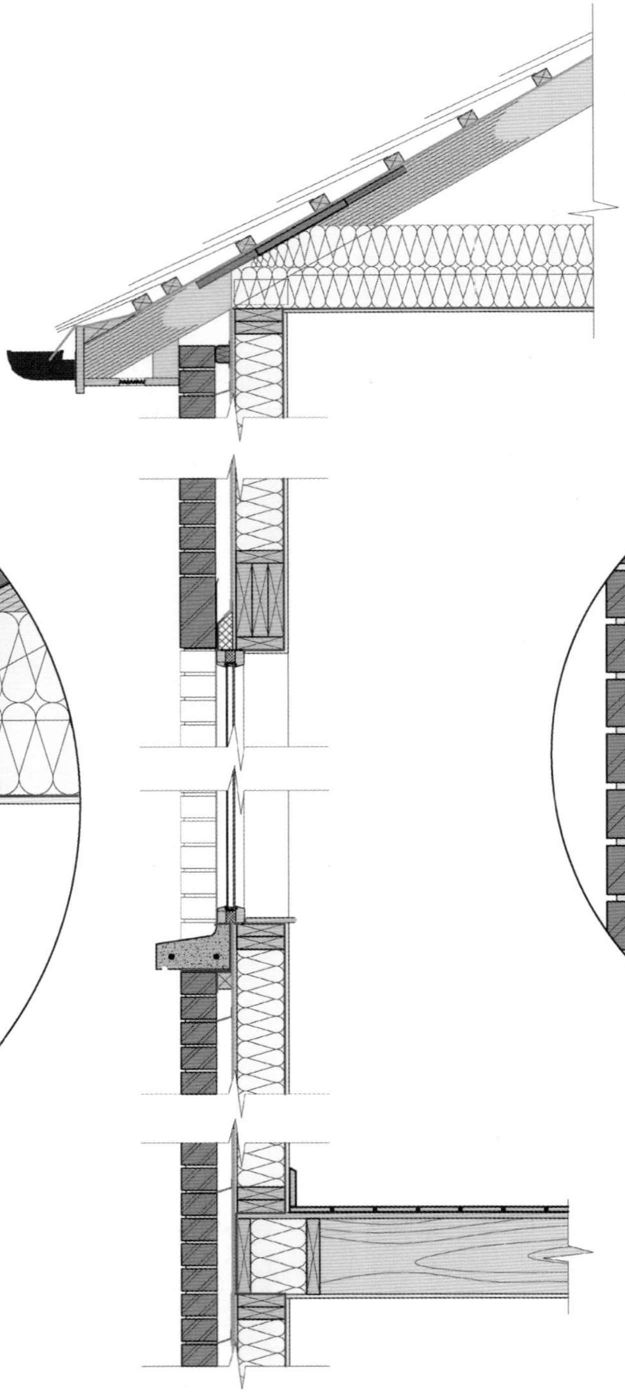

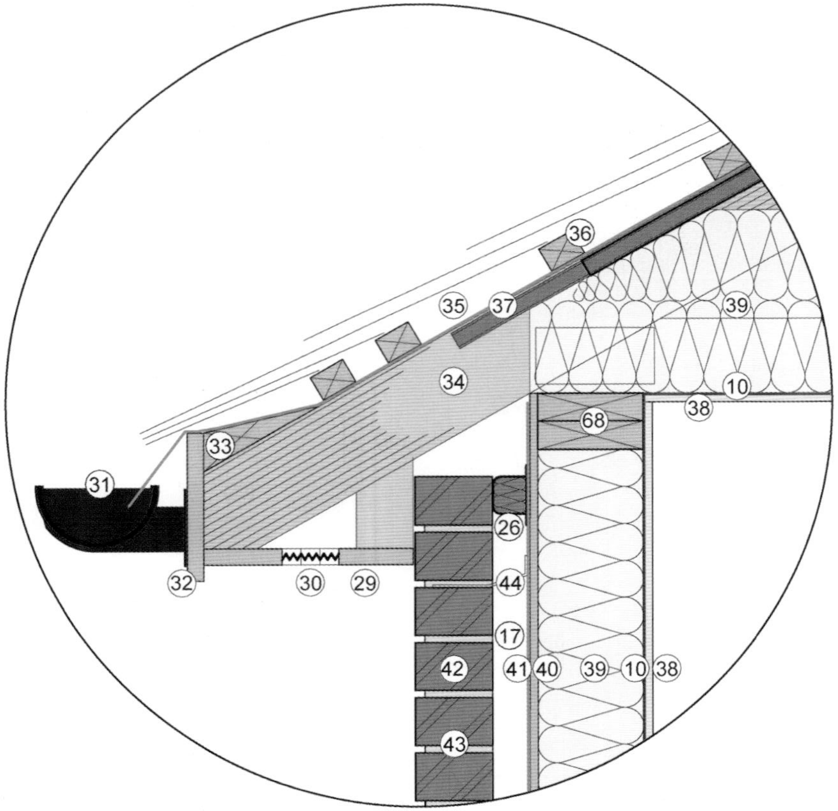

wall–roof junction (eaves)

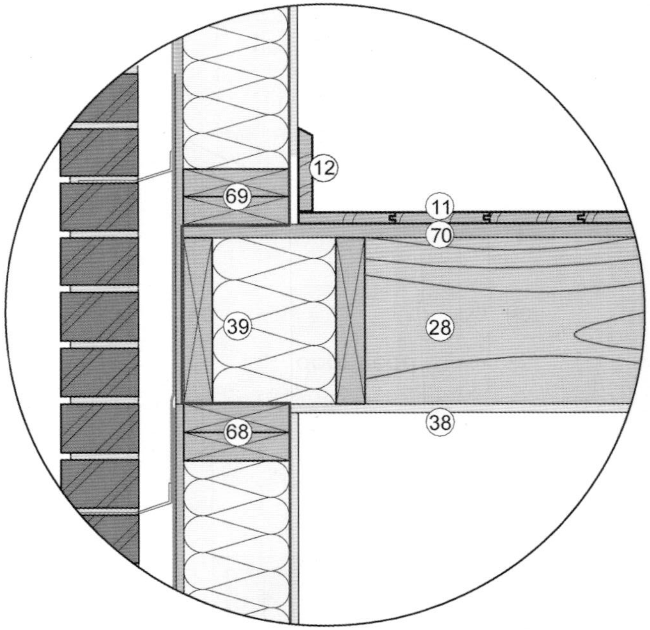

wall–first floor junction

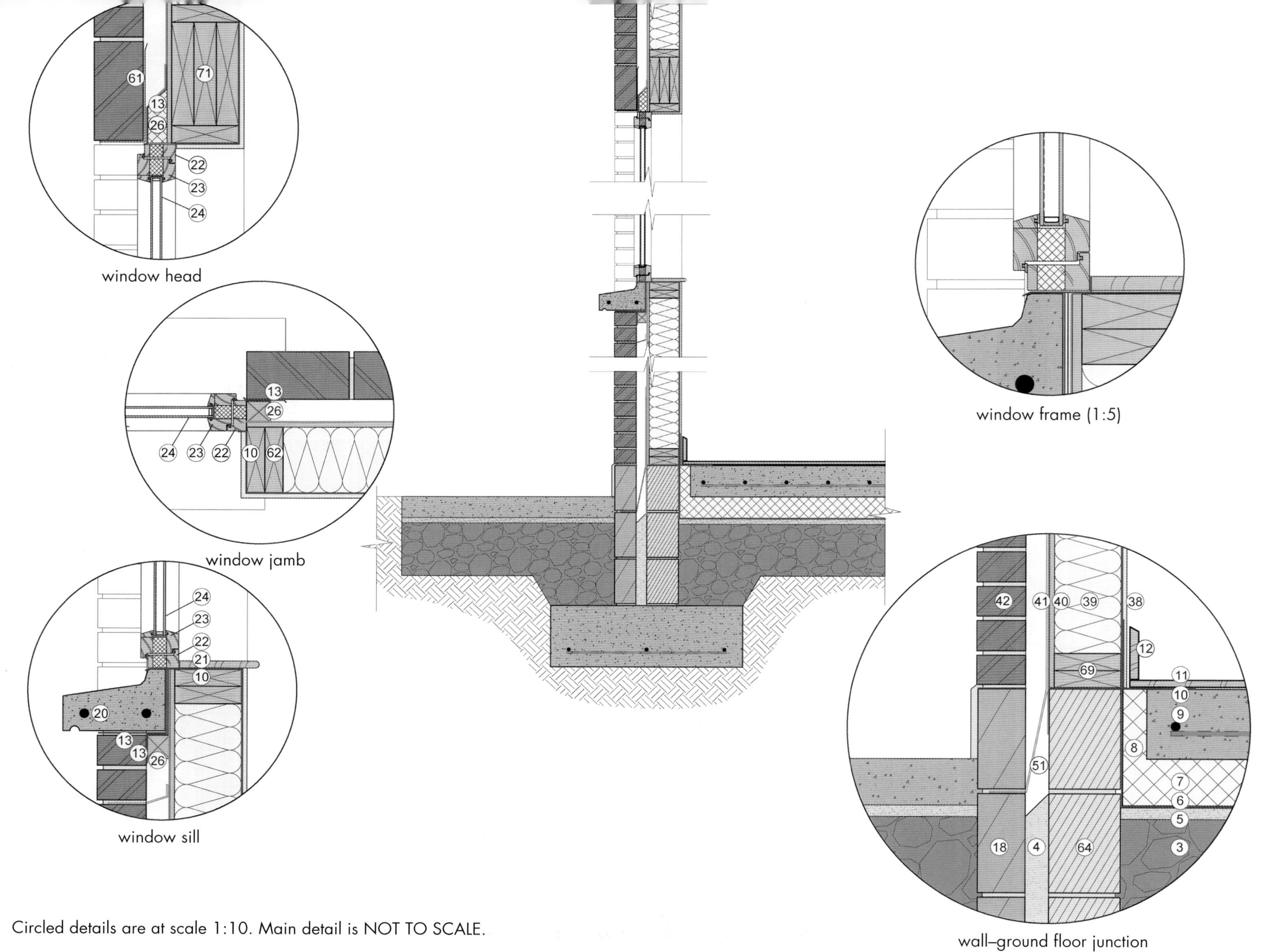

Circled details are at scale 1:10. Main detail is NOT TO SCALE.

Timber frame cavity wall: building regulations standard (longitudinal section)
244–245

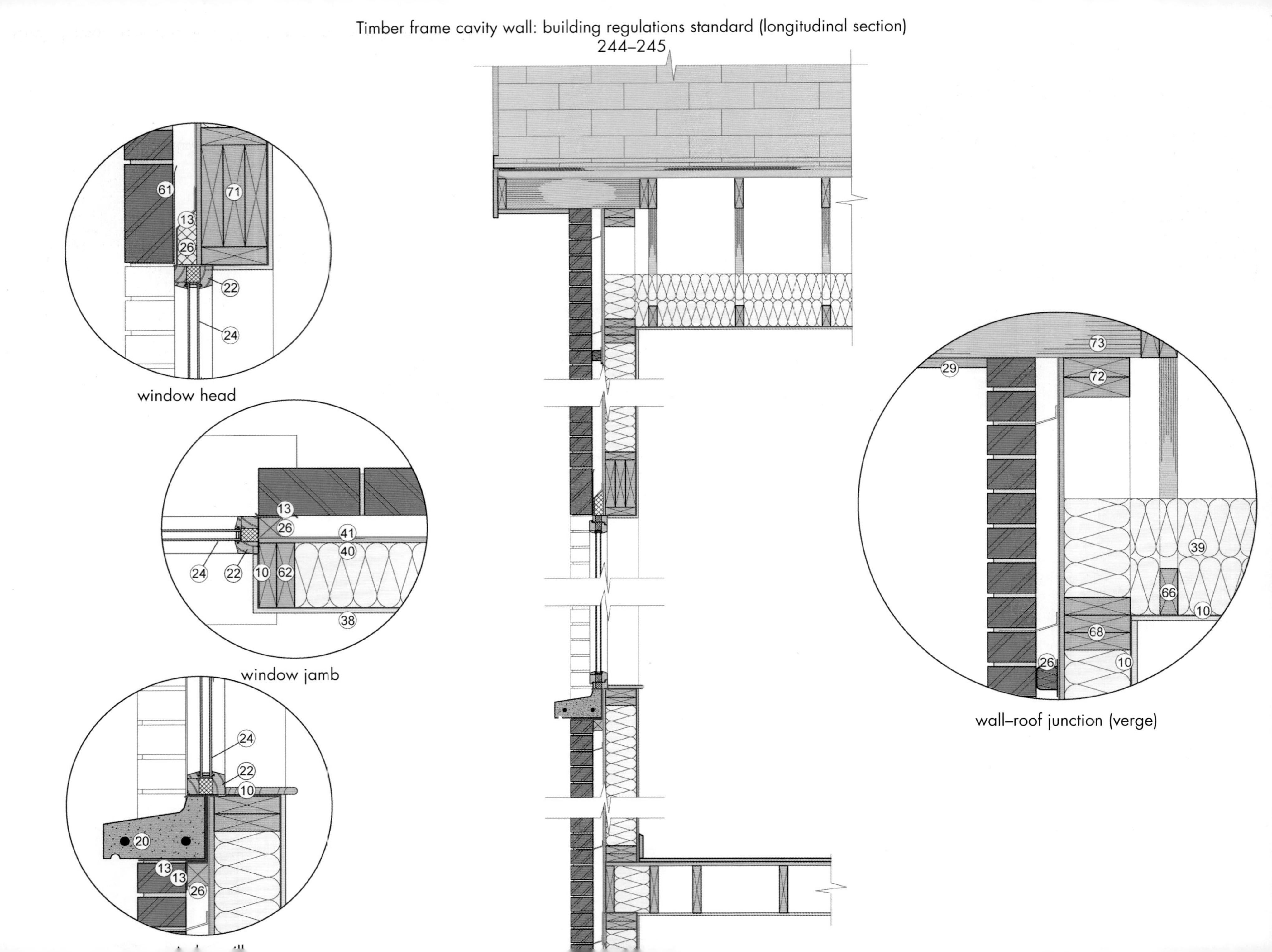

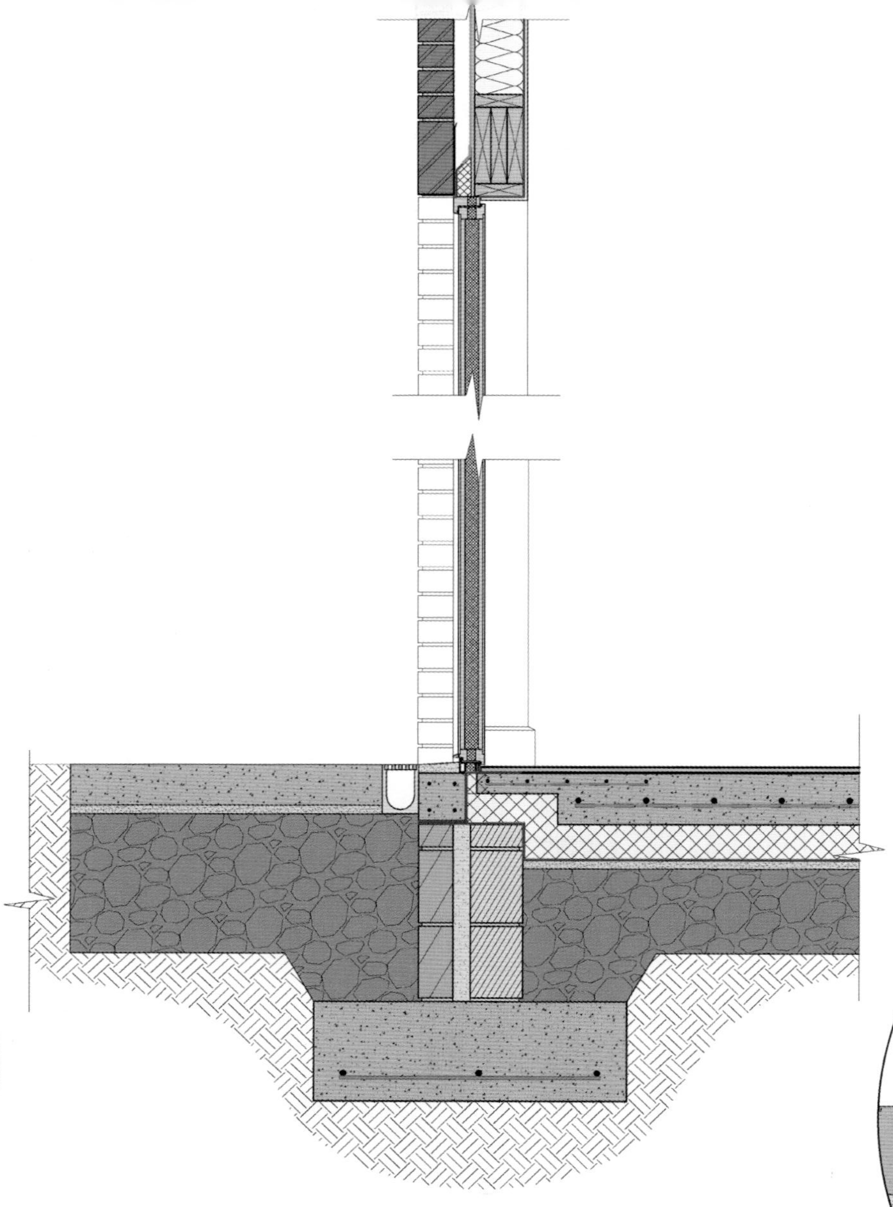

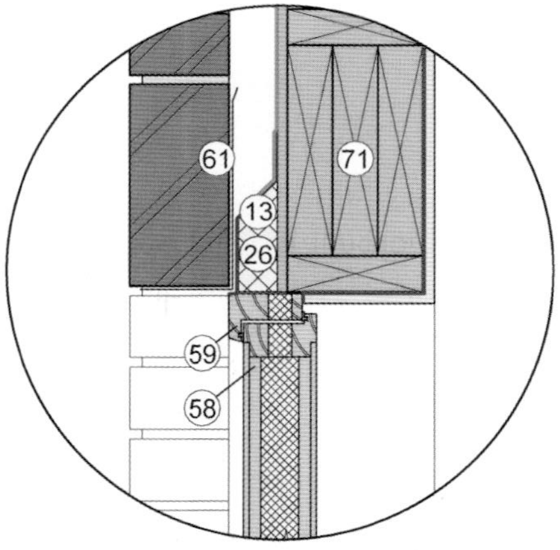

61
71
13
26
59
58

door head

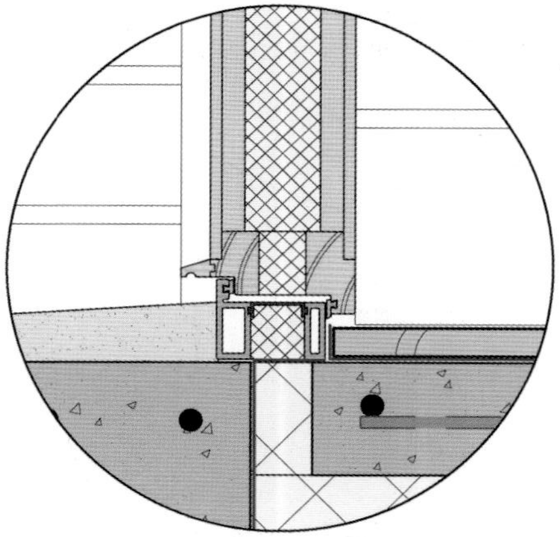

door threshold (1:5)

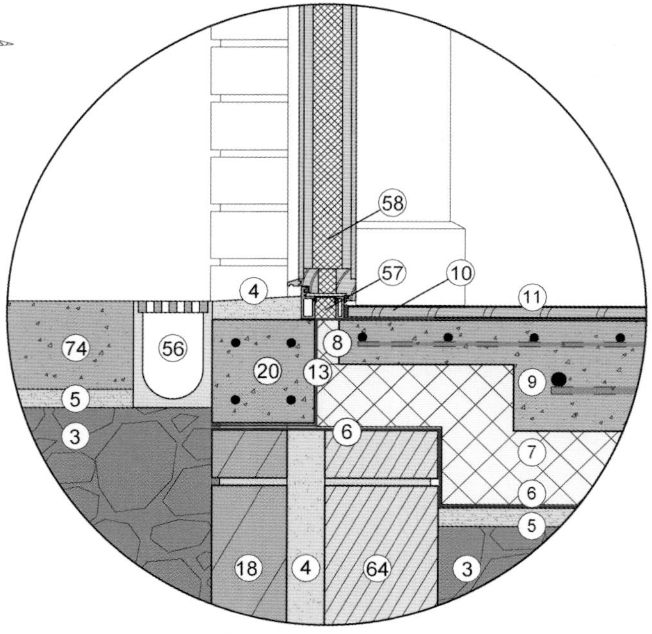

58
57
10
4
11
74
56
8
20
13
9
5
6
3
7
6
5
18
4
64
3

door sill (threshold)

Circled details are at scale 1:10. Main detail is NOT TO SCALE.

Concrete wide cavity wall: Passivhaus standard (transverse section)
246–247

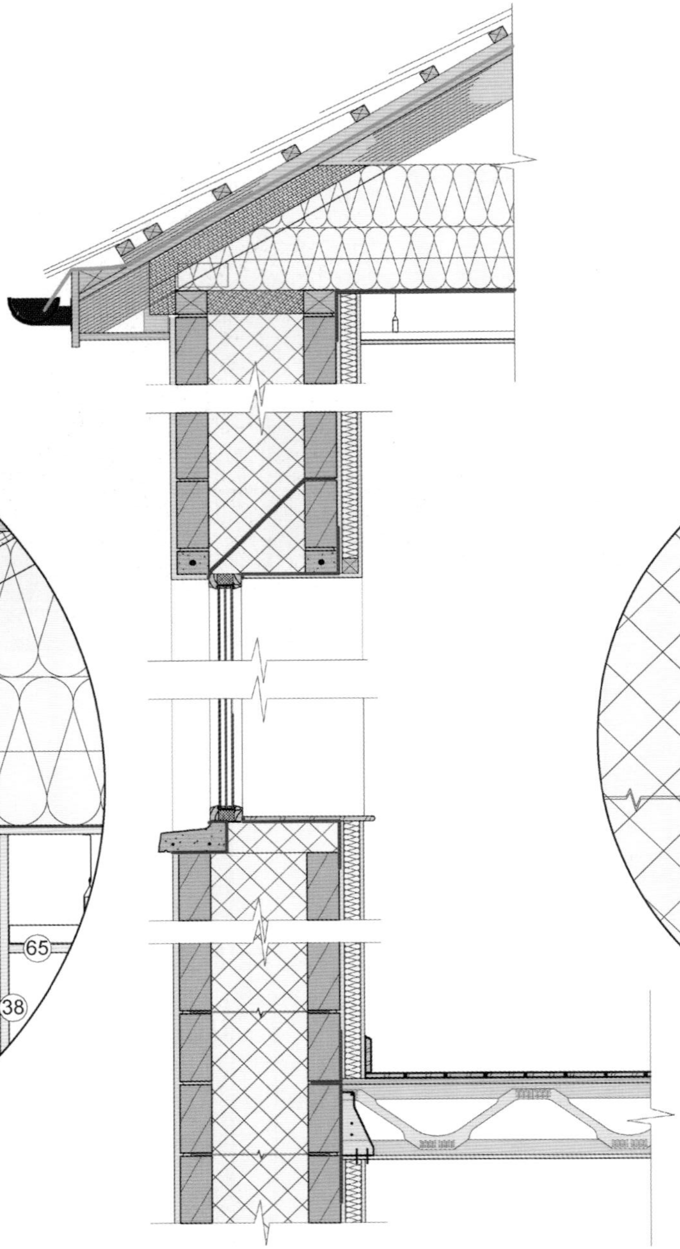

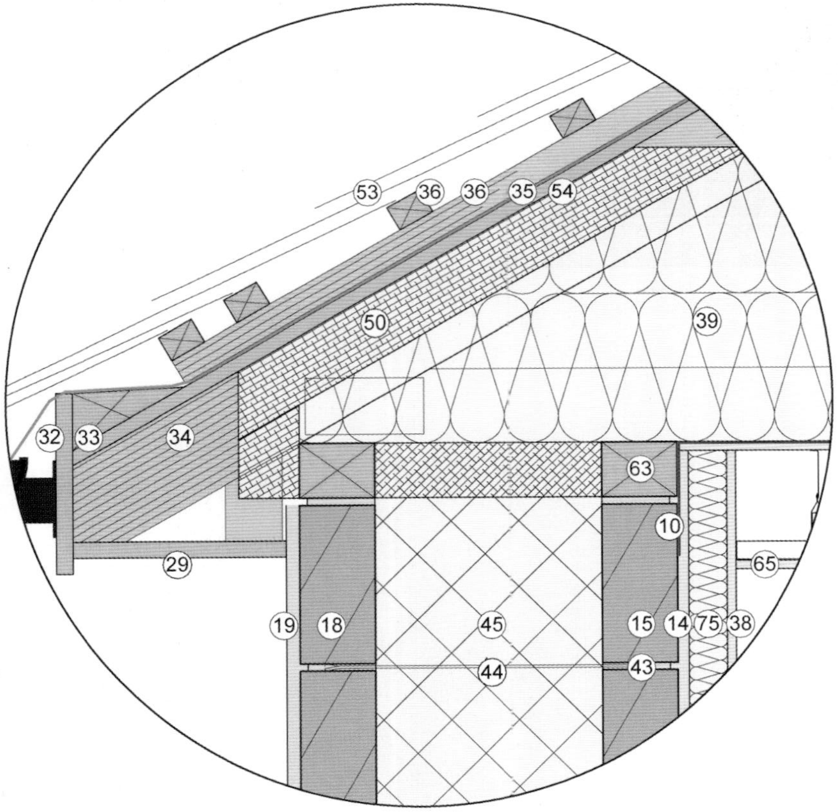

wall–roof junction (eaves)

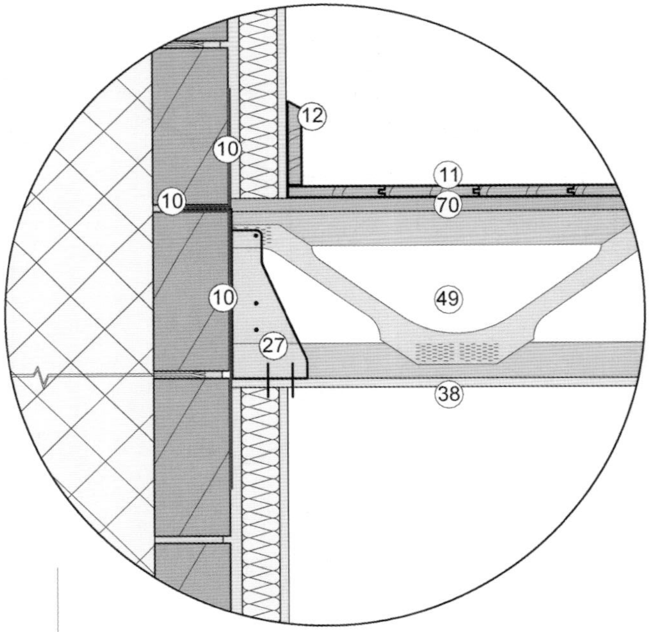

wall–first floor junction

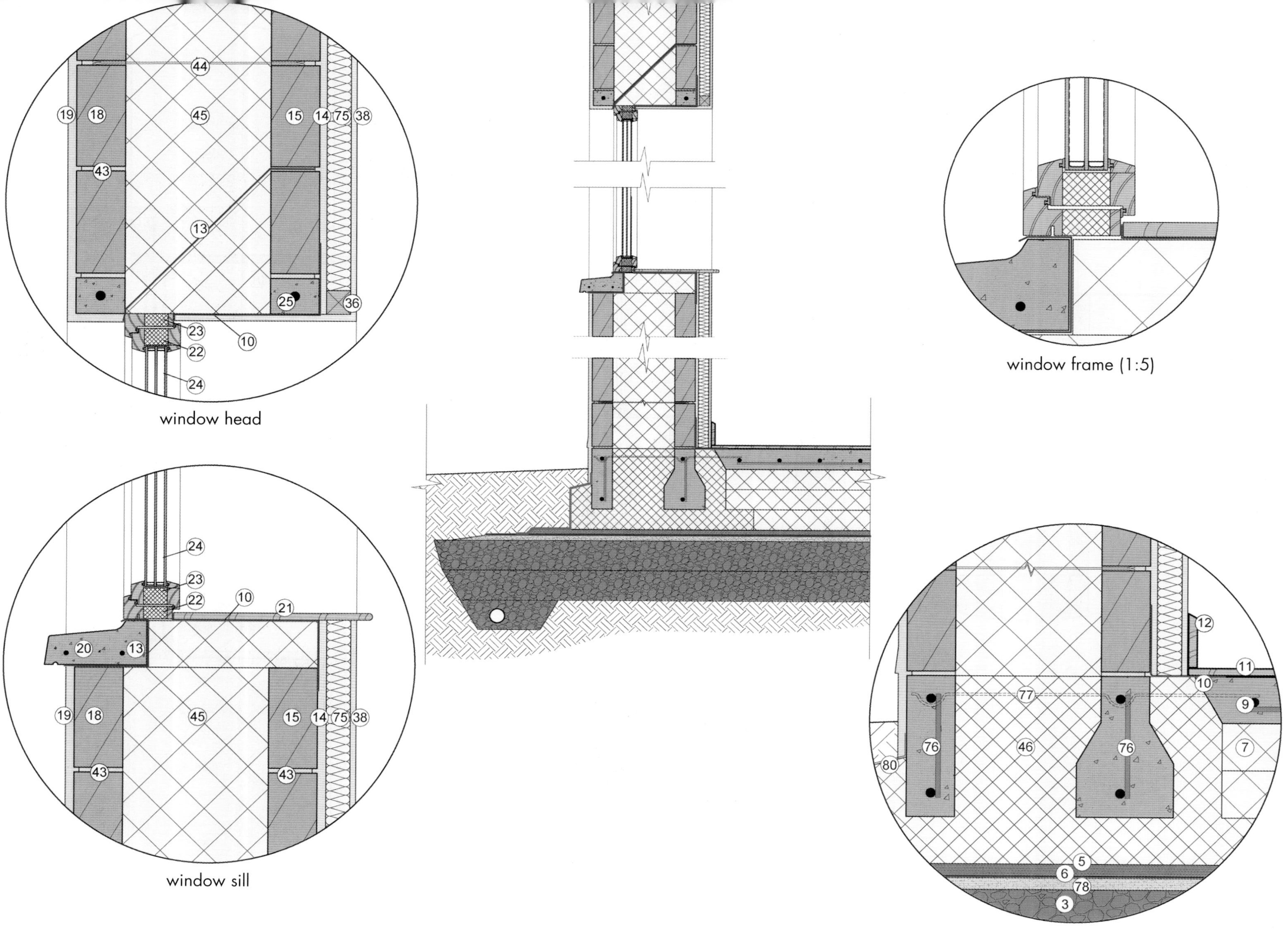

window head

window sill

window frame (1:5)

wall–ground floor junction

Circled details are at scale 1:10. Main detail is NOT TO SCALE.

Concrete wide cavity wall: Passivhaus standard (longitudinal section)
248–249

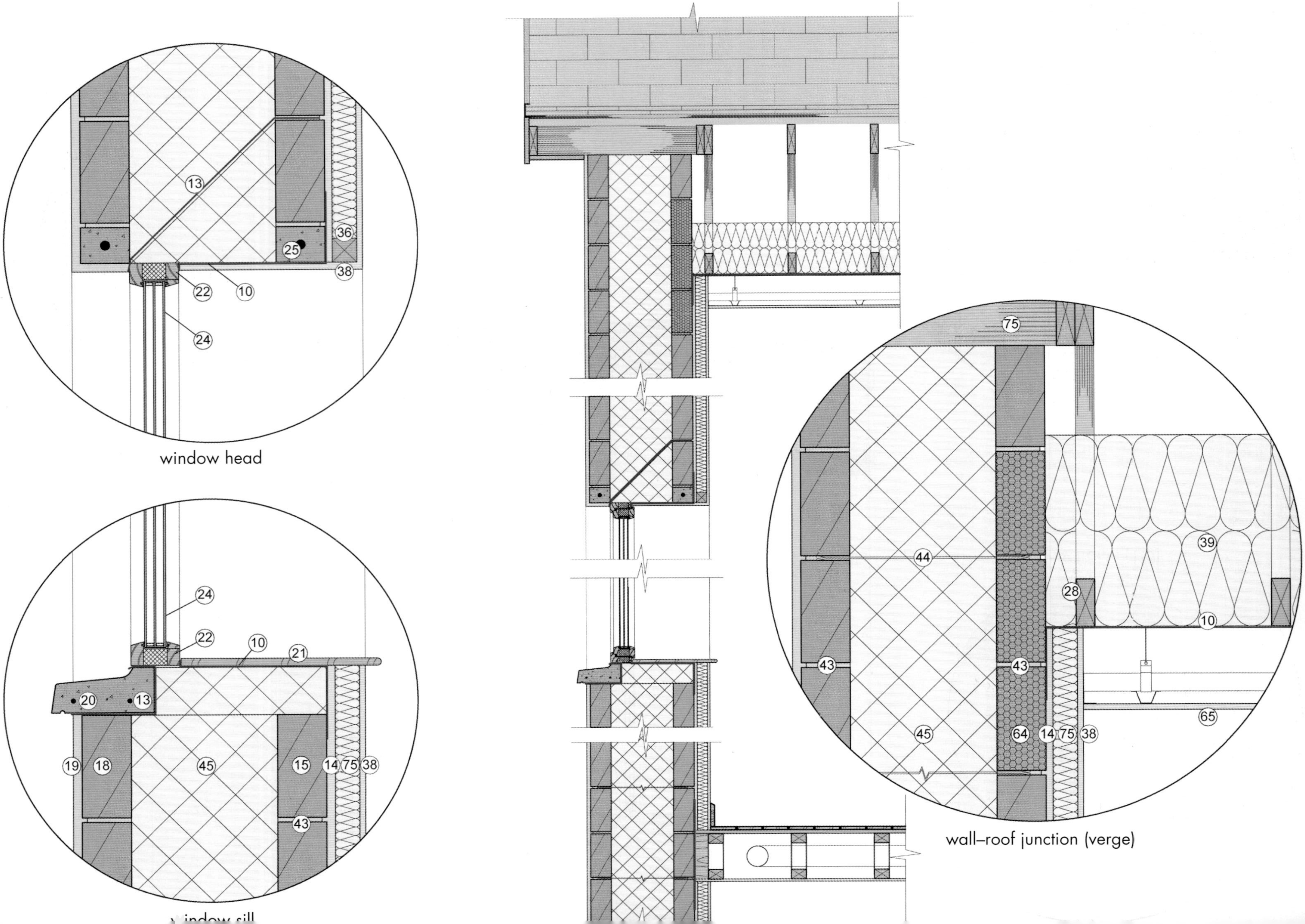

window head

window sill

wall–roof junction (verge)

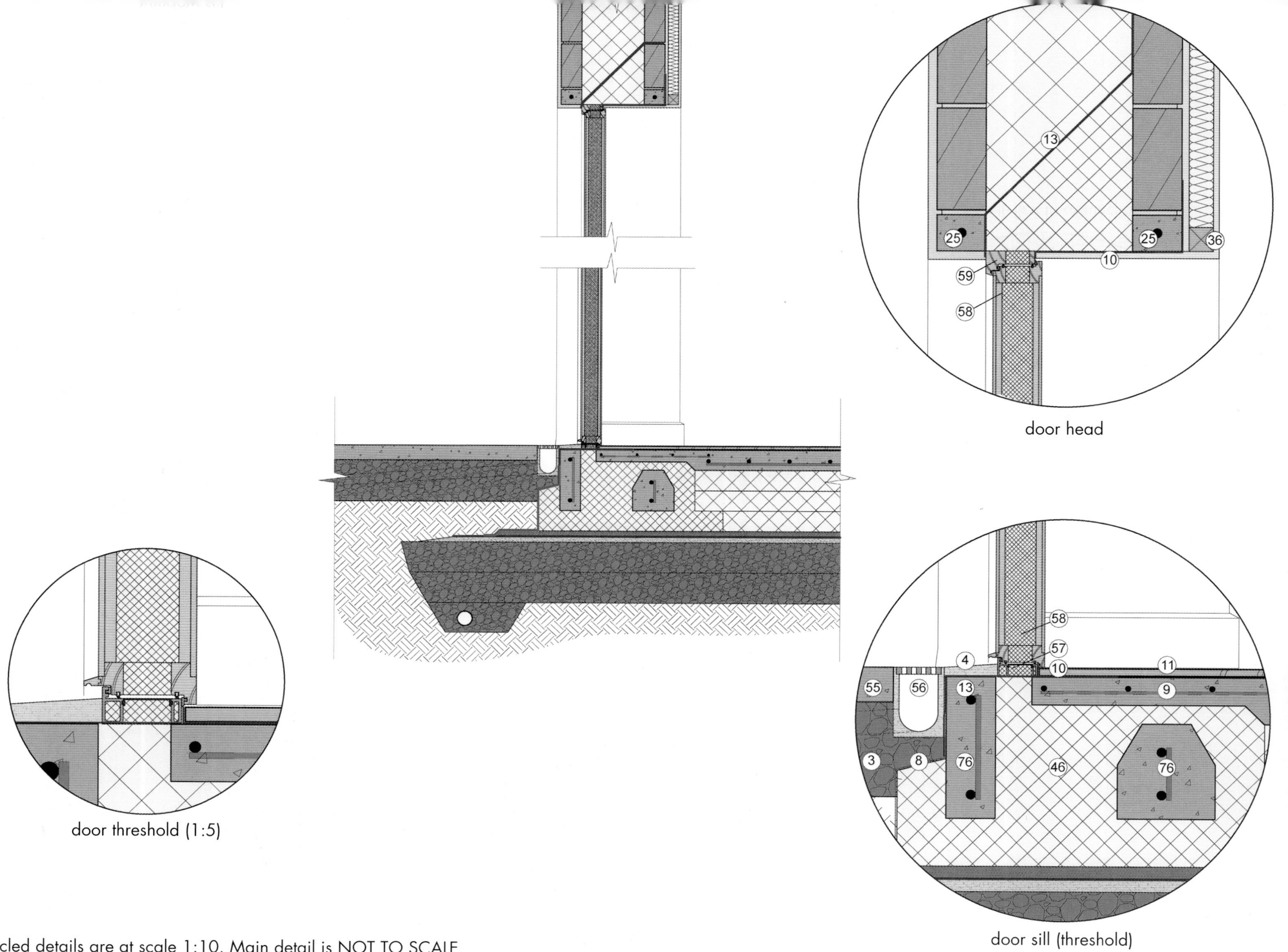

Circled details are at scale 1:10. Main detail is NOT TO SCALE.

Masonry concrete block on flat wall: Passivhaus standard (transverse section)
250–251

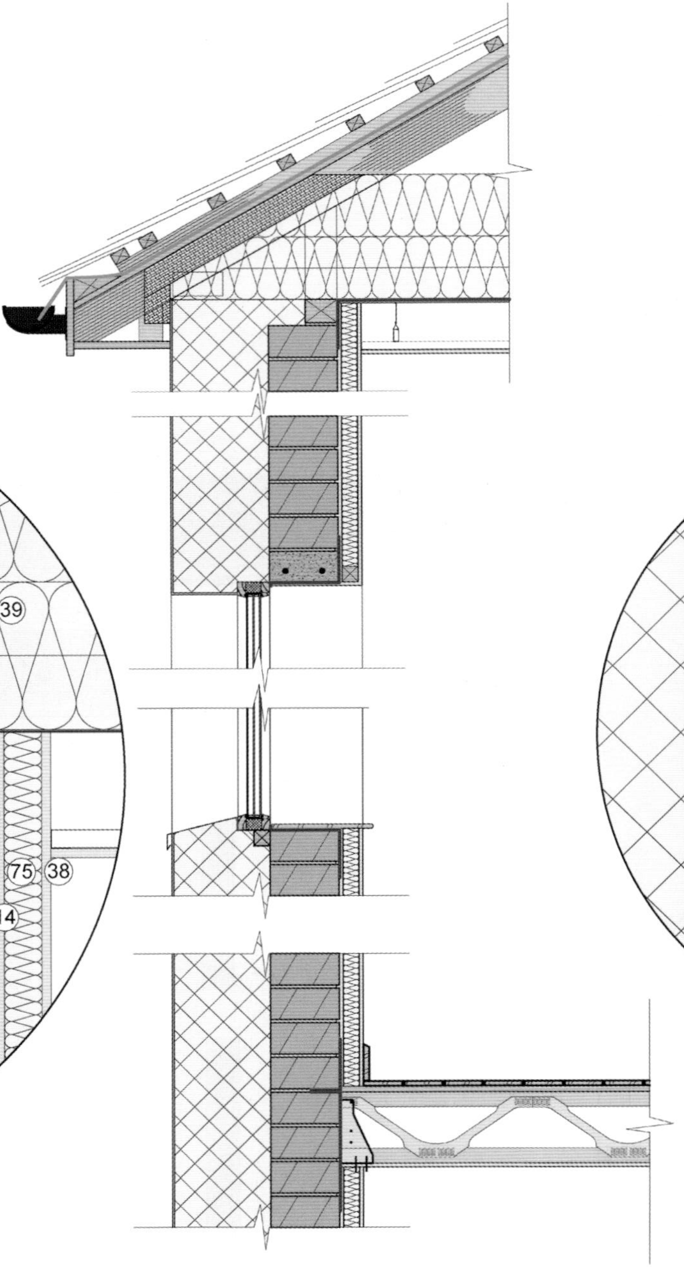

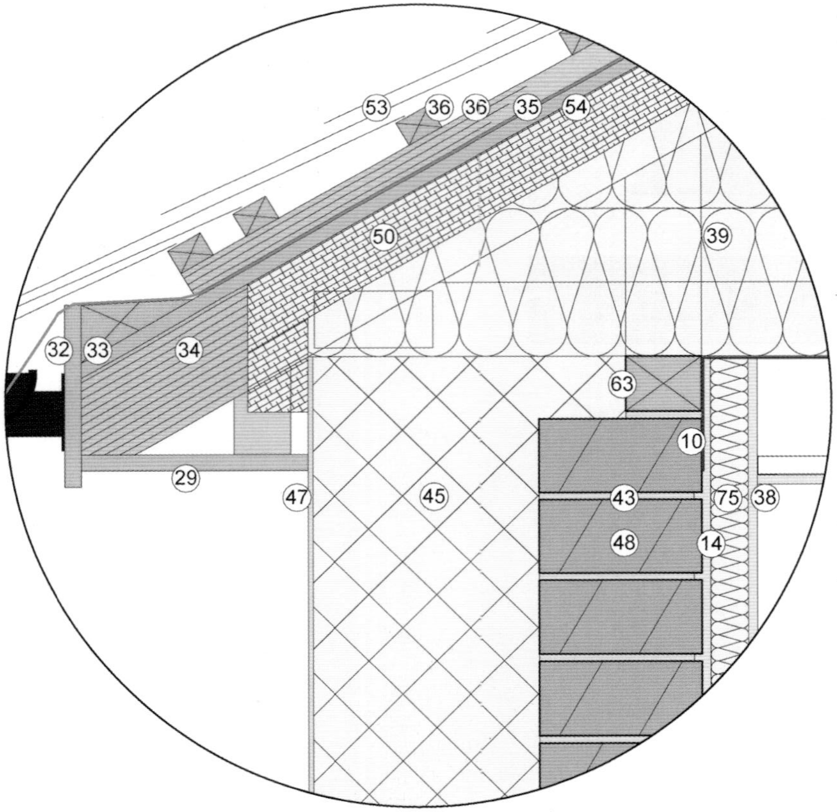

wall–roof junction (eaves)

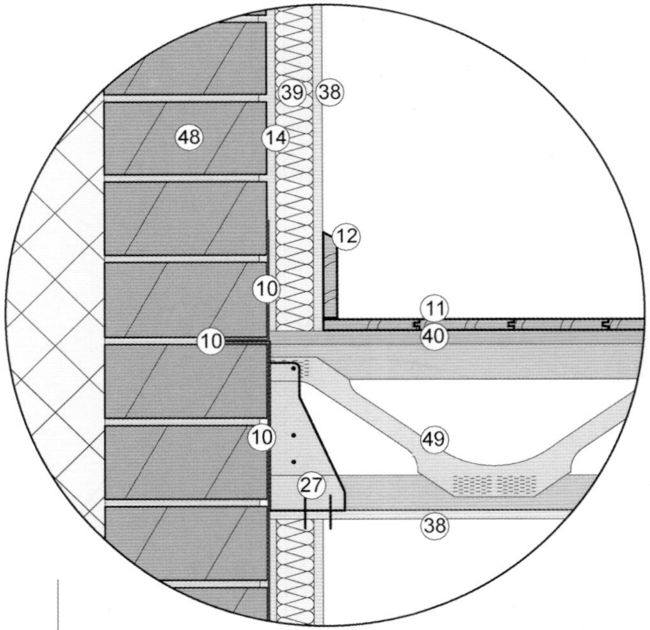

wall–first floor junction

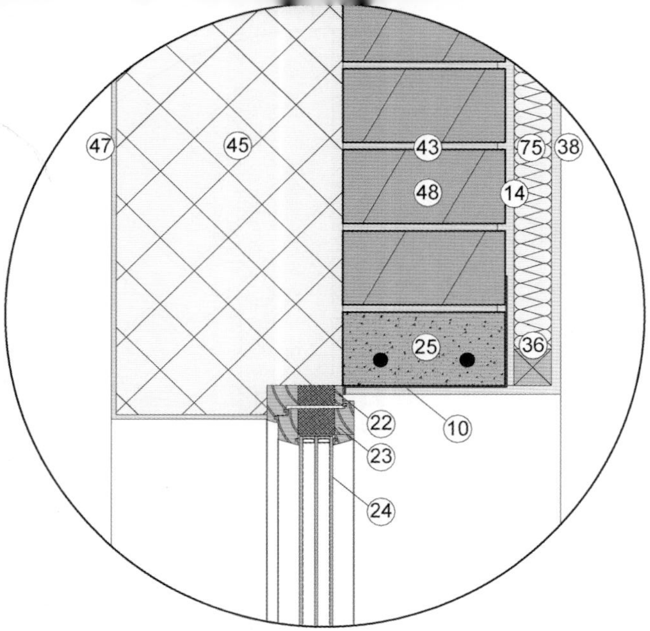

47
45
43
75
38
48
14
25
36
22
10
23
24

window head

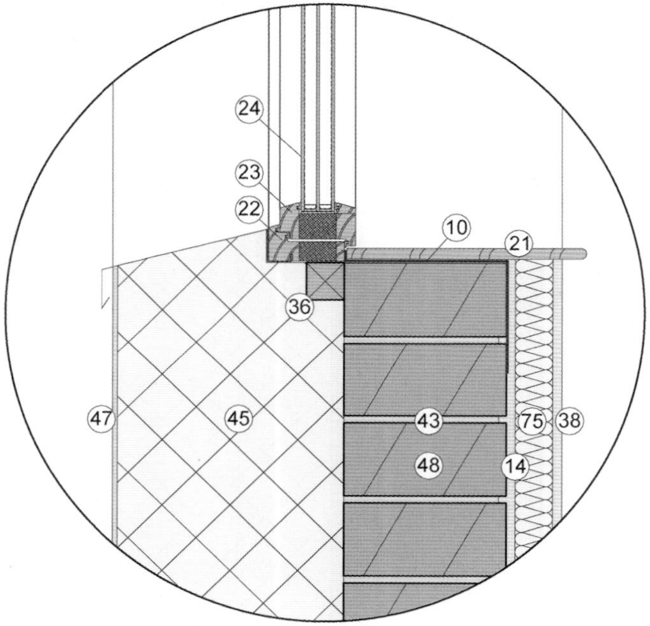

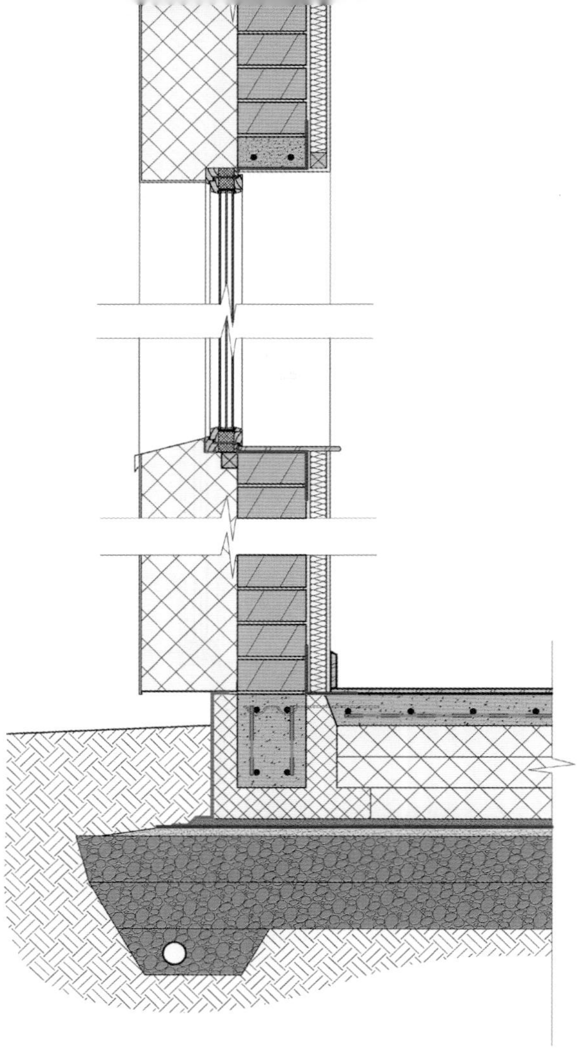

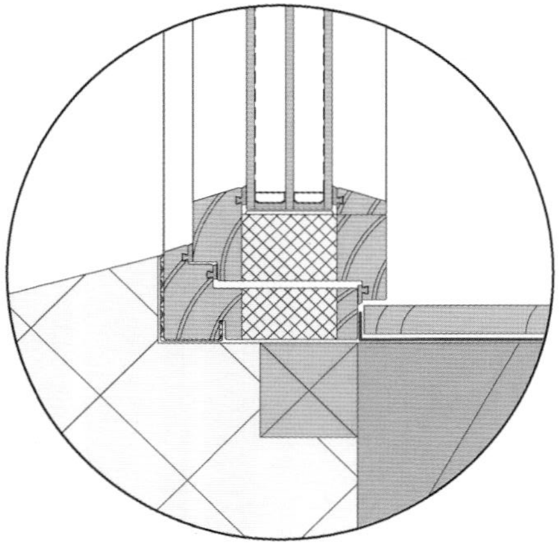

window frame (1:5)

24
23
22
10
21
36
47
45
43
75
38
48
14

window sill

12
11
10
9
77
76
7
80
7
46
7

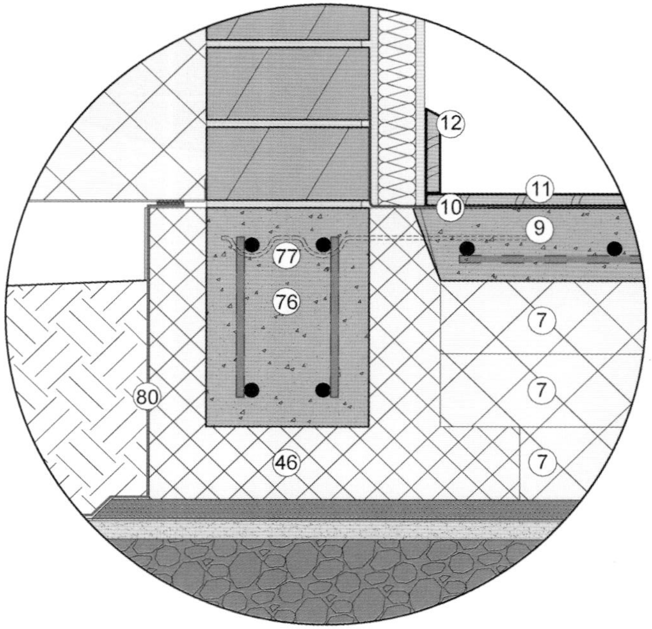

wall–ground floor junction

Circled details are at scale 1:10. Main detail is NOT TO SCALE.

Masonry concrete block on flat wall: Passivhaus standard (longitudinal section)
252–253

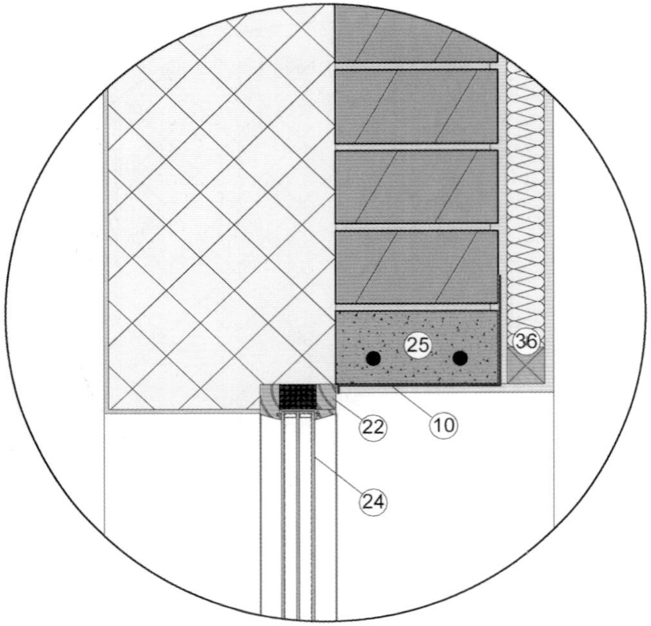

25
36
22
10
24

window head

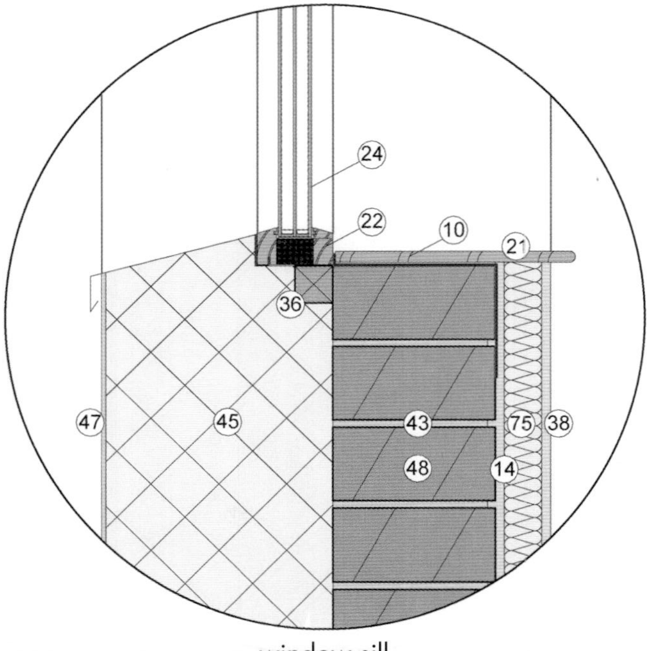

24
22
10
21
36
47
45
43
75
38
48
14

window sill

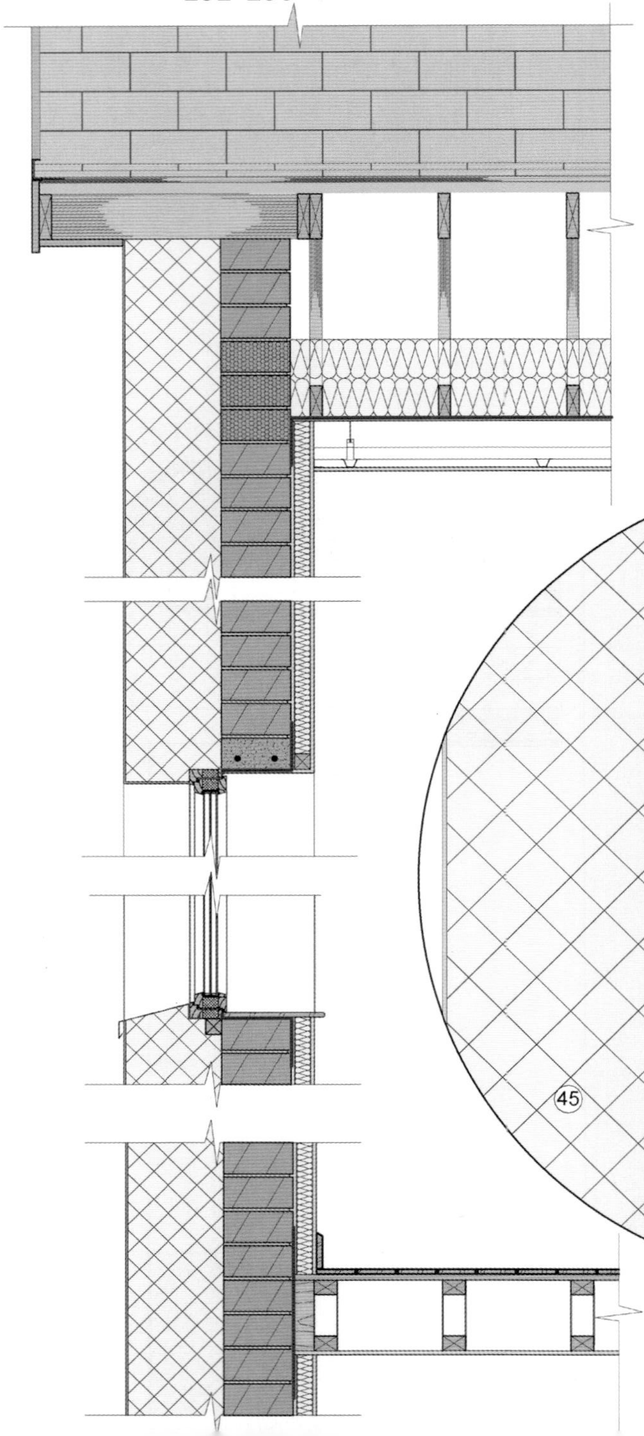

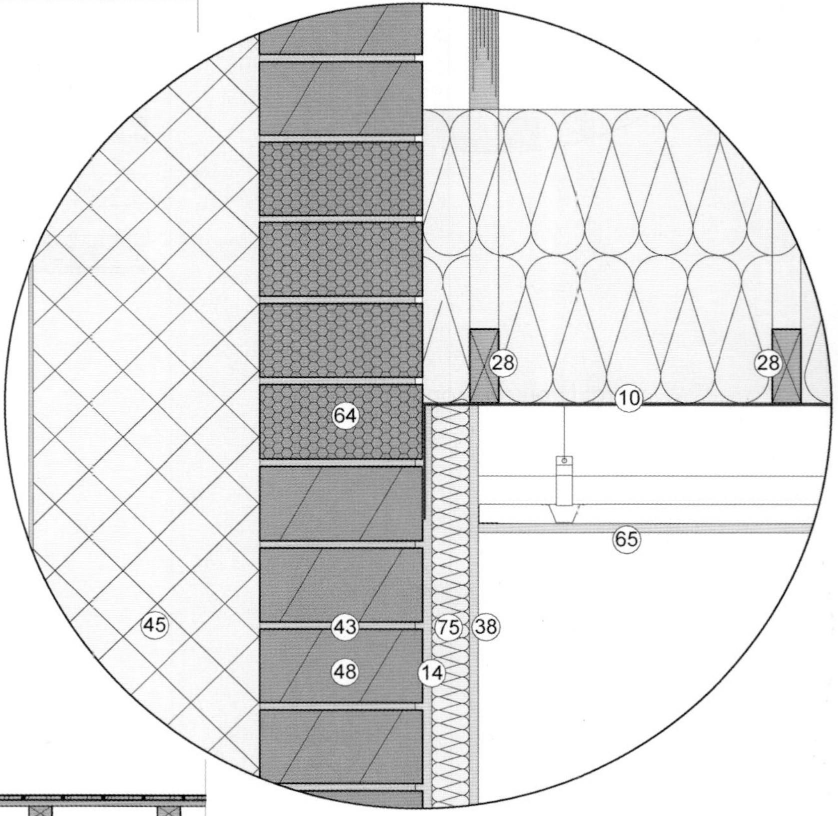

28
28
10
64
65
45
43
75
38
48
14

wall–roof junction (verge)

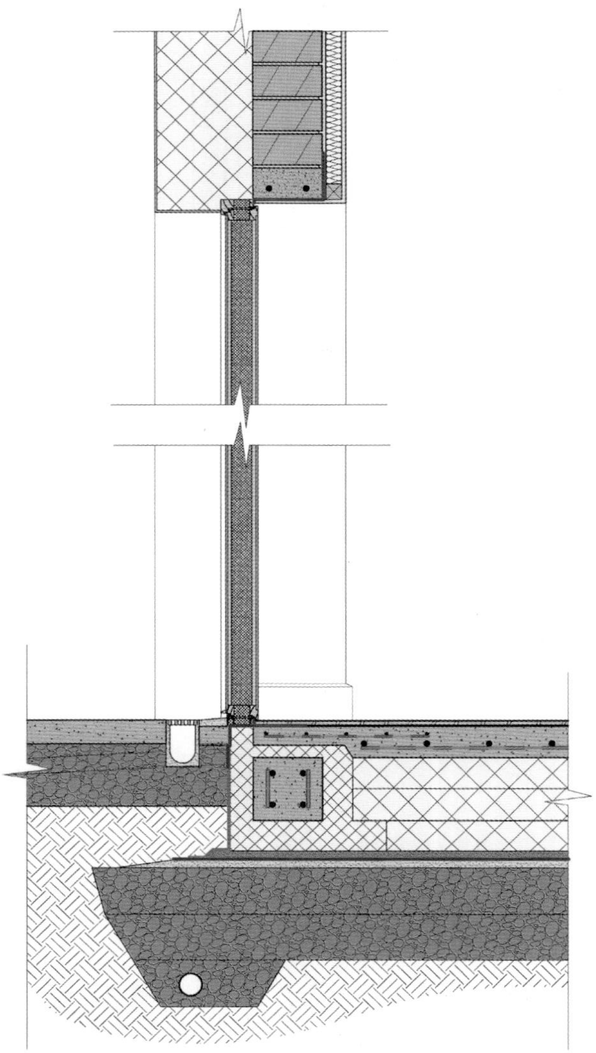

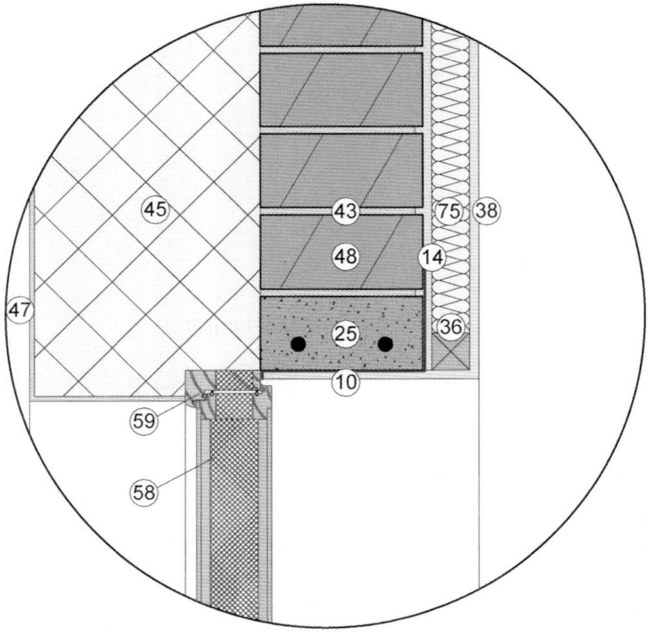

door head

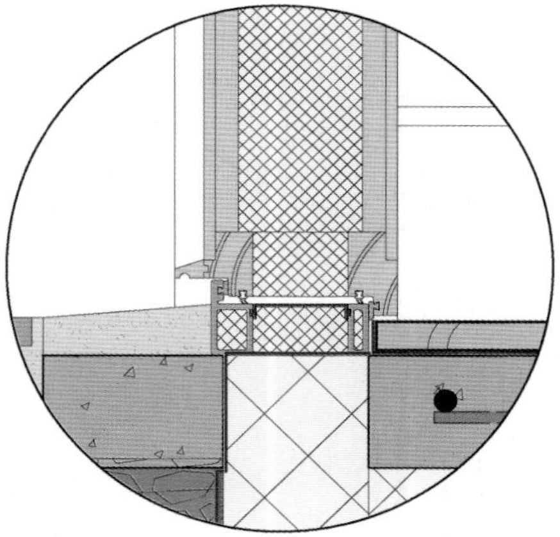

door threshold (1:5)

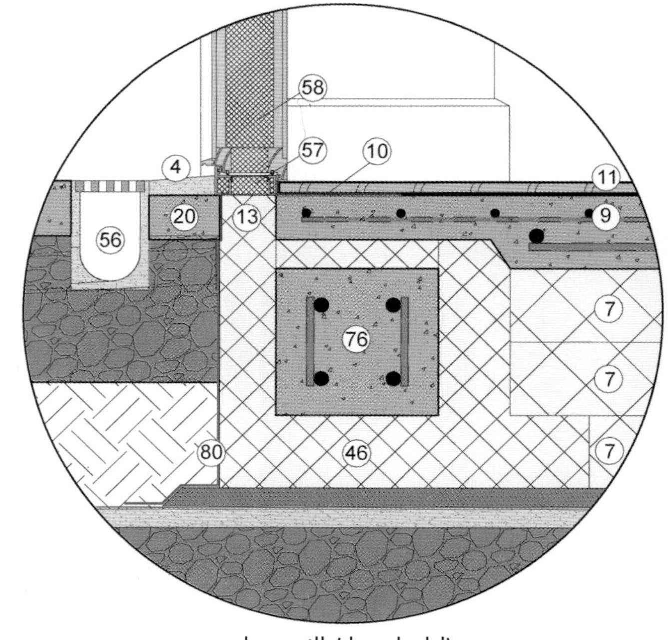

door sill (threshold)

Circled details are at scale 1:10. Main detail is NOT TO SCALE.

Timber frame external insulation wall: Passivhaus standard (transverse section)
254–255

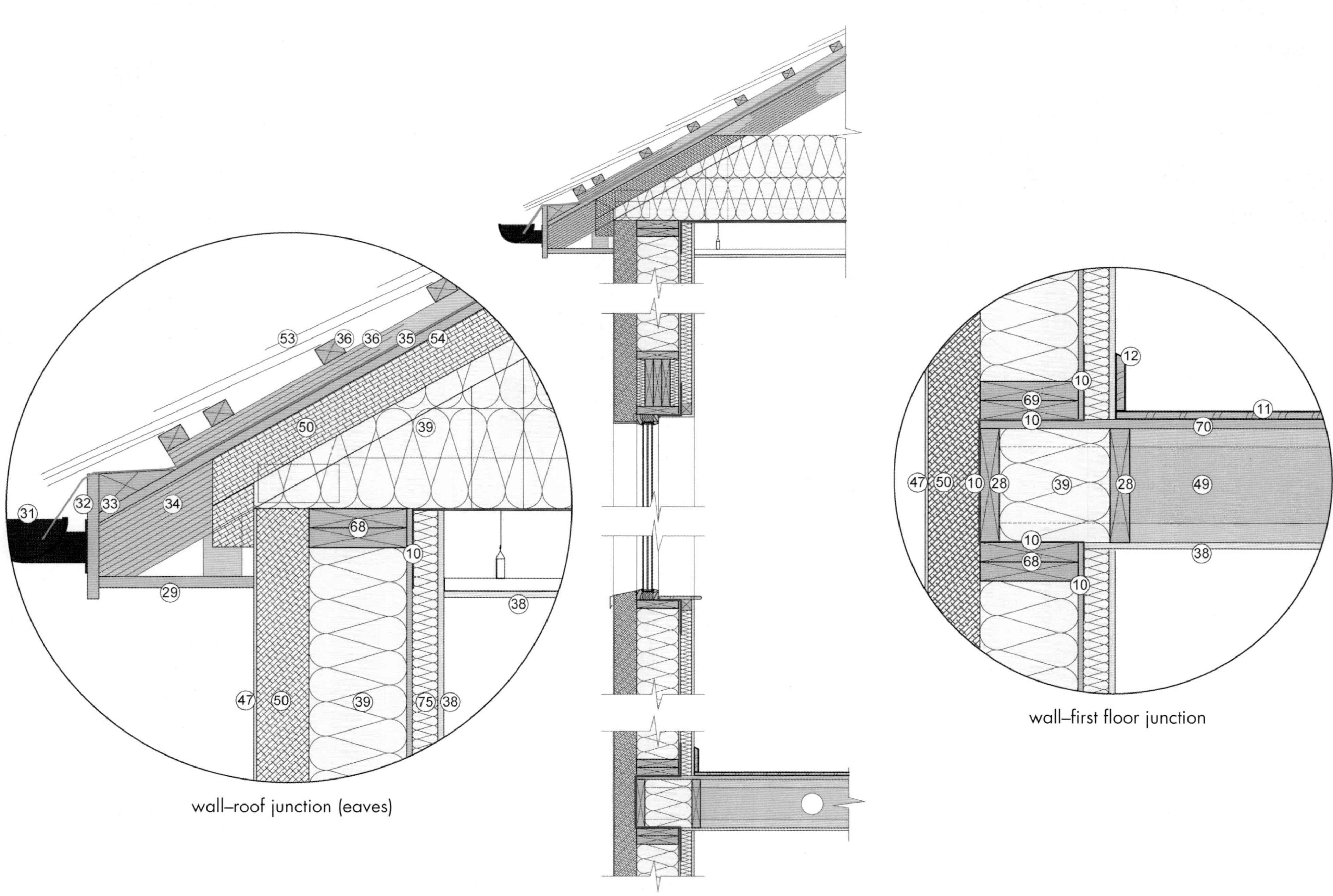

wall–roof junction (eaves)

wall–first floor junction

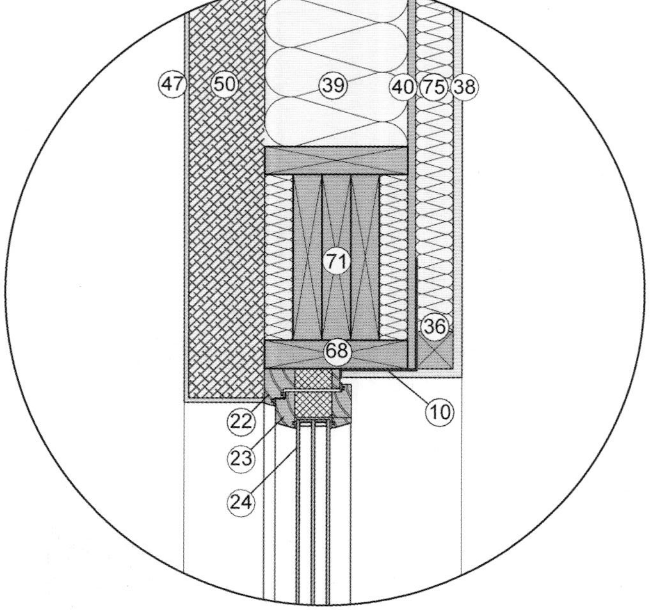

window head

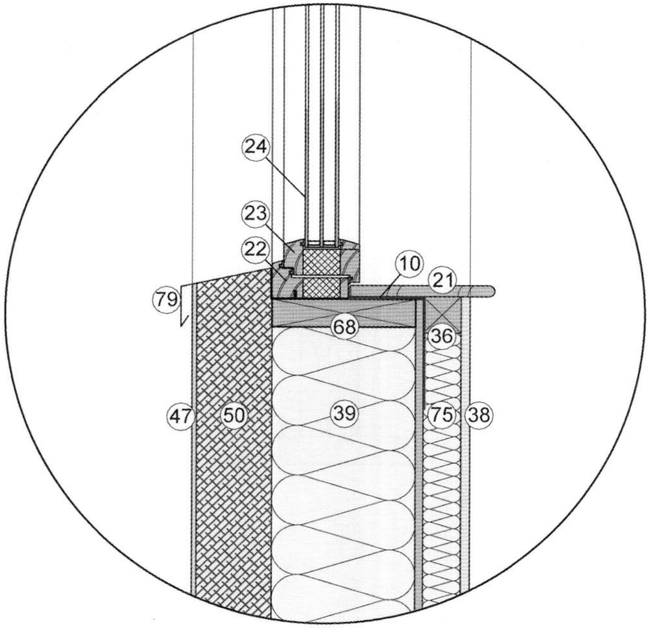

window sill

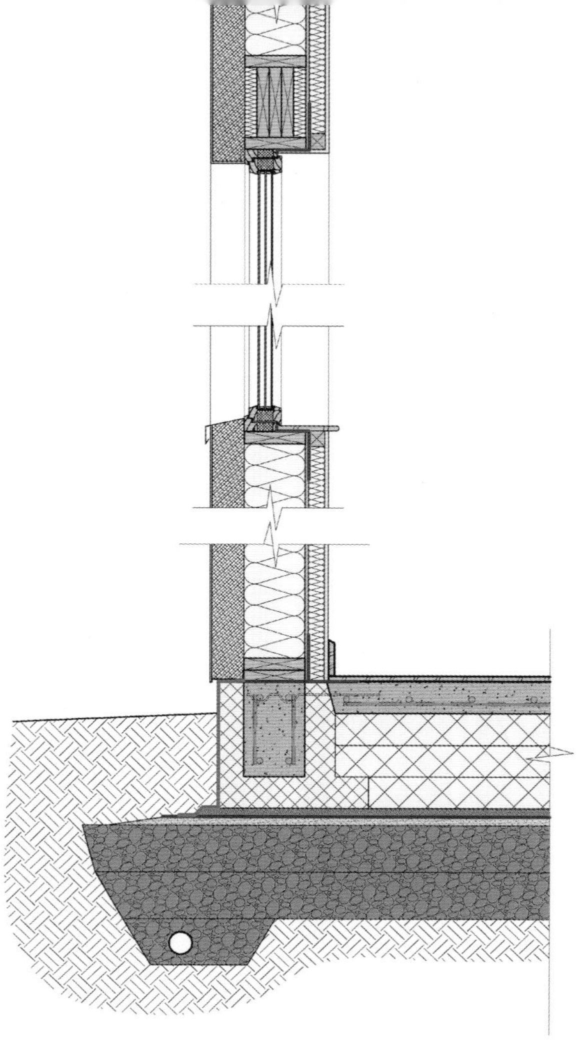

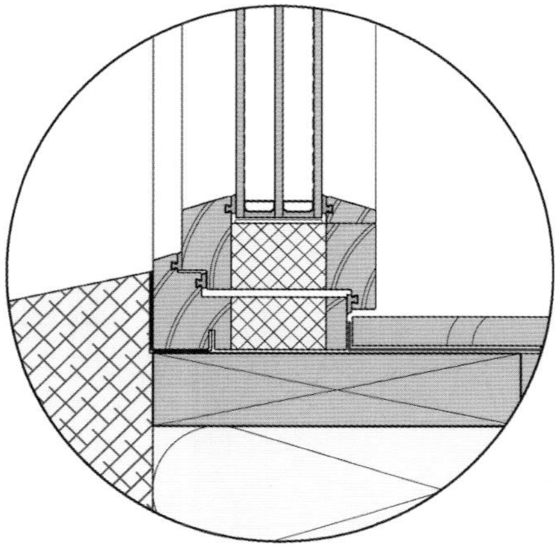

window frame (1:5)

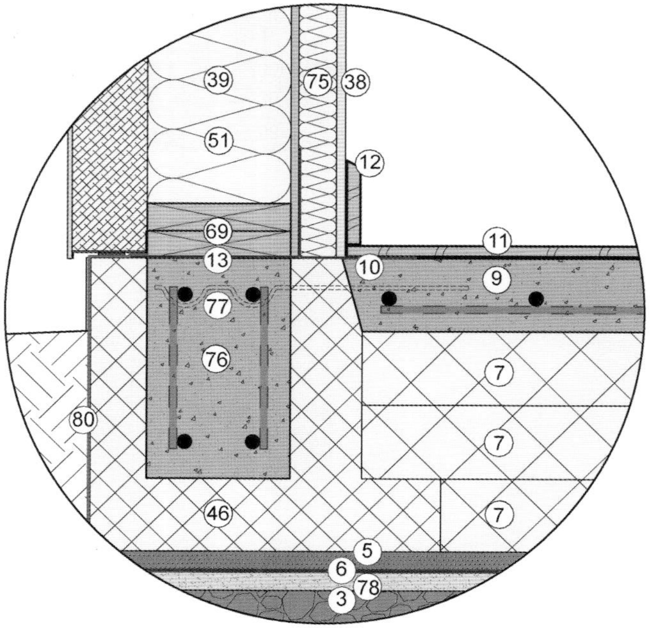

wall–ground floor junction

Circled details are at scale 1:10. Main detail is NOT TO SCALE.

Timber frame external insulation wall: Passivhaus standard (longitudinal section) 256–257

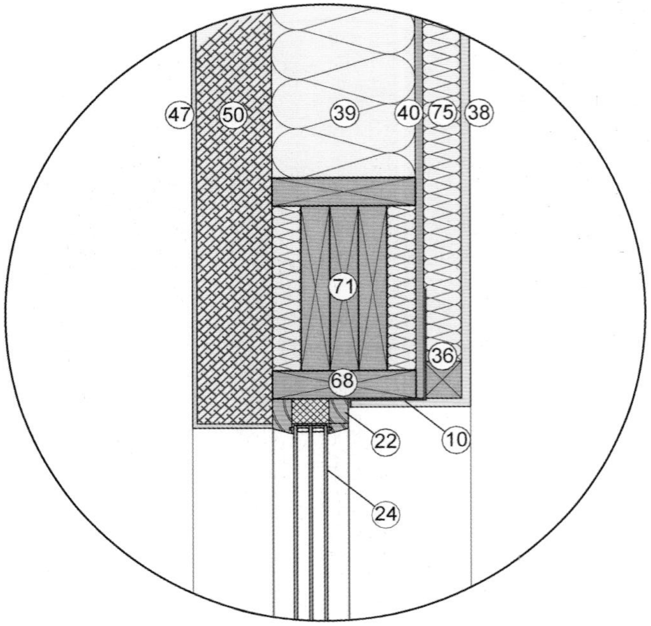

window head

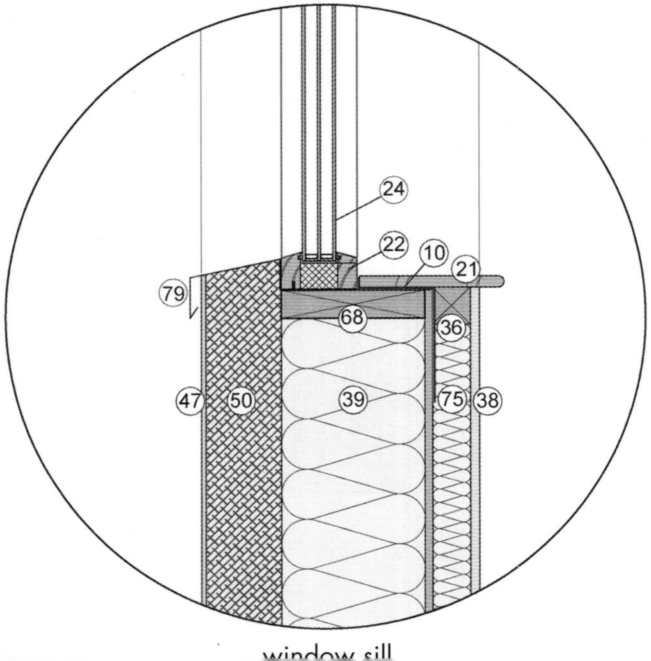

window sill

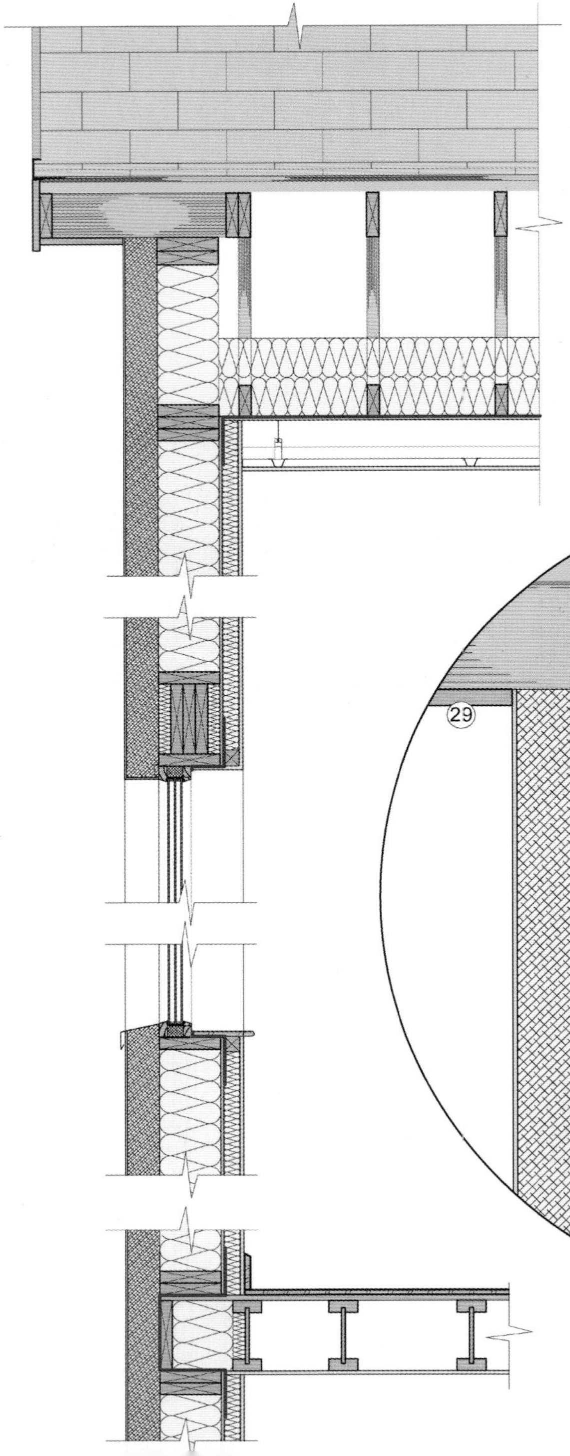

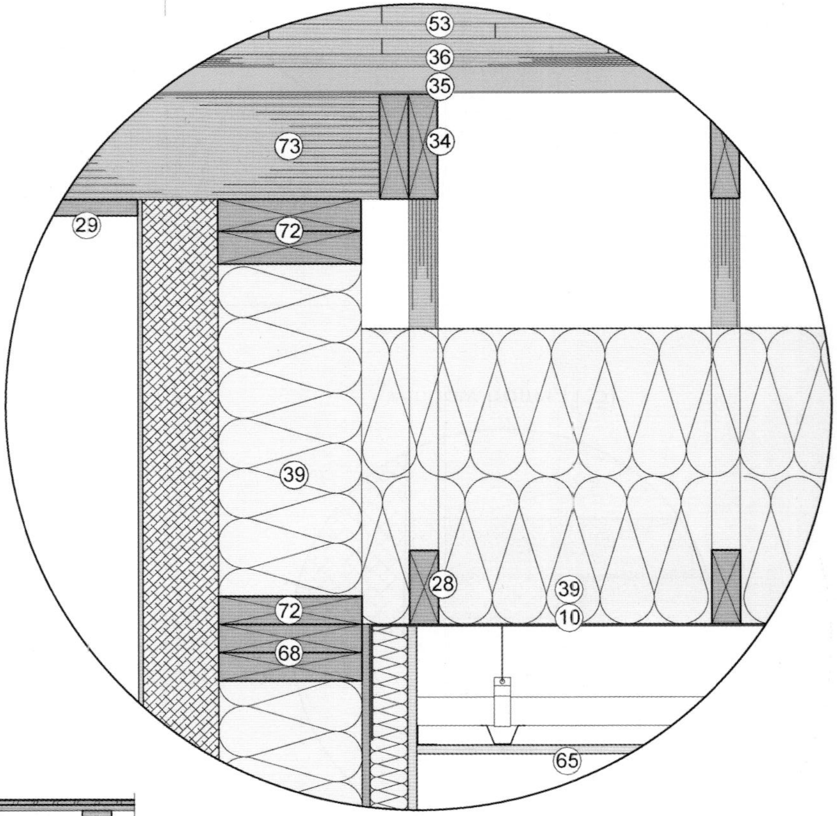

wall–roof junction (verge)

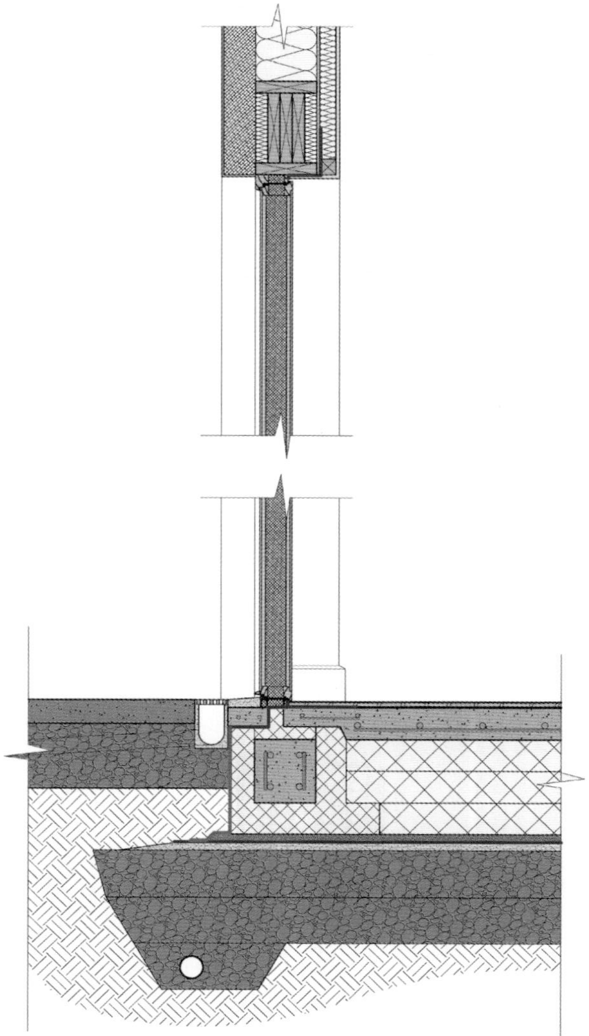

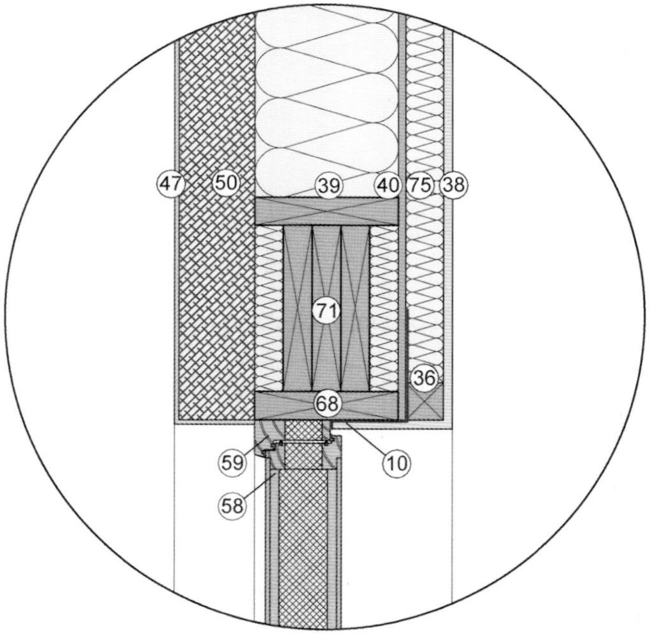

47 50 39 40 75 38
71
36
68
59 10
58

door head

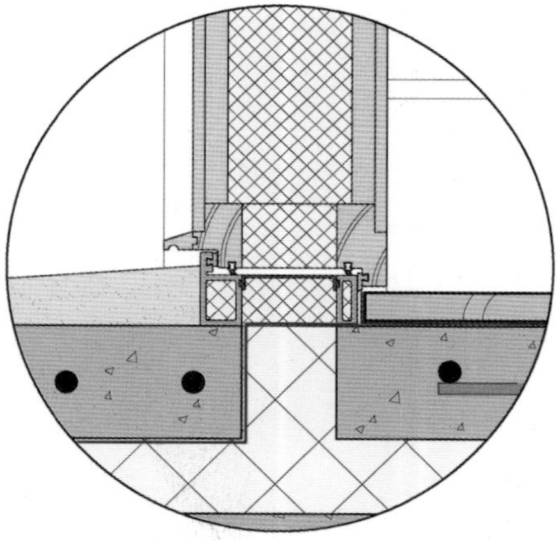

58
4 57
11
55 10
9
56
13
3
7
76
7
1 80
46 7
5
6 78
3

door sill (threshold)

door threshold (1:5)

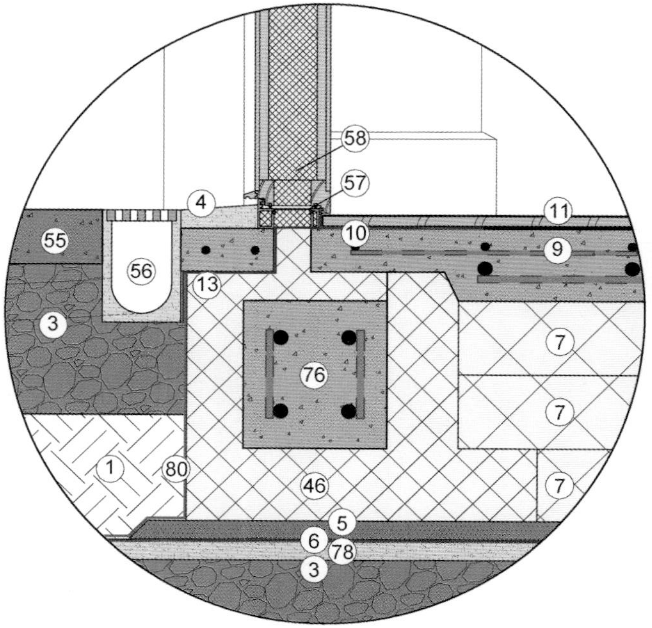

Circled details are at scale 1:10. Main detail is NOT TO SCALE.

Timber frame cladding wall: Passivhaus standard (transverse section)
258–258

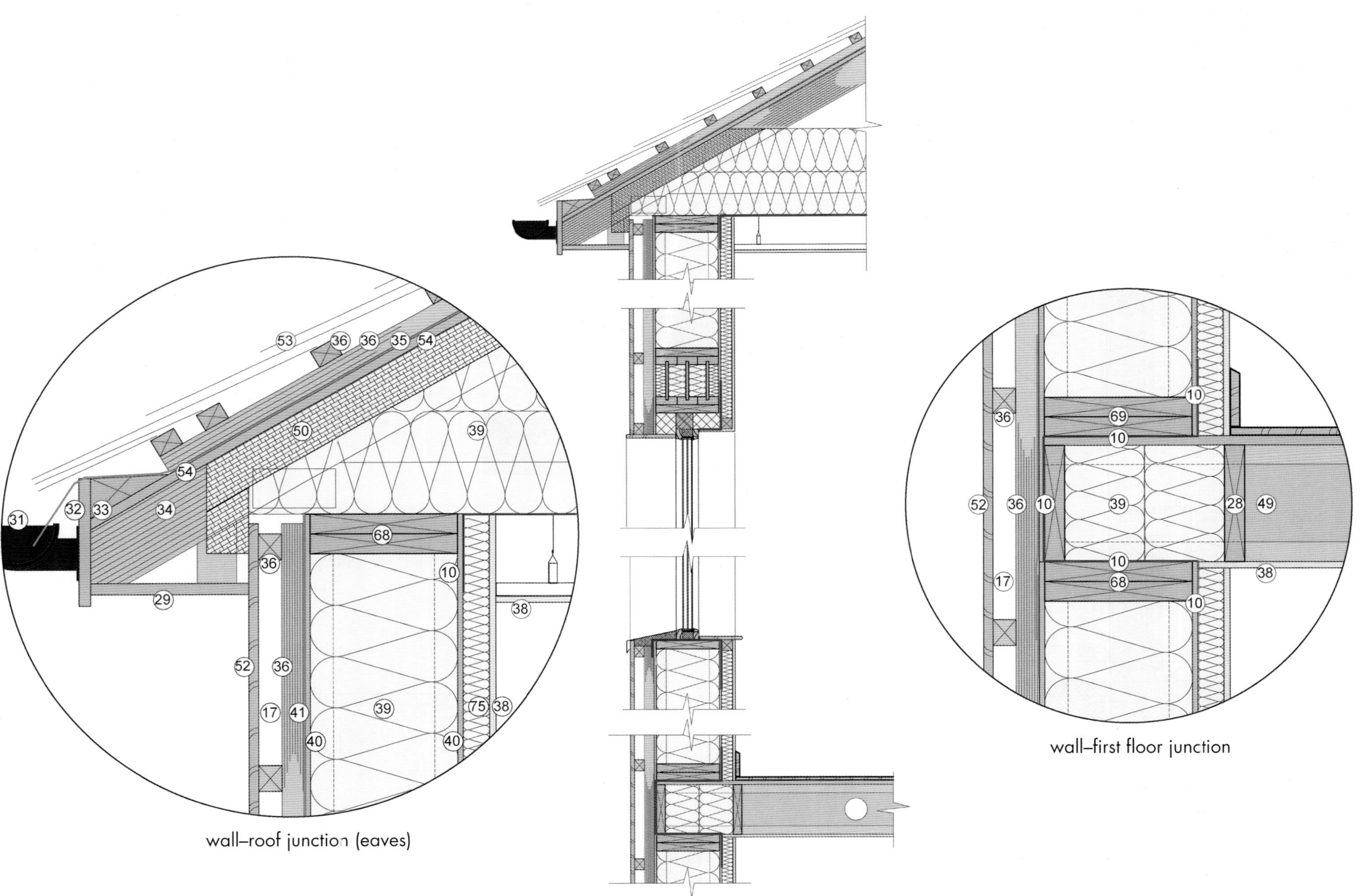

wall–roof junction (eaves)

wall–first floor junction

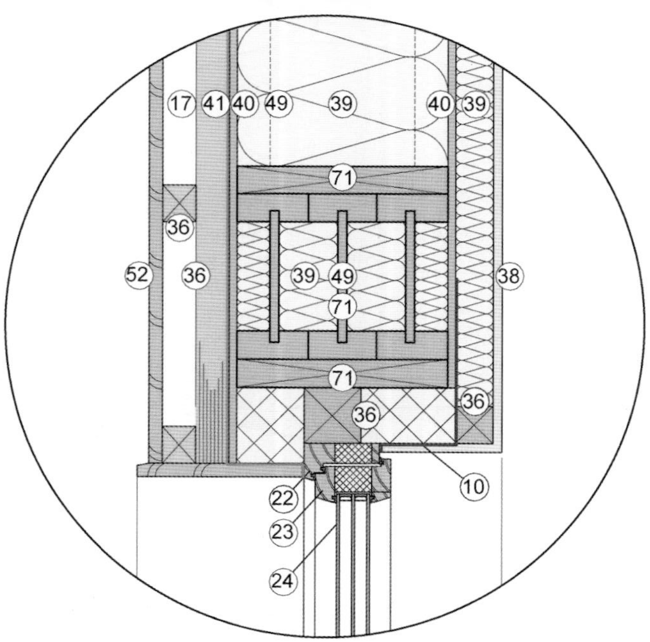

window head

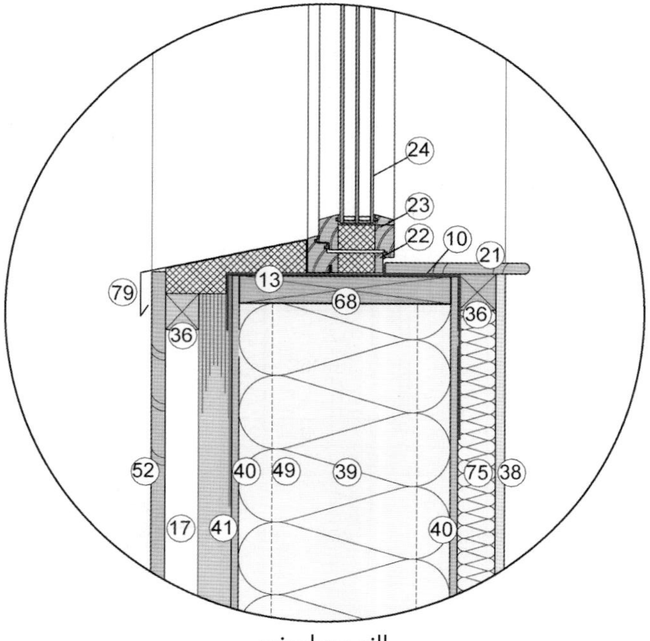

window sill

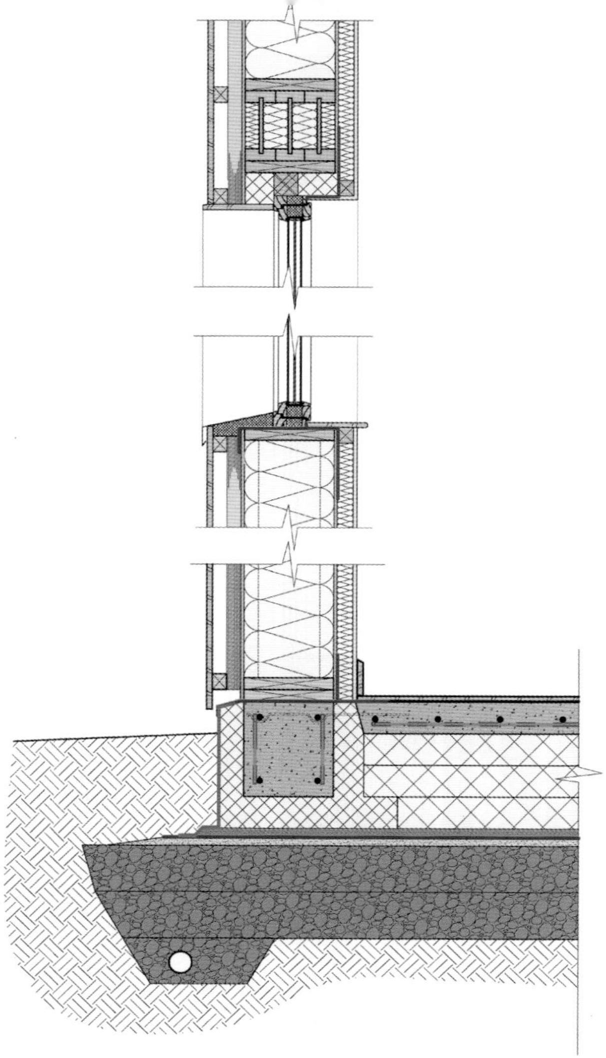

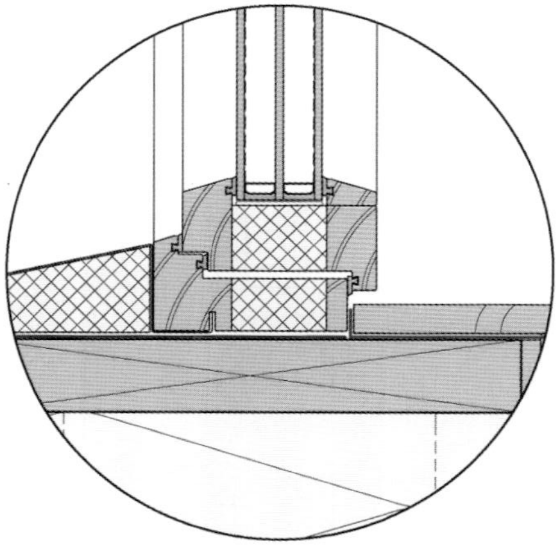

window frame (1:5)

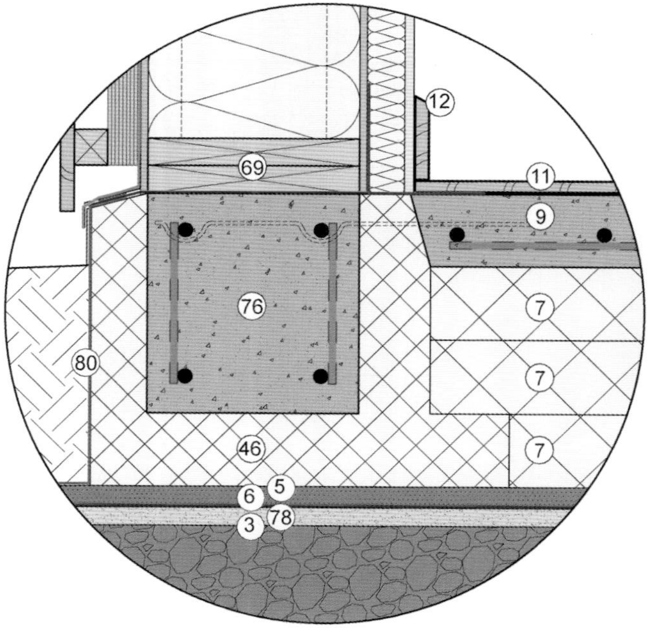

wall–ground floor junction

Circled details are at scale 1:10. Main detail is NOT TO SCALE.

Timber frame cladding wall: Passivhaus standard (longitudinal section)

260–261

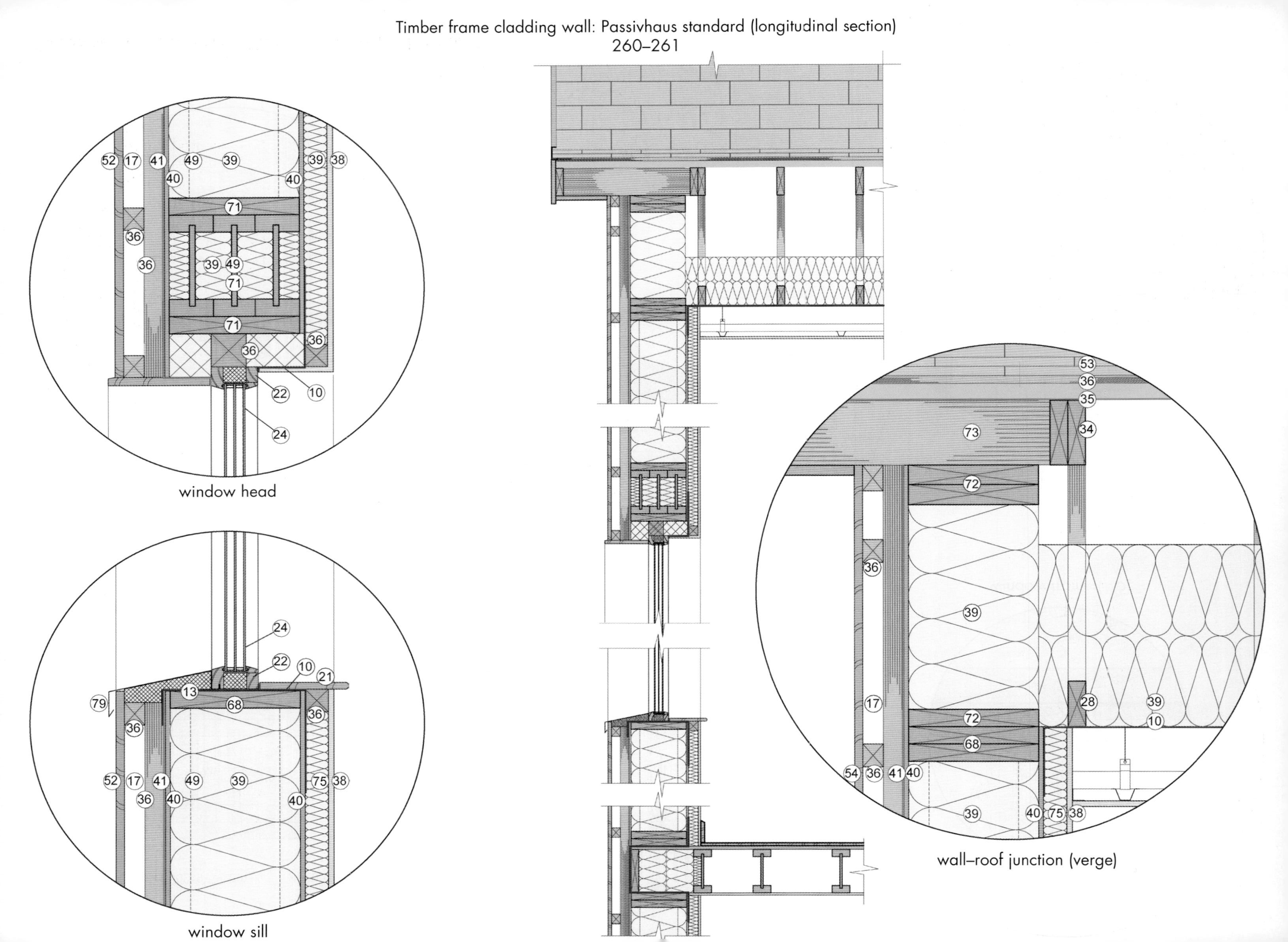

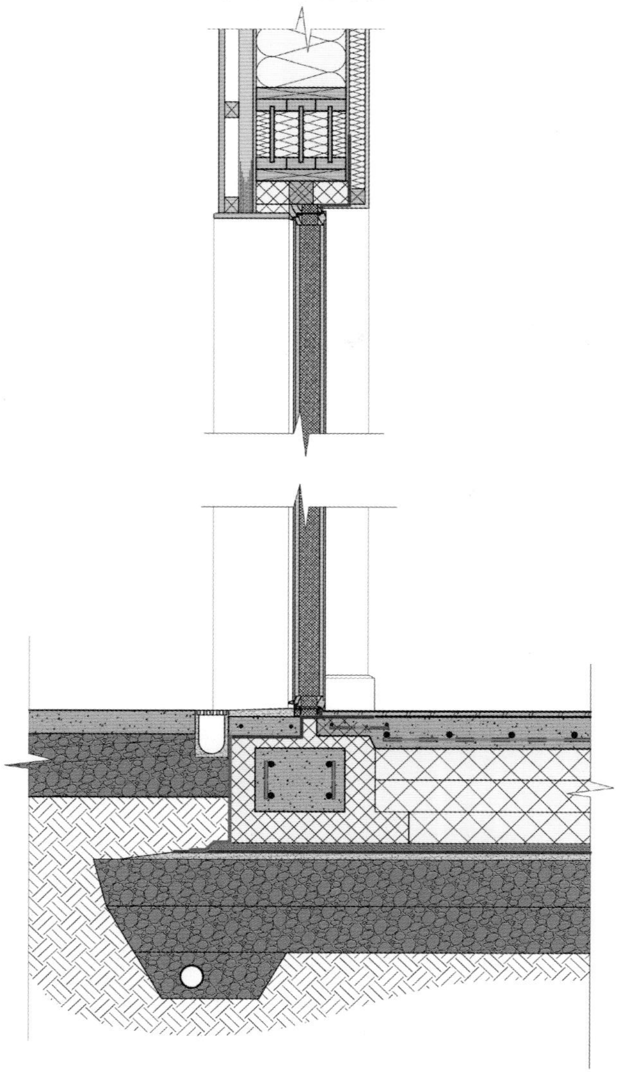

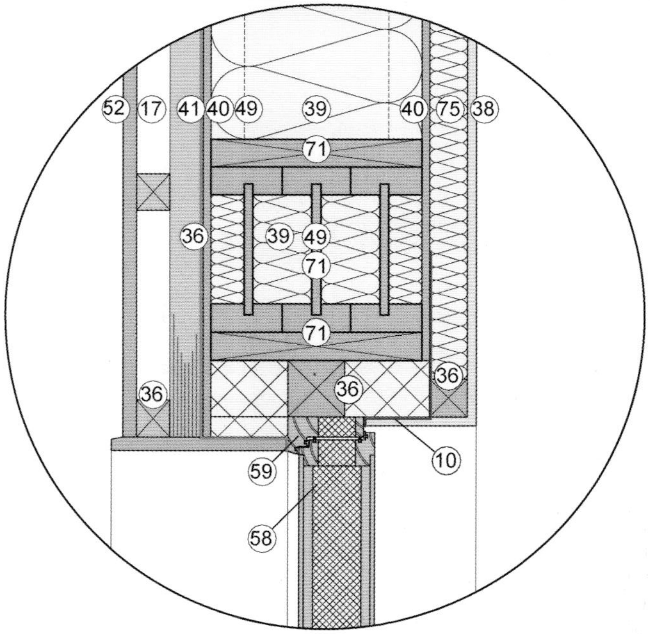

door head

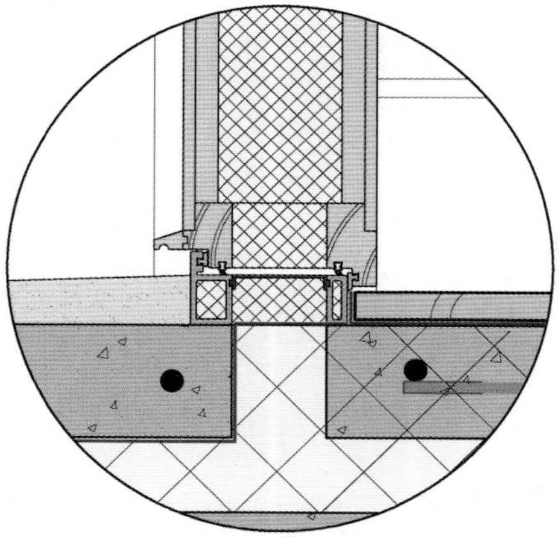

door sill (threshold)

door threshold (1:5)

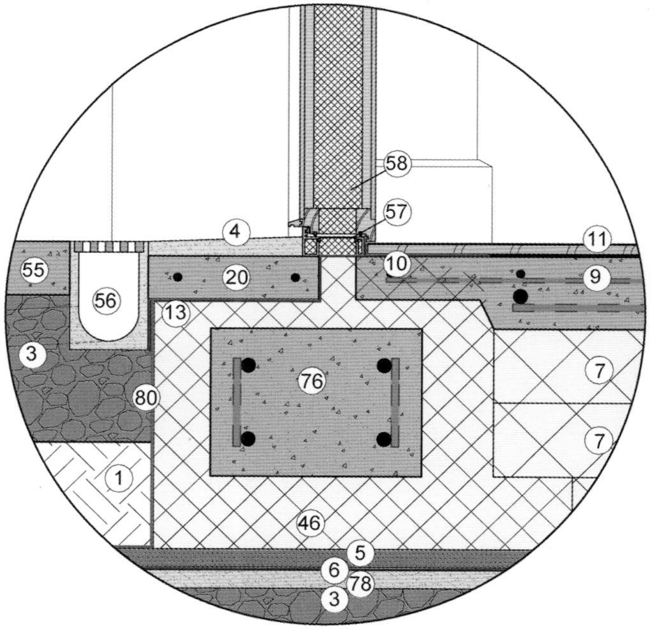

Circled details are at scale 1:10. Main detail is NOT TO SCALE.

SECTION 3

DESIGN: Comfort & Low Energy

CHAPTER 20

Healthy Indoor Environment

Comfort factors

The spaces created in a home (e.g. living room, kitchen, bedrooms) have a significant impact on how the people living there feel every day. Bright, airy, warm spaces make us feel positive and happy, while cold, damp and dark spaces make us feel miserable. It is important to realise that the environment created in a home has this effect on people. Knowing this ensures that when a home is planned, it is designed to create comfortable spaces that will have a positive impact on the lives of the people living there.

To apply this understanding to the design of homes it is essential to realise that the level of comfort experienced by the person in a home depends on two interactions. The first interaction is between the person and the internal environment; for example, when the home is too cold the person shivers. The second interaction is between the internal environment (indoors) and the external environment (outdoors); for example, when it is cold outside it will be cold inside (unless it is heated up). The home must balance these interactions so that the people inside are comfortable. This must happen at all times; day and night, spring, summer, autumn and winter.

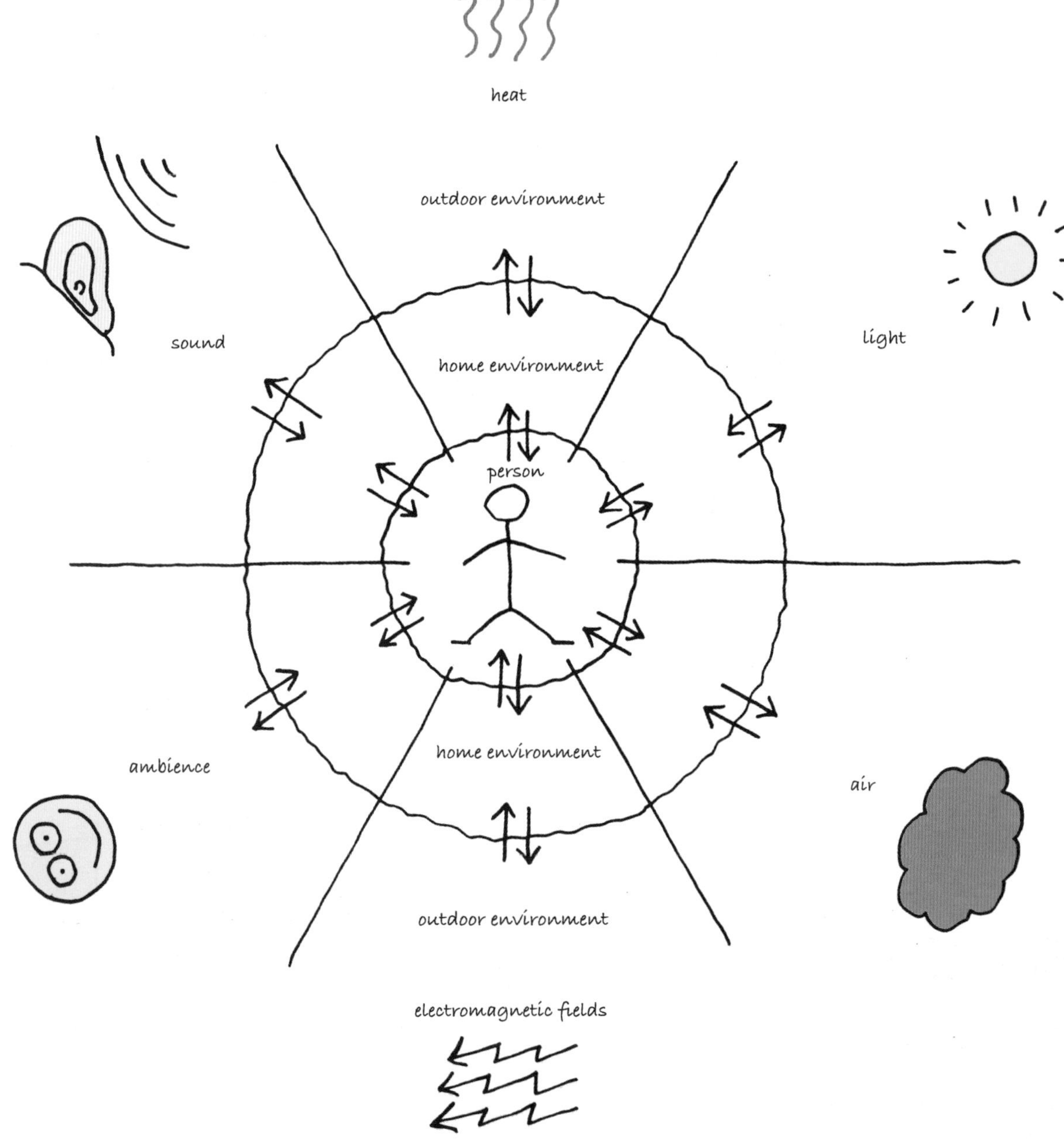

20.01 Outside–inside–person interactions: six factors for a healthy indoor environment.

KEY PRINCIPLES

There are six key factors that contribute to a healthy indoor environment.

1 Thermal comfort
- even though the temperature outdoors is constantly changing, the indoor temperature should be maintained at a steady level
- 18°C to 20°C (degrees Celsius) is comfortable for most people.

2 Light
- the light level outdoors ranges from 10,000 to 25,000 lux on a typical overcast day
- 150 to 300 lux is appropriate in most areas of a typical home.

3 Sound
- 30 decibels to 70 decibels is comfortable for most people
- noise pollution from outdoors must be excluded.

4 Air quality and movement
- a constant supply of fresh clean air (with a humidity level between 35% and 55%) must be provided
- no draughts or air movement that would have a cooling effect on the people indoors.

5 Electromagnetic fields
- all electrical devices produce an electromagnetic field – these fields may be harmful
- some EU countries are adopting standards to indicate safe levels of exposure to these fields.

6 Ambience
- ambience is achieved by using materials and furnishing to give a room warmth and comfort
- essential to creating a positive, healthy indoor environment.

	Temperature	Humidity	Sound	Lighting
	Dry Bulb Temperature	Relative Humidity	Sound Level	Illuminance
	100°C boiling point water	100% saturated air	140dB(A) threshold of pain	50,000 lux sunlight
Comfort zone	25°C summer's day	70% humid day	70dB busy office	10,000 lux shop display
Comfort zone				400 lux office lighting
Comfort zone	5°C winter's day	40% dry day	30dB quiet room	50 lux hallway
	0°C freezing point	0% dry air	0dB(A) threshold of hearing	0 lux dark

20.02 Comfort zone: the range of values highlighted in green indicate the tolerance levels for most people.

ACTIVITIES

Your favourite place ...
Think about your home. Ask yourself which part of your home is your favourite place? Explain why it is your favourite place. Does it have anything to do with the six factors of a healthy indoor environment?

Thermal comfort

The human body is very sensitive to changes in temperature. Core body temperature is approximately 37°C; typical skin temperature is usually a few degrees cooler (32° to 34°C, depending on environment and activity rate).

KEY PRINCIPLES

Several factors combine to create a person's sense of whether they feel hot, warm, neutral, cool or cold. They include:

- air temperature – the temperature of the air in a room
- radiant temperature – the combined temperature of the surfaces in a room (see below)
- relative humidity – the moisture content of the air
- air velocity – the speed at which the air in a room is moving
- activity rate – what the person is doing (e.g. sitting, dancing)
- clothing level – the type and number of layers of clothing being worn.

These factors combine to create an overall thermal environment that is sensed by the human body.

Mean radiant temperature

If there are any significant differences in the surface temperatures in a room the body will sense these and the person will feel uncomfortable. Mean radiant temperature (t_r) is the term used to describe the temperature at a point in the centre of a room as a result of the heat energy radiating from each of the surfaces in the room. It can be approximately calculated by measuring the temperature and area of each surface and calculating the proportional contribution of these surfaces to the overall temperature, using the following formula:

$$t_r = \frac{t_1.A_1 + t_2.A_2 + t_3.A_3 + t_4.A_4 + \ldots}{A_1 + A_2 + A_3 + A_4 + \ldots}$$

where:
t = temperature of surface
A = area of surface

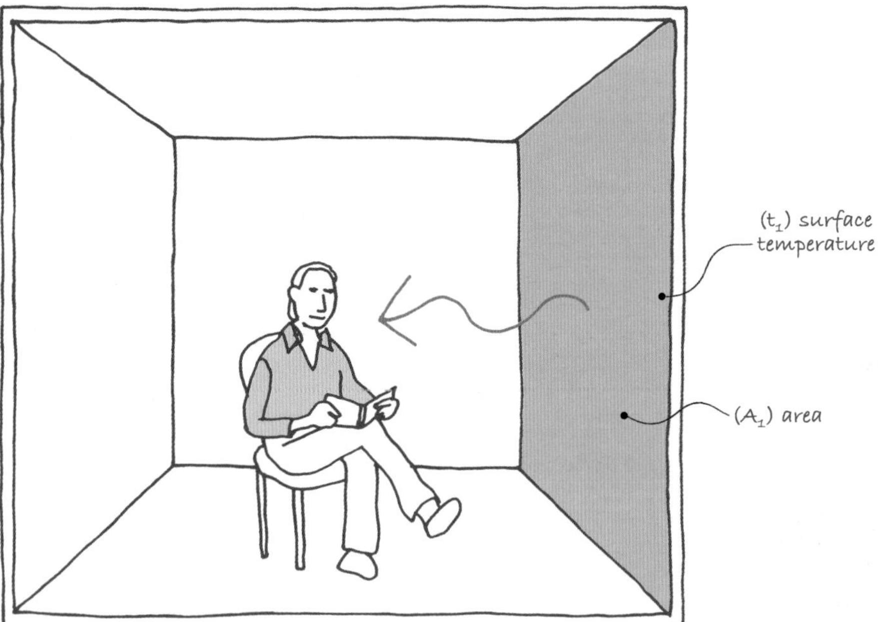

20.03 Mean radiant temperature.

Radiant asymmetry

Radiant asymmetry is the term used to describe a situation in which there is a significant imbalance in the temperature radiating from different surfaces. This happens in everyday life when a person sits near a camp fire on a cold night. The front of their body is sensing a high temperature but their back is sensing a low temperature. This makes the person feel cold and so they pull closer to the fire – but this only makes it worse! In an indoor space, any difference in radiant temperature above 4.2 degrees will make a person feel uncomfortable. Radiant asymmetry is usually associated with poorly insulated windows.

20.04 Radiant asymmetry: poor-quality windows cause radiant asymmetry and lead to an uncomfortable indoor environment.

Air temperature criteria for thermal comfort

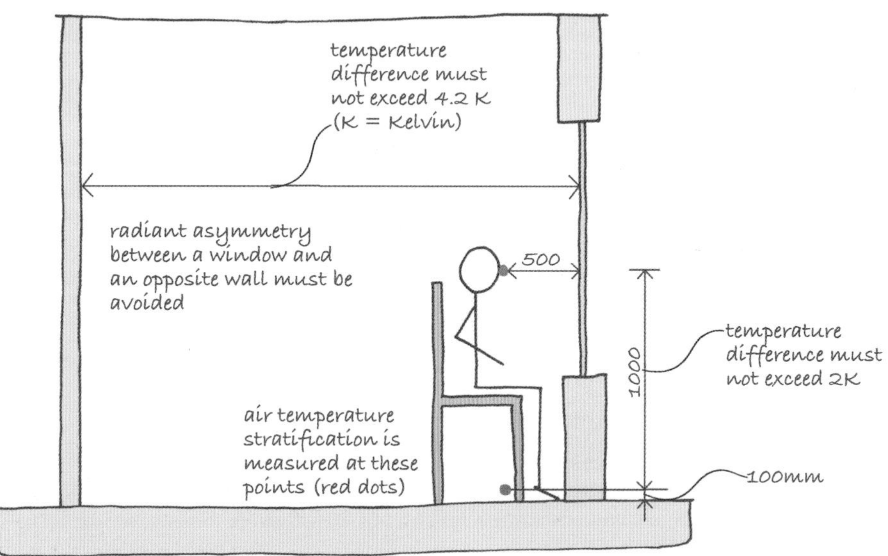

20.05 Thermal comfort: a consistent temperature throughout the room is required for comfort.

There are three air temperature criteria that should be met for comfort:

1 Vertical differences:
   - called air temperature stratification
   - temperature difference should not exceed 2K when measured from ankles to head in a sitting position.

2 Horizontal differences:
   - called radiant asymmetry
   - occurs when two surfaces in a room are at different temperatures
   - usually happens when the interior surface of window (with a high U-value) is cool because it is cold outside
   - if the temperature difference is more than 4.2K the occupants feel uncomfortable.

3 From place to place:
   - air temperature difference in different areas of a room should not exceed 0.8K.

ACTIVITIES

Examine the living room of your home. Record, in your own words, how the room meets the six comfort factors outlined above. Note also how each of these factors is controlled. For example, does the radiator have an independent temperature control valve? Can a window be opened to increase air flow?

REVISION EXERCISES

1 Summarise the key factors that contribute to a healthy indoor environment.
2 Calculate the mean radiant temperature of the room shown. (Note: there are four walls – include the one you are looking through (temp. 18.6K)).

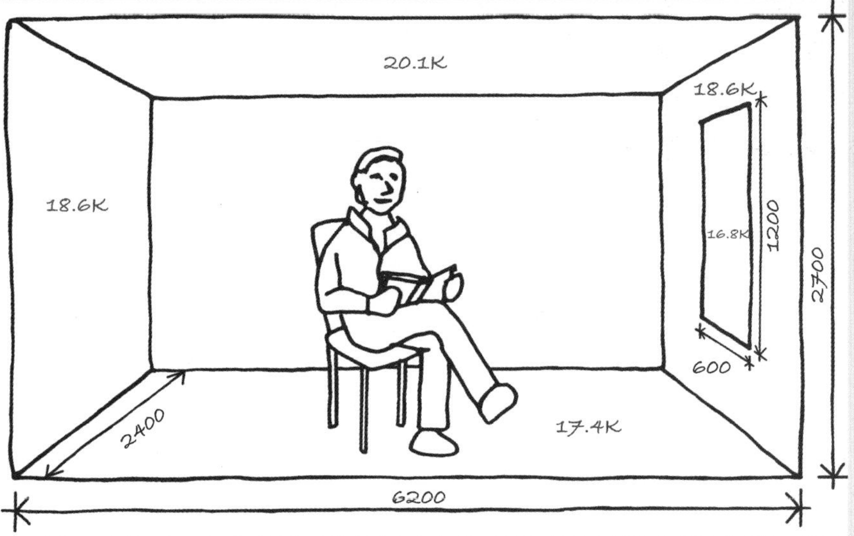

3 Describe how radiant asymmetry causes discomfort.
4 Explain, using a neat freehand sketch, the indoor temperature criteria for thermal comfort.
5 Why is air movement an important factor for thermal comfort?

CHAPTER 21 Passive Design

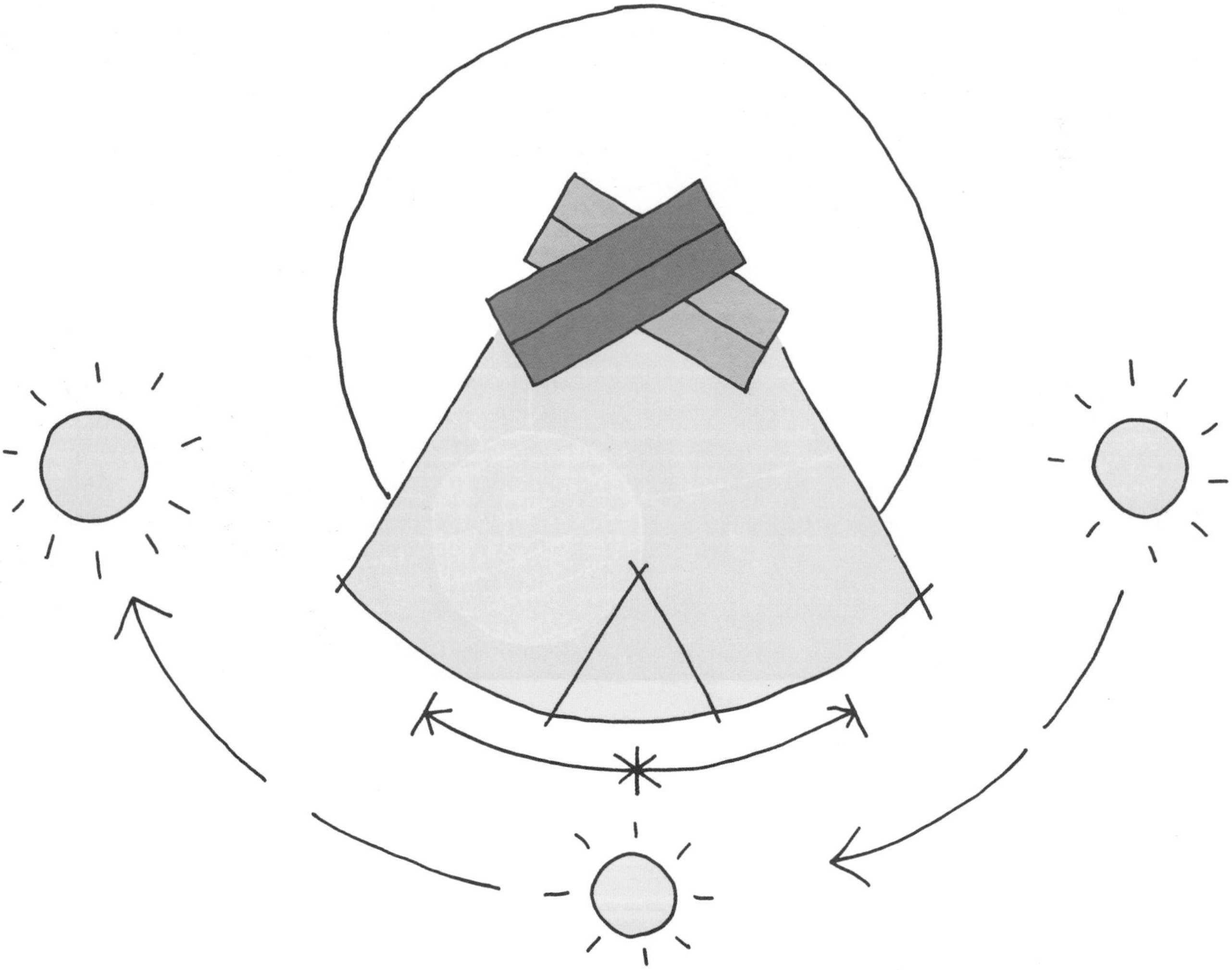

The design of low-energy housing is based on the concept of solar gain – capturing radiant energy from the sun to provide space heating, water heating and lighting.

Solar principles

When designing homes that capture the sun's energy, it is essential to understand the movement of the sun in the sky and how this changes with the seasons.

Earth's orbit

A year is the time taken for the earth to complete one orbit of the sun. The axis of the earth is tilted by 23.5° with respect to the plane that passes through the sun and the Equator. This tilt causes the change in radiation, length of day, and climate between summer and winter. If there were no tilt, there would be uniform climatic conditions throughout the year (i.e. no seasons). The intensity of radiation from the sun also varies with the season of the year. The angle at which radiation from the sun falls on a surface changes as the relative tilt and orbit of the earth around the sun changes.

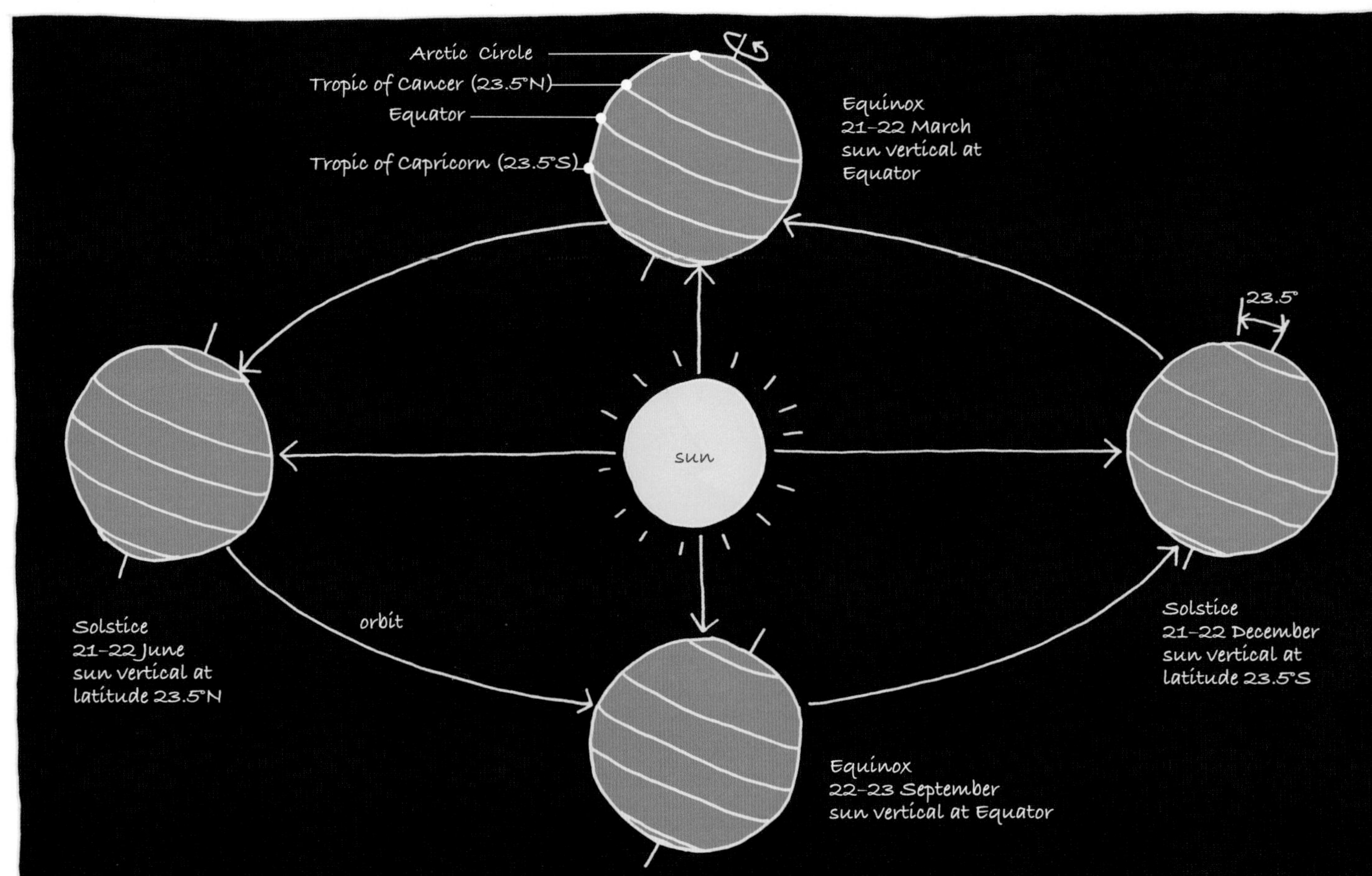

21.01 The earth's orbit: the earth rotates about the sun once per year; it rotates on its axis (towards the east, or anti-clockwise) once every 24 hours; the axis is tilted at an angle of 23.5°. Seasons depend on position in orbit.

Latitude

Geographical latitude ϕ is a measure of the position of a point on the earth's surface above (north of) or below (south of) the Equator.

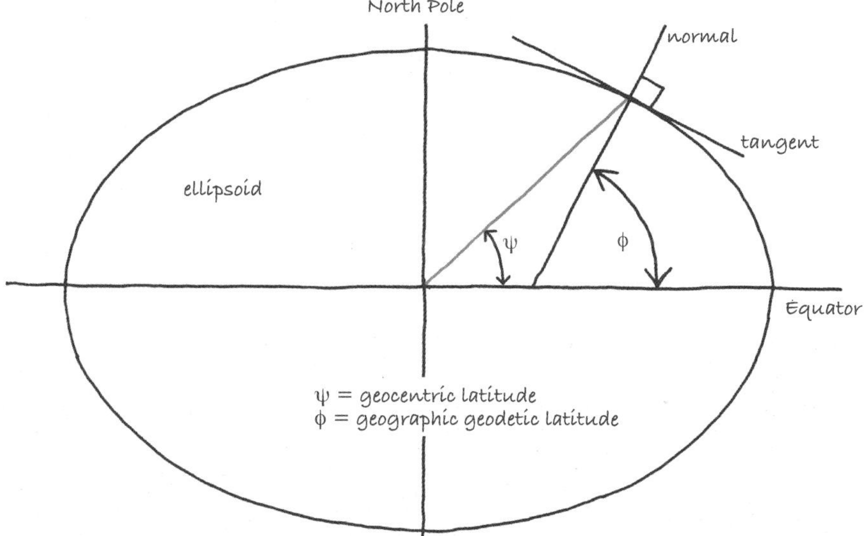

21.02 Latitude: the earth is an ellipsoid (flattened at the poles).

The radiation from the sun is at its most intense when it falls on the earth's surface at an angle of 90° to the surface – this happens at the Equator. The intensity of solar radiation decreases as latitude increases and the angle at which the solar radiation strikes the earth's surface decreases. This angle, called the altitude or sun angle, varies throughout the year. Ireland's position in the northern hemisphere means that the maximum sun angle ranges from approximately 11° to 15° in winter and from 58° to 62° in summer (depending on location).

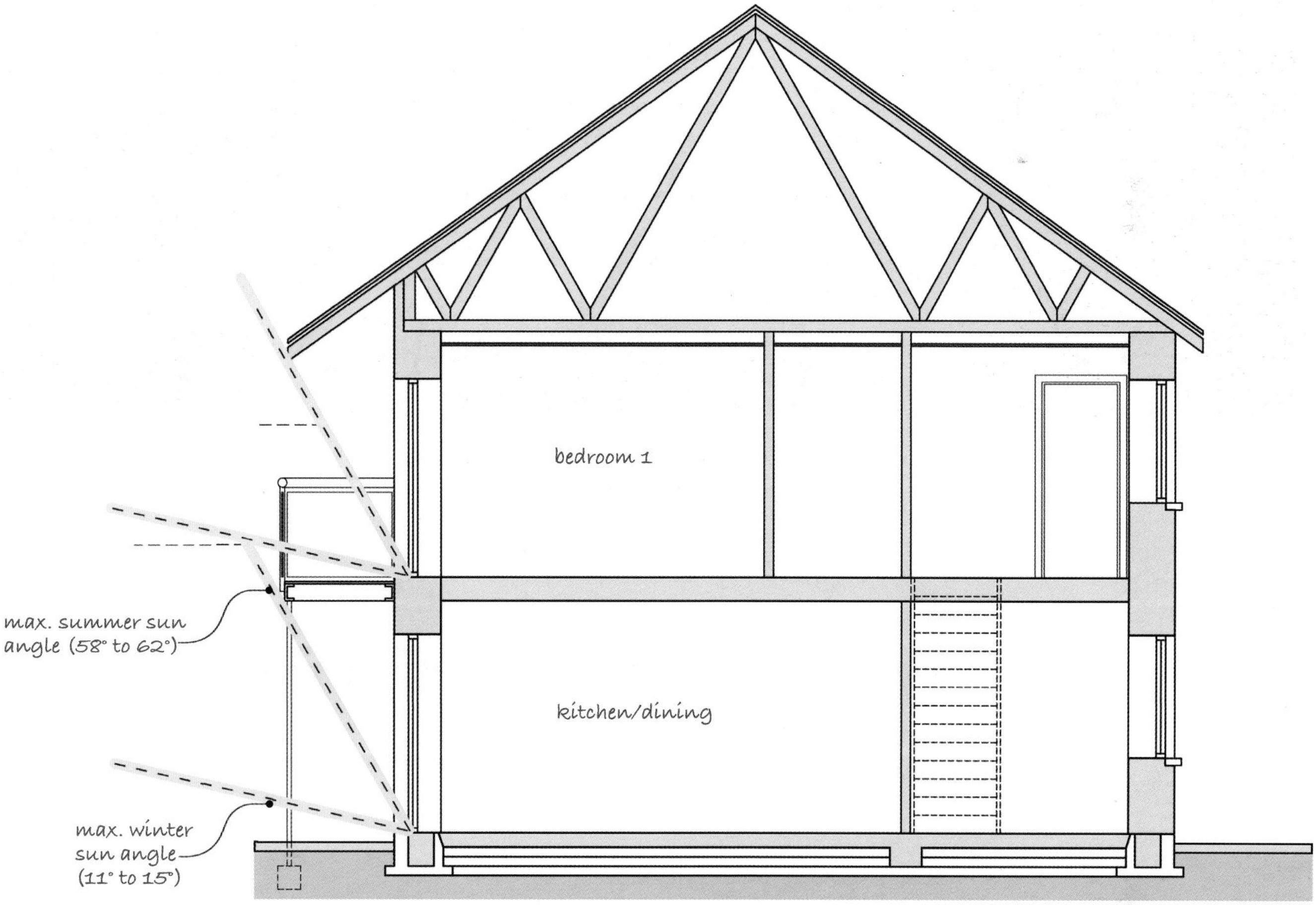

21.03 Maximum sun angle in Ireland varies from winter to summer.

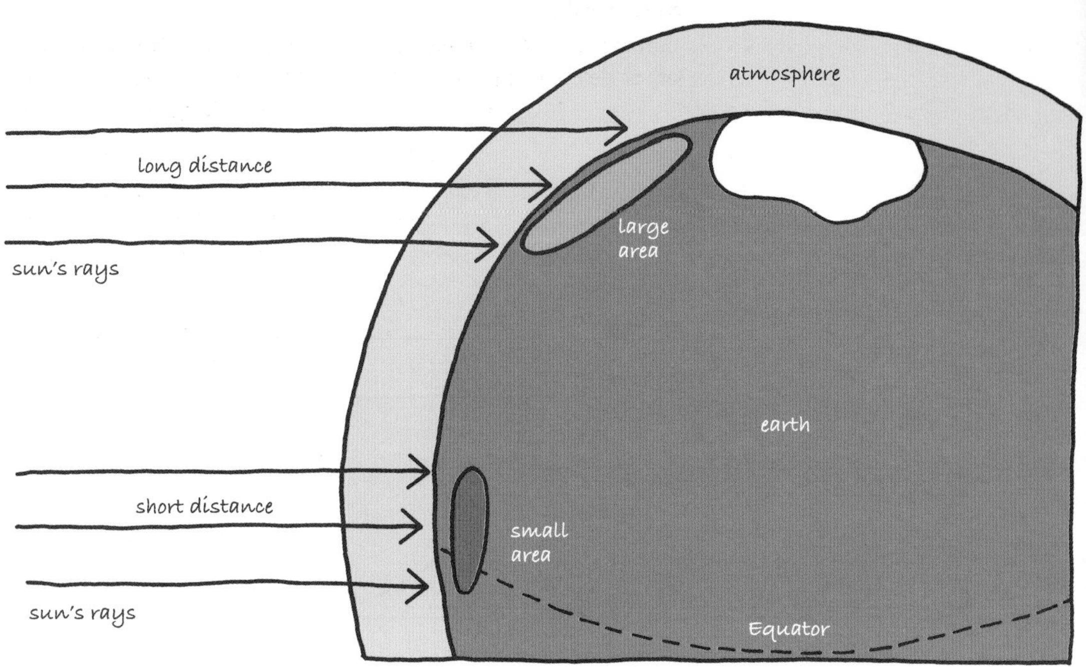

21.04 Latitude: at higher latitudes the sun's energy is spread over a larger area, and therefore weaker than if the sun is higher overhead and the energy is concentrated on smaller area.

Sun position

The position of the sun relative to the earth doesn't change. It is because of the earth's orbit around the sun that the sun appears to move in the sky. The ecliptic is the apparent path of the sun in the sky. The position of the sun in the sky is described by two angles: azimuth and altitude.

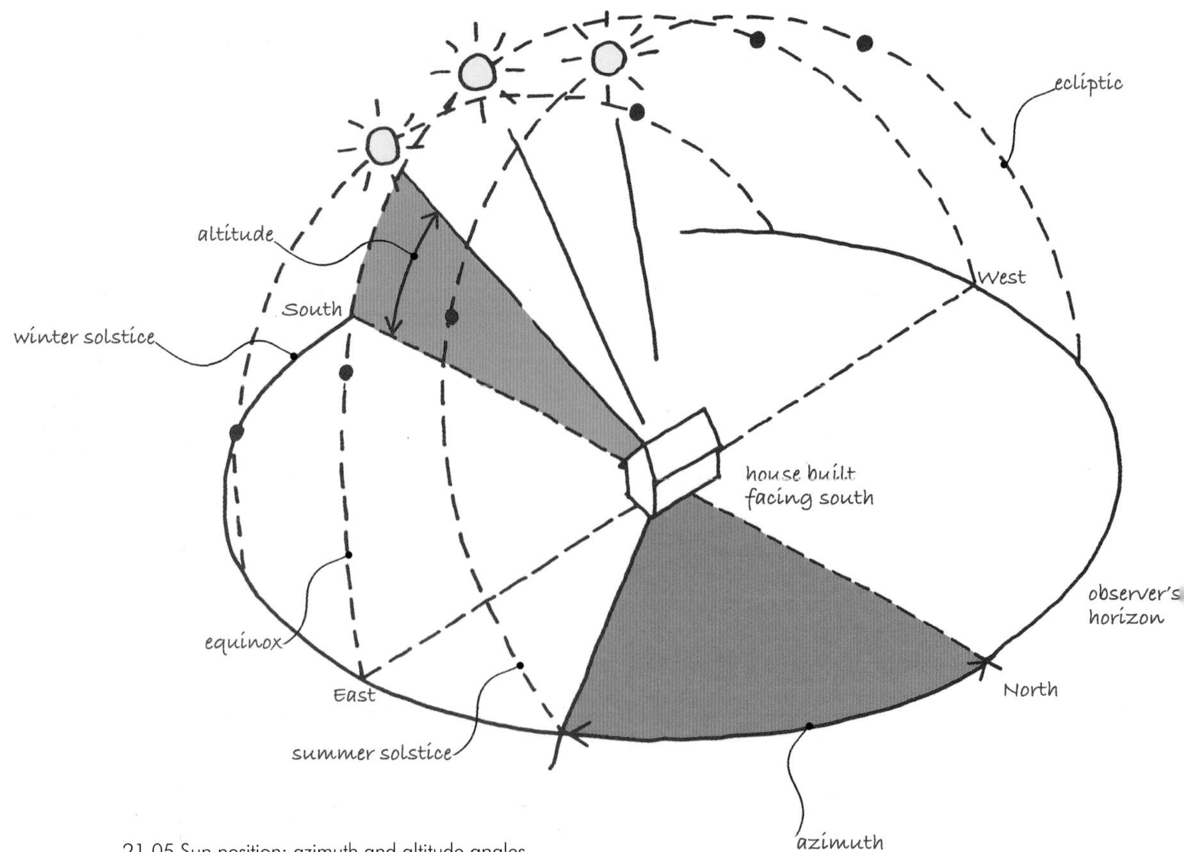

21.05 Sun position: azimuth and altitude angles.

Sun angle

The amount and quality of solar energy we receive in Ireland is influenced by our position on the planet. Ireland's position in the northern hemisphere means that the sun is to the south (over the Equator) – therefore, the south-facing side (façade) of a building receives the most solar energy.

This fact is very important when designing buildings that are going to be primarily heated by the sun's energy (i.e. passive homes). For example, it is important to know the sun angle so that features, such as shading devices, can be included in the design to prevent overheating during the summer. The sun angle is also crucial to the positioning of solar panels to ensure maximum energy gain.

The sun angle varies because the earth is tilted on its axis. In the summer the earth is leaning towards the sun; in winter it leans away from the sun.

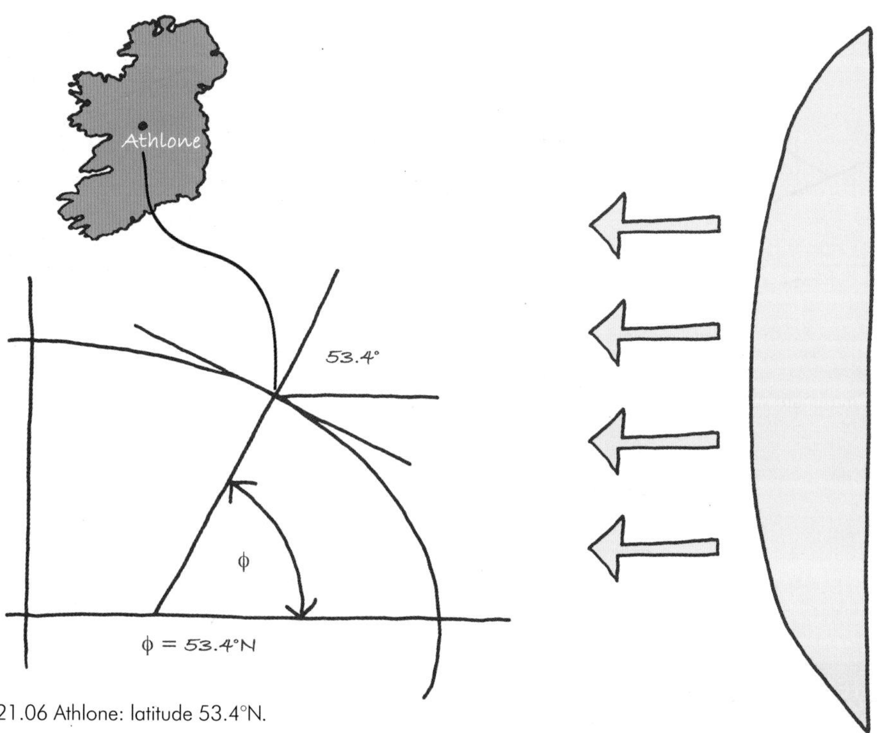

21.06 Athlone: latitude 53.4°N.

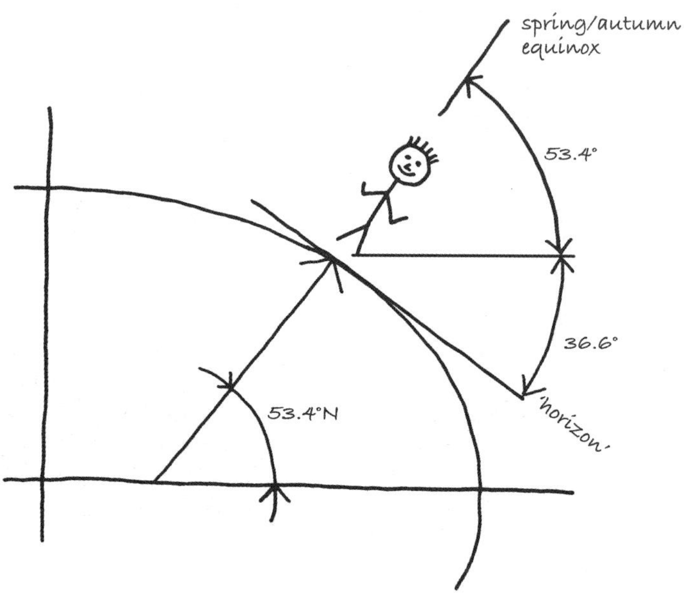

21.07 Athlone: maximum sun angle, spring/autumn equinox = 36.6°N.

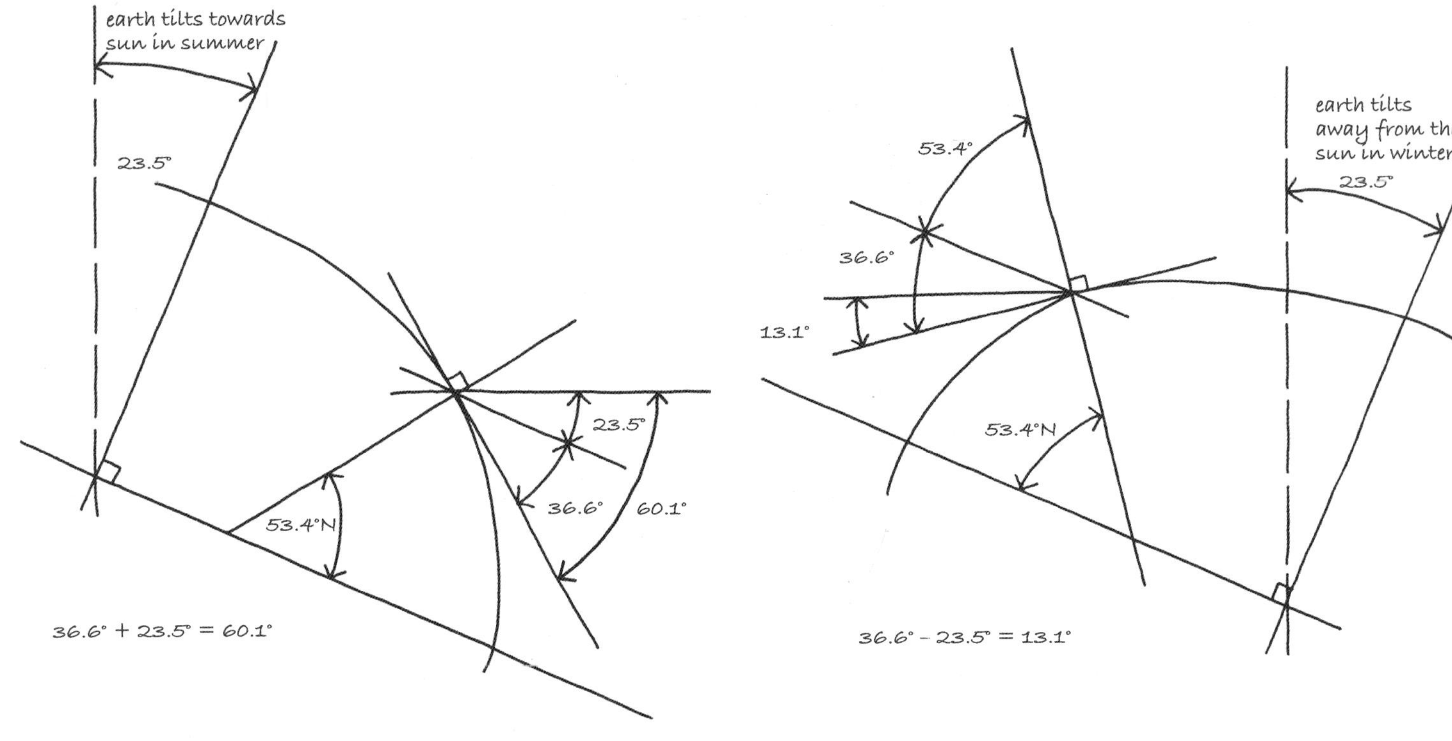

21.08 Athlone: maximum sun angle, summer solstice = 60.1°N.

21.09 Athlone: maximum sun angle, winter equinox = 13.1°N.

Once the latitude of a site is known (which can be easily found online or by using Google Earth), the maximum sun angle can be calculated using these formulae:

season	maximum sun angle
spring/autumn equinox	90° – latitude = maximum sun angle
summer solstice	90° – latitude + 23.5° = maximum sun angle
winter solstice	90° – latitude – 23.5° = minimum sun angle

21.10 Maximum sun angle formulae

ACTIVITIES

Look up the latitude of your home using the Google Earth app. Calculate the maximum sun angle in summer, winter and at the equinoxes.

Worked example

Áras an Uachtaráin in the Phoenix Park, Dublin has a latitude of 53.35 degrees.

season	maximum sun angle
spring/autumn equinox	90° – 53.35° = 36.65°
summer solstice	90° – 53.35° + 23.5° = 60.15°
winter solstice	90° – 53.35° – 23.5° = 13.15°

21.11 Maximum sun angle example.

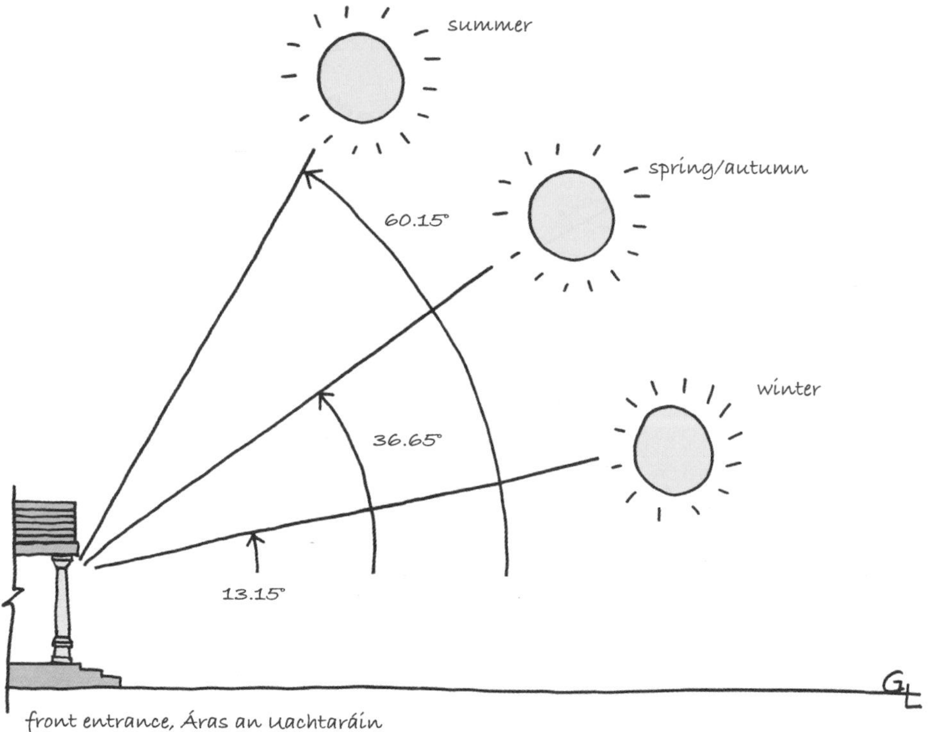

21.12 Maximum sun angle at Áras an Uachtaráin for each season.

	latitude	summer	spring/autumn	winter
Malin Head	55.39	58.11	34.61	11.11
Donegal	54.65	58.85	35.35	11.85
Athlone	53.42	60.08	36.58	13.08
Dublin	53.35	60.15	36.65	13.15
Galway	53.27	60.23	36.73	13.23
Limerick	52.66	60.84	37.34	13.84
Waterford	52.26	61.24	37.74	14.24
Cork	51.90	61.60	38.10	14.60
Mizen Head	51.45	62.05	38.55	15.05

21.13 Maximum sun angles at various locations throughout the year. Athlone, being in the middle of Ireland, has the average values.

Sun path

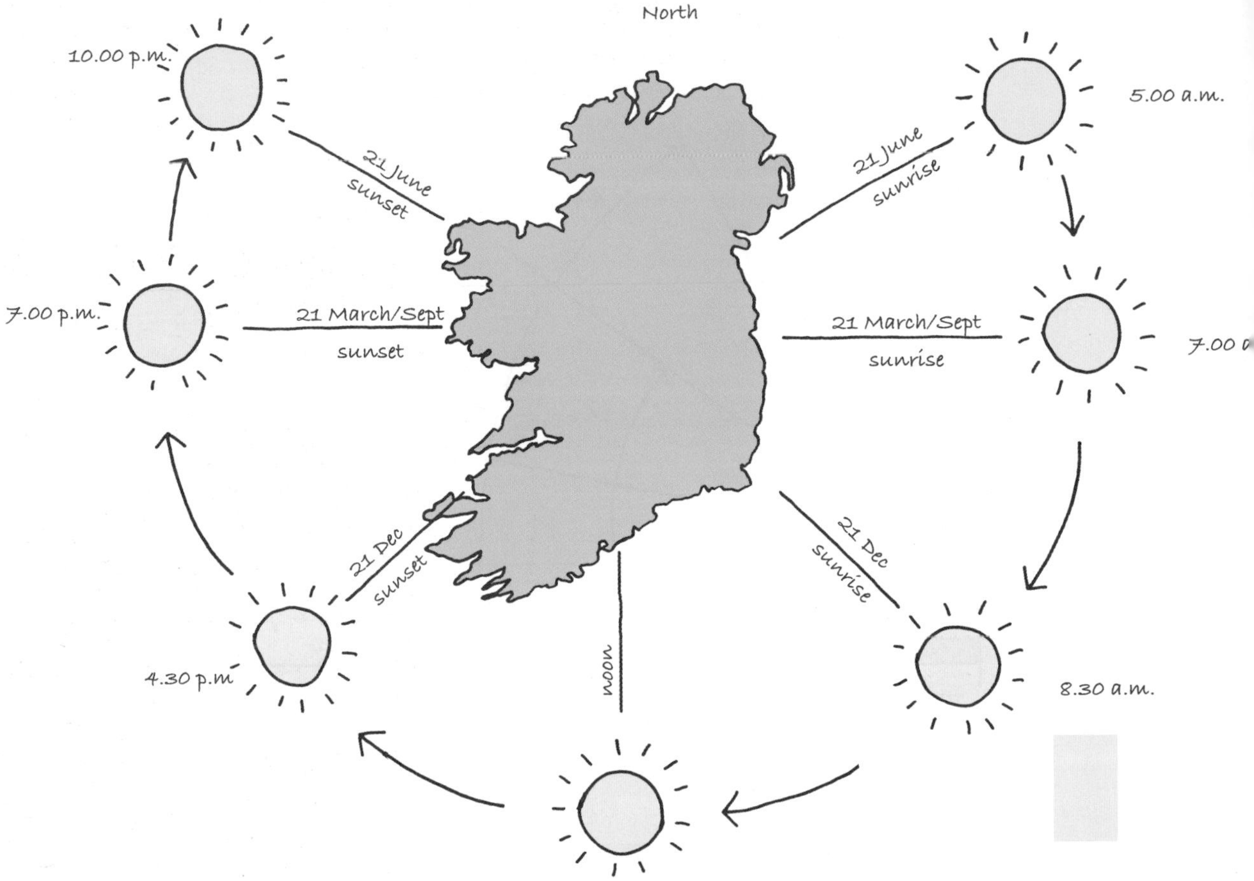

21.14 Simplified sunpath diagram showing approximate time and azimuth angle of sunrise and sunset in Ireland.

The position of the sun can be plotted using a sunpath diagram. This diagram provides an accurate picture of the sun's position when viewed from a particular point on earth at various times of the year.

KEY PRINCIPLES

Simple facts about the sun's movement:

- the sun rises (morning) in the east and sets (evening) in the west
- the sun is approximately due south at noon
- the sun is higher in the sky in summer than in winter
- summer days are long; winter days are short.

Passive design

Passive design is a general term used to describe a way of designing buildings that uses sunlight to provide heat and light. Unlike active design, which relies on burning fuels to produce energy to provide space heating, water heating and lighting, passive design uses energy from the sun to do this. Almost every home built in Ireland over the last century was based on active design. These homes waste a lot of energy in providing a comfortable indoor environment. Creating sustainable homes means shifting from an active to a passive approach.

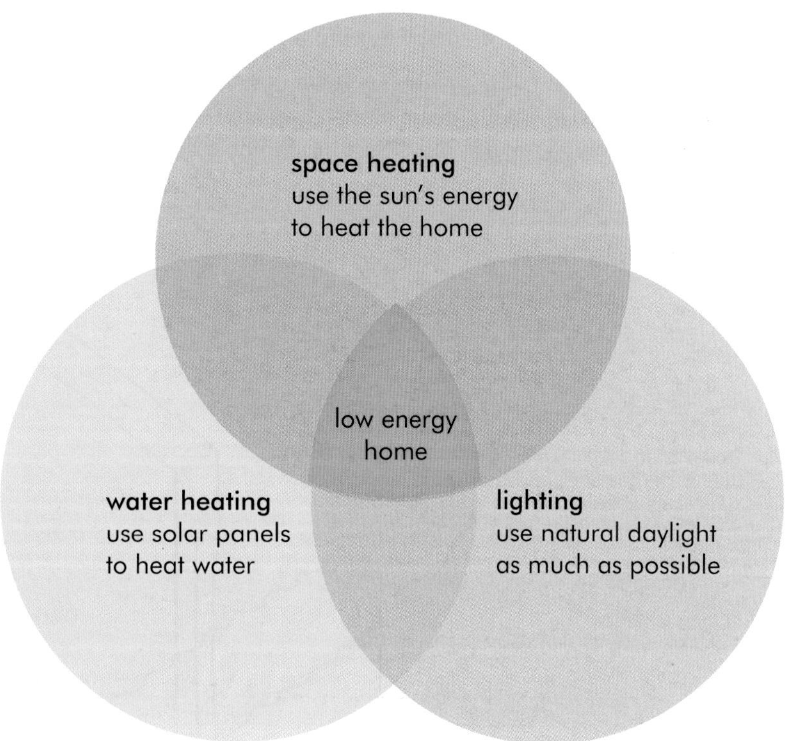

21.15 Passive design: low energy homes use solar gain to provide space heating, water heating and lighting.

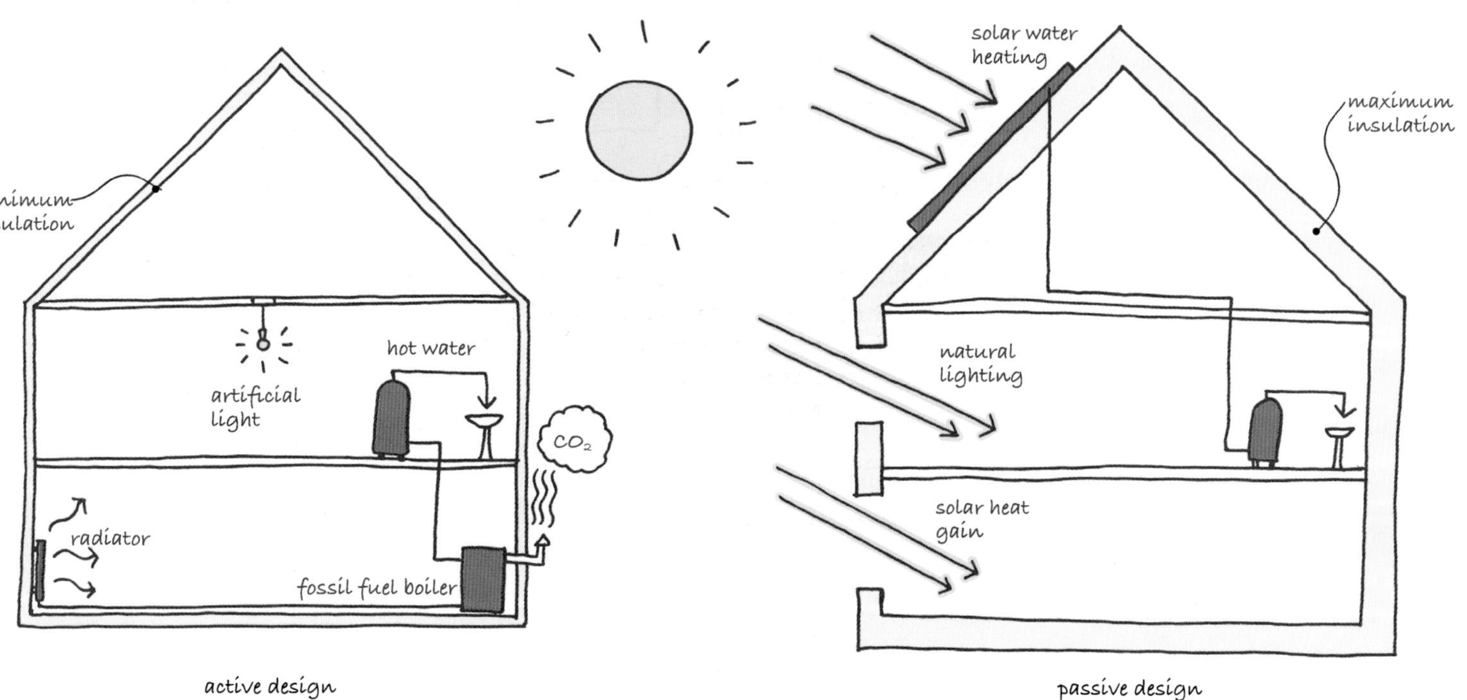

21.16 Active design (high energy consumption and high CO_2 emissions) versus passive design (low energy consumption and low CO_2 emissions).

Solar gain

Solar gain (also called solar heat gain) is a term used to describe the increase in temperature in a space or material that results from solar radiation.

The amount of solar gain increases with the strength of the sun, and with the ability of the material to absorb the radiation. Dark-coloured, rough-textured objects absorb solar radiant energy more readily than light-coloured, shiny objects. When an object is struck by sunlight it absorbs the solar energy (i.e. visible light plus a small amount of ultraviolet light) from the sunlight and later radiates this energy as infrared radiation.

When this happens in a building with low-e glazing the glass traps the energy (i.e. infrared radiation) inside. This is essentially the greenhouse effect. The application of low-emissivity coatings to the glazing makes the glass transparent to the visible light but not to the infrared radiation.

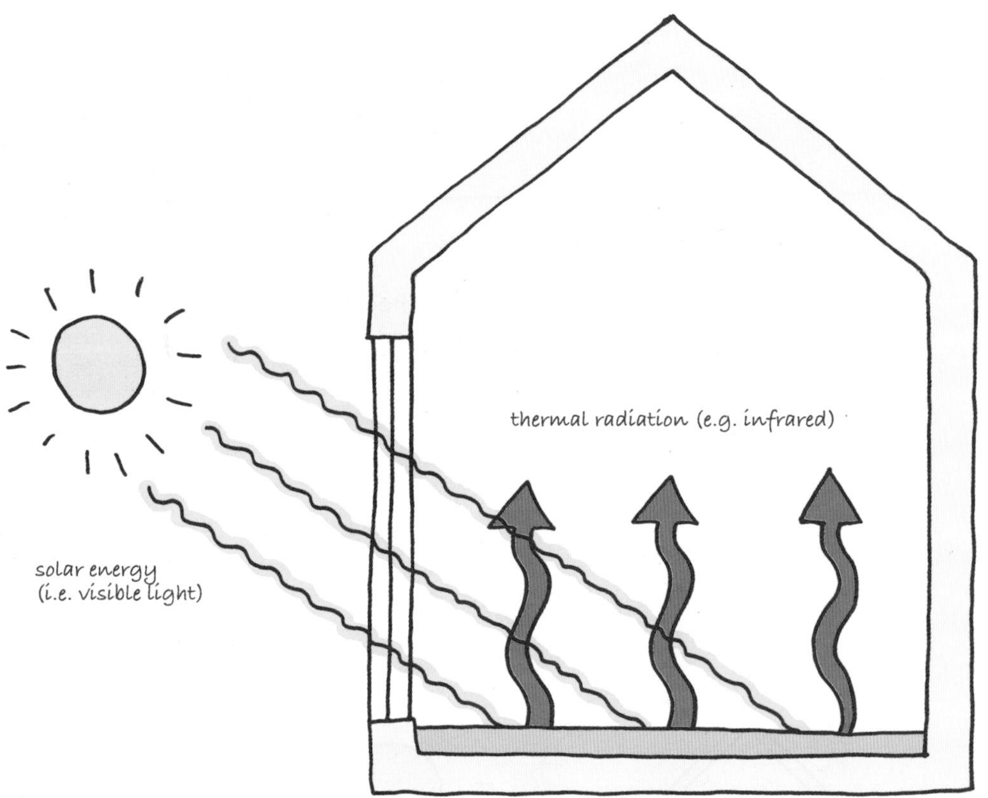

21.17 Solar gain: radiant energy from the sun warms the indoor spaces.

KEY PRINCIPLES

Homes designed to optimise solar gain have three features:

- a façade that faces south
- lots of glazing in the south-facing façade
- an interior layout that positions the main living spaces on the south side of the building.

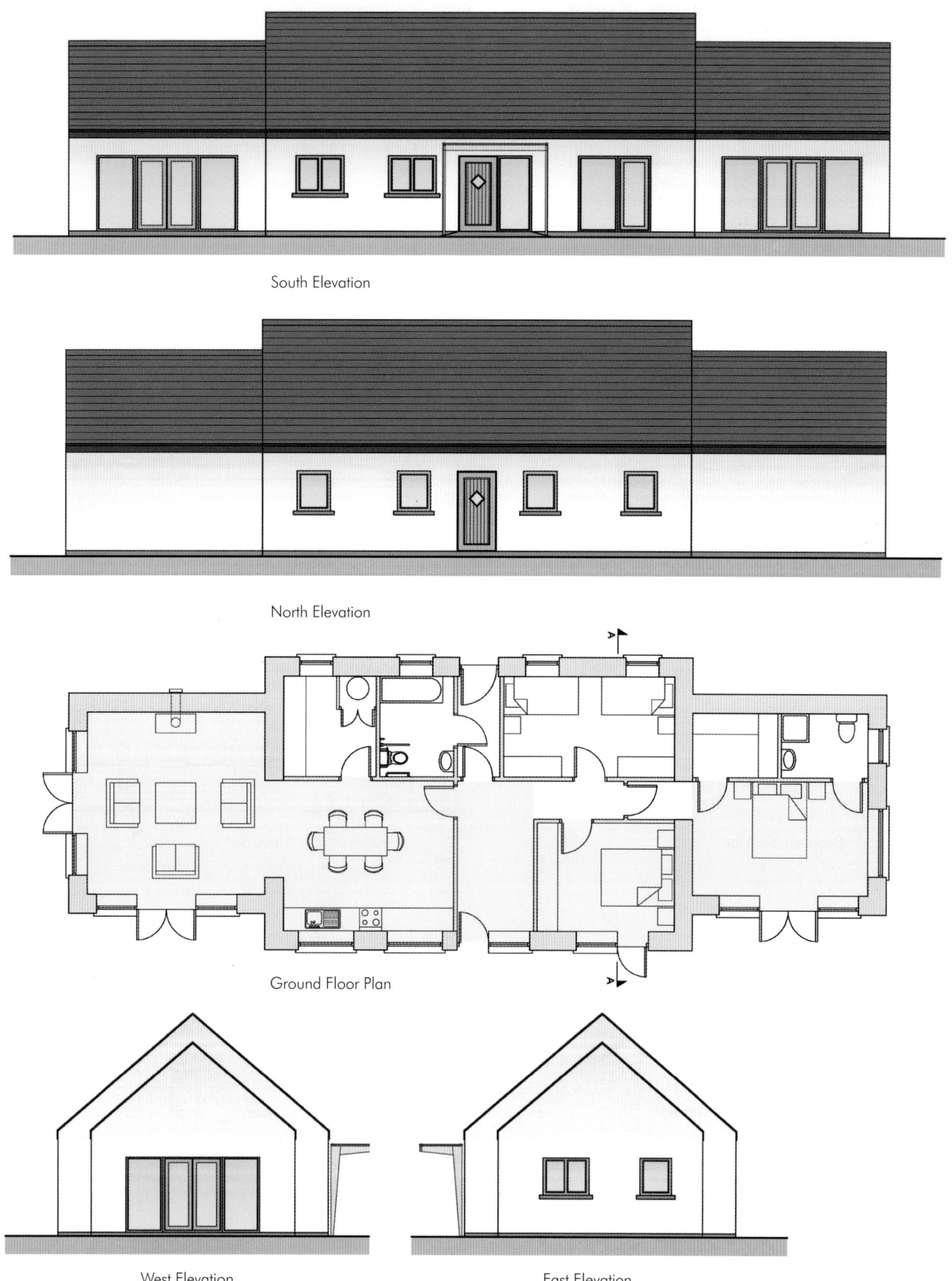

21.18 Single-storey house: orientation, glazing and interior layout combine to optimise solar gain.

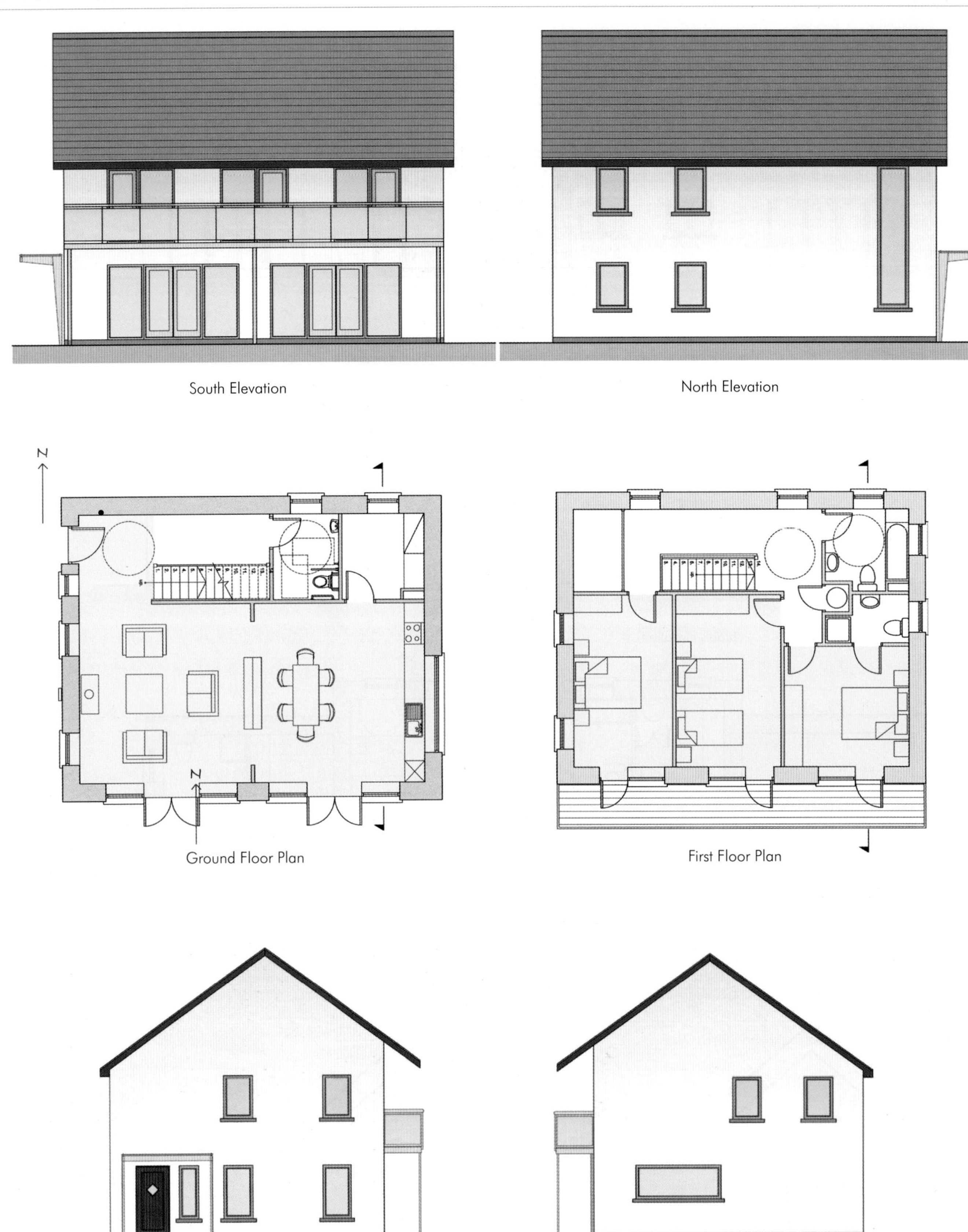

21.19 Two-storey house: orientation, glazing and interior layout combine to optimise solar gain.

21.20 Three-storey house: orientation, glazing and interior layout combine to optimise solar gain.

ACTIVITIES

Sketch the orientation of your home (check it using the Google Earth app). Then make a neat sketch of the internal layout of the ground floor of your home. Highlight the areas of the floor plan that benefit from solar gain.

Orientation

A passive house should be oriented within 30° of south. This orientation will maximise solar gain as the sun tracks across the sky. This is especially important during the cold winter months when the sun angle is low and the daylight hours are reduced.

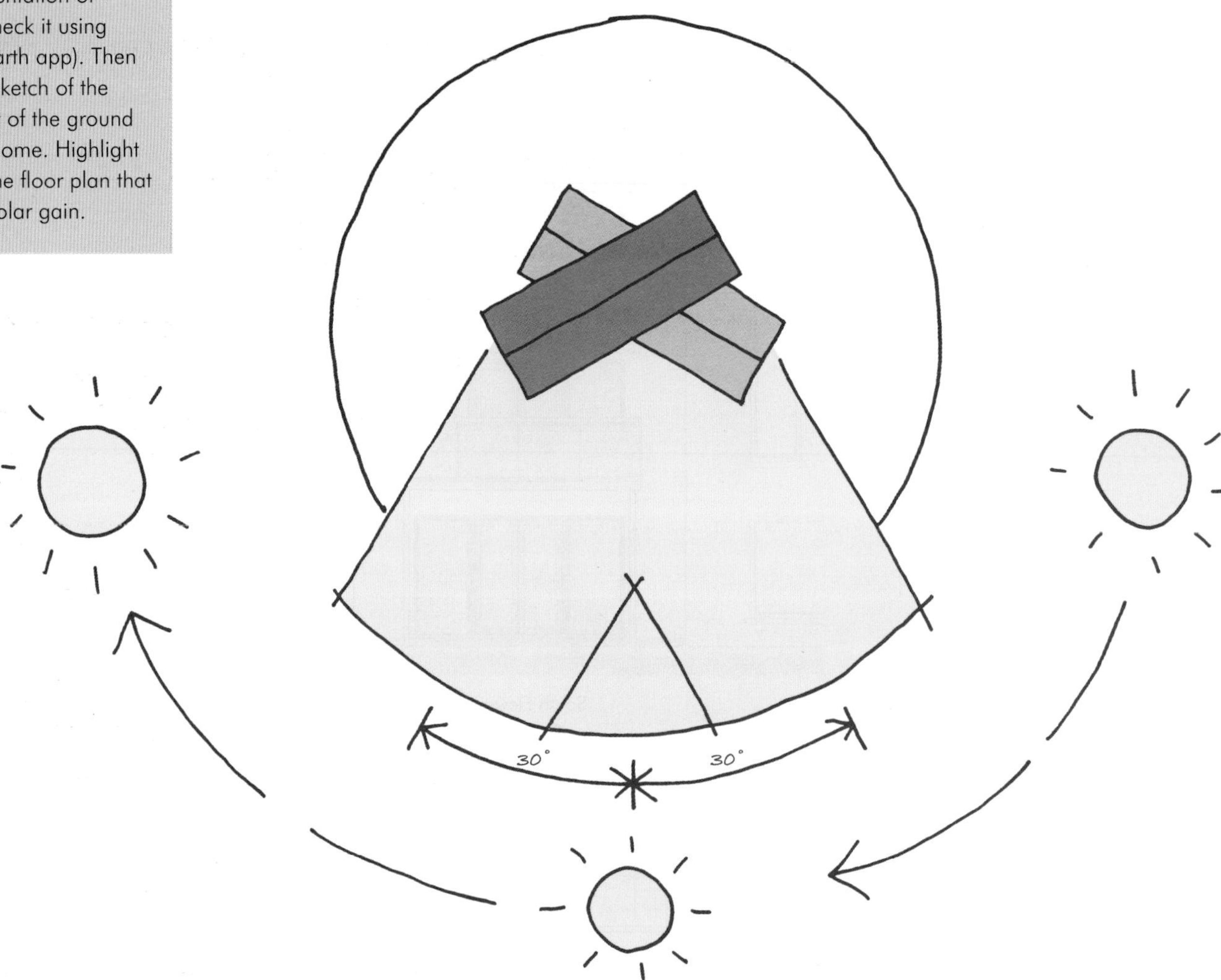

21.21 Orientation: the glazed façade should be oriented to within 30° of south.

Overheating and shading devices

Buildings that are designed to harness solar energy have the potential to overheat in the summer. This issue is addressed at the design stage. For example, if a building is being designed to the Passivhaus standard, a software tool called the Passivhaus Planning Package allows the designer to accurately calculate whether the building will overheat and to design preventative measures.

Shading devices are used to control solar gain through south-facing glazing during the summer. Permanent shading devices (e.g. brise soleils) that do not require adjustment by the occupant are preferable to those that do (e.g. shutters). Automated adjustable shading devices (e.g. blinds) are also used but these can be expensive and require regular maintenance. Planting (e.g. birch trees) can be used to the east and west. However, planting does not work on the south side of a building because the sun angle is too high. High thermal insulation of the building fabric also helps to keep the building cool during summer.

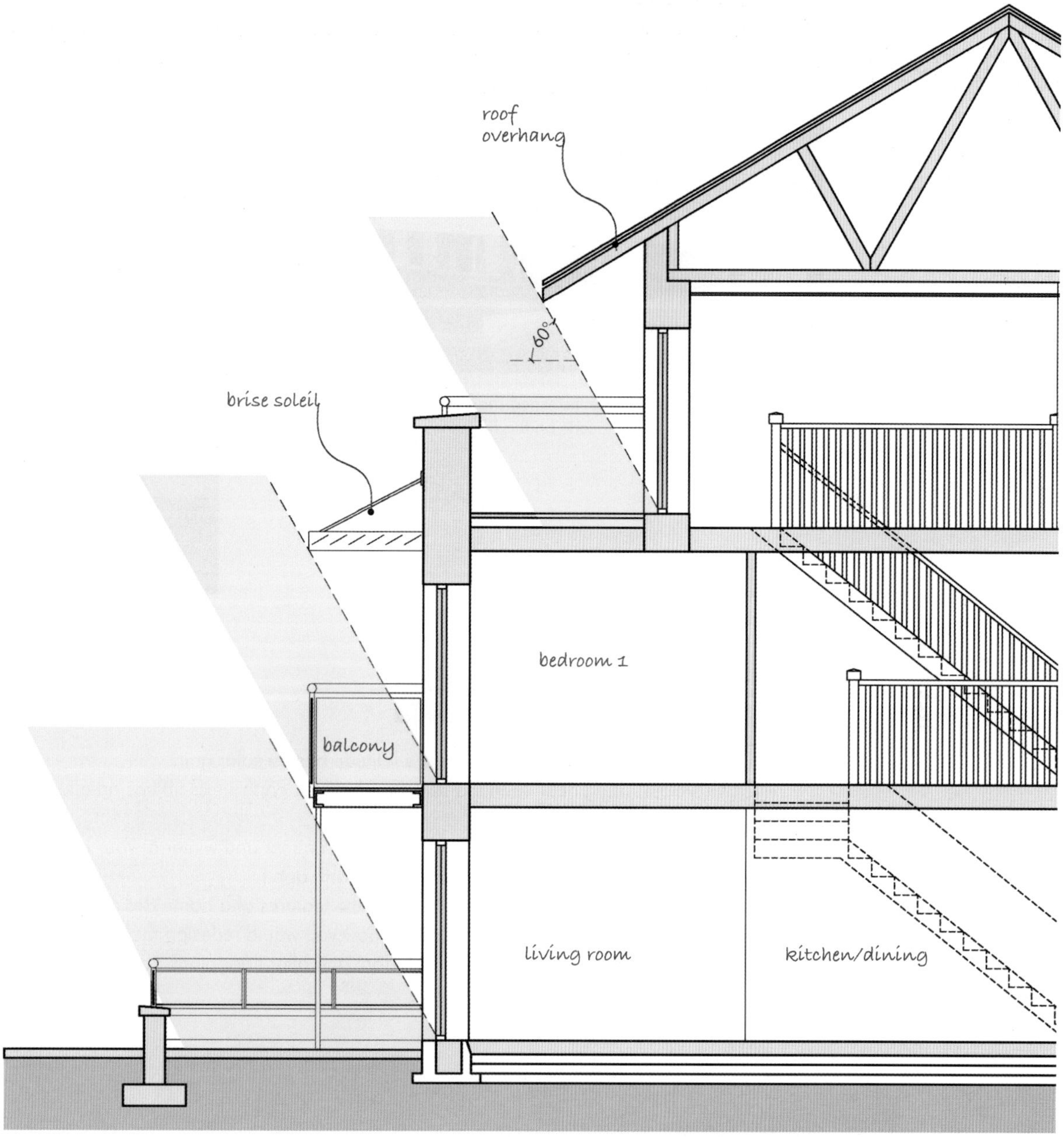

roof overhang
60°
brise soleil
balcony
bedroom 1
living room
kitchen/dining

21.22 Shading devices: roof overhangs, brise soleils and balconies are commonly used to prevent overheating. Note: 60° is the average maximum sun angle in Ireland (see Chapter 20).

21.23 Shading devices: notice the shadow cast by the roof overhang on this home by Scandinavian Homes of Co. Galway.

21.24 Shading devices: roof overhangs and balconies are both used in this house, built by Cyril Mannion in Athenry, Co. Galway.

21.25 Shading devices: notice the stiped shadow pattern cast by the brise soleil on the first floor façade on this house in Co. Wicklow.

21.26 Shading devices: the brise soleil significantly reduces solar gain, preventing overheating.

REVISION EXERCISES

1 Describe the influence that a site's latitude has on solar gain.
2 Explain, using neat freehand sketches, how the earth's axis tilt has an effect on sun angle during summer.
3 Calculate the maximum sun angle during summer and winter at your home's location. (Hint: look up your home's latitude using the Google Earth app.)
4 Explain, using neat freehand sketches, the features of a home designed to optimise solar gain.
5 Show, using neat freehand sketches, how you would redesign the ground floor of your home to optimise solar gain. (Note: show before and after floor plans and indicate the direction of North.)

CHAPTER 22

Natural Light

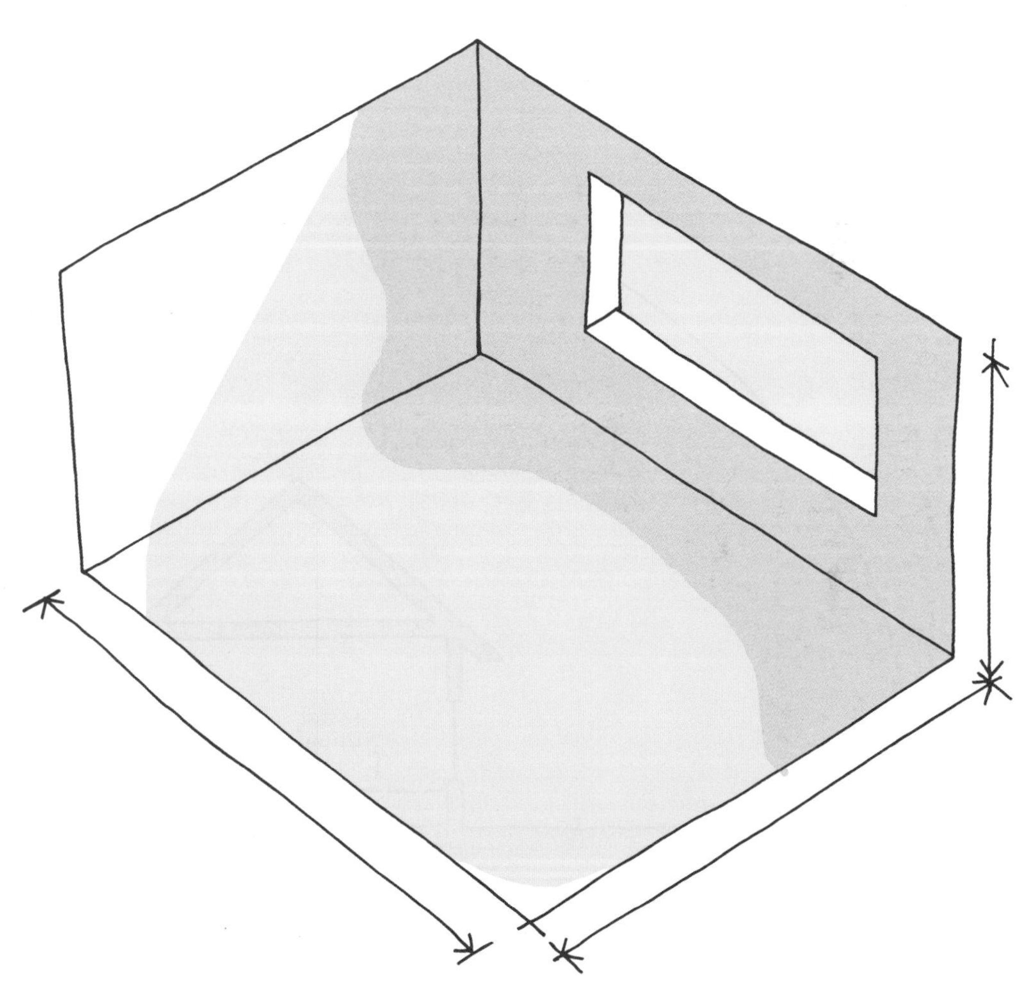

All natural light comes from the sun. The nature of this light varies with the weather. In Ireland the overcast sky is the usual source of light. This variability creates the need to adopt the idea of a standard sky.

Natural light can be classified as:
- **daylight** – diffuse light from the whole of the sky
- **sunlight** – direct 'beam' of light from the sun.

Standard sky

A standard sky is an imaginary sky that is used when designing buildings. This is necessary because the light conditions are constantly changing as the sun travels across the sky and clouds form and move.

Uniform standard sky

Uniform standard sky is the term used to describe a notional hemisphere of overcast sky that has the same level of luminance in every direction when viewed from an unobstructed point on the ground. This sky is usually assigned a value of 5,000 lux. This notional sky is used when designing fenestration patterns to ensure adequate indoor light levels.

CIE standard sky

The CIE sky is another notional sky that is used in building design. In this model, the luminance of the sky steadily increases above the horizon. The luminance of the CIE sky is three times brighter than at the horizon. This is a more realistic model and works well in the Irish context.

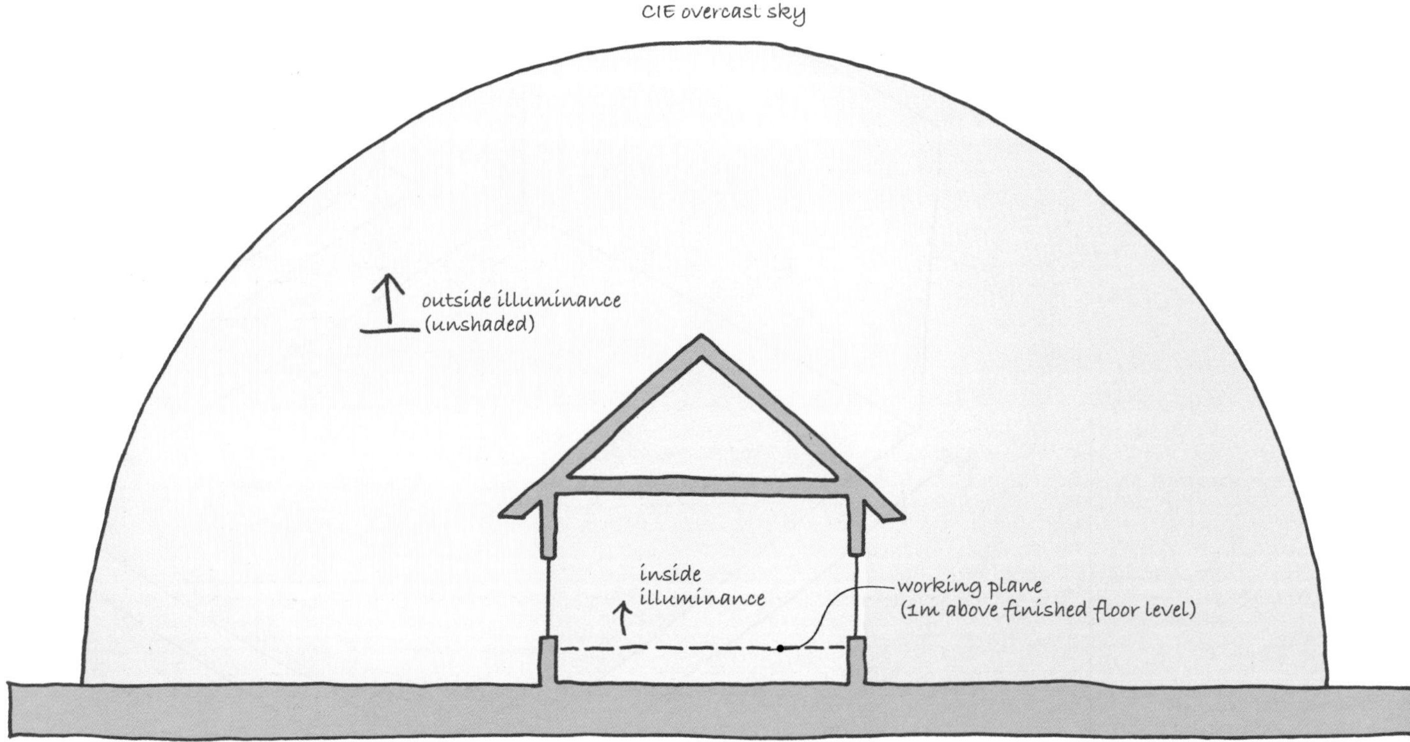

22.01 CIE standard sky.

Daylight factor

As the amount of light available from the sun/sky varies it is not possible to specify a particular amount of natural light when deciding on the window size and position for a room. Instead the amount of light to be supplied to a room is described as a proportion of the actual available light at that time. This proportion is called the daylight factor.

> **DEFINITION**
>
> Daylight factor
> The ratio between the actual illuminance at a point inside a room and the illuminance possible from an unobstructed hemisphere of the sky.

Daylight factor is expressed as a percentage and is calculated using this formula:

$$\bar{D} = \frac{E_i \times 100}{E_o}$$

where:
$\bar{D}$: daylight factor
E_i: illuminance (éclairage) inside
E_o: illuminance (éclairage) outside

In cloudy climates, the average daylight factor can be used to estimate the appearance of a room during the day.

- Less than 2%:
  - room looks gloomy under daylight alone
  - full electric lighting often needed during daytime
  - electric lighting dominates daytime appearance.
- Between 2% and 5%:
  - windows give a predominantly daylit appearance but supplementary electric lighting needed.
- 5% or more:
  - the room is strongly daylit
  - daytime electric lighting rarely needed.

A simple rule of thumb is that a window area equivalent to 4% of the floor area of a room will give a daylight factor of 2%.

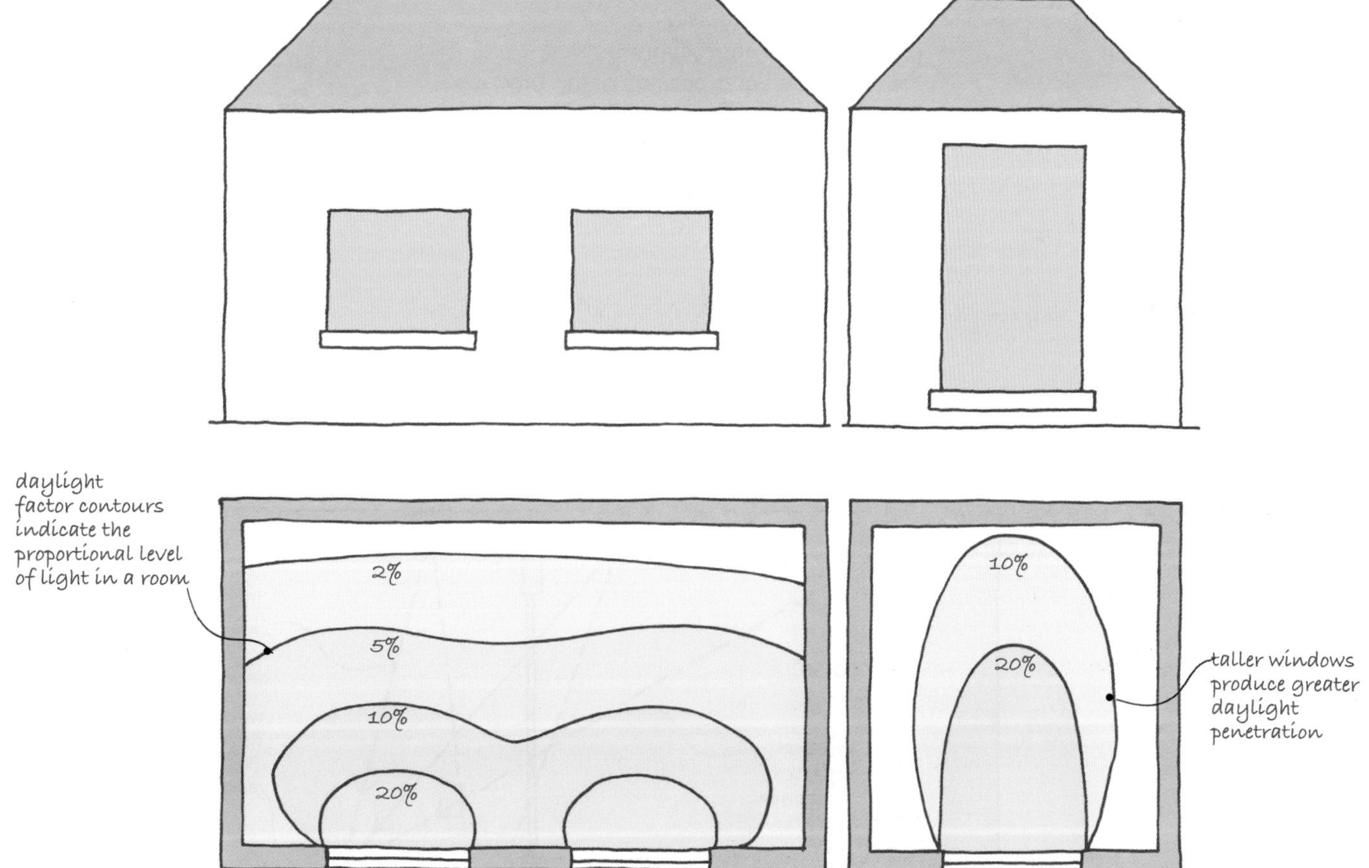

22.02 Daylight factor: window size and position determine the level of natural light indoors.

22.03 Daylight factor: the amount of artificial lighting required (and energy consumed) depends on the daylight factor.

Daylight factor components

The level of natural light indoors depends on several factors:

- the brightness of the sky
- reflections and obstructions outside
- the size, shape and position of the windows
- reflections inside the room.

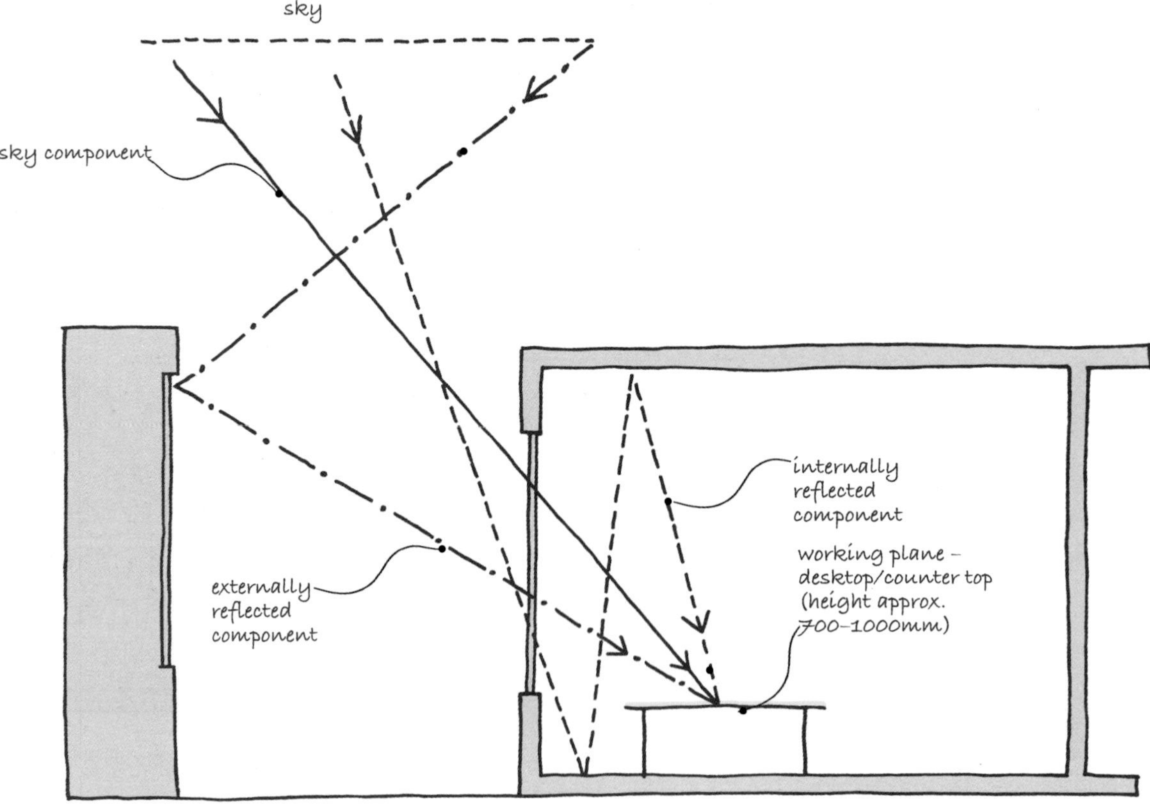

22.04 Components of daylight factor.

Daylight factor calculation

There are several methods of calculating the daylight factor in a room. The method shown here is used when calculating the daylight factor on the working plane.

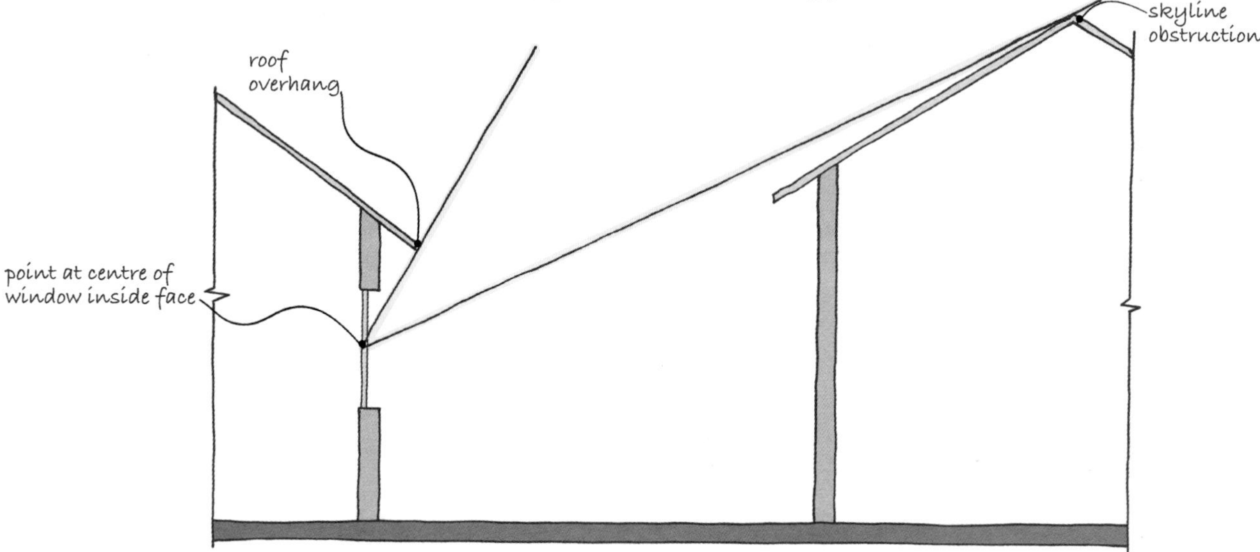

22.05 Visible sky angle: calculation of daylight factor.

The average daylight factor (or area of glazing required) can be calculated at the design stage using the formulae:

$$\bar{D} = \frac{A_g\,(\theta\tau)}{A\,(1 - \rho^2)} \quad \text{or} \quad A_g = \frac{\bar{D}A\,(1 - \rho^2)}{\theta\tau}$$

where:

$\bar{D}$ daylight factor

A total area of room surfaces (i.e. floor, walls, ceiling, windows)

A_g area of glazing

θ angle of visible sky

τ transmittance – the amount of light that can pass through glass; typically 0.5–0.7

ρ reflectance of surfaces (use 0.3 for normal living room, 0.7 for white ceiling and light-coloured walls)

Worked example

A daylight factor of 4% is required in the living room of a new home (see sketch). Using the following data, calculate the glazing area required to provide this level of light. Assume the ceiling is painted white and the walls are a cream colour.

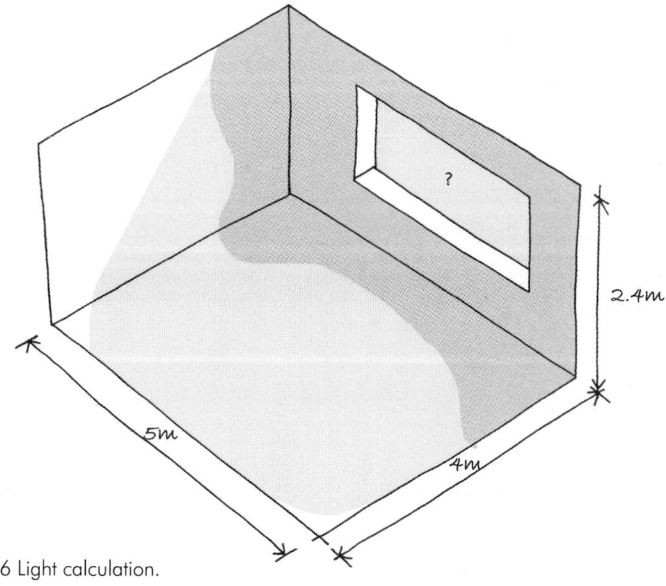

22.06 Light calculation.

$\bar{D}$ 4%
A to be calculated
A_g to be calculated
θ 52°
τ 0.6
ρ 0.7

Step 1
Calculate total surface area, A:

walls: $2(5 \times 2.4) + 2(4 \times 2.4) = 24 + 19.2 = 43.2$
floor/ceiling: $2(5 \times 4) = 40$
total area: $43.2 + 40 = 83.2$

Step 2
Input data into formula:

$$\bar{D} = \frac{A_g \quad \theta\tau}{A(1-\rho^2)} \quad \text{or} \quad A_g = \frac{\bar{D}A(1-\rho^2)}{\theta\tau}$$

$$A_g = \frac{(4)(83.2)(1-(0.7)^2)}{52 \times 0.6}$$

$$A_g = \frac{(332.8)(1-0.49)}{31.2}$$

$$A_g = \frac{(332.8)(0.51)}{31.2}$$

$$A_g = \frac{169.728}{31.2}$$

$$A_g = 5.44m^2$$

ACTIVITIES

Calculate the daylight factor of a room you use regularly.

REVISION EXERCISES

1 Describe, using a neat freehand sketch, the factors that determine the level of natural light indoors.
2 Explain the term 'CIE standard sky'.
3 Explain, using neat annotated sketches, any three features that are used to regulate the amount of daylight in houses.
4 The illuminance on the working plane in a kitchen is 300 lux. Assuming an overcast sky providing 5,000 lux, calculate the daylight factor in the kitchen. Evaluate this result (i.e. comment on the level of light).
5 Given the following data, calculate the daylight factor in a normal living room.
$\bar{D}$ to be calculated
A_g 1.6m²
θ 48°
τ 0.5
A 4.2m x 4.8m
ρ 0.3

CHAPTER 23 Heat Energy

The best way to think about heat energy and house design is to think of a home as a warm bubble floating in a cold space. In Ireland the annual mean outdoor air temperature and soil temperature (200mm depth) is 10°C. The target indoor temperature for a home is 20°C. This means that there is a mean temperature difference of 10°C. This heat energy is constantly 'trying to escape' from the home and must be prevented from doing so or be replaced (usually by burning fossil fuels).

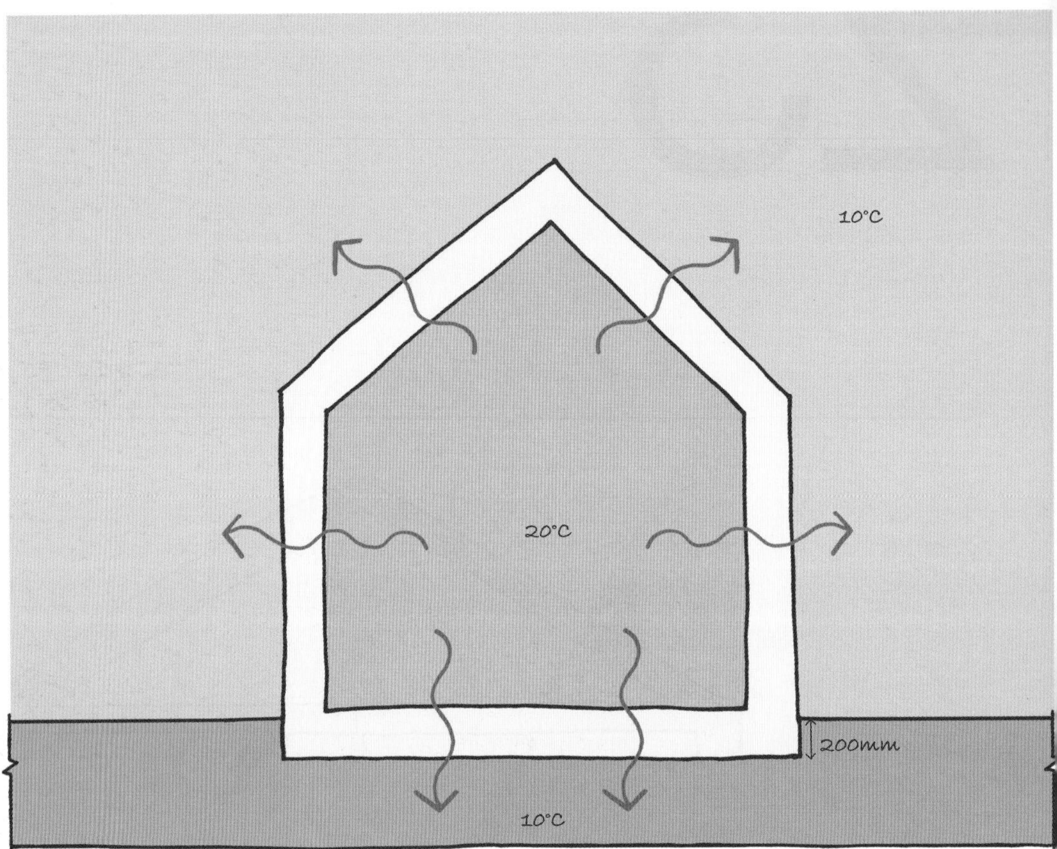

23.01 Heat energy: a house is a warm bubble in a cold space.

Low-energy housing relies on high levels of insulation and the efficient use of energy. It is essential that designers understand the fundamental principles of heat energy, particularly how heat 'moves' in and out of a building.

Principles

Heat transfer mechanisms

Heat can 'move' in one of four fundamental ways:

- conduction – transfer of energy between objects that are in physical contact
- convection – transfer of energy between an object and its environment, due to movement in a fluid (e.g. water) or gas (e.g. air)
- radiation – transfer of energy to or from a body by means of the emission or absorption of electromagnetic radiation (e.g. solar gain)
- advection – transfer of energy from one location to another by physically moving an object containing that energy (e.g. air leakage).

All these heat transfer mechanisms occur in buildings and a large part of designing low-energy housing is about designing the external envelope to limit these heat transfer mechanisms.

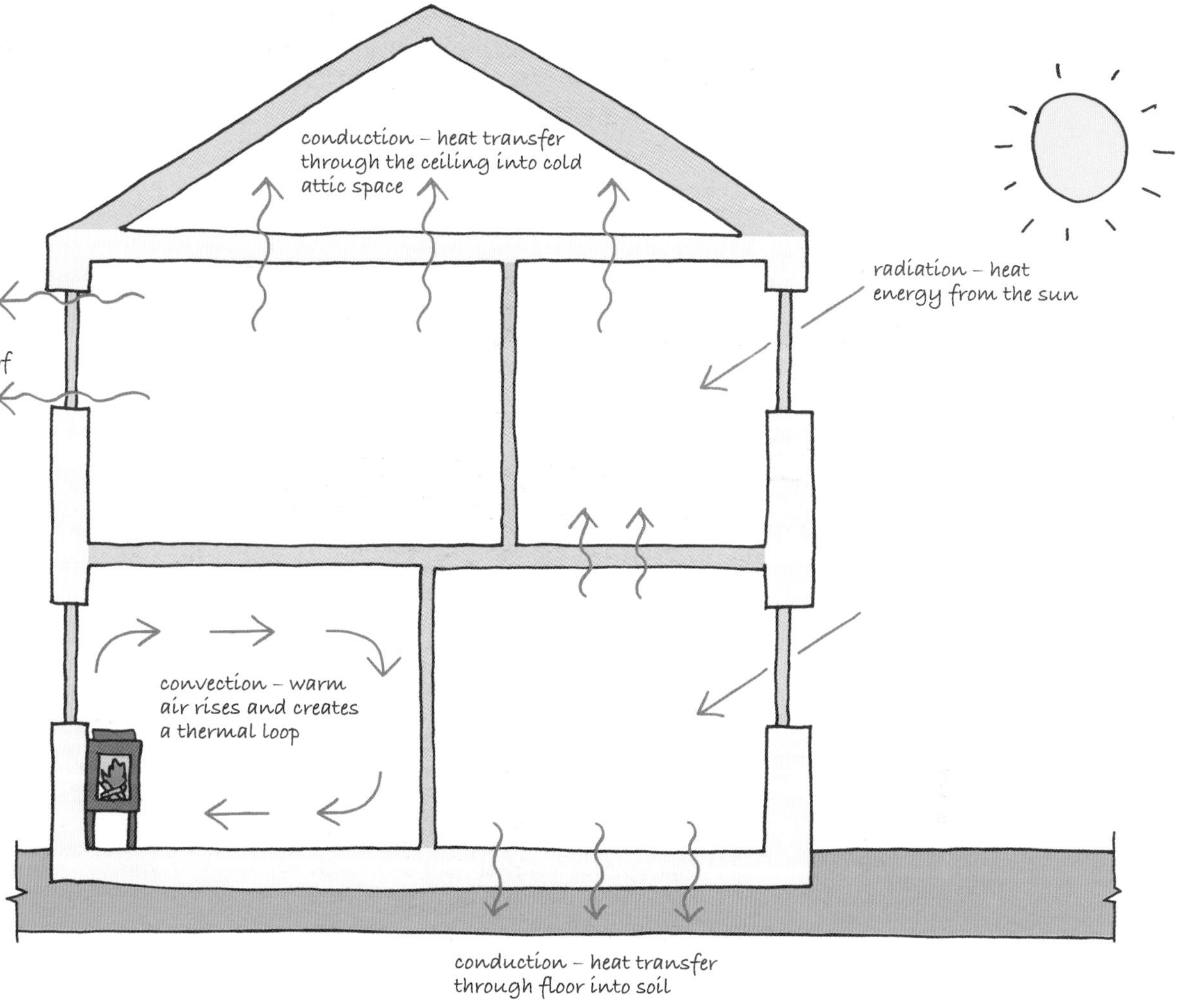

conduction – heat transfer through the ceiling into cold attic space
advection – heat loss caused by warm air leaking out of the building
radiation – heat energy from the sun
convection – warm air rises and creates a thermal loop
conduction – heat transfer through floor into soil

23.02 Heat transfer mechanisms.

Thermal properties of construction materials

Thermal conductivity, λ

1m²
1m
20°C
direction of heat flow
1m
1m
19°C

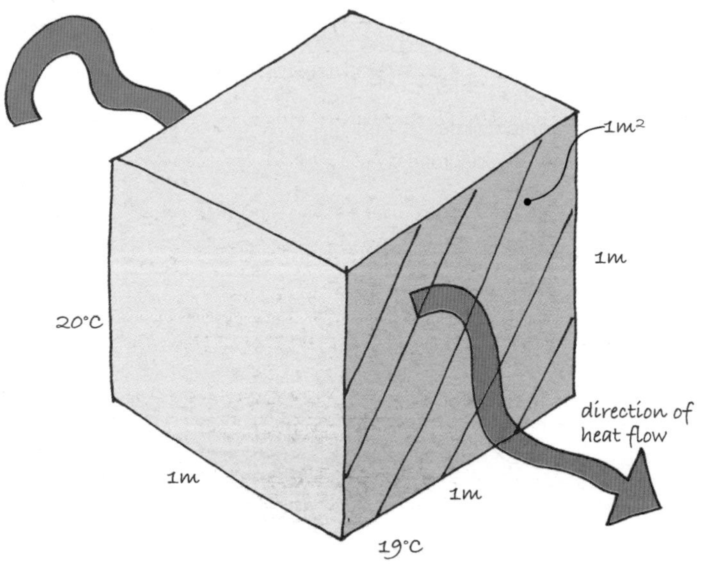

23.03 Thermal conductivity value: stated for a surface area of $1 m^2$ and a thickness of 1 m.

DEFINITION

Thermal conductivity
A measure of the rate at which heat energy is conducted through a material.

When designing a floor, wall or roof it is important to be able to compare the insulation properties of one material or product to another. The measurement used to do this is called the thermal conductivity value (λ, lambda value).

The thermal conductivity value is defined as the quantity of heat that will pass through a square metre of a material that is one metre thick, for each degree difference in temperature between one side and the other. The benefit of this measure is that, because it is stated for a one-metre cube of the material it allows various insulating materials to be easily compared. Insulants are materials, that have a low thermal conductivity.

The symbol for thermal conductivity is λ (i.e. lambda) and it is measured in W/mK (watts per metre kelvin).

Thermal conductivity of common building materials

Material	Density (kg/m³)	Thermal conductivity (W/mK)
General building materials		
Clay brickwork (outer leaf)	1,700	0.77
Clay brickwork (inner leaf)	1,700	0.56
Concrete block (heavyweight)	2,000	1.33
Concrete block (medium weight)	1,400	0.57
Concrete block (autoclaved aerated)	700	0.20
Concrete block (autoclaved aerated)	500	0.15
Concrete block (hollow)	1,800	0.84
Cast concrete, high density	2,400	2.00
Cast concrete, medium density	1,800	1.15
Aerated concrete slab	500	0.16
Concrete screed	1,200	0.41
Reinforced concrete (1% steel)	2,300	2.30
Reinforced concrete (2% steel)	2,400	2.50
Wall ties, stainless steel	7,900	17.00
Wall ties, galvanised steel	7,800	50.00
Mortar (protected)	1,750	0.88
Mortar (exposed)	1,750	0.94
External rendering (cement sand)	1,800	1.00
Plaster (gypsum lightweight)	600	0.18
Plaster (gypsum)	1,200	0.43
Plasterboard	900	0.25
Natural slate	2,500	2.20
Concrete tiles	2,100	1.50
Clay tiles	2,000	1.00
Fibre cement slates	1,800	0.45
Ceramic/porcelain tiles	2,300	1.30
Plastic tiles	1,000	0.20
Asphalt	2,100	0.70
Felt bitumen layers	1,100	0.23
Timber, softwood	500	0.13
Timber, hardwood	700	0.18
Wood wool slab	500	0.10
Wood-based panels (plywood, particle board, etc.)	500	0.13

23.04 Thermal conductivity (λ lambda value) of common construction materials. *Source*: TDGL, 2011.

Insulation material		Thermal conductivity range (W/mK)						
		0.00	0.01	0.02	0.03	0.04	0.05	0.06
Highest performance	Vacuum insulation panels	0.008						
	Aerogel		0.013					
Polyurethane	Polyurethane with pentane up to 32kg/m^3			0.027	0.030			
	Polyurethane soy based			0.026	0.030			
	Foil-faced Polyurethane with pentane up to 32kg/m^3			0.020				
	Polyurethane with CO_2				0.035			
	In-situ applied Polyurethane (sprayed or injected)			0.026				
Polyisocyanurate (PIR)	Polyisocyanurate up to 32kg/m^3			0.026				
	Foil faced Polyisocyanurate up to 32kg/m^3			0.023				
	In-situ applied Polyisocyanurate (sprayed)			0.025				
Phenolic foam	Phenolic foam			0.023				
	Foil-faced Phenolic foam			0.022				
Expanded polystyrene (EPS)	Expanded polystyrene up to 30 kg/m^3				0.030	0.045		
	Expanded polystyrene with graphite (grey)				0.031			
Extruded polystyrene (XPS)	Extruded polystyrene with CO_2			0.025	0.037			
	Extruded polystyrene with HFC 35kg/m^3			0.029	0.031			
Wool and fibre	Glass wool (up to 48kg/m^3)				0.030	0.044		
	Glass wool (equal/greater than 48kg/m^3)				0.036			
	Stone wool				0.036			
	(less than 160kg/m^3)				0.036			
	Stone wool (160kg/m^3)				0.037	0.040		
	Sheep's wool (25kg/m^3)				0.034		0.054	
	Cellulose fibre (dry blown 24kg/m^3)				0.035	0.046		
	Hemp fibre				0.038			
	Polyester fibre				0.035	0.044		
	Wood fibre (WF)				0.039	0.043		

23.05 Thermal conductivity of some common insulation materials. *Source*: NSAI and manufacturers.

Thermal resistivity, r

Thermal resistivity is an alternative index of conduction in materials. It is the 'mathematical opposite' or reciprocal of thermal conductivity, so $r = 1/\lambda$. Similarly, the unit of resistivity is mK/W (metre kelvin per watt).

Thermal resistance (R-value)

Thermal resistance is the term used to describe the ability of a material or buildup to prevent the flow of heat. The thermal resistance of each material in a structure depends on the rate at which the material conducts heat (i.e. thermal conductivity) and the thickness of the material.

Thermal resistance is calculated by dividing the thickness of the material by its conductivity:

$R = d/\lambda$

where:

R = resistance (m²K/W)
d = thickness (m)
λ = thermal conductivity of the material (W/mK)

Alternatively, it can be calculated by multiplying the thickness of the material by its resistivity:

$R = d \times r$

where:

R = resistance (m²K/W)
d = thickness (m)
r = thermal resistivity of the material (mK/W)

Surface resistance, R_{si} and R_{se}

As heat moves through the external envelope of a building, the heat energy is transferred from one surface of the structure, through each layer of the buildup, to the other surface. Each layer of the buildup offers some resistance to the flow of heat. The inner and outer surfaces of the buildup also resist the flow of heat energy. These are referred to as the internal surface resistance, R_{si}, and the external surface resistance, R_{se}.

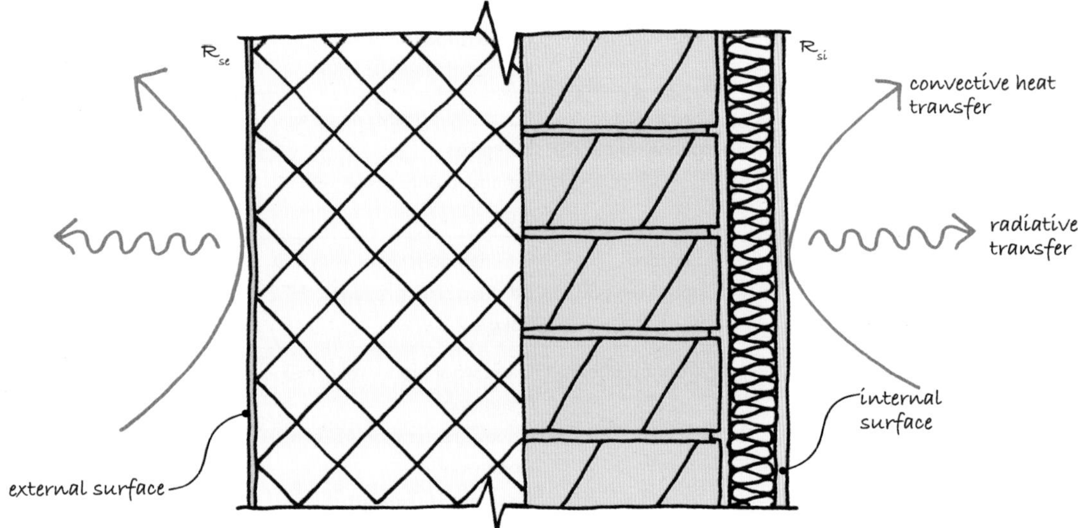

23.06 Surface resistance: heat is transferred from the surface by convection (i.e. air movement) and radiation (i.e. infrared radiation).

The level of resistance at the surfaces depends on:

- surface properties – typical building materials have high emissivity
- direction of energy flow – upwards (e.g. roof), downwards (e.g. floor) or horizontal (e.g. wall)
- climate – sheltered or exposed (especially the wind chill effect for external surface resistance).

When calculating the heat energy transmitted through a building element the constant values shown in the tables below are used.

23.07 Surface resistance: the constant values used in thermal transmittance calculations are shown on the left. The actual value of external surface resistance varies depending on wind speed; the higher the wind speed, the lower the resistance (see table on the right).

	Surface resistance (m²K/W)	
Direction of heat flow	R_{si}	R_{se}
upwards	0.10	0.04
horizontal	0.13	0.04
downwards	0.17	0.04

Wind speed m/e	R_{se}(m²K/W)
1	0.08
2	0.06
3	0.05
4	0.04
5	0.04
7	0.03
10	0.02

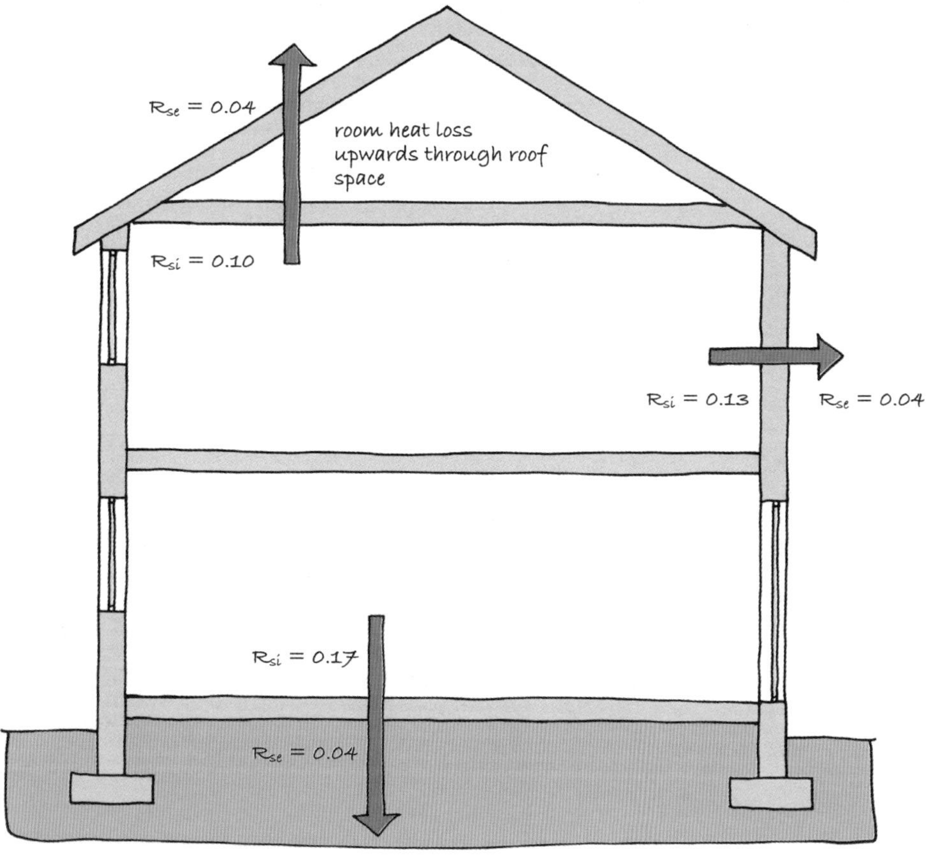

23.08 Surface resistance values (W/m²K).

Thermal transmittance (U-value)

Thermal transmittance is the term used to describe the rate of heat energy transfer through a structure. In other words, how much heat energy is lost through the fabric of the building (i.e. floor, walls, roof). It is the reciprocal of the sum of the thermal resistances of all of the components of the buildup including the internal and external surface resistances:

$$U = \frac{1}{R_T}$$

where:

$$R_T = R_{si} + R_1 + R_2 + R_3 + R_4 + \dots + R_{se}$$

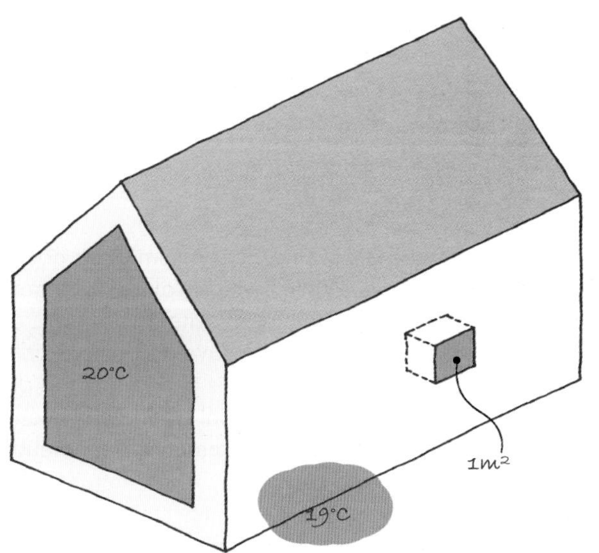

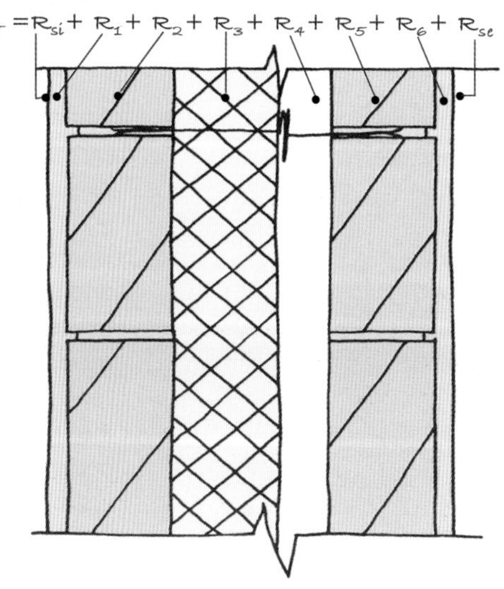

23.09 Thermal transmittance: the rate of heat loss for one square metre of structure when there is a one degree temperature difference between inside and outside.

The amount of thermal transmittance occurring is described per square metre of structure. This is useful because it allows a comparison to be made between one structural system and another (e.g. concrete cavity walls versus timber frame cavity walls).

The amount of thermal transmittance occurring is also described per degree temperature difference from inside to outside. This is useful because it doesn't matter what the actual temperature is, the rate is based on a one degree difference. Once the rate of heat loss is known, it can be used to work out the total amount and cost of the heat energy lost.

The rate of thermal transmittance is referred to as the U-value and is expressed in watts per square metre per kelvin, or W/m²K. Well-insulated parts of a building have a low thermal transmittance, whereas poorly insulated parts of a building have a high thermal transmittance. In other words, low U-values are good; high U-values are bad.

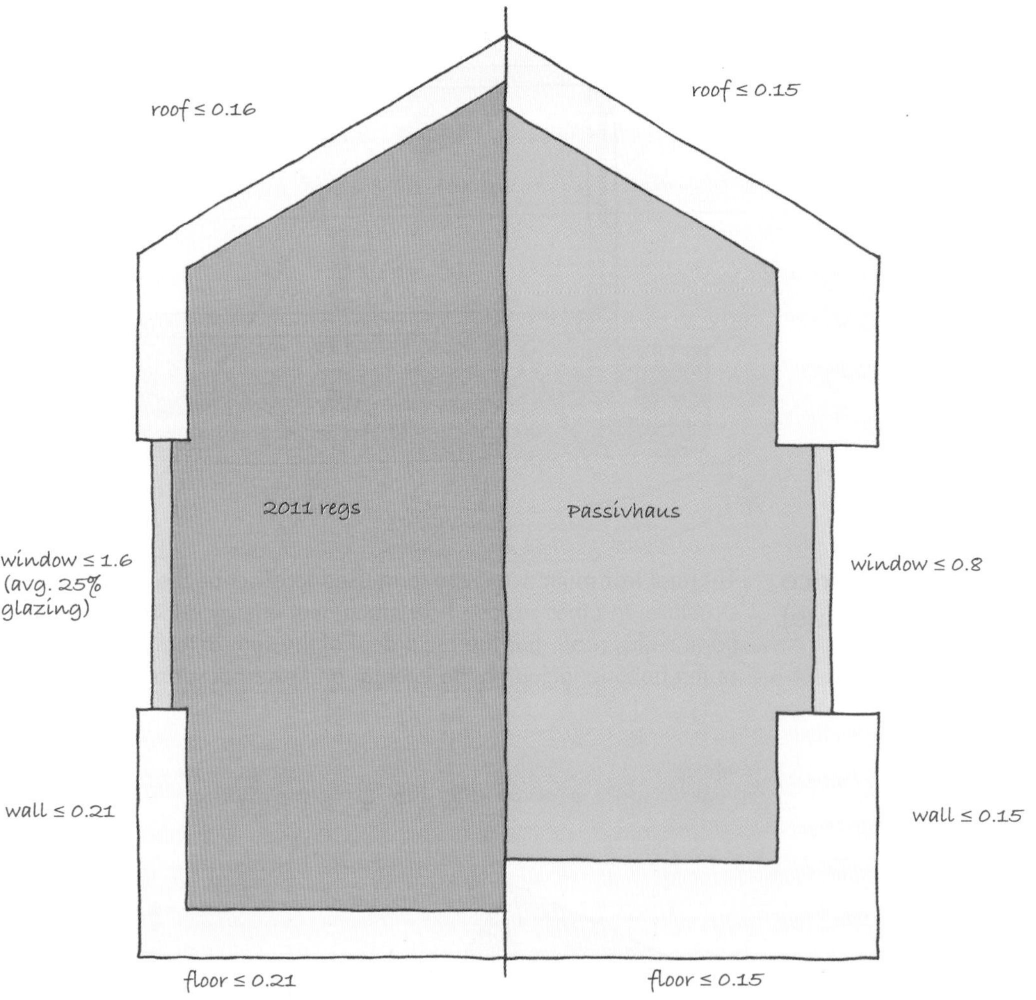

23.10 U-values (W/m²K): maximum permitted U-values – TGD L 2011 building regulations compared to Passivhaus standard.

U-values for typical construction buildups are based on certain assumptions about the materials and using standard values for surface resistances. While these U-values are a good indicator of future performance, they are at best a theoretical estimate. On site, the climatic conditions (e.g. exposure, wind), storage of materials and workmanship can have a significant influence on the real-world performance of insulation products in particular. It is because of this difference between the design performance of construction materials and their real world performance that a good designer will always try to exceed the minimum U-value requirements. A theoretical U-value that is just below the requirement will likely be above it on site.

Thermal transmittance (U-value) calculation

The thermal transmittance, or U-value, is calculated as the reciprocal of the total resistance:

$$U = \frac{1}{R_T} \qquad \text{(unit: W/m}^2\text{K)}$$

There are four different thermal transmittance calculations used when calculating the rate of heat loss from a typical house:

1 homogenous (e.g. masonry wall)
2 non-homogenous (e.g. ceiling/timber frame wall)
3 floor
4 window/door.

The calculation methods used differ for each of these four areas.

U-value: homogenous structure calculation

In this calculation the sum of the thermal resistances of the components is calculated first. The reciprocal of this value gives the U-value.

A typical homogenous U-value calculation involves the following steps:

1 Sketch a cross section of the structure to ensure you don't skip any layer.
2 Create a table into which you can input the data.
3 List each layer in order from inside to out (from high temperature to low temperature) in the first column (starting with the internal surface resistance and finishing with the external surface resistance).
4 Convert the thickness of each layer from millimetres to metres (divide by one thousand).
5 Input the conductivity/ resistivity value of each material.
6 Line by line for each layer, divide the thickness by the conductivity (or multiply the thickness by the resistivity) to get the resistance.
7 Input any given values/constants (e.g. surface resistances, air cavity resistance).
8 Add up the resistances to get a total resistance.
9 The U value is the reciprocal (i.e. 'one over') of this.
10 Values used in the intermediate calculations should be calculated to three places of decimals.
11 The final U-value should be stated to two places of decimals because the conductivity values and standard values (e.g. surface resistance) are not precise enough for higher accuracy.

Worked example (homogenous structure)

Calculate the U-value of a traditional cavity wall, given the following data:

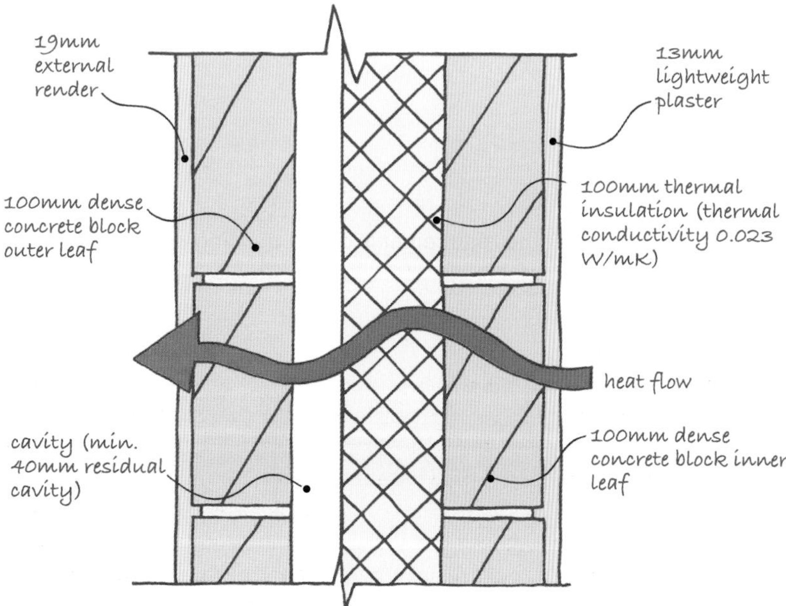

23.11 Traditional cavity wall.

	thickness (mm)
• external render	19
• concrete block outer leaf	100
• cavity	150
• insulation	100
• concrete block inner leaf	100
• internal plaster	13

	resistance (m^2K/W)
• internal surface resistance	0.13
• external surface resistance	0.04
• cavity (air) resistance	0.18

	conductivity value (w/mK)
• internal plaster	0.180
• external render	1.000
• concrete blockwork	1.330
• insulation	0.023

Layer/surface	Thickness (m)	Conductivity (W/mK)	Resistance (m^2K/W)
Internal surface	–	–	0.130
Plaster	0.013	0.180	0.072
Inner leaf	0.100	1.330	0.075
Insulation	0.100	0.023	4.348
Cavity	–	–	0.180
Outer leaf	0.100	1.330	0.075
Render	0.019	1.000	0.019
External surface	–	–	0.040
Total resistance (R_T)			**4.939**

The U-value is calculated using the formula:

$$U = \frac{1}{R_T}$$

$$U = \frac{1}{4.939}$$

$$U = 0.20245$$

$$U = 0.20\ W/m^2K$$

This wall would meet the requirements of the building regulations; U-value ≤ 0.21 W/m^2K.

Worked example (homogenous structure)

Calculate the U-value of a wide cavity wall (fully filled with insulation), given the following data:

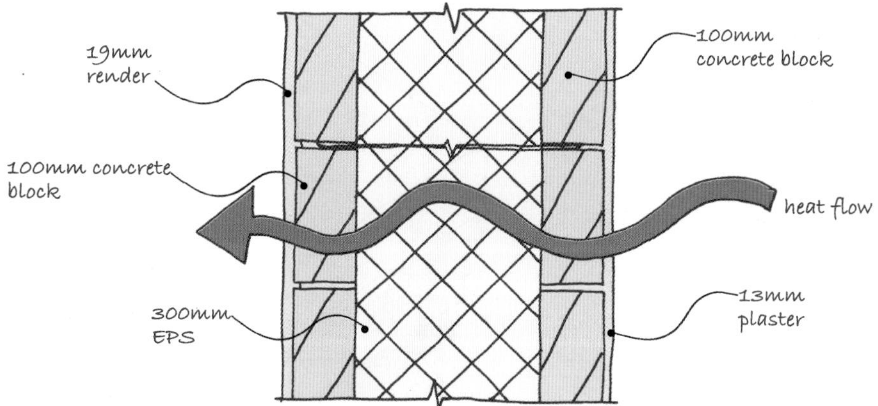

23.12 Wide cavity wall.

	thickness (mm)
• external render	19
• concrete block outer leaf	100
• insulation	300
• concrete block inner leaf	100
• internal plaster	13

	resistance (m^2K/W)
• internal surface resistance	0.13
• external surface resistance	0.04

	conductivity value (w/mK)
• internal plaster	0.180
• external render	1.000
• concrete blockwork	1.330
• insulation	0.034

Layer/surface	Thickness (m)	Conductivity (W/mK) 4	Resistance (m^2K/W)
Internal surface	–	–	0.130
Plaster	0.013	0.180	0.072
Inner leaf	0.100	1.330	0.075
Insulation	0.300	0.034	8.824
Outer leaf	0.100	1.330	0.075
Render	0.019	1.000	0.019
External surface	–	–	0.040
Total resistance (R_T)			9.235

The U-value is calculated using the formula:

$$U = \frac{1}{R_T}$$

$$U = \frac{1}{9.235}$$

$$U = 0.10828$$

$$U = 0.11 \text{ W/m}^2\text{K}$$

This wall would meet the requirements of the Passivhaus standard; U-value ≤ 0.15 W/m^2K.

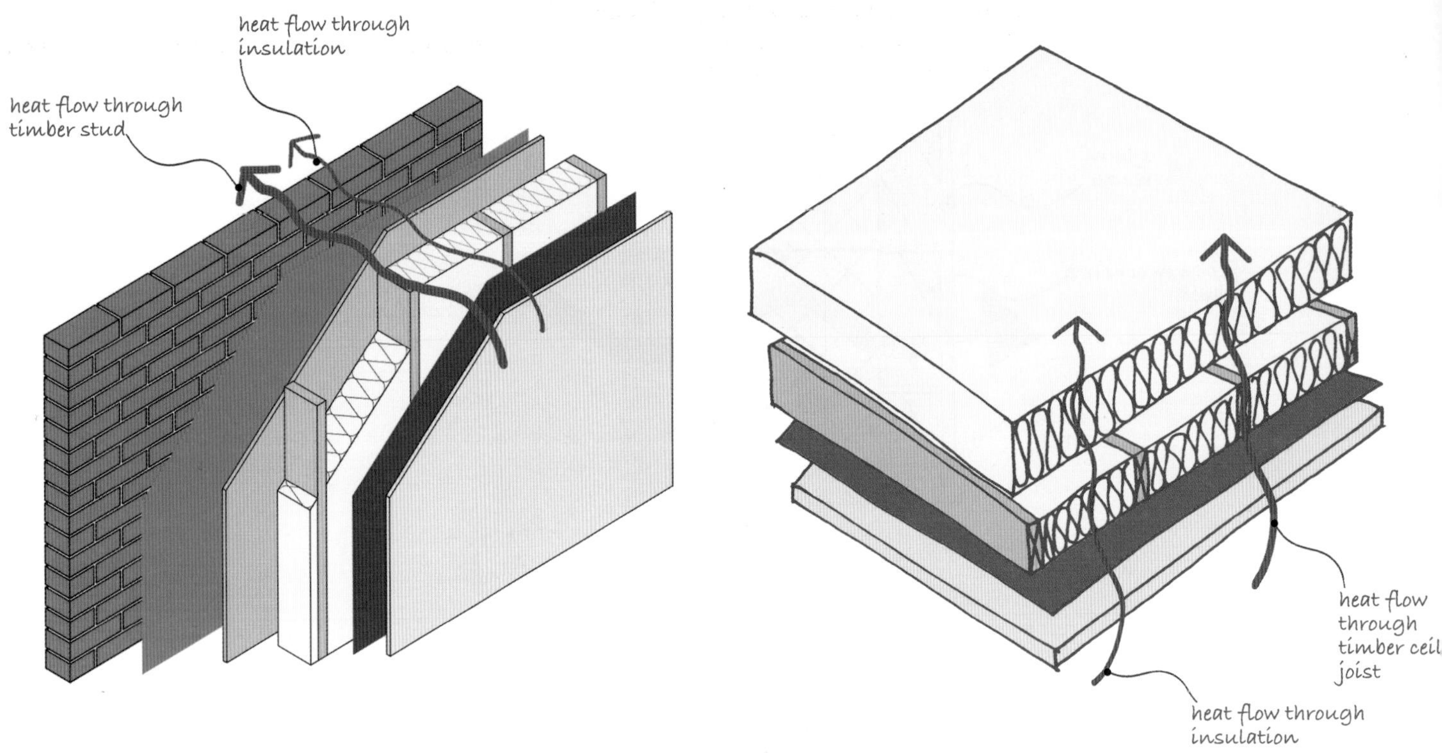

23.13 U-values: heat flow through non-homogenous structures with multiple heat flow paths.

A typical timber frame wall is an example of a U-value calculation where the element is made up of a number of layers, some of which are bridged. The outer leaf (brick) is of uniform construction and it does not change along its length. However, the inner leaf is bridged by timber studs. Therefore, there are two possible heat flow paths: across the studs or across the insulation between the studs.

The heat flow path across the studs cannot be dismissed as being negligible, because the thermal conductivity of softwood timber is usually three to four times higher than that of a typical insulant. In a typical timber frame structure, the thermal conductivity of the timber studs is over five times higher than that of the insulant. Similarly, the studs typically make up a significant portion of the wall area (e.g.15%).

U-value calculations for non-homogenous structures are complex and best done using specialist software.

U-value and thermal bridging: window calculation

The heat loss through a window is determined by calculating the thermal transmittance through each of the four heat flow paths:

- through the glazing
- through the spacers
- through the frame
- through the window–wall junction.

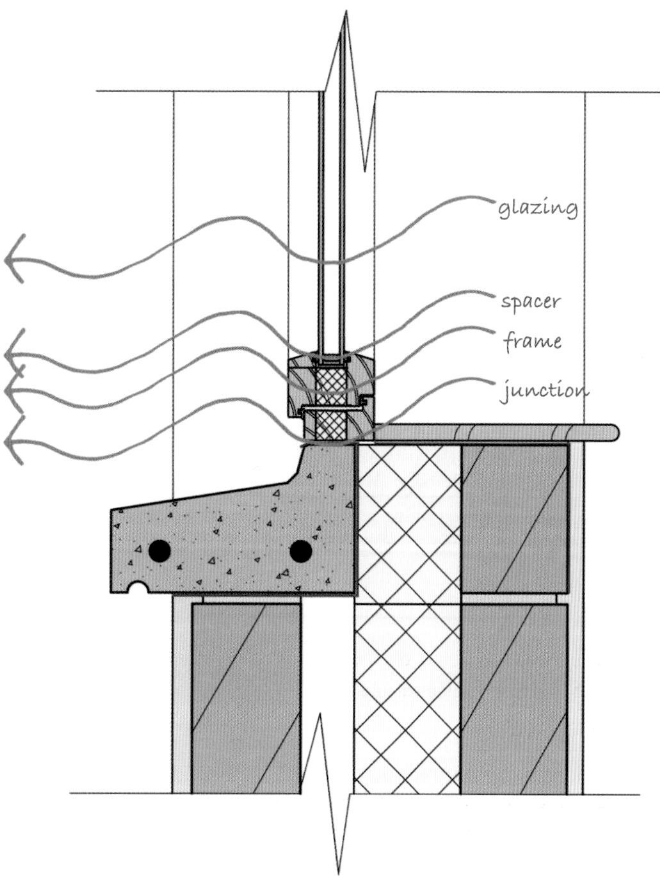

23.14 Windows thermal resistance: multiple heat flow paths through a typical window installation.

The heat flow paths for the glazing and frame are calculated by multiplying the U-value by the area. The heat flow paths for the spacer and window – wall junction are calculated by multiplying the psi value (Ψ) by the length, where Ψ is the linear thermal transmittance.

The U-value of an installed window is calculated using the formula:

$$U_{window\ installed} = \frac{(U_{glass} \times A_{glass}) + (U_{frame} \times A_{frame}) + (\Psi_{spacer} \times L_{spacer}) + (\Psi_{installation} \times L_{installation})}{A_{window}}$$

When selecting a window product it is useful to calculate the U-value of the window alone (before installation) so products can be compared. This can be done using the same formula, excluding the installation data:

$$U_{window} = \frac{(U_{glass} \times A_{glass}) + (U_{frame} \times A_{frame}) + (\Psi_{spacer} \times L_{spacer})}{A_{window}}$$

The required areas and lengths are calculated using the formulae:

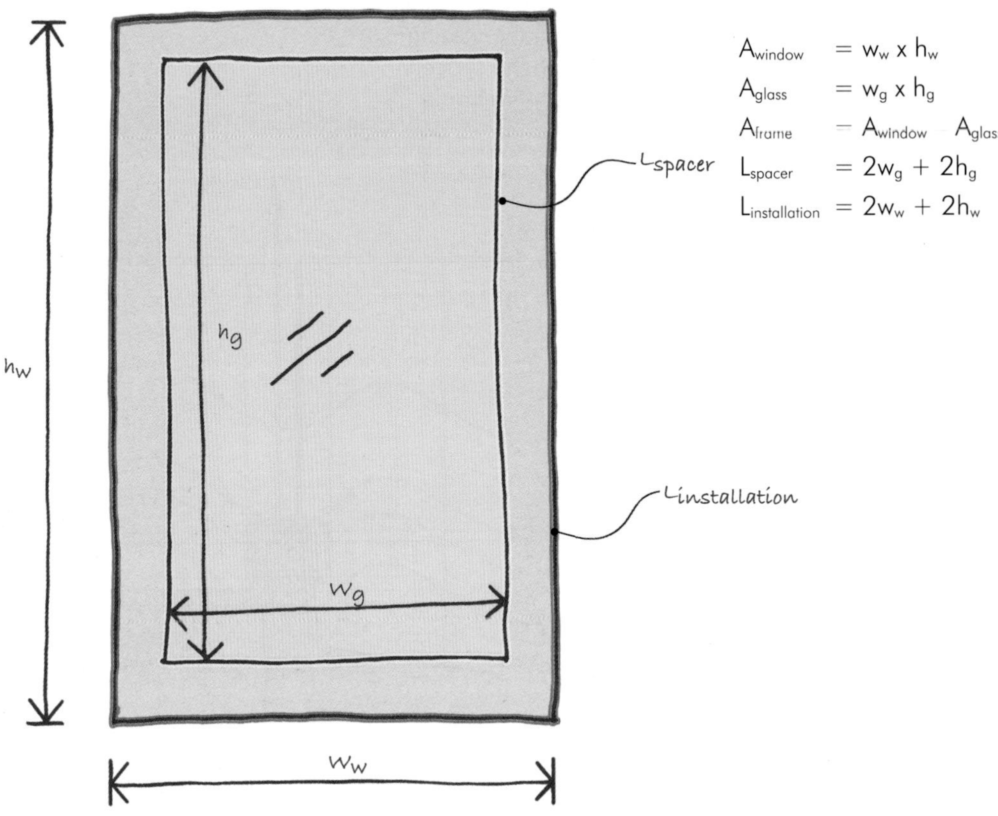

23.15 Window U-value calculation.

Worked example (window)
Calculate the U-value of a window, given the following data:

Window dimensions:

- window size = 1.23m x 1.48m
- frame width top and side = 117mm
- frame width bottom = 134mm
- frame thickness = 68mm

U-values:

- U-value glazing (U_g) = 0.6 W/m²K
- U-value frame (U_f) = 1.6 W/m²K

Thermal bridge values:

- spacer (Ψ_{spacer}) = 0.08 W/mK
- window–wall junction ($\Psi_{installed}$) = 0.15 W/mK

Calculate window areas and lengths:

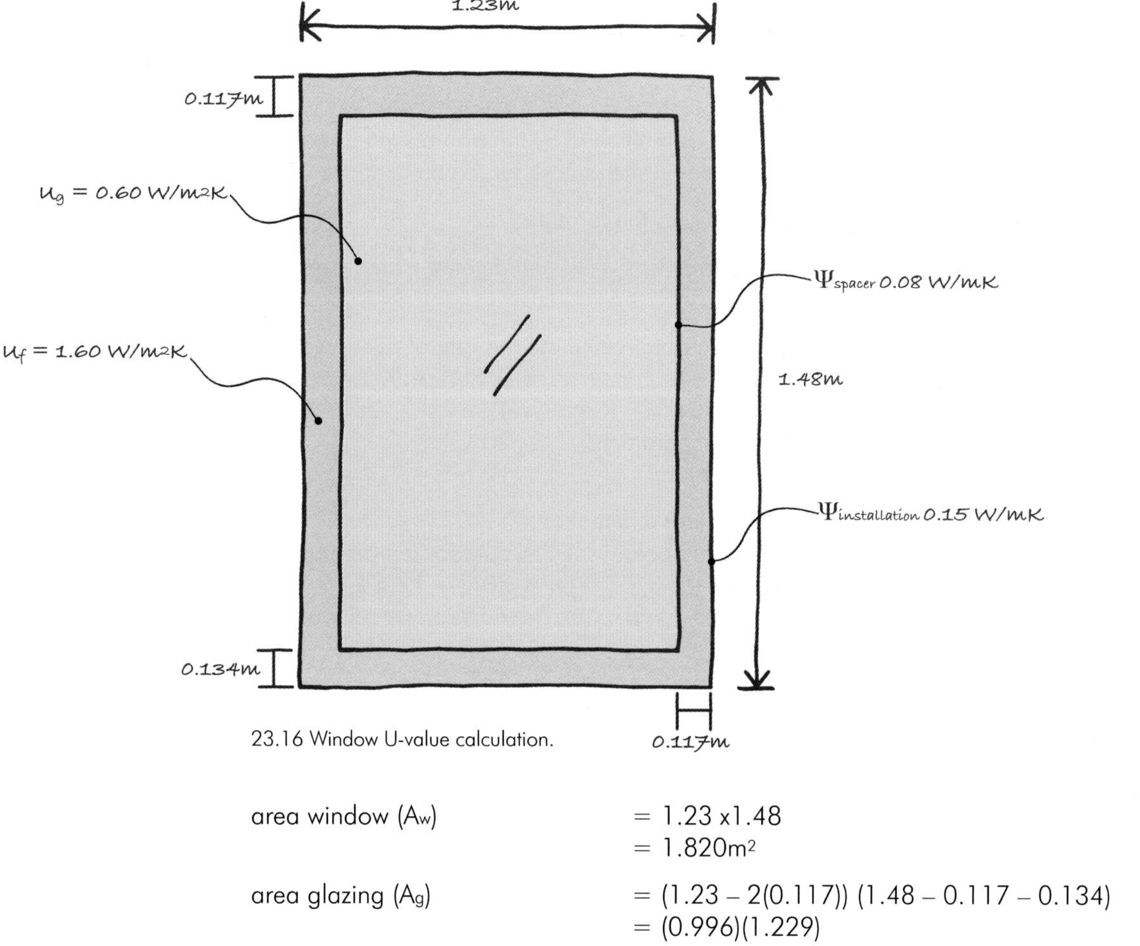

23.16 Window U-value calculation.

area window (A_w) = 1.23 x1.48
= 1.820m²

area glazing (A_g) = (1.23 – 2(0.117)) (1.48 – 0.117 – 0.134)
= (0.996)(1.229)
= 1.224m²

area frame (A_f) = Aw – Ag
= 1.820 – 1.224
= 0.596m²

length installation ($L_{installation}$) = 2(1.23) + 2(1.48)
= 5.42m

length spacer (L_{spacer}) = 2((1.23 – 2(0.117)) + 2((1.48 – 0.117 – 0.134))
= 2(0.996) + 2 (1.229)
= 1.992 + 2.458
= 4.45m

Input data into formula:

$$U_{window\ installed} = \frac{(U_{glass} \times A_{glass}) + (U_{frame} \times A_{frame}) + (\Psi_{spacer} \times L_{spacer}) + (\Psi_{installation} \times L_{installation})}{A_{window}}$$

$$U_{window\ installed} = \frac{(0.6)(1.224) + (1.6)(0.596) + (0.08)(4.45) + (0.15)(5.42)}{1.820}$$

$$U_{window\ installed} = \frac{(0.7344) + (0.9536) + (0.356) + (0.813)}{1.820}$$

$$U_{window\ installed} = \frac{2.857}{1.820}$$

$$U_{window\ installed} = 1.569$$

$$U_{window\ installed} = 1.57\text{W/m}^2\text{K}$$

This window would meet the requirements of the building regulations; U-value ≤ 1.60 W/m²K (assuming the windows and doors comprise 25% of the floor area).

Rate, amount and cost of energy loss calculations

Rate of energy loss

While the U-value is a very important and useful measurement, it is limited by the fact that it represents the rate of energy loss for one square metre of the structure when there is a one degree temperature difference between indoors and outdoors.

To get a more complete picture of the rate of energy loss, the U-value of an element (e.g. floor, wall, window, roof) is multiplied by the appropriate area and the temperature difference to calculate actual rate of energy loss for the building.

This can be done using the formula:

rate of total energy loss = U-value x area x temperature difference

Worked example

Given the following data, calculate the rate of energy loss through the walls of a house.

- U-value walls = $0.21 W/m^2K$
- area walls = $42m^2$
- mean indoor temperature = 20°C
- outdoor temperature = 12.5°C

Calculate temperature difference:

temperature difference = outdoor temperature – indoor temperature
= 20°C – 12.5°C
= 7.5°C
= 7.5K

Input data into formula:

rate of total energy loss = U-value x area x temperature difference

rate of total energy loss = 0.21 x 42 x 7.5

rate of total energy loss = 66.15W

The units of each part of the formula are treated the same way as the numbers. So, for this calculation:

$$\frac{W}{m^2K} \times m^2 \times K = W$$

Note: 1 watt = 1 joule per second

SUPPLEMENTARY INFORMATION

Air and surface temperatures are usually stated in degrees Celsius in Ireland (and degrees Fahrenheit in some other parts of the world). When doing calculations, the SI unit for temperature, degrees Kelvin (unit: K), is used. This uppercase K is not to be confused with lowercase k, which is the symbol for kilo (e.g. kilogram).

Amount of energy loss

The amount of energy loss is calculated for a period of time, usually the heating period. The heating period is that time of the year when the occupant has the heating turned on to maintain a comfortable indoor temperature. This can be calculated using the formula:

amount of energy loss = rate of total energy loss x period of time

Worked example

Calculate the amount of energy lost through the walls of a house, given the following data:

- rate of total energy loss = 66.15W
- period = 5 hours per day for 45 weeks

Calculate time in seconds:

time = 60 x 60 x 5 x 7 x 45
= 5,670,000 seconds

Calculate amount of energy loss:

amount of energy loss = rate of total energy loss x period of time
amount of energy loss = 66.15 x 5,670,000
= 375,070,500 joules

Convert to kilowatt hours:

conversion factor: 3,600,000 joules = 1 kWh

$$\frac{375{,}070{,}500}{3{,}600{,}000} = 104.19 \text{ kWh}$$

Cost of energy loss

The rising cost of energy is one of the main reasons why people upgrade their homes (e.g. install insulation or solar panels). The most accurate way to calculate the annual cost of energy losses is to look at the actual cost per unit of energy supplied to the home. This is called the 'delivered energy cost'. The delivered energy cost of each type of fuel varies with changes in demand in the market. Up-to-date data is available from the Sustainable Energy Authority of Ireland (SEAI).

Fuel	Form	Unit of Supply	Average Price per Unit (€)	Gross Calorific Value (kWh/unit)	Delivered Energy Cost cent/kWh	Percentage Change since 1 July 2012
Peat	Briquettes, baled	Bale	4.30	67.0	6.42	+10.3%
Coal	Nuggets (lignite)	Tonne	355.00	5,763.5	6.16	+9.2%
	Premium coal	Tonne	395.00	8,267.2	4.78	+8.2%
	Standard coal	Tonne	380.00	7,900.0	4.81	+8.6%
	Standard anthracite	Tonne	465.00	8,735.2	5.32	+6.9%
	Grade A anthracite	Tonne	505.00	8,960.0	5.64	+6.3%
	Ovoids (smokeless)	Tonne	440.0	8,850.0	4.97	+7.3%
Oil	Gas oil	Litre	1.02	10.55	9.68	+0.2%
	Kerosene	Litre	0.99	10.18	9.69	+0.0%
L.P.G.	Bulk L.P.G.	Litre	0.95	7.09	13.41	+8.4%
	Bottled butane	11.35kg Cylinder	33.38	155.7	21.44	-
	Bottled propane	34kg Cylinder	90.50	471.0	19.21	-
	Bottled propane	47kg Cylinder	123.29	651.0	18.94	-
Natural Gas	Band D1 $<5{,}556$ kWh p.a.	kWh	0.077	1.0	7.72	+13.8%
	Band D2 $>5{,}656$ $<55{,}556$ kWh p.a.	kWh	0.067	1.0	6.73	+9.5%
	Band 3 $\geq 65{,}558$ kWh p.a.	kWh	0.062	1.0	6.18	+6.5%
Electricity	Band DA: $<1{,}000$kWh p.a.	kWh	0.59	1.0	59.01	+8.0%
	Band DB: $\geq 1{,}000$ $<2{,}600$kWh p.a.	kWh	0.28	1.0	27.86	+6.4%
	Band DC: $\geq 2{,}500$ $<5{,}000$ kWh p.a.	kWh	0.23	1.0	22.89	+6.2%
	Band DD: $\geq 5{,}000$ $<15{,}000$ kWh p.a.	kWh	0.20	1.0	20.16	+7.1%
	Band DE: $\geq 15{,}000$ kWh p.a.	kWh	0.17	1.0	17.33	+6.0%
	Night rate	kWh	0.09	1.0	9.37	
Wood	Pellets bulk delivery	kg	0.24	4.8	5.10	+1.6%
	Pellets bagged	kg	0.32	4.8	8.69	+1.1%
	Briquettes	kg	0.39	4.8	8.06	+1.7%

23.17 Domestic fuels: comparison of energy costs (July 2013). Most residential consumers are in Band D2 for natural gas and DB and DC for electricity. *Source:* SEAI.

If the amount of energy loss has been calculated previously, the following formula can be used to calculate the annual cost of energy loss:

cost = amount of energy loss x unit price of energy

If no previous calculations have been done, the annual cost of heat loss can be calculated in one step using the following formula:

$$\text{cost} = \frac{\text{time} \times \text{rate} \times \text{price}}{3{,}600{,}000}$$

where:

time = heating period (unit: seconds, s)
rate = U-value x area x temperature difference (unit: watt, W)
price = delivered cost per unit of energy (unit: cent per kilowatt hour, c/kWh)

ACTIVITIES

Check the energy bill for your home to determine the current cost of each unit of energy (e.g. electricity/gas, etc.) consumed.

SUPPLEMENTARY INFORMATION

Where does the 3,600,000 in the formula come from?

$$\text{Cost} = \frac{\text{U-value} \times \text{area} \times \text{temp diff} \times \text{time} \times \text{price}}{3{,}600{,}000}$$

$$= \frac{W}{m^2k} \times m^2 \times K \times s \times \frac{c}{kWh}$$

$$= \frac{j/s}{m^2k} \times m^2 \times K \times s \times \frac{c}{3{,}600{,}000\,j}$$

$$= \frac{c}{3{,}600{,}000}$$

Note:
- W = Watt
- K = Kelvin
- k = kilo
- m = metre
- h = hour
- s = second
- j = joule
- c = cent

Note:
- 1W = 1 joule per second
- W = j/s
- 1kWh = 3,600,000 j/s

Worked example

Given the following data, calculate the annual cost of the energy loss through the walls of a home heated using oil (kerosene):

- U-value walls = $0.21 W/m^2K$
- area walls = $65m^2$
- mean indoor temperature = 20°C
- outdoor temperature = 9.5°C
- heating period = 10 hours per day for 42 weeks
- price of kerosene = 9.69c/kWh (from table)

time = 60 x 60 x 10 x 7 x 42
= 10,584,000 seconds

rate = U-value x area x temperature difference
= 0.21 x 65 x (20 – 9.5)
= 143.325

$$\text{cost} = \frac{\text{time} \times \text{rate} \times \text{price}}{3{,}600{,}000}$$

$$\text{cost} = \frac{10{,}584{,}000 \times 143.325 \times 9.69}{3{,}600{,}000}$$

$$\text{cost} = \frac{14{,}699{,}262{,}940}{3{,}600{,}000}$$

cost = 4,083.13c
= €40.83

Cost of energy loss (alternative method)

If instead of the 'delivered energy cost', the calculation was based on the cost per unit of energy (e.g. litre of oil) then the calorific value of the fuel must be used. The cost is calculated using the following formula:

$$\text{cost} = \frac{\text{time x rate x price}}{\text{1,000 x calorific value}}$$

where:

time = heating period (unit:seconds, s)

rate = U-value x area x temperature difference (unit: Watt, W)

price = price per unit of fuel (e.g. litre of oil)(unit: cent, c or euro, €)

Worked example

Given the following data, calculate the annual cost of the energy loss through the walls of a home heated using oil (kerosene):

- U-value walls = $0.13W/m^2K$
- area walls = $91m^2$
- mean indoor temperature = 21°C
- outdoor temperature = 7°C
- heating period = 12 hours per day for 39 weeks
- price of kerosene = 95c/litre
- calorific value of kerosene = 36,648kj/litre (gross calorific value of kerosene 10.18kWh/litre (from table)1kWh= 3,600kj)

time = 60 x 60 x 12 x 7 x 39
= 11,793,600 seconds

rate = U-value x area x temperature difference
= 0.13 x 91 x (21 – 7)
= 118.3

Input data into formula:

$$\text{cost} = \frac{\text{time x rate x price}}{\text{1,000 x calorific value}}$$

$$\text{cost} = \frac{11{,}793{,}600 \times 118.3 \times 95}{36{,}648{,}000}$$

$$\text{cost} = \frac{132{,}542{,}373{,}600}{36{,}648{,}000}$$

cost = 3,616.63cc

cost = €36.16

REVISION EXERCISES

1 Describe, using examples, the four mechanisms of heat transfer.

2 Compare the thermal conductivity of the following construction materials:
- brick
- concrete block (medium weight)
- concrete block (autoclaved aerated)
- softwood timber
- expanded polystyrene insulation (with graphite)
- polyisocyanurate insulation (foil faced)
- sheep's wool insulation
- cellulose insulation
- wood fibre insulation

3 Given the following data, calculate the U-value of the structure:

	thickness (mm)
• external render	18
• concrete block outer leaf	100
• cavity	140
• insulation	100
• concrete block inner leaf	100
• internal plaster	13
	resistance (m^2K/W)
• internal surface resistance	0.13
• external surface resistance	0.04
• cavity (air) resistance	0.18
	conductivity value (w/mK)
• internal plaster	0.180
• external render	1.000
• concrete blockwork	1.330
• insulation	0.031

4 Given the following data, calculate the U-value of the window:

	window dimensions
• window size	= 1.36m x 1.54m
• frame width top and side	= 112mm
• frame width bottom	= 140mm
• frame thickness	= 55mm
	U-values (W/m^2K)
• U-value glazing (U_g)	= 0.55
• U-value frame (U_f)	= 1.40
	thermal bridge values (W/mK)
• spacer (Ψ_{spacer})	= 0.06
• window–wall junction ($\Psi_{installed}$)	= 0.12

5 Given the following data, calculate:

a) the rate of energy loss through the structure

b) the amount of energy loss through the structure

c) the cost of energy loss through the structure.

• U-value walls	= $0.19W/m^2K$
• area walls	= $65m^2$
• mean indoor temperature	= 20°C
• outdoor temperature	= 9.5°C
• period	= 7 hours per day for 42 weeks
• price (natural gas: D2)	= 6.73c/kWh

CHAPTER 24

Energy Standards

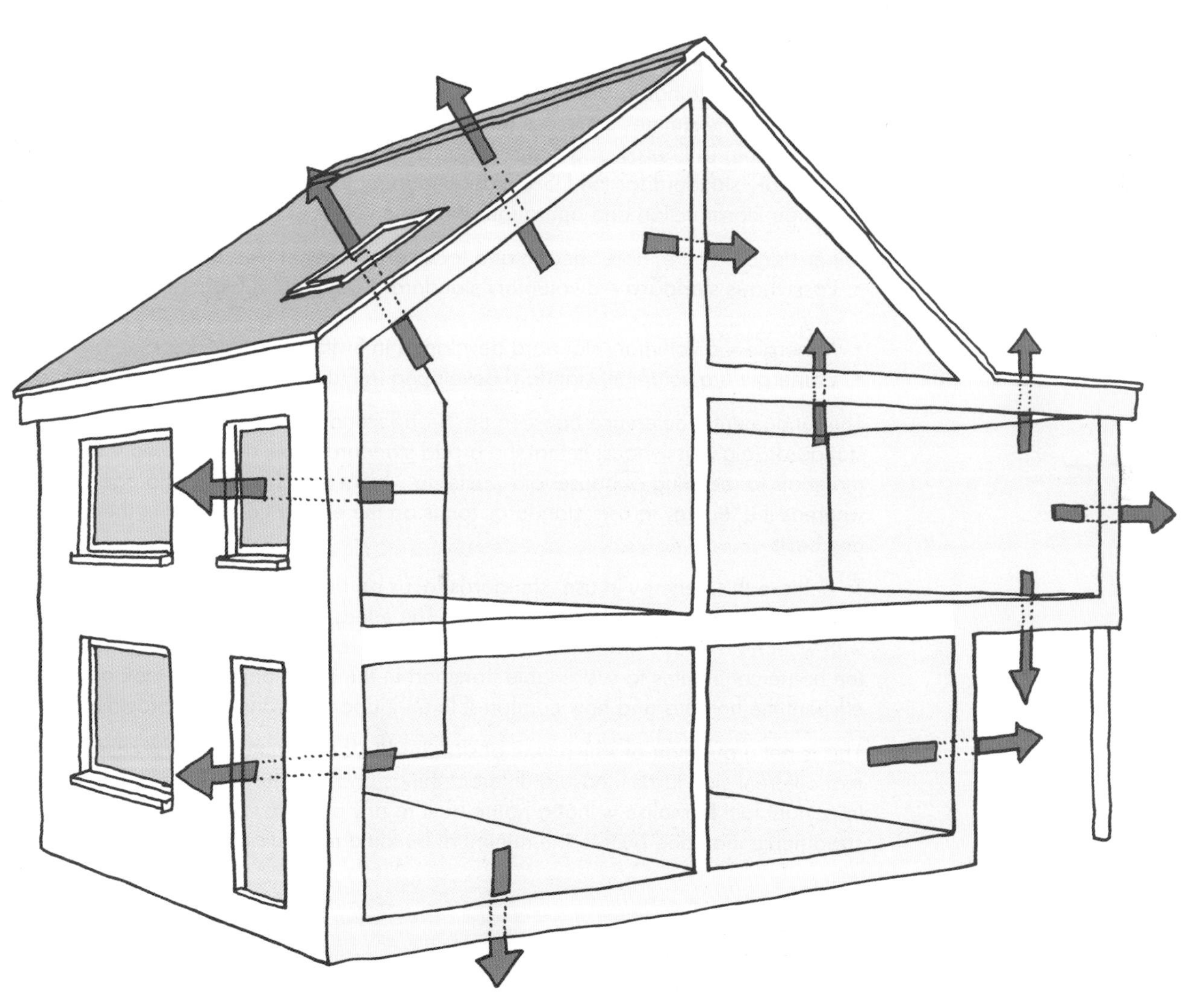

There are several key facts driving change in the standards to which homes are built:

- over 90% of Ireland's energy supply comes from non-renewable sources (e.g. oil, natural gas, solid fuels)
- almost 30% of Ireland's energy supply is consumed by the residential sector (houses, flats, apartments)
- approximately 30% of Ireland's carbon emissions come from the residential sector:
  - almost every home (98.4%) in Ireland has central heating
  - almost four out of five homes (78%) consume oil or natural gas
- carbon emissions are causing global warming, which is leading to climate change
- energy costs are rising and more people are experiencing energy poverty.

In response to these facts the government has increased the energy efficiency requirements for newly built houses. This means that a home built today must be significantly more energy efficient than one built ten or twenty years ago. These changes are expected to continue with regular updates to the building regulations until new homes are at a net zero energy standard.

Design and performance standards

Regulatory authorities all over the world are trying to tackle these same problems. Some countries have introduced standards that promote a higher quality of sustainable design above the minimum standards set out in their building regulations. The idea is to encourage the construction industry to build sustainable homes.

Some standards are very broad and take into account all aspects of the building's impact. Examples include:

- **Code for Sustainable Homes (CSH)** – a voluntary standard for England, Wales and Northern Ireland that examines 34 issues related to how a home is designed, constructed and used
- **Leadership in Energy and Environmental Design for Homes (LEED for Homes)** – a voluntary standard for the USA and Canada that comprises a suite of rating systems for the design, construction and operation of homes.

Other standards are more specific and focus on energy in use. Examples of these include:

- **Passivhaus standard** – a voluntary standard developed in Germany and used all over the world
- **Minergie** – a voluntary standard developed in Switzerland
- **Effinergie** – a voluntary standard developed in France.

The fundamental difference between the broad standards (e.g. CSH) and the 'energy in use' standards (e.g. Passivhaus) is that the broad standards look at everything – from construction materials to recycling of household waste, to whether the home has storage space for bicycles; whereas the 'energy in use' standards focus on the energy consumed in the home on a day-to-day basis.

To achieve this, 'energy in use' standards focus on building fabric (i.e. thermal insulation and airtightness) and services (i.e. ventilation). The energy in use standards are not concerned with whether a house is built using materials from renewable resources (e.g. timber) or how the home contributes to sustainable transport in the community; they look only at how energy efficient the home is and how comfortable an indoor environment is provided.

This is not a question of which type of standard is 'better'; it is simply a case of recognising that different standards measure different things and that they all have a role to play. The most important fact to realise is that a home built to any of these voluntary standards will be more sustainable than one built to the minimum building regulations requirements.

Categories	Issue
Energy and CO_2 emissions	Dwelling emission rate (M) Fabric energy efficiency (M) Energy display devices Drying space Energy labelled white goods External lighting Low and zero carbon technologies Cycle storage Home office
Water	Indoor water use (M) External water use
Materials	Environmental impact of materials (M) Responsible sourcing of materials – basic building elements Responsible sourcing of materials – finishing elements
Surface Water Run-off	Management of surface water run-off from developments (M) Flood risk
Waste	Storage of non-recyclable and recyclable household waste (M) Construction site waste management Composting
Pollution	Global warming potential (GWP) of insulants NO_x emissions
Health and Well-being	Daylighting Sound insultaion Private space Lifetime homes (M)
Management	Home user guide Considerate Constructors Scheme Construction site impacts Security
Ecology	Ecological value of site Ecological enhancement Protection of ecological features Change in ecological value of site Building footprint

24.01 Code for Sustainable Homes: assessment categories. (M) denotes issues with mandatory elements.

Building regulations (TGD L 2011)

The Technical Guidance Documents provide detailed information on the design features required to comply with the building regulations. Each document addresses a different area of building design. Technical Guidance Document L: Conservation of Fuel and Energy – Dwellings (TGD L) sets out the requirements for energy efficiency and carbon emissions.

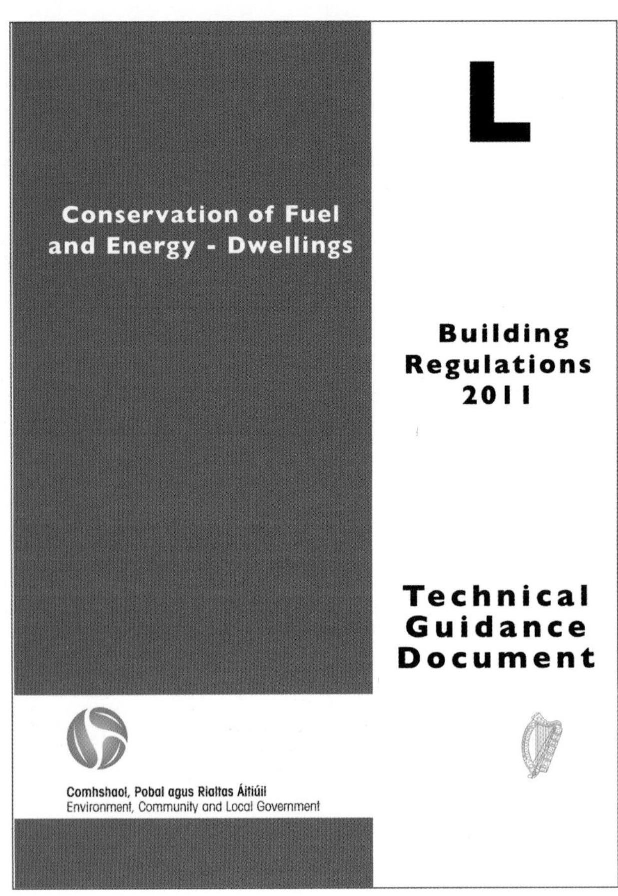

24.02 Technical Guidance Document L: Conservation of Fuel and Energy – Dwellings (2011 edition).

Energy consumption and carbon emissions

The building regulations specify the requirements for energy consumption and carbon emissions that must be met by all newly constructed houses.

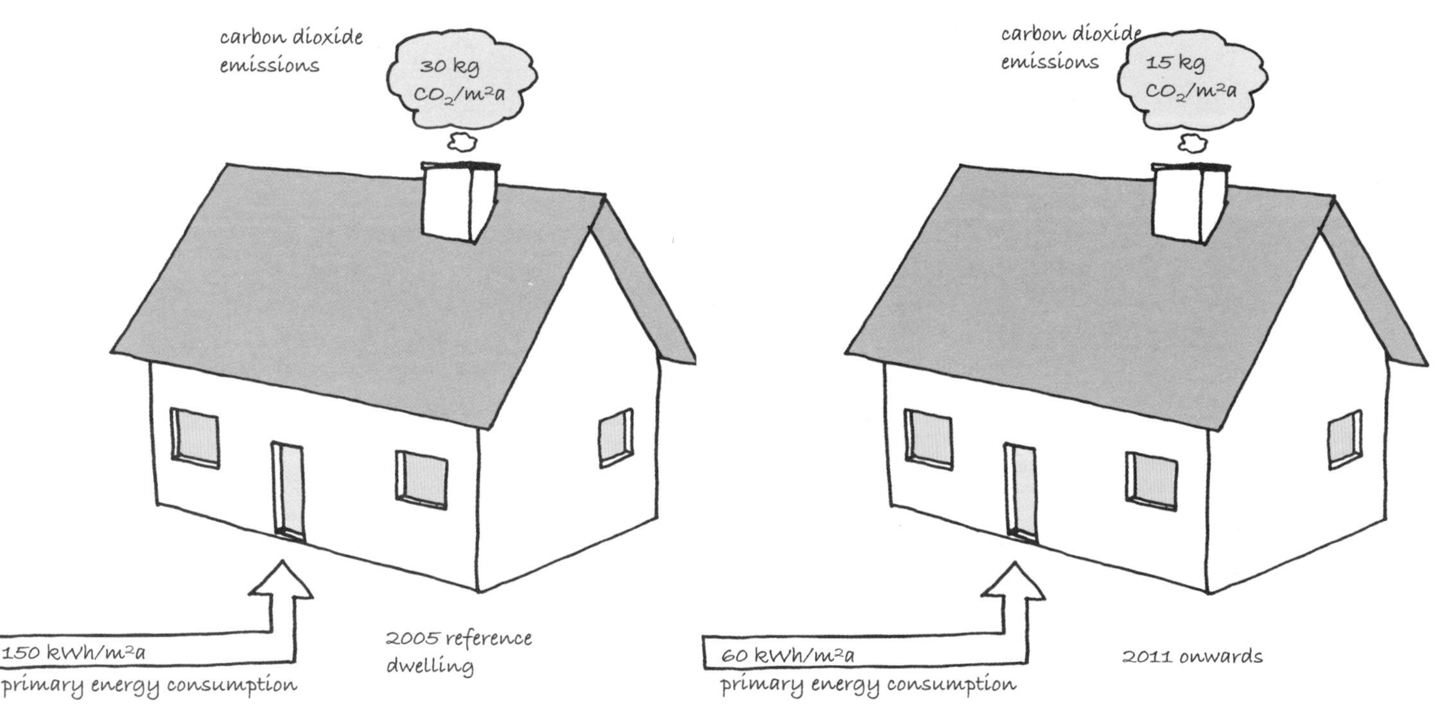

24.03 Baseline reference dwelling (2005) and proposed dwelling (2011 onwards) with 40% relative energy consumption and 49% relative carbon emissions.

Reference dwelling

The requirements for energy efficiency and carbon emissions are stated relative to a 'reference dwelling'. This is based on the idea that the proposed home must outperform a similar house (i.e. the reference dwelling) built in the past. There isn't a single reference dwelling; it is a notional version of the proposed house.

The reference dwelling complies with the building regulations that were in force in 2005. So the question becomes: How much better is the proposed house compared to the same house built to the 2005 standards?*

* The minimum acceptable performance is 40% relative energy consumption and 49% relative carbon dioxide emissions.

Energy consumption and carbon emission limits

The amount of energy consumption and carbon emissions permitted under the building regulations have reduced gradually in recent years.

Performance indicator	2005 (baseline reference dwelling)		2007		2011		2016	
			reduction factor		reduction factor		reduction factor	
Primary energy consumption	1.0	150	0.60	90	0.40	60	0.30	45
Carbon dioxide emissions	1.0	30	0.69	21	0.46	14	0.30	9
Building energy rating	1.0	B3		B1		A3		A2

24.04 Maximum permitted energy consumption and carbon emissions for an average dwelling.

The energy consumption rate (per square metre of floor area) of the proposed home is stated as the energy performance coefficient (EPC):

$$\text{EPC} = \frac{\text{primary energy consumption of the proposed dwelling (kWh/m}^2\text{a)}}{\text{primary energy consumption of the reference dwelling (kWh/m}^2\text{a)}}$$

The maximum permitted energy coefficient (MPEPC) is 0.4, or 40%.

The carbon emission rate (per square metre of floor area) of the proposed dwelling is stated as the carbon performance coefficient (CPC):

$$\text{CPC} = \frac{\text{CO}_2\text{ emission rate of the proposed dwelling (kgCO}_2\text{/m}^2\text{a)}}{\text{CO}_2\text{ emission rate of the reference dwelling (kgCO}_2\text{/m}^2\text{a)}}$$

The maximum permitted carbon performance coefficient (MPCPC) is 0.46, or 46%.

Both energy consumption and carbon dioxide (CO_2) emissions are calculated using the Dwelling Energy Assessment Procedure (DEAP) software tool.

Renewable energy requirement

TGD L (2011) also requires that some of the energy consumed by a home is generated on site using renewable energy technologies. The minimum level of required is:

- 10 kWh/m^{2}a contributing to energy use for domestic hot water heating, space heating or cooling; or
- 4 kWh/m^{2}a of electrical energy; or
- a combination of these which would have an equivalent effect.

Renewable energy technologies means technology, products or equipment that supply energy derived from renewable energy sources, including:

- solar thermal systems
- solar photovoltaic systems
- biomass systems
- systems using biofuels
- heat pumps
- wind turbines
- other small-scale renewable systems.

Building fabric insulation: U-values

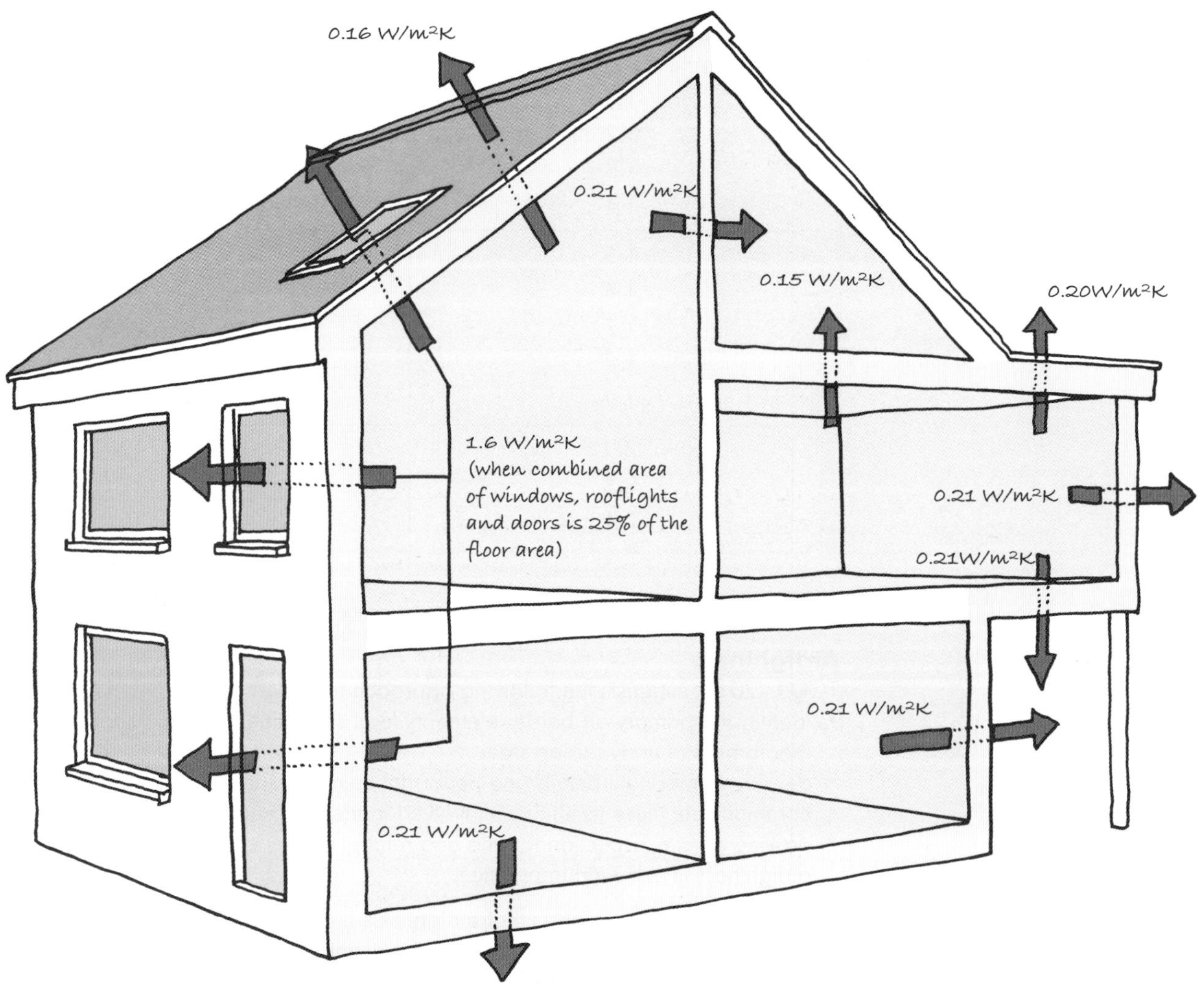

24.05 U-values: maximum permitted U-values for the building fabric (TGDL, 2011).

The maximum permitted rate of energy loss through the building fabric is outlined in TGD L (2011). The average U-value of U ≤ 1.60W/m²K for windows and doors assumes that the windows and doors comprise 25% of the area of the floor. A house that has a greater proportion of glazing is required to meet a higher building standard (i.e. a lower U-value).

Average U-value of windows, doors and rooflights (W/m²K)	Maximum combined area of external doors, windows, rooflights and doors expressed as a percentage of floor area (A_1)
0.8	58.9
1.0	44.8
1.2	35.1
1.3	31.9
1.4	29.2
1.5	26.9
1.6	**25.0**
1.7	23.3
1.8	21.9
1.9	20.6
2.0	19.4
2.2	17.5
2.4	15.9
2.6	14.5

24.06 U-values: maximum permitted variation in U-values for windows, rooflights and doors.

Airtightness

TGD L (2011) suggests the following approach to airtightness:

- identify the primary air barrier elements (e.g. sheathing, plaster, vapour control layer, breather membrane) at early design stage
- develop appropriate details and performance requirements to ensure continuity of the air barrier
- communicate these to all those involved in the construction process
- provide on-site inspection regime and related quality control procedures to ensure that airtightness is achieved in practice.

While this procedure suggests that airtightness is important, the requirement is only <7 m³/h.m² (less than 7 cubic metres of air per hour for every square metre of floor area). This is a very poor standard compared to the Passivhaus standard.

Building Energy Rating (BER)

A Building Energy Rating (BER) is an approximate measure of how much energy a building consumes every year. When a BER assessment is completed a certificate is produced. This certificate is similar to the energy efficiency label for household electrical appliances (e.g. fridges, cookers) and it also states the annual amount of the greenhouse gas carbon dioxide (CO_2) that the home produces. By law, a BER certificate must be available for every home rented or sold in Ireland.

BER certificates are useful for comparing the performance of homes built to building regulations standards. However, they lack the accuracy and scientific methodology to provide a true picture of the energy performance of a home.

KEY PRINCIPLES

The benefits of having a BER system include:

- increases awareness – labelling every home will allow consumers to make an informed decision when renting or buying a home and should encourage people to buy/rent more energy-efficient homes
- changes behaviour – making people more aware of the energy performance of buildings will encourage them to reduce their energy consumption
- encourages better design – architects, builders and developers will build more energy-efficient homes to make their houses more attractive to buyers
- fights climate change – improving the energy performance of homes will lower energy consumption and reduce CO_2 emissions.

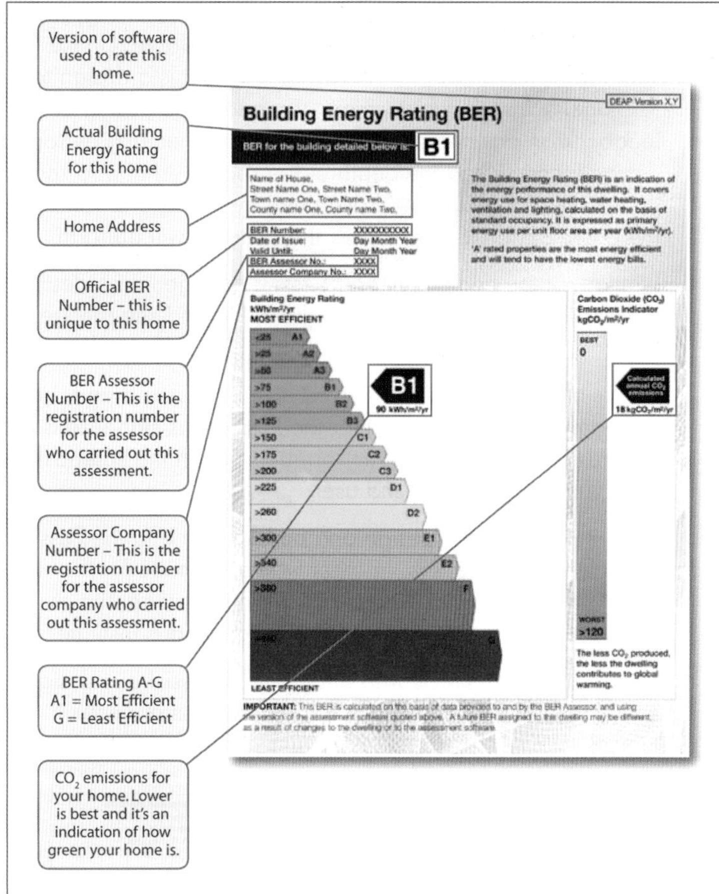

24.07 Building Energy Rating (BER) certificate (*Source:* Sustainable Energy Authority of Ireland).

To conduct a BER, the assessor follows the Dwelling Energy Assessment Procedure (DEAP). Carrying out an assessment on an existing building involves visiting the building, taking measurements and recording certain details. This information is then entered into the DEAP software tool and the calculations are combined to produce an overall estimation of annual primary energy demand and carbon dioxide (CO_2) emissions. The dwelling is then given a rating on a scale of A1 (best) to G (worst). As well as the certificate, the homeowner is also given an advisory report. The report explains the changes that could be made to the home to improve its energy performance and reduce CO_2 emissions.

Year of construction	Pre-1972	1972–1978	1979–1981	1982–1991	1992–2001	2002–2008
Typical rating	E2–G	E1–E2	D1–D2	C3–D1	C2	C1

24.08 Existing houses: typical BER ratings prior to retrofitting insulation.

ACTIVITIES

Find out the BER for your home or a similar home nearby. Hint: Whenever a home is sold/rented a BER must be provided to the new owner/tenant.

SUPPLEMENTARY INFORMATION

The information gathered during the assessment visit includes:

- **dwelling type and age** – detached, semi-detached, terraced, ground floor apartment, etc.
- **structural details** – wall, roof and floor construction
- **room-by-room survey** – dimensions, openings (doors, windows), chimneys, fans, vents, radiators, lighting
- **ventilation system** – natural ventilation, mechanical ventilation, etc.
- **space heating system** – type (radiators, storage heaters, underfloor, etc.), fuel type (gas, oil, electricity, etc.), boiler type
- **water heating system** – heat source, fuel type, insulation (e.g. water cylinder insulation), solar water heating system, controls (e.g. thermostats, timers, etc.).

Passivhaus standard

The Passivhaus standard is the world's leading 'energy in use' standard. It is the most reliable and scientifically rigorous methodology available. Unlike the other standards, the Passivhaus standard is not merely an assessment tool; it is a design tool. Using the PHPP (Passivhaus Planning Package) software, the designer can adapt the design of the building and receive immediate feedback on how the changes will affect the energy performance of the building. For example, the designer can extend the depth of the roof overhang to see how this will impact on solar gain and contribute to the control of overheating. When one variable is changed, the software recalculates the entire design to assess how the building will perform.

Similarly, if the homeowner requests a change to the design during construction, the designer can enter the proposed change into the PHPP and see precisely what impact it will have on the energy performance of the building.

Critics of the Passivhaus standard dismiss it as a brand. While there is some truth in this, it is important to acknowledge that the Passivhaus standard is 'open source'. The PHPP is simply a series of spreadsheets. The formulae within the spreadsheets are not hidden and can be manipulated to suit the end user.

Also, it is possible to design and build a home to the Passivhaus standard without going through the certification process. In other words, somebody who wants an energy-efficient home but isn't interested in achieving certification can adopt the principles and methods of the Passivhaus standard without ever contacting the Passivhaus Institute.

In fact, many architects who are certified Passivhaus designers are bringing their Passivhaus knowledge and techniques to non-Passivhaus projects.

DEFINITION

Passivhaus
A Passivhaus building is a building in which thermal comfort can be maintaines by post-heating the fresh air, supplied to maintain acceptable indoor air quality, without the need for additional re-circulation of air.

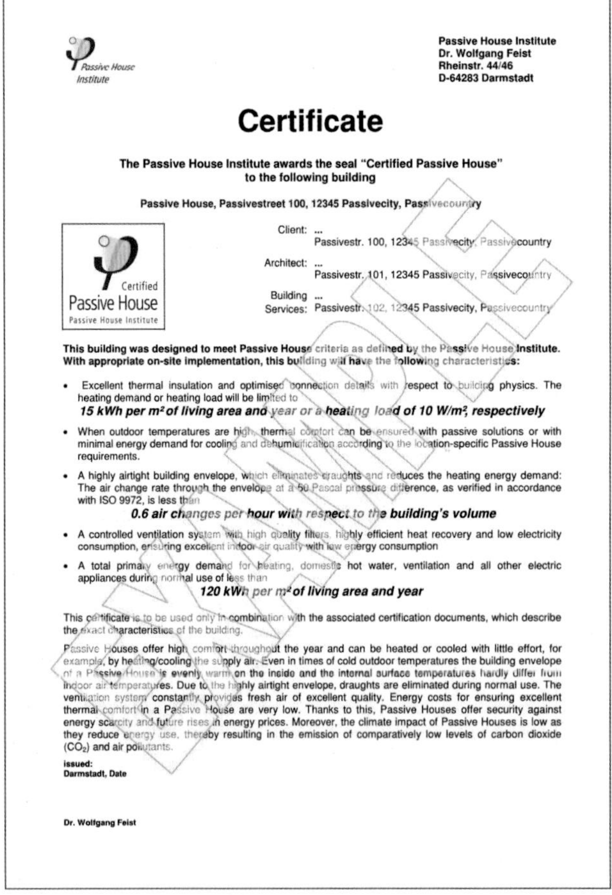

Passive House Institute

Passive House Institute
Dr. Wolfgang Feist
Rheinstr. 44/46
D-64283 Darmstadt

Certificate

The Passive House Institute awards the seal "Certified Passive House" to the following building

Passive House, Passivestreet 100, 12345 Passivecity, Passivecountry

Certified Passive House
Passive House Institute

Client: ...
Passivestr. 100, 12345 Passivecity, Passivecountry

Architect: ...
Passivestr. 101, 12345 Passivecity, Passivecountry

Building Services: ...
Passivestr. 102, 12345 Passivecity, Passivecountry

This building was designed to meet Passive House criteria as defined by the Passive House Institute. With appropriate on-site implementation, this building will have the following characteristics:

- Excellent thermal insulation and optimised connection details with respect to building physics. The heating demand or heating load will be limited to
  15 kWh per m² of living area and year or a heating load of 10 W/m², respectively
- When outdoor temperatures are high, thermal comfort can be ensured with passive solutions or with minimal energy demand for cooling and dehumidification according to the location-specific Passive House requirements.
- A highly airtight building envelope, which eliminates draughts and reduces the heating energy demand: The air change rate through the envelope at a 50 Pascal pressure difference, as verified in accordance with ISO 9972, is less than
  0.6 air changes per hour with respect to the building's volume
- A controlled ventilation system with high quality filters, highly efficient heat recovery and low electricity consumption, ensuring excellent indoor air quality with low energy consumption
- A total primary energy demand for heating, domestic hot water, ventilation and all other electric appliances during normal use of less than
  120 kWh per m² of living area and year

This certificate is to be used only in combination with the associated certification documents, which describe the exact characteristics of the building.

Passive Houses offer high comfort throughout the year and can be heated or cooled with little effort, for example, by heating/cooling the supply air. Even in times of cold outdoor temperatures the building envelope of a Passive House is evenly warm on the inside and the internal surface temperatures hardly differ from indoor air temperatures. Due to the highly airtight envelope, draughts are eliminated during normal use. The ventilation system constantly provides fresh air of excellent quality. Energy costs for ensuring excellent thermal comfort in a Passive House are very low. Thanks to this, Passive Houses offer security against energy scarcity and future rises in energy prices. Moreover, the climate impact of Passive Houses is low as they reduce energy use, thereby resulting in the emission of comparatively low levels of carbon dioxide (CO_2) and air pollutants.

issued:
Darmstadt, Date

Dr. Wolfgang Feist

24.09 Passivhaus Certificate. Each house is individually tested and assessed to ensure that it meets the Passivhaus standard and a certificate is issued by the Passivhaus Institute in Germany.

Principles

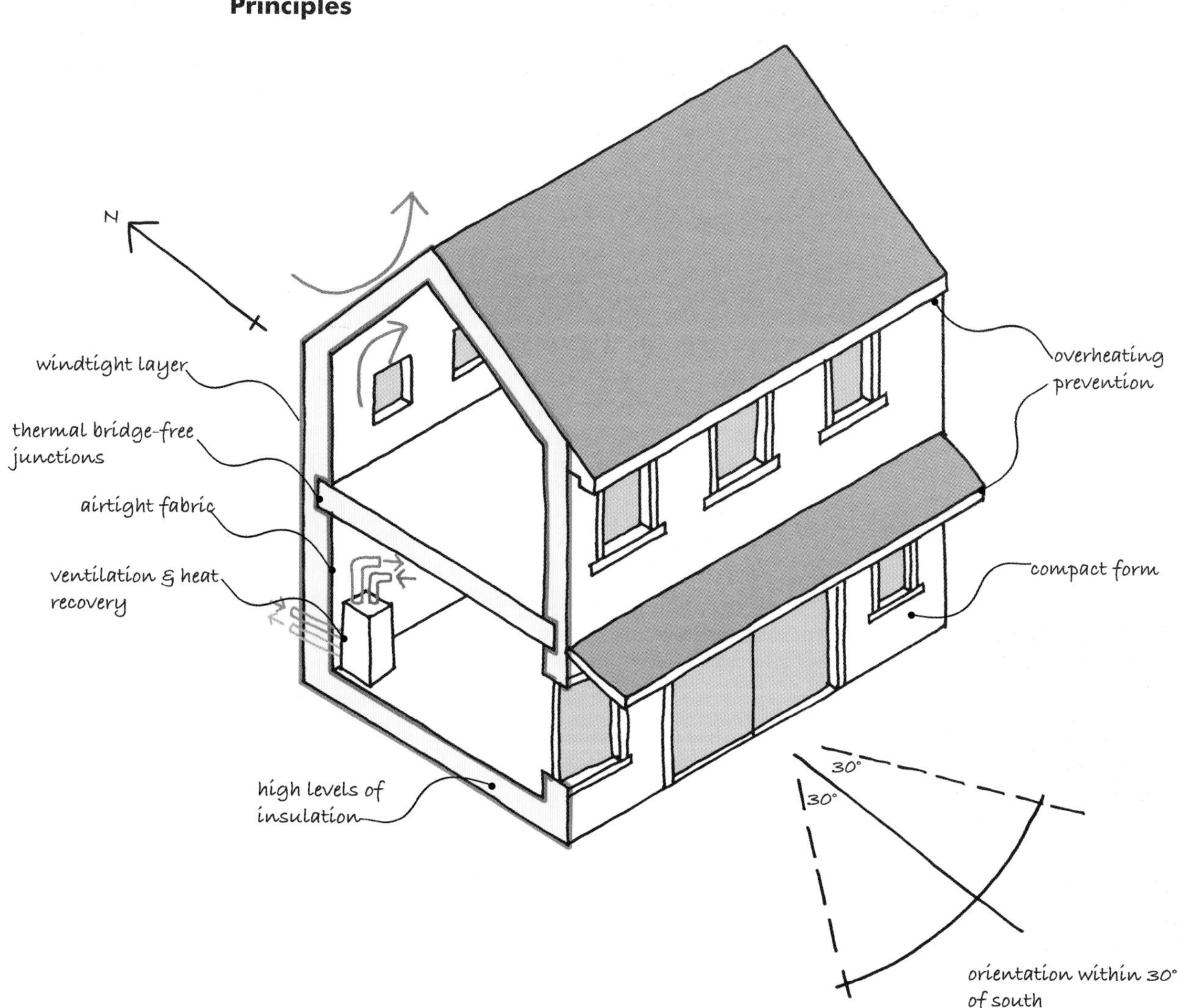

24.10 Passivhaus principles.

The Passivhaus approach to building design is based on seven simple principles:

1. **orientation** – using high-performance south-facing windows to capture the sun's energy
2. **insulation** – using very high levels of insulation throughout the structure
3. **preventing thermal bridges** – ensuring that there is no heat loss at joints
4. **airtightness** – sealing the entire structure to reduce heat loss caused by leakage of warm air
5. **heat recovery ventilation** – providing a constant supply of warm, clean, fresh air
6. **compactness** – having a low surface area to volume ratio
7. **preventing overheating** – the indoor temperature should not rise above 25°C for more than 10% of the year.

These design principles should inform the design of the building, but there is some flexibility in relation to their implementation. For example, it is possible to build a less compact house or on a site with poor solar exposure; it just means that other measures (e.g. extra insulation) will be needed to compensate.

ACTIVITIES

Visit the Passivhaus database (www.passivhausprojekte.de) to see examples of houses that have been built to the Passivhaus standard.

Criteria

There are two types of criteria set out in the Passivhaus standard:

1. **evaluation criteria** – absolute requirements that must be met
2. **functional criteria** – limiting backstop values that should not be exceeded to ensure thermal comfort.

Evaluation criteria

To achieve passive house standard a house must meet the following energy performance criteria:

- space heating demand ≤ 15 kWh/m^{2}a. The space heating demand is the energy required to maintain an indoor temperature of 20°C all year round. Space heating refers to the heating of the indoor rooms; it does not include hot water heating or other energy needs.

OR

- heating load ≤ 10 W/m^2. The heating load is the energy required to maintain an indoor temperature of 20°C on a given day. The heating load should not exceed the amount of heat that can be supplied to the house via the fresh air required for good indoor air quality (≤ 10W/m^2).

AND

- primary energy demand ≤ 120 kWh/m^{2}a. The primary energy demand is the total energy consumed for all requirements (i.e. space heating, water heating, ventilation and all electricity use).

AND

- building airtightness: air changes ≤ 0.6 h^{-1}@ n50

AND

- excess temperature frequency (above 25°C) ≤ 10% of the year.

Functional criteria

There are several functional criteria in relation to thermal performance:

- opaque elements (floors,walls, roofs):
  - U-value ≤ 0.15 W/m^{2}K

Windows:

- triple glazing with U-value glazing: Ug ≤ 0.70 W/m^{2}K
- solar transmittance value, g value > 0.55
- low conductivity glazing spacers
- thermal bridge-free window frame and sash/casement
- installed window U-value: $U_{window\ installed}$ ≤ 0.80 W/m^{2}K

Doors:

- $U_{door\ installed}$ ≤ 0.80 W/m^{2}K

Thermal bridging:

- linear thermal bridges (psi value)ψ < 0.01W/mK
- point thermal bridges (chi value)$\sum\chi$ / A < 0.01W/K

The criteria for ventilation equipment include:

- heat recovery efficiency, η_{HR} > 75% – this refers to the ability of the heat exchanger to capture heat energy from the exhaust air leaving the building
- electricity efficiency, < 0.45Wh/m^2 – this is the maximum amount of energy (per square metre of floor area) that the ventilation unit can consume
- noise protection, < 25 dB(A) in living spaces.

Another criterion is compactness. This describes the relationship between the surface area of the home and its volume:

- a ratio of 0.7 or less (i.e. surface area ÷ volume ≤ 0 7).

Compactness

Heat is lost through external surfaces; the greater surface area, the greater the heat loss. A simple house design that has a minimum of extensions or additions is best. Despite what might seem intuitive, building small does not necessarily mean building compact.

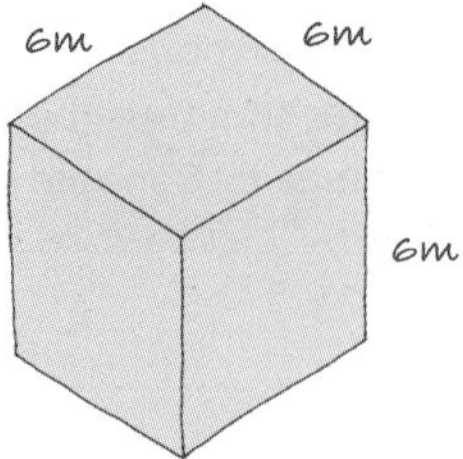

24.11 Compactness.

For example, taking a regular cube with a side length of 6m:

- area of one side = (6 x 6)
- total area = 6 x (6 x 6) = 216m^2
- volume = 6 x 6 x 6 =216 m^3
- compactness ratio = surface area ÷ volume = 216/216 = 1.0
- 1.0 > 0.7 – therefore does not meet Passivhaus recommendation.

For a regular cube with a side length of 10m:

- area of one side = (10 x 10)
- total area = 6 x (10 x 10) = 600m^2
- volume = 10 x 10 x 10 = 1,000m^3
- compactness ratio = surface area ÷ volume = 600/1,000 = 0.6
- 0.6 < 0.7 – therefore meets Passivhaus recommendation.

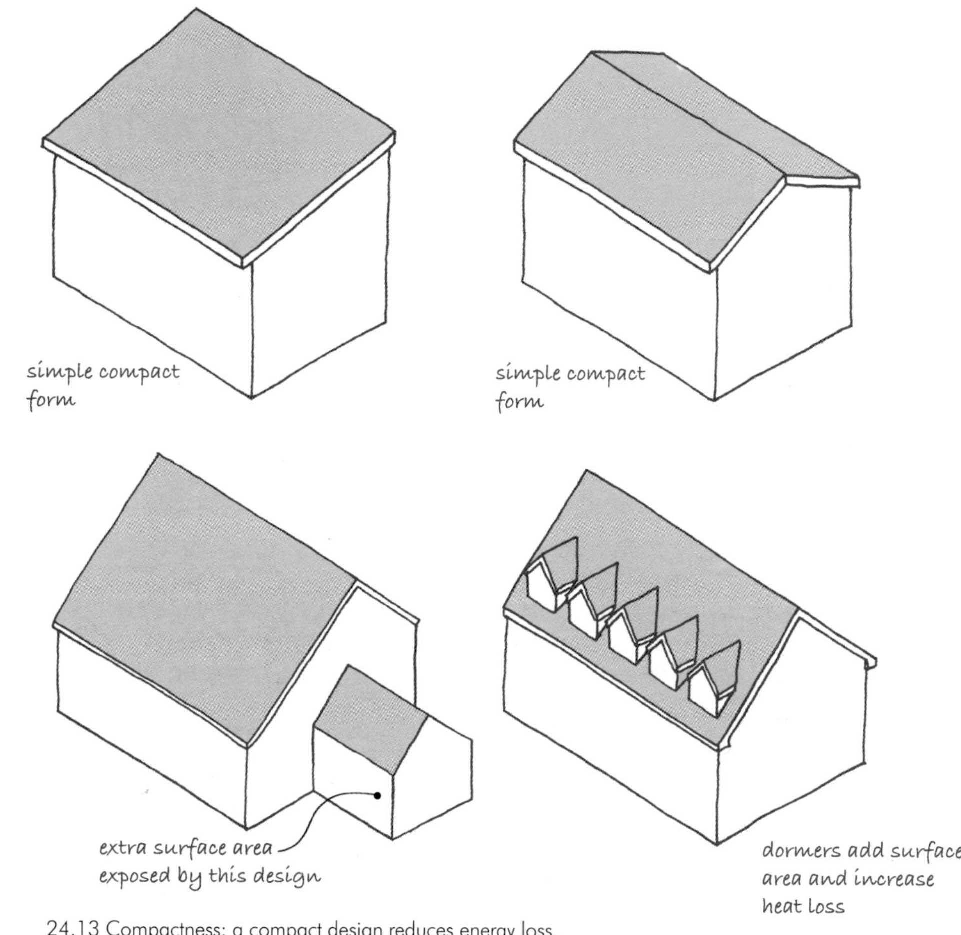

24.13 Compactness: a compact design reduces energy loss.

Certificate

Certified Passive House component
for cool, temperate climate, valid until 31.12.2013

Passive House Institute
Dr. Wolfgang Feist
64283 Darmstadt
GERMANY

Category: **Window Frame**
Manufacturer: **Munster Joinery**
Ballydesmond, Mallow, IRELAND
Product name: **PassiV Future Proof**

The following comfort criteria were used in awarding this certificate:

Given a U_g value of 0.70 W/(m²K) and a window size of 1.23 m by 1.48 m,

U_W = **0.78 W/(m²K) ≤ 0.80 W/(m²K)**

Taking into account the installation based thermal bridges, and provided that the installation is, with regard to the thermal bridges, equal or better than shown in the data sheet, the window meets the following criterion.

$U_{W,installed}$ **≤ 0.85 W/(m²K)**

Thermal data of the window frame

	U_f-value [W/(m²K)]	Width [mm]	Ψ_g [W/(mK)]	$f_{Rsi=0.25}$ [-]
Spacer			Superspacer TriSeal*	
Bottom	0.77	102	0.024	0.74
Side/top	0.77	102	0.024	

*Spacers of lower thermal quality, especially those made of aluminium, lead to significantly higher thermal losses and lower temperature factors.

Further information see data sheet

Passive House Efficiency Class

phA advanced component
phB basic component
phC certifiable component

phA
CERTIFIED COMPONENT
Passive House Institute

www.passivehouse.com **0064wi03**

24.12 Certified component: certificate for a window.

Certified components

Components such as windows, doors and ventilation units that are used in passive houses can be submitted for certification to the Passivhaus Institute in Germany. Each product submitted is subjected to rigorous tests to ensure it performs as designed. For example, a window will only be certified as installed in a particular wall buildup. So the certificate will include detailed installation drawings showing precisely how the window is to be installed on site to ensure optimal performance.

Certified components do not have to be used in the construction of a passive house. However, when uncertified products are used, the Passivhaus Institute will only allow 75% of the manufacturer's claimed energy performance when entering figures in the passive house planning package for certification. This is to guard against exaggerated claims by manufacturers.

Energy balance

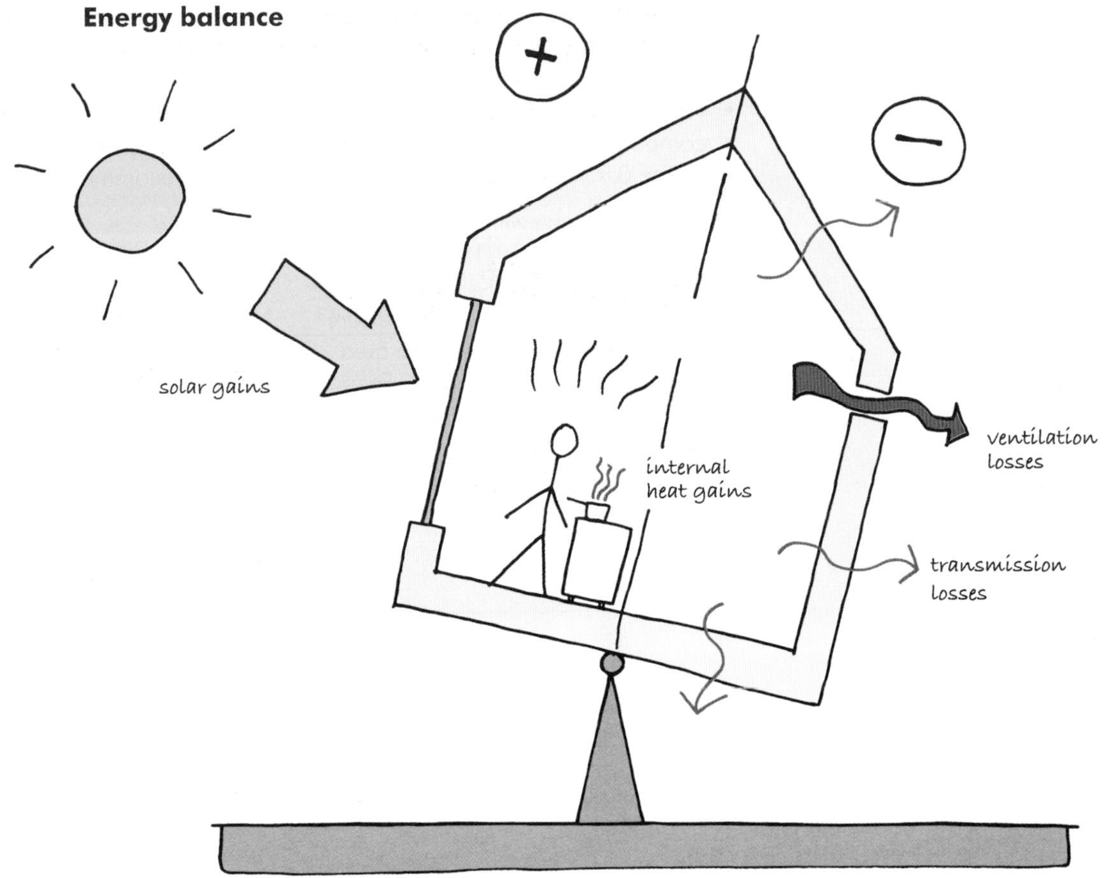

24.14 Energy balance: in cool climates the losses 'outweigh' the gains ... so we supply heat.

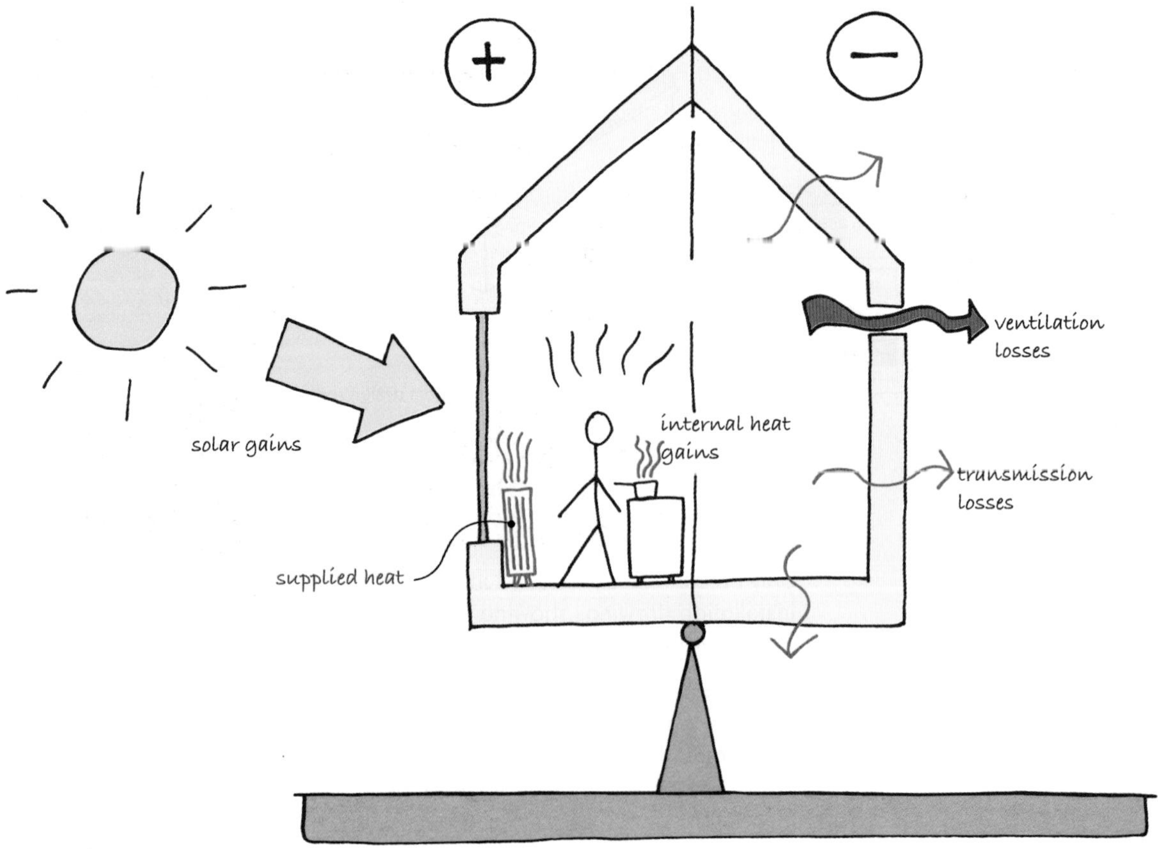

24.15 Energy balance: supplied heat brings the system into balance – the Passivhaus limit is 15 kWh/m^{2}a.

The law of energy conservation states that the sum of all heat losses must equal the sum of all heat gains. In a typical home energy is gained from the sun and from people and appliances inside the home. These are called 'solar heat gains' and 'internal heat gains'. Energy is lost through the building fabric and through air leaving the building. These are called 'transmission losses' and 'ventilation losses'. In cool climates the total losses exceed the total gains and the difference must be made up by the heating system so that the law of energy conservation is satisfied. In a Passivhaus, this heating demand is limited to 15 kWh/(m^2a).

KEY PRINCIPLES

Energy balance: in a cool climate (e.g. Ireland) the losses always outweigh the gains over the course of a year. Heat energy must be supplied to bring the system into balance – this is the space heating demand.

space heat demand = (transmission losses + ventilation losses) – (solar gains + internal heat gains)

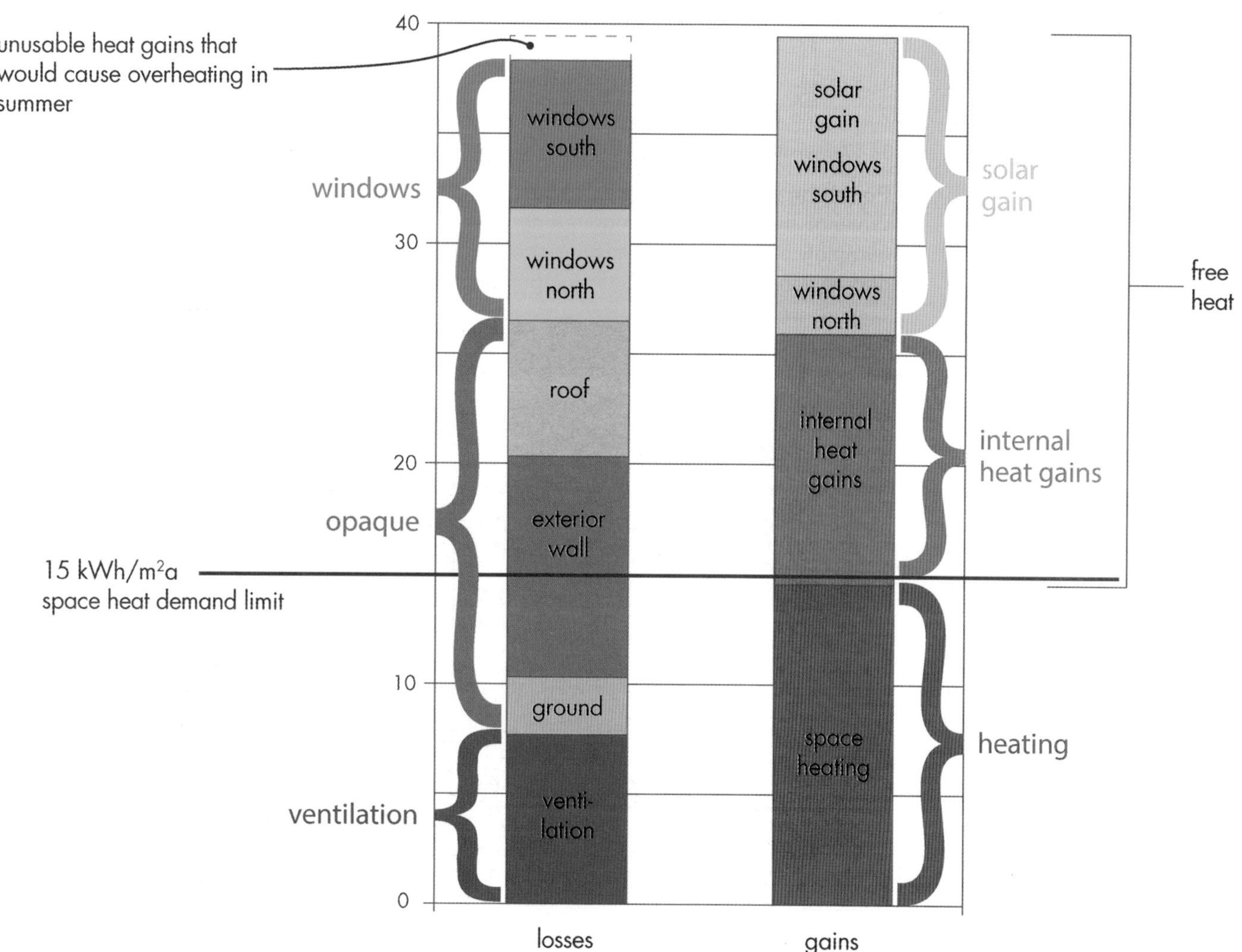

24.16 Energy balance: losses minus gains equal heating requirement.

24.17 Internal heat gains: the human body (core temperature 37°C) is constantly emitting heat energy.

Passivhaus planning package

While all the calculations required during the design phase of a Passivhaus project are completed automatically in the PHPP, it is important to have a basic understanding of what is being calculated and how this influences the design process.

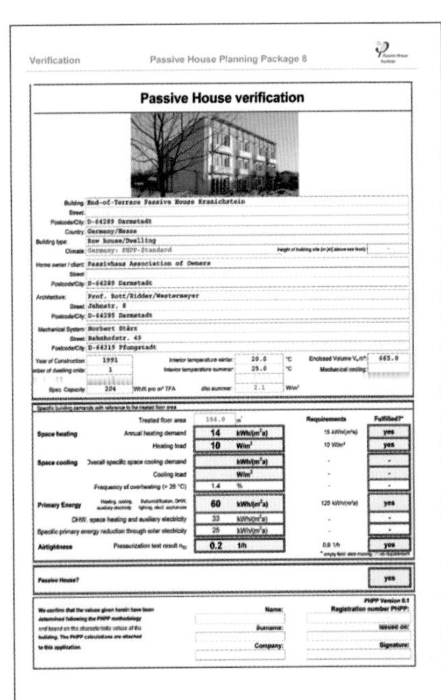

Verification — Passive House Planning Package 8

Passive House verification

Building: End-of-Terrace Passive House Kranichstein
Street:
Postcode/City: D-64289 Darmstadt
Country: Germany/Hesse
Building type: Row house/Dwelling
Climate: Germany: PHPP-Standard
Home owner / client: Passivhaus Association of Owners
Street:
Postcode/City: D-64289 Darmstadt
Architecture: Prof. Bott/Ridder/Westermeyer
Street: Jahnstr. 8
Postcode/City: D-64285 Darmstadt
Mechanical System: Norbert Stärz
Street: Bahnhofstr. 49
Postcode/City: D-64319 Pfungstadt
Year of Construction: 1991 — Interior temperature winter: 20.0 °C — Enclosed Volume V_e m³: 665.0
Number of dwelling units: 1 — Interior temperature summer: 25.0 °C — Mechanical cooling:
Spec. Capacity: 204 Wh/K per m² TFA — dito summer: 2.1 W/m²

Specific building demands with reference to the treated floor area

		Value	Unit	Requirements	Fulfilled?*
	Treated floor area	156.0	m²		
Space heating	Annual heating demand	14	kWh/(m²a)	15 kWh/(m²a)	yes
	Heating load	10	W/m²	10 W/m²	yes
Space cooling	Overall specific space cooling demand		kWh/(m²a)	-	-
	Cooling load		W/m²	-	-
	Frequency of overheating (> 25 °C)	1.4	%	-	-
Primary Energy	Heating, cooling, dehumidification, DHW, auxiliary electricity, lighting, electr. appliances	60	kWh/(m²a)	120 kWh/(m²a)	yes
	DHW, space heating and auxiliary electricity	33	kWh/(m²a)	-	-
	Specific primary energy reduction through solar electricity	25	kWh/(m²a)	-	-
Airtightness	Pressurization test result n_{50}	0.2	1/h	0.6 1/h	yes

Passive House? yes

We confirm that the values given herein have been determined following the PHPP methodology and based on the characteristic values of the building. The PHPP calculations are attached to this application.

Name: / Surname: / Company:
PHPP Version 8.1 — Registration number PHPP: / Issued on: / Signature:

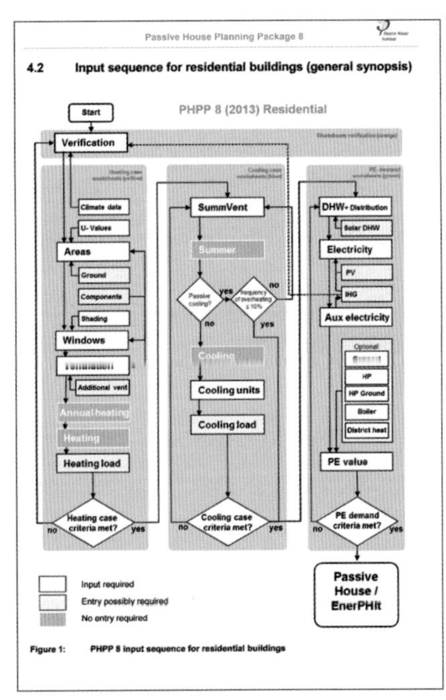

24.18 Passivhaus Planning Package (PHPP): summary page and workflow.

The PHPP allows a designer to calculate, during the design stage, the exact energy performance of the house. The designer has complete control over every aspect of the design and can accurately calculate how changes to the design will affect the energy performance of the home.

The information required for the PHPP is much more detailed than that required for DEAP. It is the greater amount and accuracy of the information used that makes the PHPP so much more accurate than DEAP. Practice has shown that the actual performance of a passive house in use in usually extremely close to the results calculated using the PHPP at the design stage.

When the PHPP process is complete the designer has several key indicators of energy performance, including space heating demand, heating load and primary energy demand.

KEY PRINCIPLES

The benefits of using the PHPP include:

- better design outcomes – the house design can be modified to optimise its energy efficiency
- different energy efficiency measures can be tested to establish which provide(s) the best result
- problems can be anticipated before they arise, which reduces costly errors on site
- changes to the design that are suggested on site can be tested to see what impact they might have on overall energy efficiency
- reduction in the amount of energy the home consumes
- reduction in CO_2 emissions.

REVISION EXERCISES

1 Explain the purpose of the building regulations.
2 Outline the improvement in energy and emissions standards that has occurred through revisions to TGD L.
3 Describe the requirement for renewable energy generation in TGD L and give one example of how this can be achieved.
4 Describe, using a neat annotated sketch, the seven principles of Passivhaus design.
5 Explain the concept of energy balance.

CHAPTER 25

Airtightness

In this chapter airtightness testing and calculations are discussed. This chapter should be read in conjunction with Chapter 11, which looked at airtightness standards, methods and materials. Airtightness and ventilation go hand in hand, so Chapter 26 on ventilation should also be read in conjunction with this chapter.

Airtightness is the term used to describe the measures taken to control the unwanted movement of air into and out of a building. The movement of air is classified as:

- **infiltration** – the unwanted movement of air from the outside to the inside of a building (traditionally referred to as a draught)
- **exfiltration** – the unwanted movement of air from the inside of a building to the outside (commonly called air leakage).

Airtightness standards

Achieving the airtightness requirement for the building regulations is reasonably straightforward because it is a low standard. However, achieving the airtightness requirement for the Passivhaus standard is extremely challenging because it is a very high standard. When all the tiny air leaks in a typical Passivhaus are added up they would usually be the equivalent of a hole that could be covered with the palm of one hand. Getting to this level of airtightness is usually the hardest part of any building project that is aiming for Passivhaus certification.

It is important to note the difference in the units used to describe airtightness in both standards. In the building regulations the rate of air leakage is expressed per square metre of floor area; in the Passivhaus standard it is expressed as a fraction of air volume per hour. This means that a direct comparison cannot be made; a calculation (like that shown below) must be completed.

The real difference between the building regulations and Passivhaus airtightness standard can be seen when a typical 150m^2 home is used as an example:

- building regulations: < 7m^3/h.m^2 @50Pa
  - acceptable air leakage is 150 x 7 =1,050 m^3/h
- Passivhaus standard: < 0.6 air changes per hour @50Pa
  - acceptable air leakage is 150 x 2.4m ceiling height x 0.6 = 216 m^3/h.

In this example, the acceptable air leakage rate of a house built to the building regulations is almost five times higher than an equivalent house built to the Passivhaus standard.

Airtightness and energy loss

Airtightness is important because when warm air leaks out of a building it takes heat energy with it. The extent of the heat loss depends on the volume of air leakage and the temperature difference between indoors and outside. The amount of heat energy that air can hold is described as its specific heat capacity. The specific heat capacity of air is 0.33 Wh/(m^{3}K) (at normal pressure and a temperature of approximately 21°C).

Taking the 150m^2 home from the example above, and assuming an outdoor temperature of 10°C, the amount of heat energy lost per hour from each house can be calculated as:

heat loss per hour = V x Cpρ x Δt

where:

V = air leakage volume
Cpρ = heat capacity of air – the amount of heat that air can hold (0.33 Wh/m^{3}K)
Δt = temperature difference

House built to building regulations standard:

heat loss per hour	= V x cpρ x Δt
	= 1,050 x 0.33 x 11
	= 3,811.5Wh
	= 3.81 kWh
heat loss per annum	= 3.81 x 24 x 365
	= 33.4 MWh

Passive house standard:

heat loss per hour	= V x cpρ x Δt
	= 216 x 0.33 x 11
	= 784.1 Wh
	= 0.78 kWh
heat loss per annum	= 0.78 x 24 x 365
	= 6.8 MWh

ACTIVITIES

Check the living room of your home for airtightness. On a cold night, close the internal doors and go around the room, wall by wall, and feel for air movement at the following locations:

- wall–floor junction (external walls)
- wall–window junction (around the frame)
- window sash–casement frame junction (where the opening part of the window meets the frame)
- wall vents.

Permeability testing

From this calculation it is clear that for an average size house, under similar conditions, the rate of energy lost through air leakage is almost five times greater in the house built to the building regulations standard than the house built to Passivhaus standard.

Once the airtightness layer is in place a test is carried out to check for leaks. This test is called a permeability test – also known as the blower door test. The idea behind the test is to simulate a windy day and determine how the airtightness layer will perform under these conditions.

A large fan is installed in a door or window. When the fan is running it changes the air pressure inside the building to levels that correspond to a dynamic pressure on the windward side of a house at wind speeds of 4–10 m/s (i.e. 15–35 km/h), i.e. equivalent to a very windy day.

The speed of the fan is gradually increased so that the pressure difference between inside and outside rises to around 60Pa (pascal). The performance of the airtightness layer is noted at exactly 50Pa. Based on the volume of the building, the computer software controlling the fan determines the leakage rate by measuring the flow rate supplied by the fan.

25.01 Permeability testing is carried out to simulate a windy day.

Procedure

Despite the fact that the test is commonly referred to as the 'blower door test', it is best carried out by installing the fan in a window so that the door is included in the test. Doors are generally harder to make airtight than windows and so are more likely to be a source of leaks.

25.02 Permeability testing: fan installed in doorway.

25.03 Blower door test: the screen bulges outward as the air pressure inside the home increases.

The test is quite straightforward to carry out.

1 Check that the weather is suitable for the test: wind speed below 6m/s or 3 on the Beaufort scale.
2 Temporarily seal all fans, flues, chimneys, vents, etc. with airtight membrane/tape.
3 Install the door blower fan in a window or the doorway of the principal entrance to the dwelling.
4 Connect the fan to the control unit and laptop computer.
5 Input the required data into the software.
6 Run the fan.
7 Record the results: at least five readings must be taken at different pressure points of no more than 10Pa differences, e.g. 10Pa, 20Pa, 30Pa, 40Pa, 50Pa, 60Pa.
8 Carry out the test for pressurisation and depressurisation.

The result is called the 'air change rate' and is stated in air changes per hour (ACH); for example, 0.6ACH or simply 0.6/h or $0.6h^{-1}$ means that 0.6 of the air volume in the building leaks per hour.

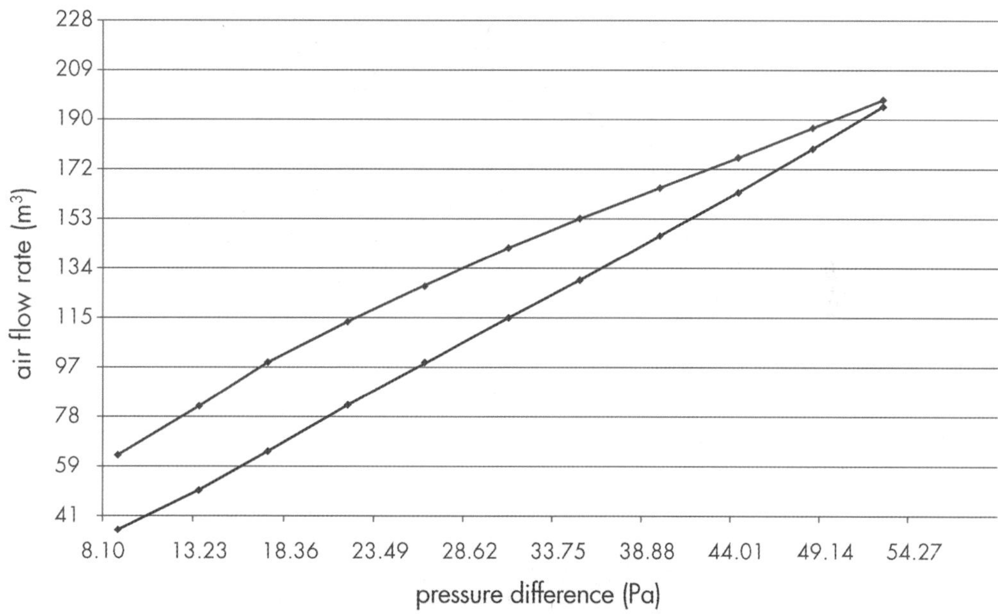

25.04 Permeability testing: a graph showing the results of the pressurisation (red) and depressurisation (blue) tests. Note: the air flow rate is relative to the volume of the building.

The test is carried out twice – once for pressurisation and once for depressurisation – for the following reasons:

- to test the airtightness layer by simulating the pressure and suction of the wind blowing on the dwelling from different directions
- to test that the window and door seals perform adequately in both directions: for example, the seals of an inward opening would be 'helped' during a pressurisation test when the air pressure pushes the casement against the frame; however, under a depressurisation test the seals would be truly tested.

Checking for leaks

During the test, if the results are above 0.6 air changes per hour (for Passivhaus standard) the leaks have to be found and sealed. This can be done using several methods:

- smoke taper
- thermal imaging
- anemometer.

Once any leaks have been sealed the test is repeated.

25.05 Finding leaks: thermal imaging highlights cold surfaces caused by air movement – this works best in cold weather.

25.07 Finding leaks: a smoke taper highlights air movement.

25.06 Finding leaks: an anemometer gives a precise reading of air movement speed.

Calculations

The number of air changes per hour (at 50Pa) can be calculated by dividing the measured air flow rate by the net interior air volume using the formula:

$$n_{50} = \frac{V_{50}}{V_{air}}$$

Worked example

Given the following data, calculate the air change rate.

- net air volume, V_{air}: 702 m^3
- air flow rate @50Pa: 184 m^3/h

Calculate air change rate:

$$n_{50} = \frac{V_{50}}{V_{air}}$$

$$n_{50} = \frac{184\ m^3}{700\ m^3/h}$$

$$n_{50} = 0.26\ /h$$

Worked example

This formula can also be used to calculate the maximum permitted air change rate.

Given the following data, calculate the maximum permitted air change rate so that the limit of $0.6h^{-1}$ is not exceeded.

- net air volume,
  V_{air}: 450 m^3
  $n_{50} = 0.6h^{-1}$
  $n_{50} = \frac{V_{50}}{V_{air}}$

therefore:

$V_{50} = V_{air} \times n_{50}$

$V_{air} = 450 \times 0.6$

$V_{air} = 270m^3$

Worked example

The equivalent air leakage area is the area that would result if all of the tiny leaks throughout the structure were added up to form one single hole. It can be calculated using the formula:

$$\text{leakage area} = \frac{V_{50}\ (m^3/h)}{0.02\ (m^3/h.mm^2)}$$

Given the following data, calculate the equivalent air leakage area from the house.

- $V_{50} = 224m^3$

$$\text{leakage area} = \frac{V_{50}\ (m^3/h)}{0.02\ (m^3/h.mm^2)}$$

$$\text{leakage area} = \frac{224\ (m^3)}{0.02\ (m^3/h.mm^2)}$$

leakage area $= 11{,}200mm^2$ (or a square of side 106mm)

REVISION EXERCISES

1 Explain why it is essential to make a building airtight.
2 Compare the standards for airtightness in TGD L and the Passivhaus standard.
3 Describe the test used to determine the airtightness performance of a building.
4 Compare the heat loss per annum from a house of floor area $120m^2$:
(a) built to TGD L standard – airtightness result: $6.2m^3/h.m^2$ @50Pa
(b) built to Passivhaus standard – airtightness result: 0.54 air changes per hour @50Pa: assume 2.5m ceiling height.
5 Calculate the equivalent leakage area for both of the houses in question 4.

CHAPTER 26

Ventilation

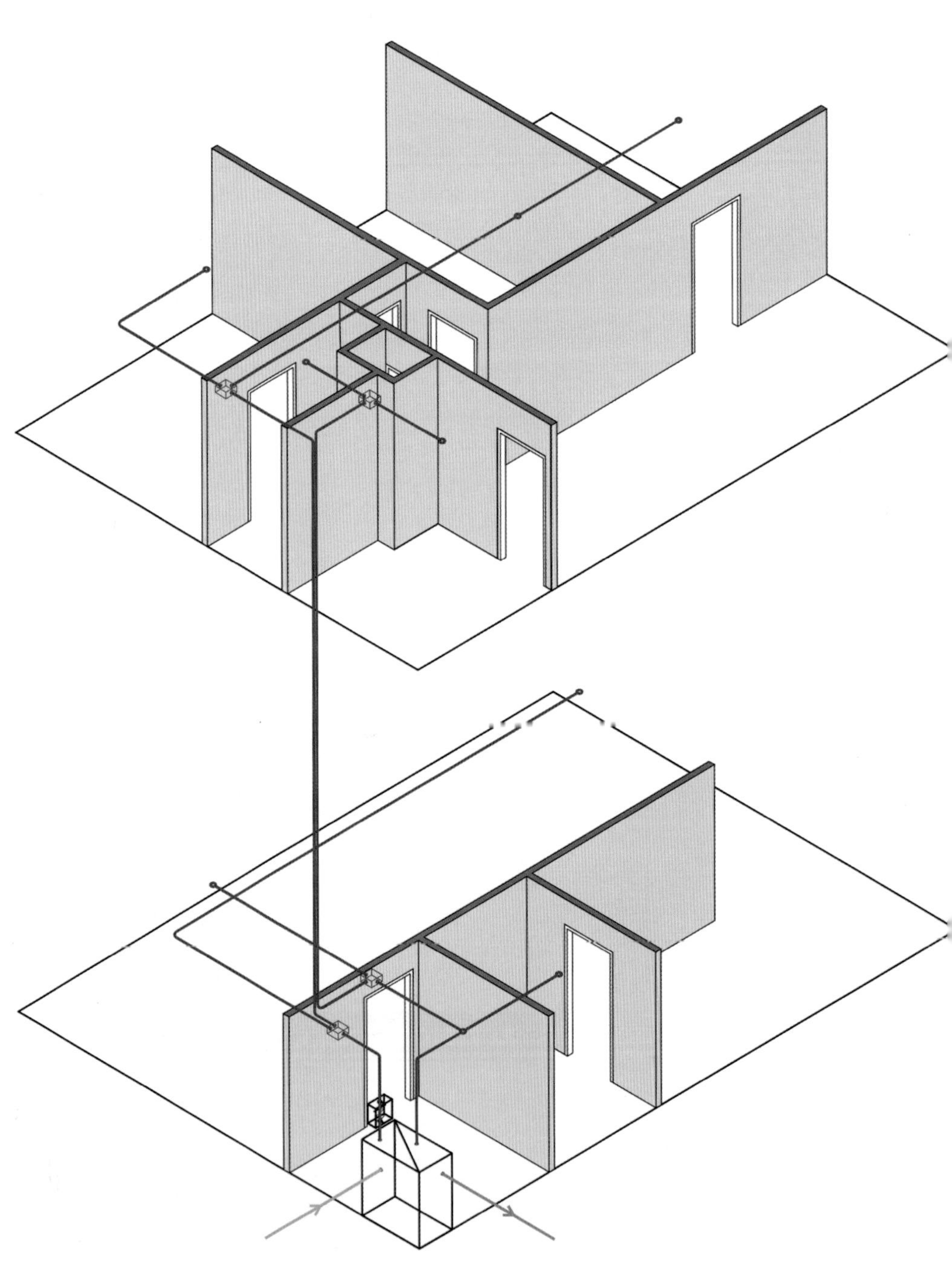

Ventilation is the term used to describe the measures taken to ensure that the home has a constant supply of fresh clean air. Ventilation and airtightness go hand in hand, so the previous chapter on airtightness should be read in conjunction with this chapter.

Ventilation control

There are two design approaches to ventilation:

1 **controlled** – an airtight building with a mechanical ventilation system that provides a constant supply of fresh air

2 **uncontrolled** – a non-airtight building that relies on a combination of air leakage and ventilation holes in the structure to provide a 'background' supply of fresh air plus window openings to provide rapid or 'purge' ventilation.

The fundamental difference between the two approaches is that a controlled system is carefully designed to ensure that a good standard of indoor air quality is always maintained. The level of ventilation and indoor air quality provided by an uncontrolled system depends on the weather and the temperature difference between indoors and outdoors.

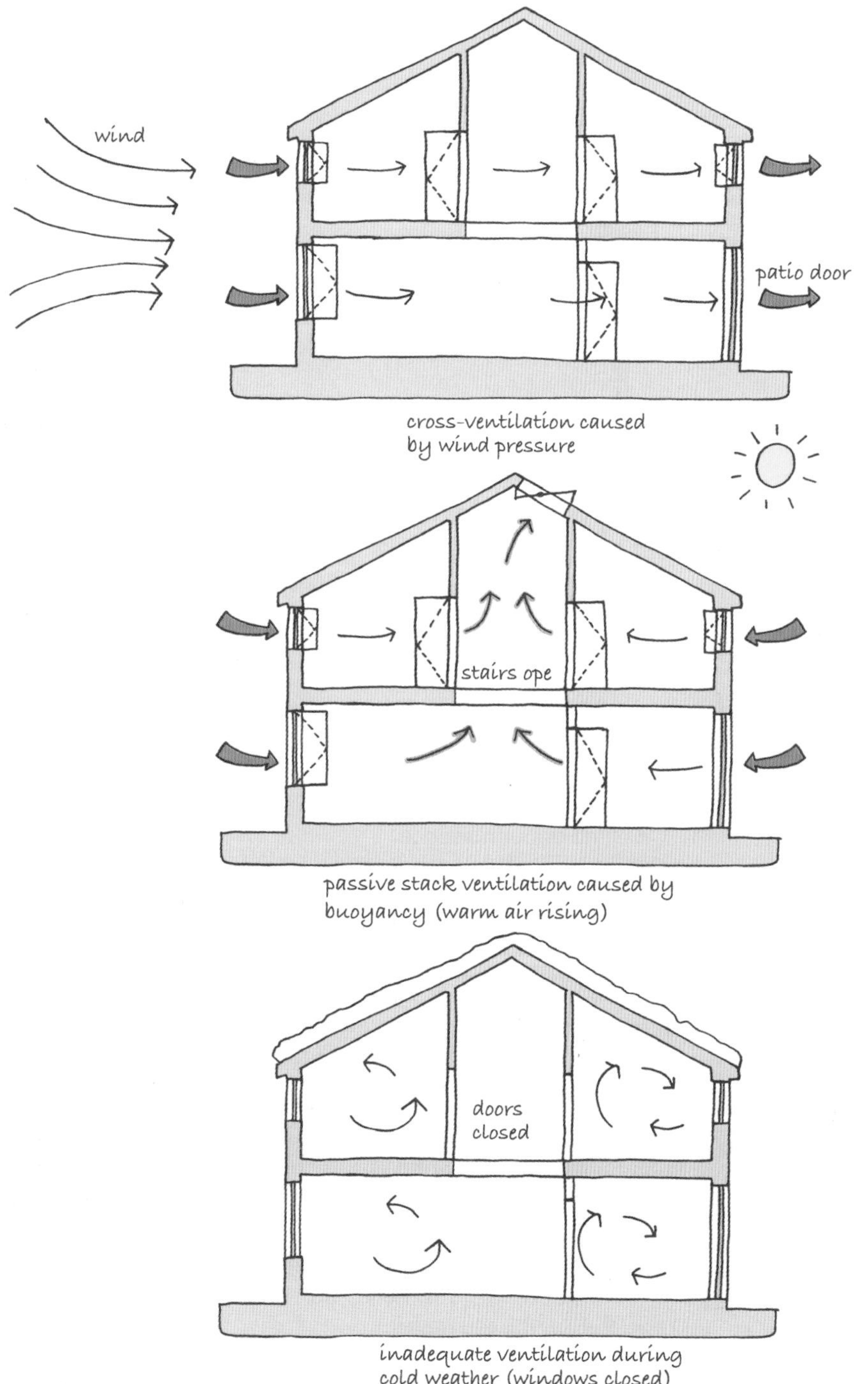

26.01 Ventilation: uncontrolled ventilation provides an unreliable level of indoor air quality and leads to significant heat energy losses.

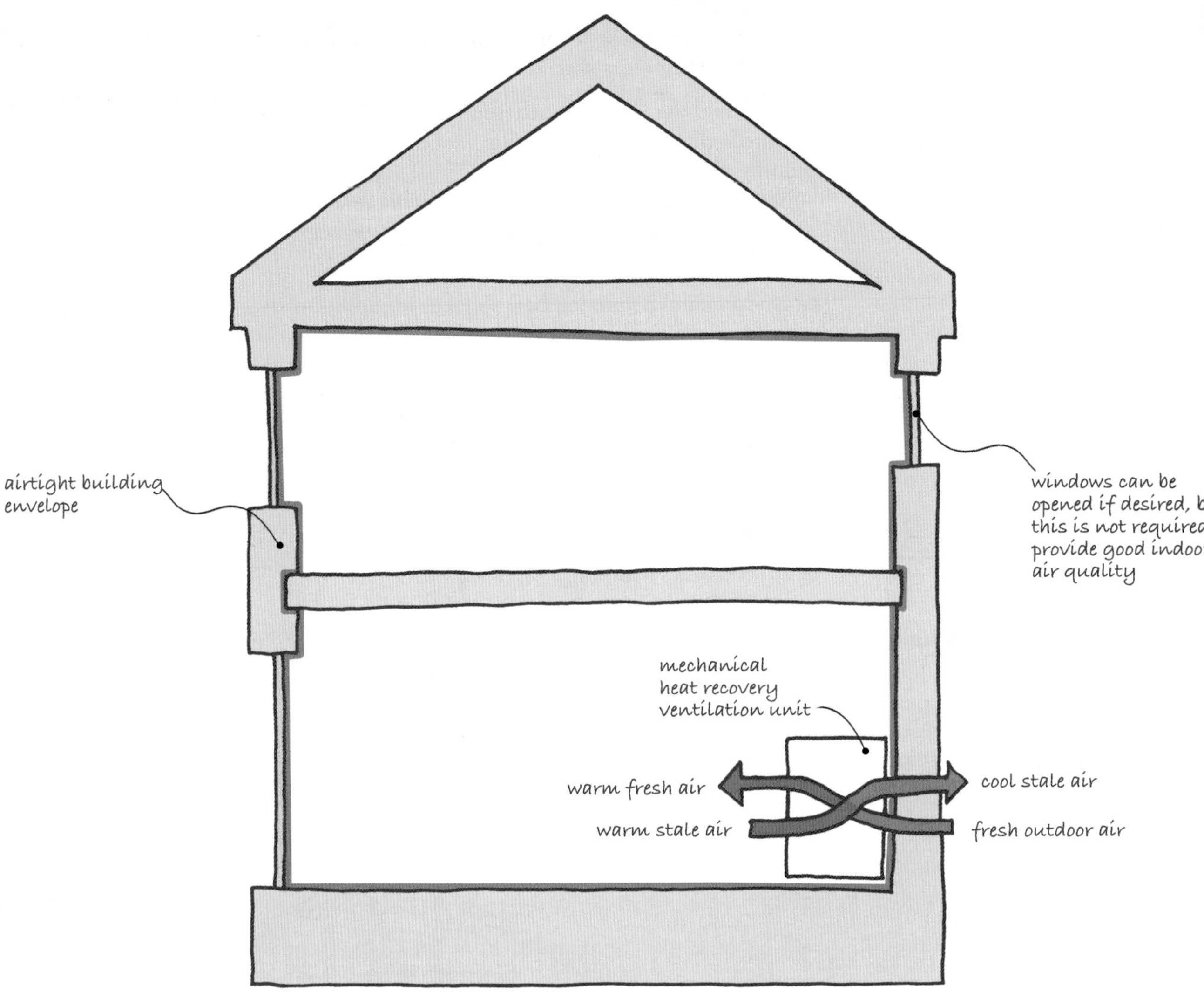

26.02 Controlled ventilation: an airtight building with mechanical heat recovery ventilation.

Function of ventilation

Ventilation performs several important roles:

1 primary functions – renewal of indoor air:
- limit humidity/prevent mould growth
- avoid concentration and build-up of pollutants
- limit odour nuisance.

2 secondary functions – conditioning the indoor air:
- cleaning (filters)
- heating/cooling
- humidification/dehumidification.

3 tertiary functions – passive heat recovery:
- reduction of ventilation heat losses
- increase in comfort due to higher supply air temperatures.

Air quality

Air quality is fundamental to human health. The ventilation system must ensure a reliable supply of high quality indoor air and ensure that the following gases are not present above the safe limit.

1 Water vapour:
- if the air is too dry:
  - the mucous membranes of the upper respiratory tract dry up
  - household dust builds up.
- if the air is too moist:
  - condensation on indoor surfaces
  - mould growth
  - dust mites multiply.

2 Carbon dioxide:
- colourless and odourless at low concentrations; has a sharp acidic odour at higher concentrations
- humans are the main indoor source of carbon dioxide – the more people present in an indoor space, the more quickly CO_2 levels will increase and oxygen levels will decrease
- high levels indoors may cause occupants to grow drowsy, get headaches, or function at lower activity levels
- outdoor air contains approximately 0.35–0.4% (i.e. less than half of one per cent)
- carbon dioxide in indoor air should not exceed 1.0%.

3 Carbon monoxide:
- colourless, odourless, tasteless, highly toxic (above 0.67% can be fatal)
- produced by burning fossil fuels (e.g. boilers).

4 Nitrogen-based gases (N_20, NO, NO_2) – in high concentrations cause lung damage.

5 Formaldehyde vapours – cause impairment of the eyes and upper respiratory tract (above 100 micrograms/m^3).

6 Radon:
- radioactive particles adhere to dust particles in the air and are inhaled
- causes lung cancer
- level should not exceed 200Bq/m^3.

Air change rate

Controlling the rate of air flow is essential to energy conservation and comfort. It is important that there are no draughts or air movement that would have a cooling effect on the people indoors. There is a significant difference between the requirements for ventilation under the building regulations and the Passivhaus standard.

Building regulations air change rates

TGD F (2009) states that for a typical dwelling (where the air permeability is above 5m^3/h.m^2), ventilation is provided in two ways:

1 background ventilation – wall vents that are always open.

2 purge ventilation – windows and doors that can be opened to provide high levels of short-term or 'purge' ventilation.

The requirement is:
- habitable rooms (living rooms, bedrooms, etc.):
  - background ventilation – vent opening with cross-sectional area 5,000mm^2
  - purge ventilation – 5% of the floor area.
- kitchen:
  - background ventilation – vent opening with cross-sectional area 2,500mm^2
  - purge ventilation – 30 litres/second extractor fan in cooker hood.
- utility room:
  - background ventilation – vent opening with cross-sectional area 2,500mm^2
  - purge ventilation – 30 litres/second extractor fan.
- bathroom:
  - background ventilation – vent opening with cross-sectional area 2,500mm^2
  - purge ventilation – 15 litres/second extractor fan.
- toilet (no bath/shower):
  - background ventilation – vent opening with cross-sectional area 2,500mm^2
  - purge ventilation – 6 litres/second extractor fan.

Passivhaus standard air change rates

The rate of air change in a Passivhaus must meet three criteria:

1 supply requirement:
- $30m^3$/hour/person of fresh air must be supplied (to the whole house – not to each room).

2 extract requirement:
- kitchen – $60m^3$/hour
- bathroom – $40m^3$/hour
- toilet/store/utility/en suite bathroom – $20m^3$/hour.

3 air change requirement:
- the system must be balanced for the entire dwelling to ensure that a minimum rate of 0.3 air changes per hour is achieved.

When determining the actual air change rate the air change requirement must be met. There is some flexibility in relation to the supply and extract requirements; these can be relaxed by approximately one-third if required. Over-supply, especially during winter in smaller households (i.e. fewer people), can cause the humidity level to drop to uncomfortable levels.

Worked example

Calculate the ventilation rate required to ensure indoor air quality in a home designed for four people, with a floor area of $120m^2$. The home has 4 habitable rooms, 1 kitchen and 1 bathroom. Assume a ceiling height of 2.5m:

- supply requirement: 4 people x 30 m^3/h/person = 120 m^3/h
- extract requirement: 60 (kitchen) + 40 (bathroom) = 100 m^3/h
- air change requirement: 0.30/h x 120 m^2 x 2.5m = 64 m^3/h.

The minimum ventilation rate for this dwelling is 120 m^3/h.

ACTIVITIES

Compare the ventilation requirements for a kitchen under both standards (building regulations standard and Passivhaus standard). Discuss the difference and consider why this is the case.

SUPPLEMENTARY INFORMATION

If the same dwelling were to be designed for two people the supply requirement would be:
- supply requirement: 2 people x 30 m^3/h/p = 60 m^3/h

In this scenario the extract requirement is now greatest at 100 m^3/h. This is the maximum level of extract required during meal preparation, so it is acceptable to design the system so that this level of extraction is achieved when the ventilation unit is in boost mode. Boost mode is normal performance plus 30%.
- extract requirement: 60 + 40 = 100 m^3/h = 130% of normal performance
- extract requirement: 100/130 x 100 = $77m^3$/h

Comparing the ventilation requirements, the values are:
- supply = $60m^3$/h
- extract = $77m^3$/h
- air change requirement = $64m^3$/h

So the minimum ventilation rate for the dwelling when designed for two people is $77m^3$/h.

Mechanical heat recovery ventilation

Mechanical heat recovery ventilation (MHRV) is the term used to describe a controlled ventilation system in which air is pumped into and out of the building, combined with a system that transfers heat energy from the stale air leaving the building to the fresh air entering the building. This type of system only works efficiently in an airtight building.

In a controlled ventilation system the incoming air can be heated to maintain a comfortable indoor air temperature. This is, in fact, the technical definition of a Passivhaus – a home in which a comfortable indoor temperature can be maintained solely by heating the air that is being supplied to maintain indoor air quality.

The heat is added in two steps:
- heat exchange – heat is transferred from the warm stale air leaving the building to the cooler incoming fresh air
- post heating (optional) – the incoming fresh air passes over a heating element.

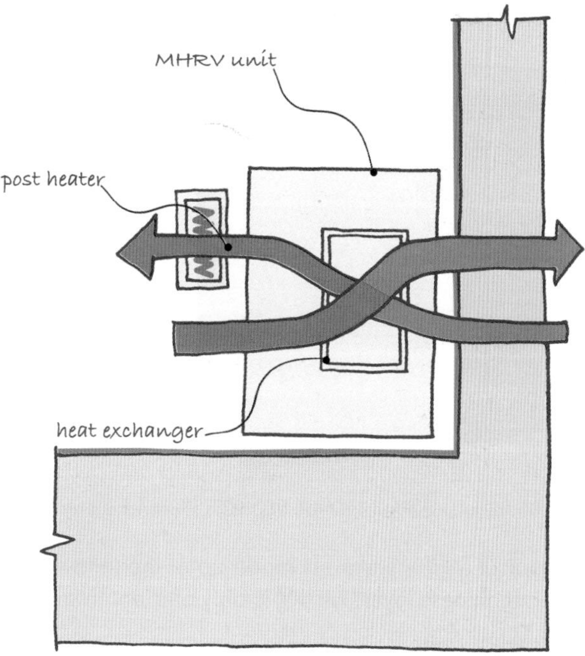

26.03 Heating the fresh air: heat exchange plus post heating.

The heating requirement doesn't have to be met by heating the air – it just has to be theoretically possible. In practice, many designers/home owners choose to supply this heat using wood-burning stoves or electrical radiators in bathrooms or by other methods.

MHRV system design

The principal concept of MHRV is to provide a constant gentle flow of warm air to living spaces (e.g. living rooms/bedrooms) while extracting warm moist air from kitchens, utility rooms, toilets and bathrooms. When designing a home it is best to try to group the extract rooms together. This improves the energy efficiency of the system and reduces the length of ducting required.

MHRV system balance

From a whole house perspective, the amount of air supplied should equal the amount of air extracted so that the system is in balance. The rooms receiving a fresh supply of air are usually larger than the extract rooms. This is helpful because it means that the rate of extraction is greater in the smaller rooms because the same volume of air is being removed from a smaller space.

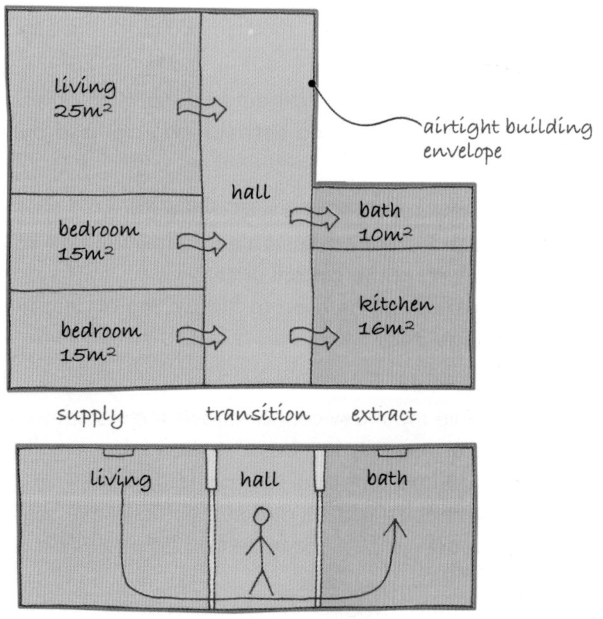

26.04 MHRV: system balance – when total supply volume equals total extract, the rate of extract volume is higher than the rate of supply because the extract rooms are generally smaller than the supply rooms.

MHRV system components

26.05 MHRV unit (PAUL NOVUS 300:93% effective heat recovery rate, electricity consumption: 0.23Wh/m³).

A typical MHRV system is made up of the following components.

- airtightness layer: MHRV is only efficient in an airtight building.
- MHRV unit:
  - two fans – supply and extract
  - heat exchange module
  - filters:
    - supply filter – fine particle filter that captures dust, pollen and other suspended particles
    - exhaust filter – coarse particle filter that captures household dust, odours, etc.
    - kitchen filter – the exhaust inlet in the kitchen has a grease filter.
  - frost protection – a small heating element that ensures the outdoor air entering the system is never below 0°C
  - post heater (optional) – heating element to warm the supply air (supply ducting should be insulated)
  - condensate drain – when warm extract air cools as it passes through the heat exchanger it releases moisture.
- ducting:
  - supply ducting – delivers fresh air from the MHRV unit to the living spaces
  - extract ducting – removes stale air from the kitchen, utility, bathrooms
  - exhaust ducting – transfers stale air from the MHRV unit to the outside
  - outdoor air ducting – transfers fresh air from outside to the MHRV unit.
- silencer:
  - between first supply/extract and the MHRV unit
  - on the supply ducting between bedrooms to prevent 'cross talk'.
- diffusers:
  - the 'vent covers' at the end of the ducts
  - these are usually adjustable to allow the flow rate to be controlled and to facilitate the balancing of the overall system
  - jet nozzles can be used to 'throw' the air into the centre of the room (see 'Coanda effect' on page 345).
- control panel:
  - a simple input device that allows the system to be controlled
  - there are usually five basic settings:
    - standard – normal air flow rates
    - set back – a 30% reduced air flow rate (e.g. used when most of the occupants are away)
    - boost – a 30% increased air flow rate (e.g. used when cooking or when having lots of visitors)
    - summer bypass – used to bypass the heat exchanger during the summer months (in practice this can be up to nine months of the year)
    - off – nobody at home for several days.

Counter flow heat exchanger

25.06 MHRV system: heat exchange module.

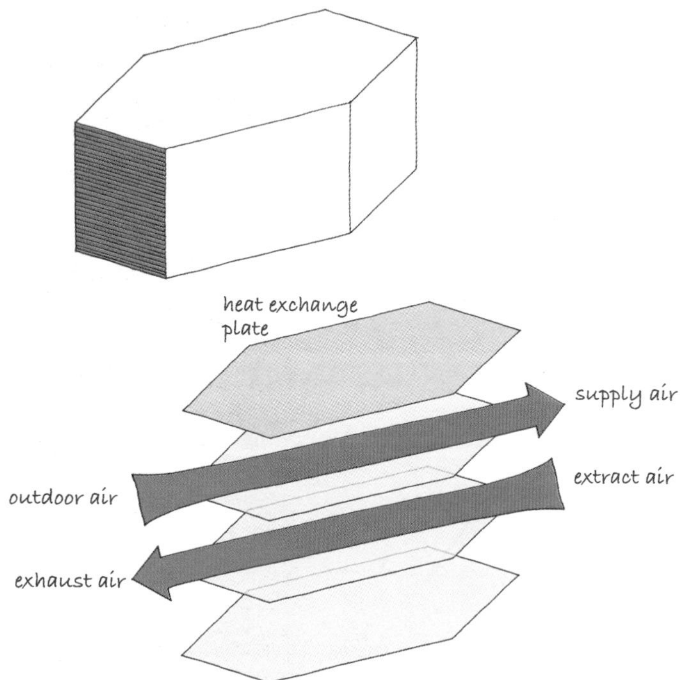

26.07 Heat exchange unit: counter flow plate heat exchangers.

The heat exchanger is where the heat energy is transferred from the warm stale extract air to the cool fresh outdoor air as it is drawn into the system. This is actually a surprisingly 'low-tech' device. It consists of a series of evenly spaced plates, which are commonly made from very thin plastic material.

The warm stale air passes on one side of the plate; the cool fresh air passes on the other side travelling in the opposite direction. The heat energy is conducted through the very thin plates and is transferred from the warm stale air to the cool fresh air. The two bodies of air do not mix as they pass on opposite sides of each plate. This type of unit can typically recover over 80% of the heat energy.

More advanced heat exchangers have a honeycombed or cellular structure instead of plates. This creates more surface area for the heat exchange to take place. This type of unit can typically recover over 90% of the heat energy.

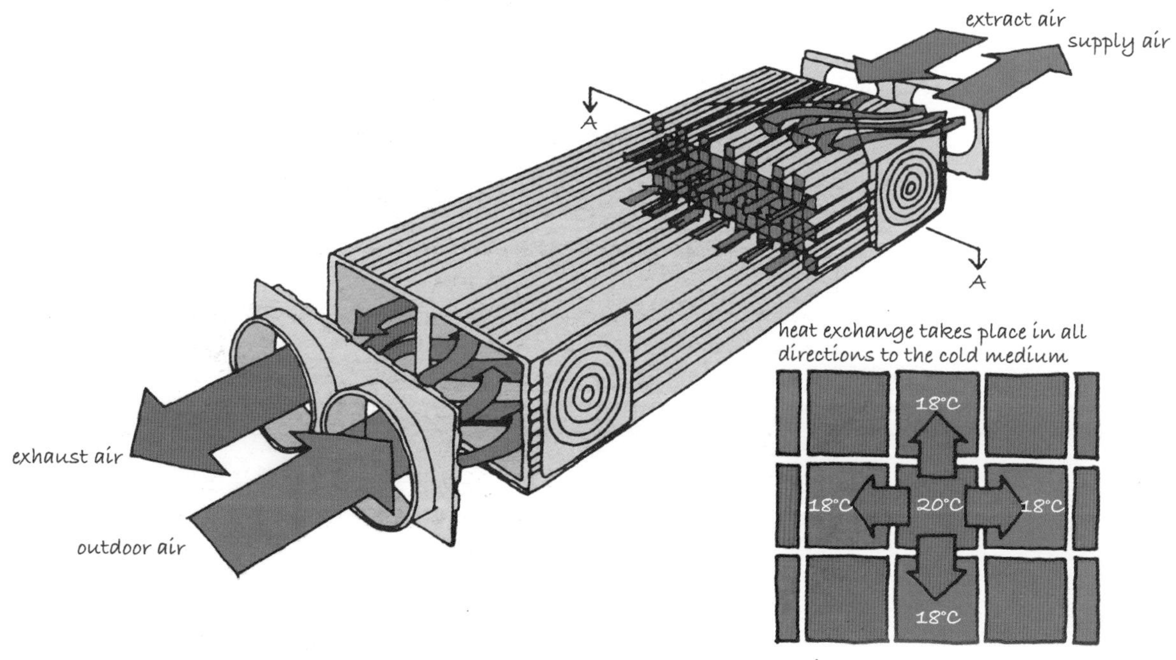

26.08 Heat exchange unit: counter flow cellular heat exchangers.

Summer bypass

In the mild Irish climate it is usually only necessary to recover the heat from the exhaust air during the three coldest months of the year. The solar and internal heat gains are usually adequate to maintain a comfortable indoor temperature of 20°C for the other nine months of the year.

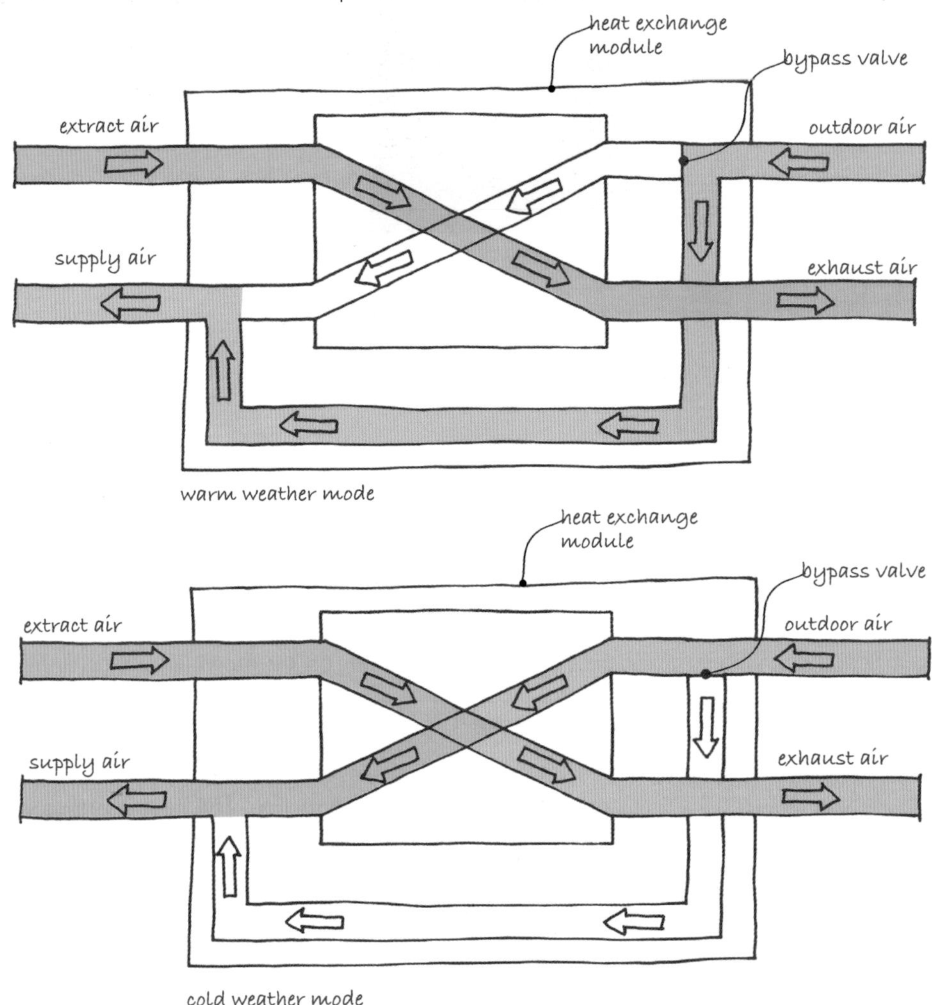

26.09 Heat recovery: during the summer a bypass valve redirects the outdoor air so it bypasses the heat exchange module.

This is managed automatically by the mechanical heat recovery ventilation unit. The outdoor and indoor air temperatures are monitored by temperature sensors connected to the controller in the unit and when the indoor temperature is greater than the outdoor air temperature the unit switches to bypass mode. This diverts the outdoor air intake so that it does not pass through the heat exchange module.

Summer bypass is an important feature of an MHRV system. It helps to cool the building and prevent overheating.

Coanda effect

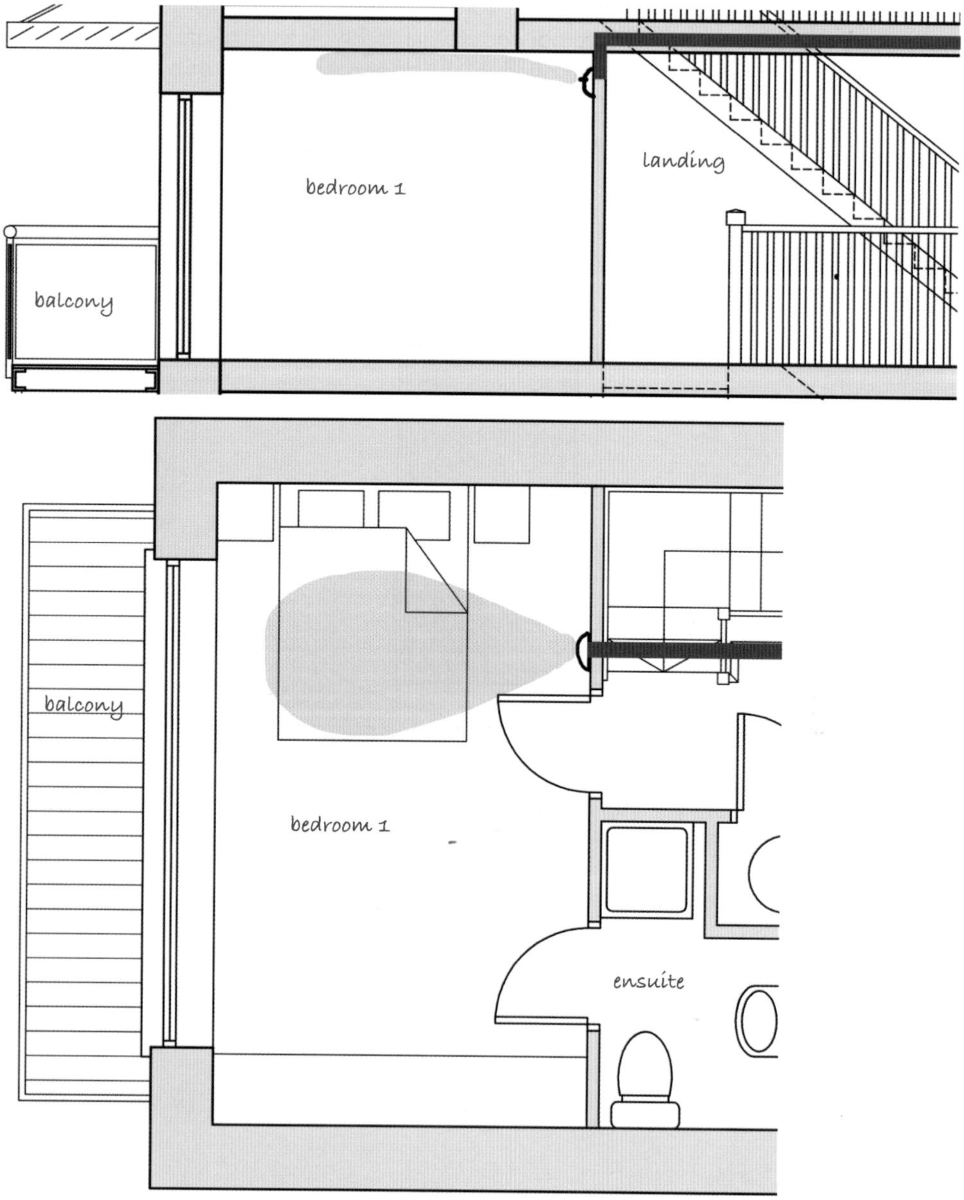

26.10 Coanda effect: the tendency of a stream of air to 'stick' to the ceiling carries the fresh air stream deep into the room.

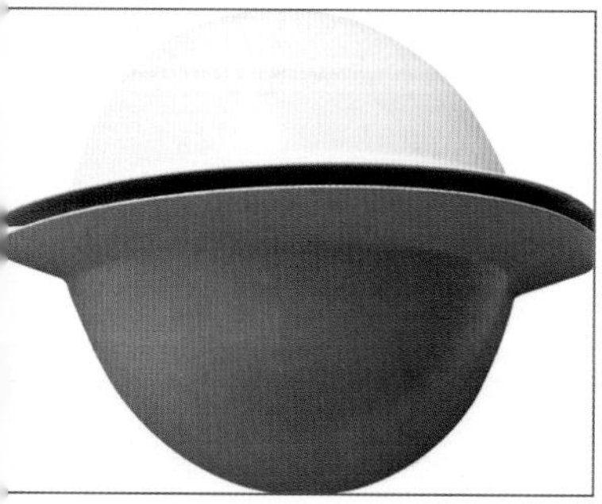

26.11 Linear or slot diffuser maximises the Coanda effect.

The Coanda effect is the tendency of a stream of air to be attracted to a nearby surface. It effectively causes air discharged from the diffuser to 'stick' to the ceiling and travel further before dropping.

Linear or slot diffusers create a greater length of contact with the ceiling and so provide a greater Coanda effect. Using the Coanda effect means that instead of running a duct into the centre of the ceiling it can be terminated at the wall. The Coanda effect is then used to 'throw' the air into the centre of the room.

Transferred air

Hallways and landings are neither supply nor extract zones. They are transition zones where the air moves from a supply zone to an extract zone. To facilitate this, there must be clearance at each internal door to allow the air to circulate freely. This can be achieved by leaving a gap between the bottom of the door and the floor or by using hidden door head vents.

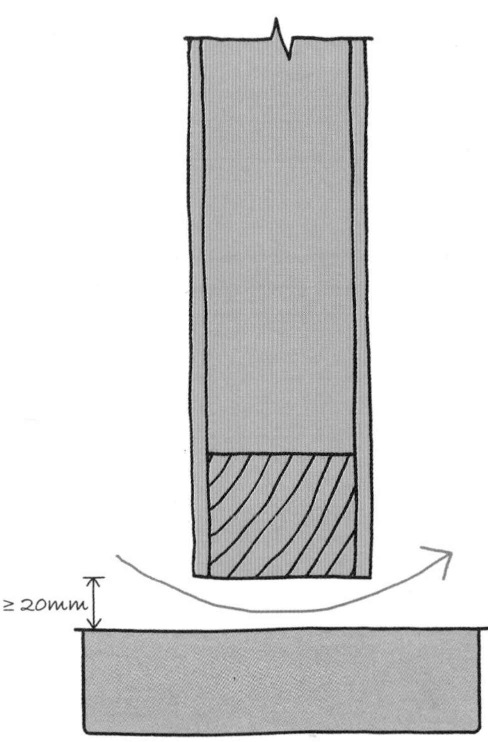

26.12 Transition zone door clearance: a clear gap of at least 20mm is required.

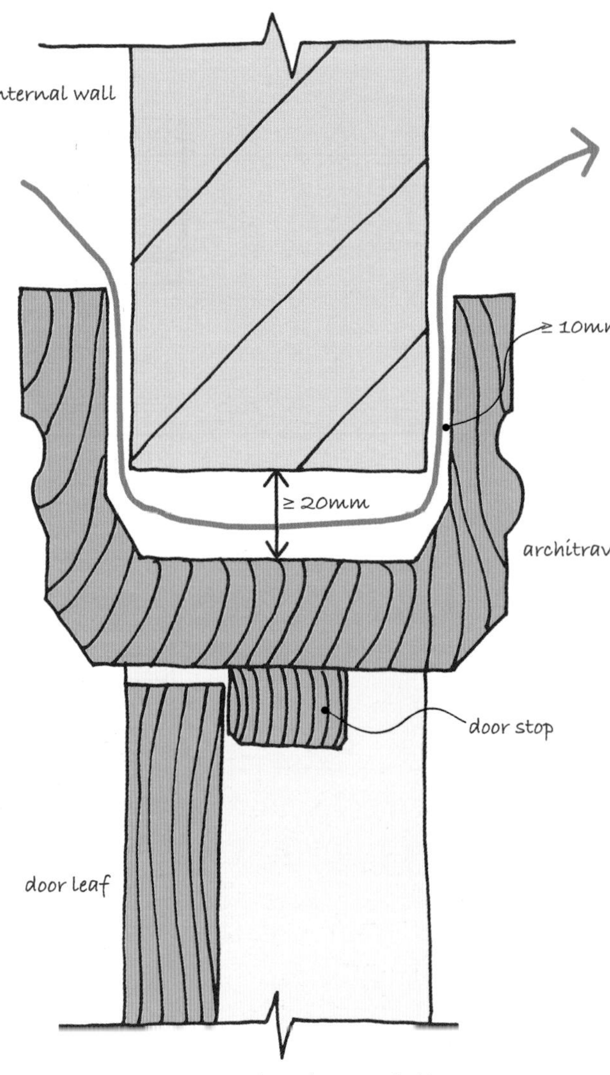

26.13 Transition zone door clearance: hidden ventilation gap in the door architrave at the door head.

ACTIVITIES

Redesign the MHRV ducting layouts shown in the two-storey house floor plans so as to optimise the use of the Coanda effect and reduce the length of ducting required.

System layout

MHRV systems do not limit the design of a home in any way. However, the following guidelines optimise system efficiency and reduce installation time and cost:

- locate the MHRV unit in an accessible location –
  - for ease of maintenance (e.g. changing filters)
  - avoid attic spaces.
- install the MHRV unit on an external wall –
  - this shortens the length of outdoor air and exhaust ducts
  - these ducts should be insulated to minimise heat energy loss.
- group extract rooms close together –
  - this shortens the length of extract ducts
- use the Coanda effect to shorten the length of ducts.

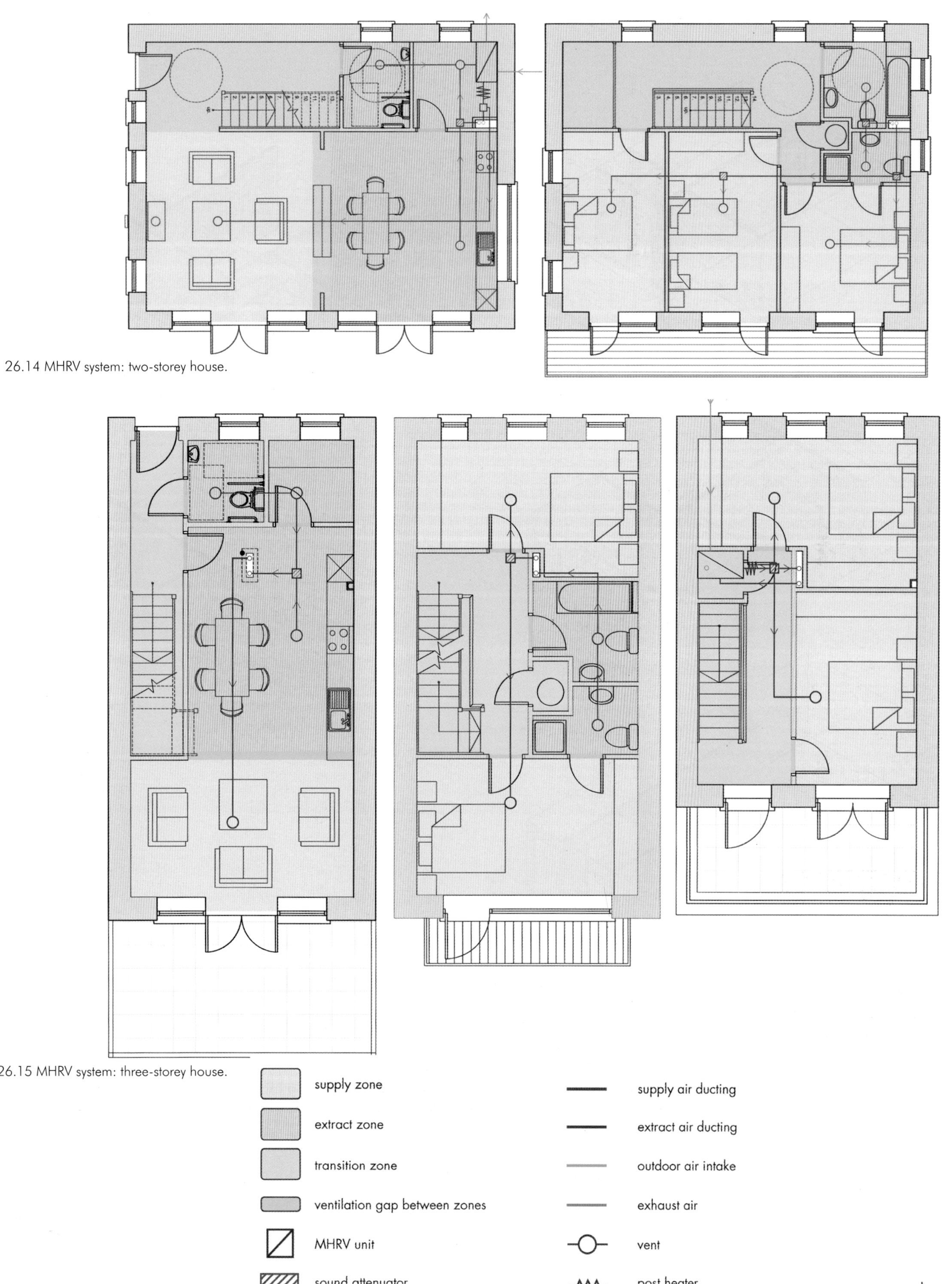

26.14 MHRV system: two-storey house.

26.15 MHRV system: three-storey house.

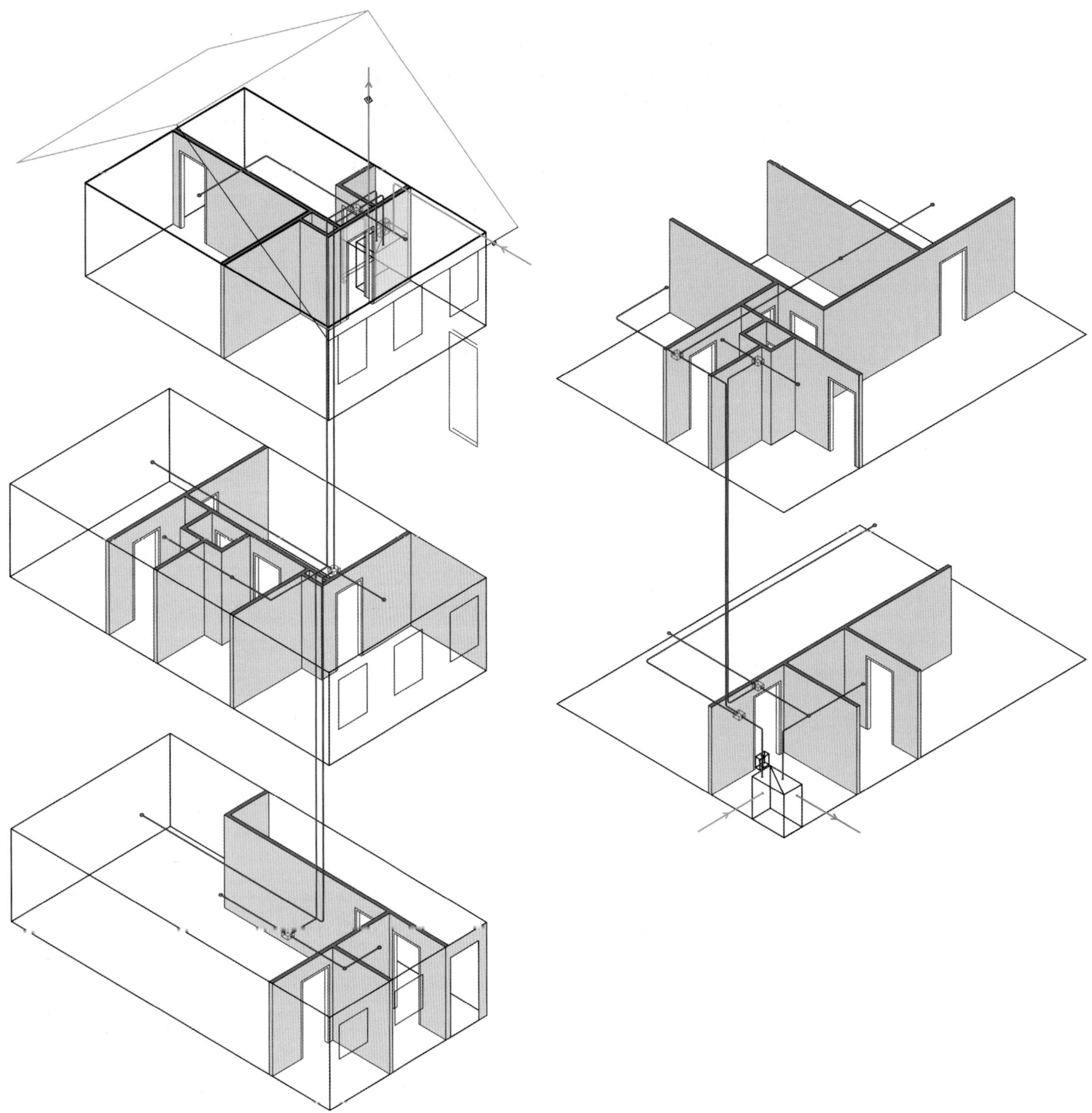

26.16 Mechanical ventilation heat recovery: pictorial view of systems shown on previous page.

Maintenance

A well-designed and installed system should require a minimal amount of maintenance. General guidelines include:

- outdoor air and exhaust filters should be replaced when necessary:
  - the control unit indicates when this required
  - this usually happens annually, depending on outdoor air quality
- kitchen filters should be replaced as necessary
- ducts should be short and easy to inspect
- cleaning should be possible or ducts should be easy to replace
- ducts should have smooth, antistatic interior surfaces.

Advantages/disadvantages

26.17 Certified Passivhaus home, Co. Kerry.

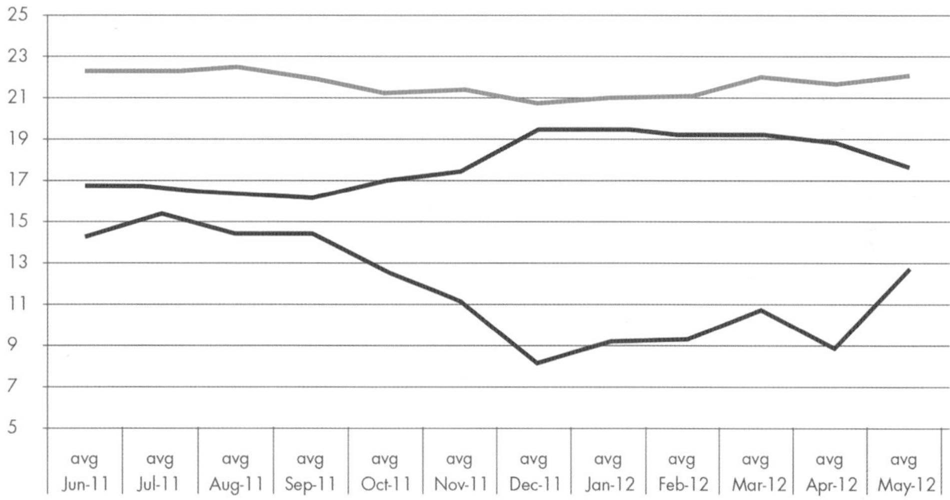

26.18 System performance: the consistent indoor air temperature and supply air temperature from this system, installed in the house shown in the photograph, is typical of the performance of a well-designed and installed MHRV system.

There are many advantages to a mechanical heat recovery ventilation system:

- comfort – MHRV combined with an airtight structure provides a high level of thermal comfort
- active temperature control – the system responds to outdoor air temperature
- indoor air quality – filters clean the outdoor air before it enters the building
- energy efficiency – recovery of 'waste' heat from stale air reduces energy consumption
- costs – less energy consumption means lower energy bills.

Most of the disadvantages associated with MHRV systems relate to the 'newness' of this technology in the Irish context:

- training required for installers
- high level of workmanship required: poorly installed systems do not perform as designed
- maintenance: filters must be changed regularly (at least annually)
- back-up – if the MHRV unit breaks down or if there is an electricity outage the windows have to be opened to provide ventilation.

Passivhaus criteria

MHRV systems that are used in houses built to the Passivhaus standard must meet the following quality criteria:

- comfortable supply air temperatures (≥16.5°C)
- low air flow velocities:
  - fast-moving air creates a 'wind chill' effect
  - air movement speeds should not exceed 0.8m/s @ 20°C
- heat recovery efficiency – more than 75% of the 'waste' heat must be recovered from the stale exhaust air
- electricity efficiency – maximum electricity consumption: 0.45Wh/m^3
- balance – total supply and total extract rates should be balanced
- control – the system should have three levels of operation:
  - setback mode: 70%
  - normal mode: 100%
  - boost mode: 130%
- noise
  - max. 25 dB(A) in living spaces
  - max. 35 dB(A) in the room housing the unit (e.g. utility room)
- filters
  - outdoor air filter (F7 type)
  - exhaust air filter (G4 type)
- frost protection – the system should pre-warm the outdoor air intake when the outdoor air temperature is below 0°C.

REVISION EXERCISES

1 Describe, using neat freehand sketches, the two approaches to ventilation.
2 Discuss the requirements for air quality.
3 Outline the requirements for air change rates under the Passivhaus standard.
4 Explain, using a neat annotated sketch, how a heat exchange module works.
5 Show, using a neat annotated sketch, how a mechanical heat recovery ventilation system could be installed in the home shown.

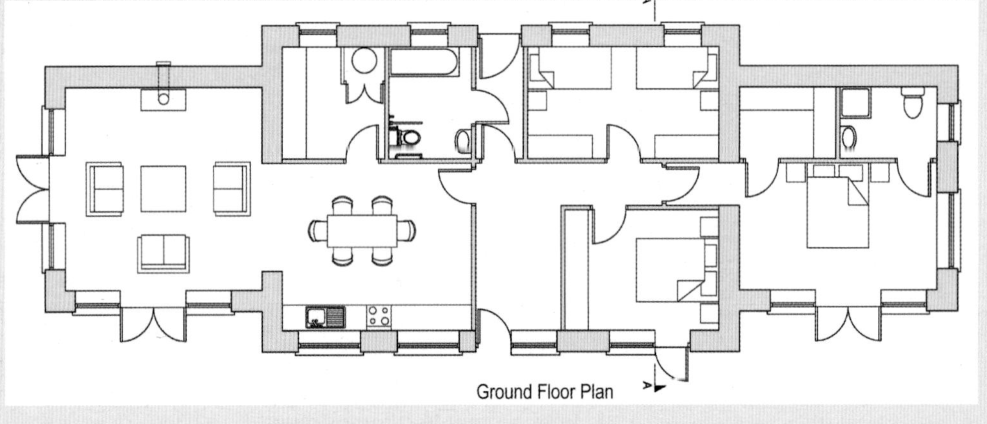

CHAPTER 27

Electrical Energy

Electricity generation

A generator is an electrical machine that converts mechanical energy into electrical energy. When a simple loop of copper wire is rotated between the poles of a magnet the wire 'cuts' through the magnetic field. When the loop is rotated an electromotive force is induced in the wire. This force causes electrical current to flow in the wire. This fundamental principle is used in power stations to convert mechanical energy to electrical energy.

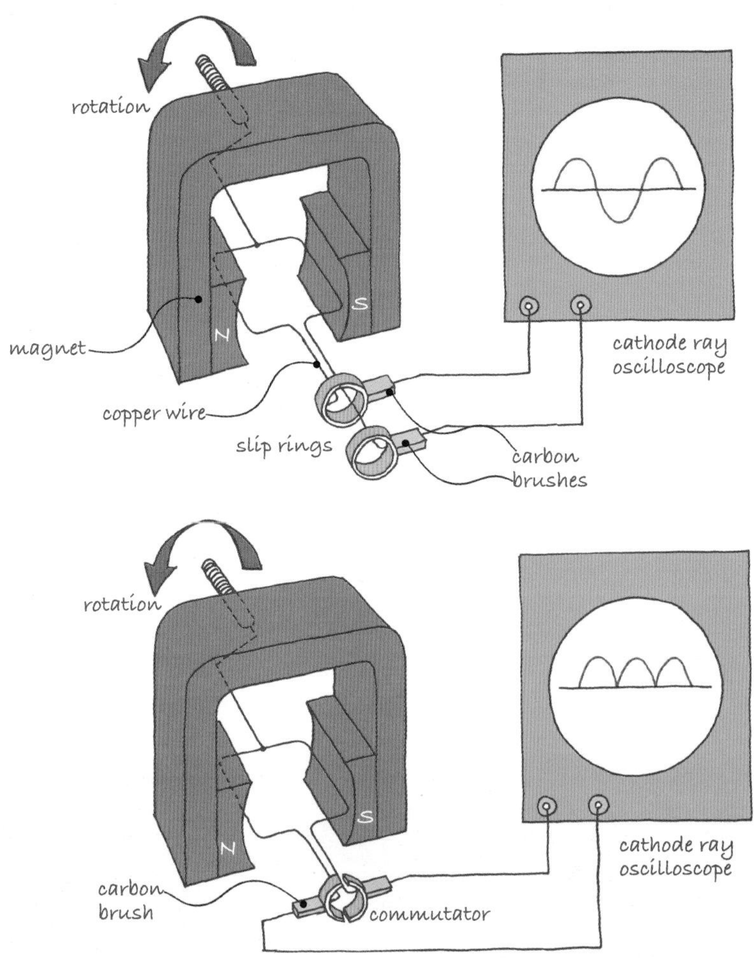

27.01 Simple generators: an alternating current (AC) (top) and a direct current (DC) generator.

A simple generator can be used to produce two types of current: direct current and alternating current. Direct current is used in low-voltage applications like batteries and photovoltaic solar panels. Alternating current is used as the mains supply in houses and most other buildings. One of the reasons alternating current is used for mains supply is because it is easy to change the voltage of alternating current using transformers (which only work on alternating current). This is very important for efficient electricity transmission.

Electrical machines

mechanical energy input → generator → electrical energy output

electrical energy input → motor → mechanical energy output

27.02 Electrical machines: energy converters.

An electrical machine is a device that converts mechanical energy or vice versa:

- generator – converts mechanical energy into electrical energy
- motor – converts electrical energy into mechanical energy.

Note: mechanical energy is the sum of potential energy and kinetic energy.

Power stations

A power station is a facility that converts mechanical energy into electrical energy. In Ireland, the source of the mechanical energy is hydro (water), thermal (heat) or wind. Thermal stations generate heat by burning fossil fuels including coal, oil, natural gas and milled peat, most of which is imported. Ireland consumes approximately 27 billion kilowatt-hours of electricity per annum. There are approximately 60 power stations in Ireland; many of these are small local stations.

Thermal power station

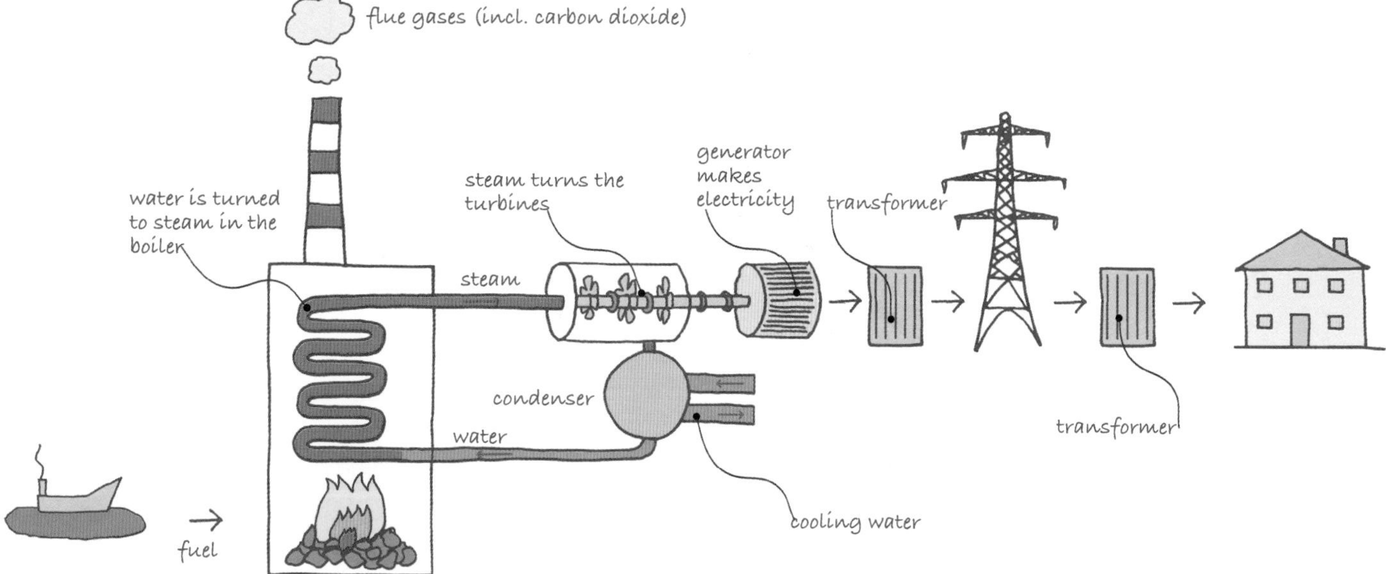

27.03 Thermal power station.

27.04 Moneypoint thermal power station, Co. Clare. Power output rate: 915MW. The station can consume up to 7,000 tonnes of coal per day and it has a 600,000 tonne storage area.

Hydro power station

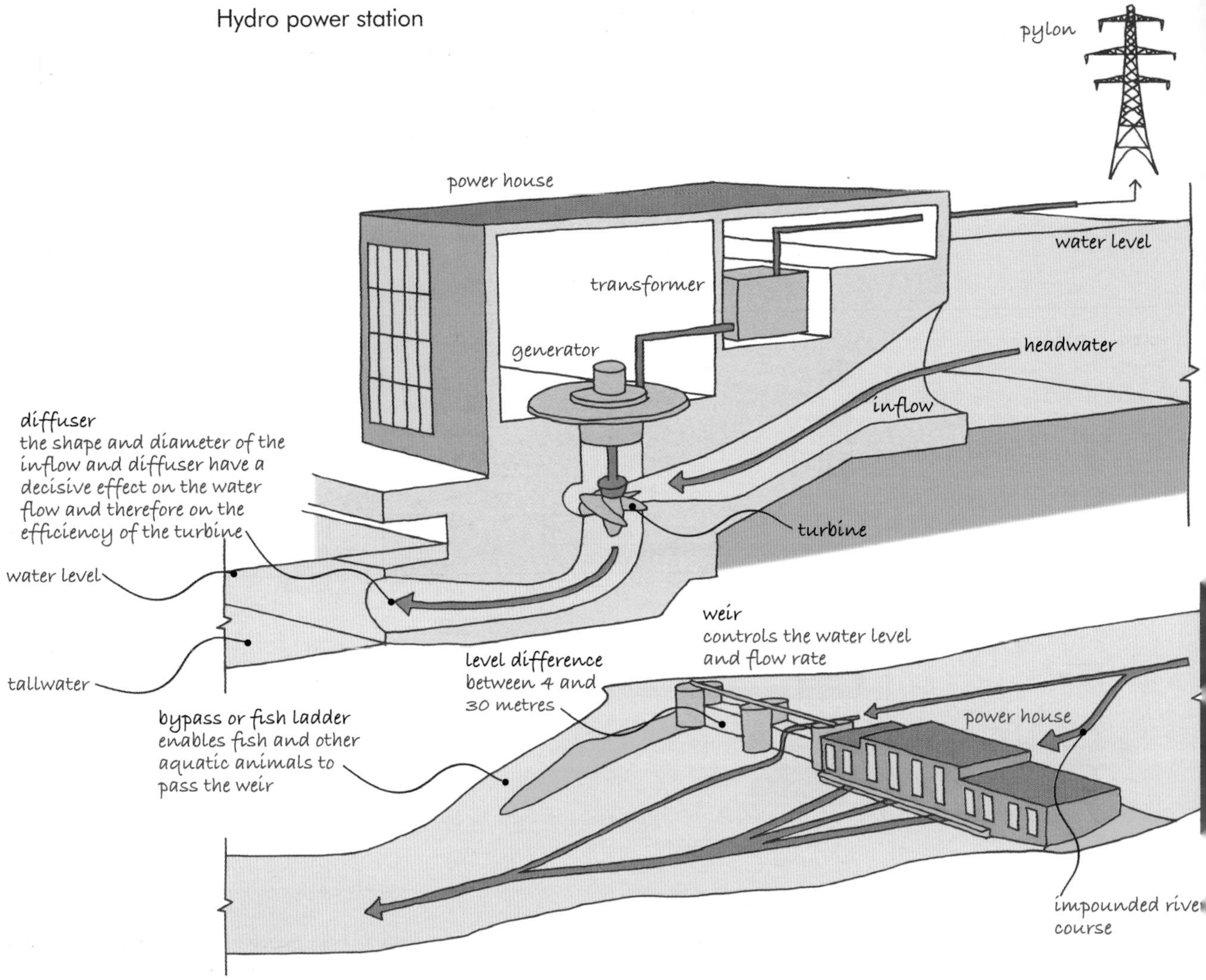

pylon

power house

water level

transformer

generator

headwater

inflow

diffuser
the shape and diameter of the inflow and diffuser have a decisive effect on the water flow and therefore on the efficiency of the turbine

turbine

water level

weir
controls the water level and flow rate

level difference
between 4 and 30 metres

tallwater

bypass or fish ladder
enables fish and other aquatic animals to pass the weir

power house

impounded river course

27.05 Hydro power station.

27.06 Ardnacrusha Hydro power station, Co. Clare. Power rate: 86MW. When it was opened in 1929, the plant was able to meet the electricity demand of the entire country. It now represents about 2% of the ESB's total capacity.

Wind power station

Wind turbines are connected to the grid via an intermediate direct current circuit. The alternating current generated by the generator is first converted into direct current and is then converted back into alternating current with the correct frequency and voltage. This enables variable-speed operation of the wind turbine and reduces mechanical stresses.

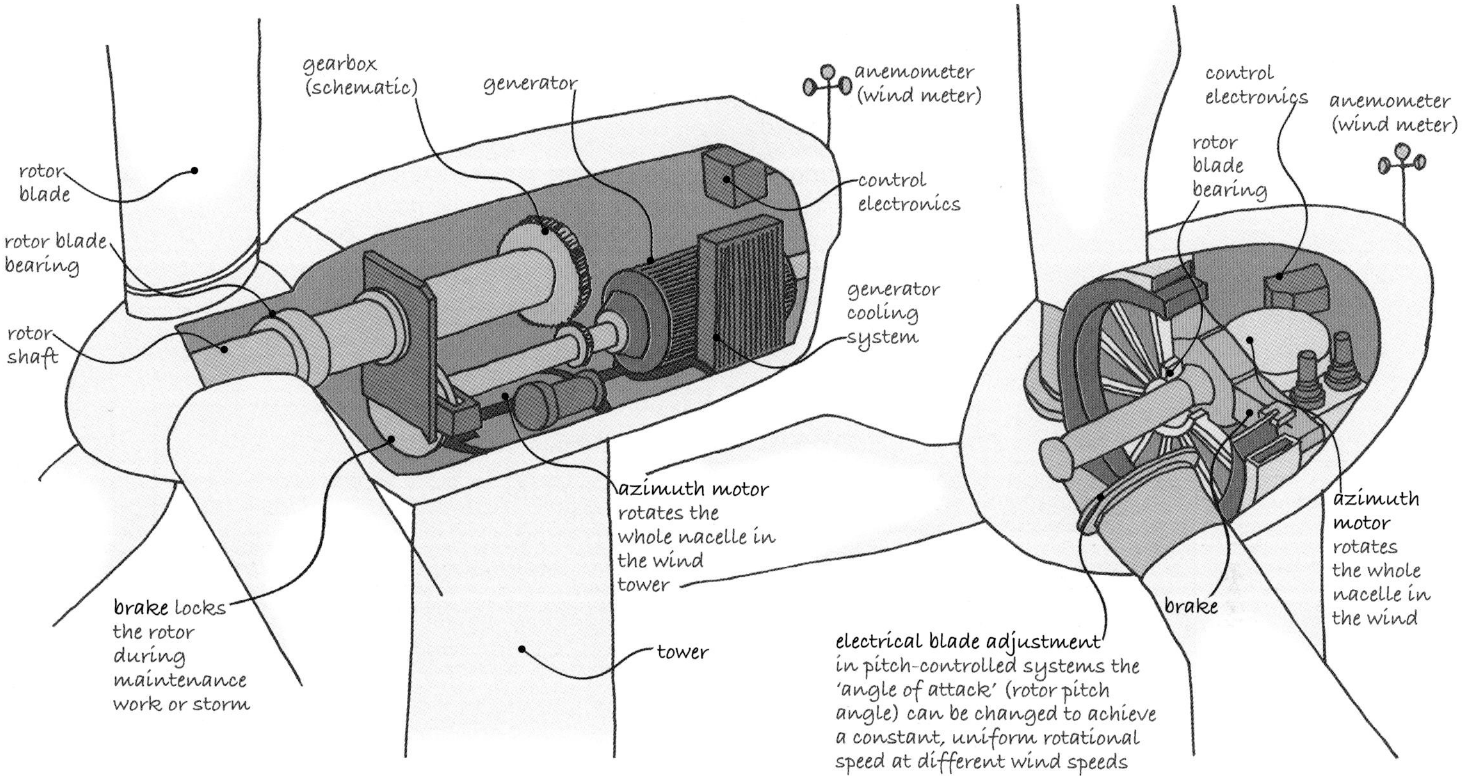

rotor blade
rotor blade bearing
rotor shaft
gearbox (schematic)
generator
anemometer (wind meter)
control electronics
generator cooling system
azimuth motor rotates the whole nacelle in the wind
tower
brake locks the rotor during maintenance work or storm
tower

control electronics
anemometer (wind meter)
rotor blade bearing
azimuth motor rotates the whole nacelle in the wind
brake
electrical blade adjustment in pitch-controlled systems the 'angle of attack' (rotor pitch angle) can be changed to achieve a constant, uniform rotational speed at different wind speeds

1 Example of a system with gearbox
Output: 2.0 MW
Rotor diameter: 80m
Tower height: approx. 80m
Speed: 9–19 revolutions per minute

2 Example of a system without gearbox
Output: 5.0 MW
Rotor diameter: 114m
Tower height: approx. 124m
Speed: 8–13 revolutions per minute

27.07 Wind turbines: some systems use a gearbox to increase the low speed of the rotors to a better speed for the generator.

27.08 Meentycat Wind Farm in Co. Donegal. Power rate: 84MW. Ireland's largest wind farm.

Transmission and distribution

Once the electricity is generated it needs to be delivered to the consumer. This is done via the transmission system (often referred to as the 'national grid'), a network of approximately 6,500km of high-voltage overhead lines and underground cables and over 100 substations. This infrastructure is divided into four elements (generation, transmission system, distribution system and retail suppliers) with various companies involved at each stage.

Electricity is transmitted at very high voltages to reduce the heating effect in the cables and the amount of energy lost during transmission. The amount of heat energy produced in a cable is proportional to the current squared. In other words, if the current is doubled the heat generated in the cable is quadrupled.

When the power is transmitted at high voltage and low current, the same amount of power is transmitted but much less heat energy is lost through the transmission lines.

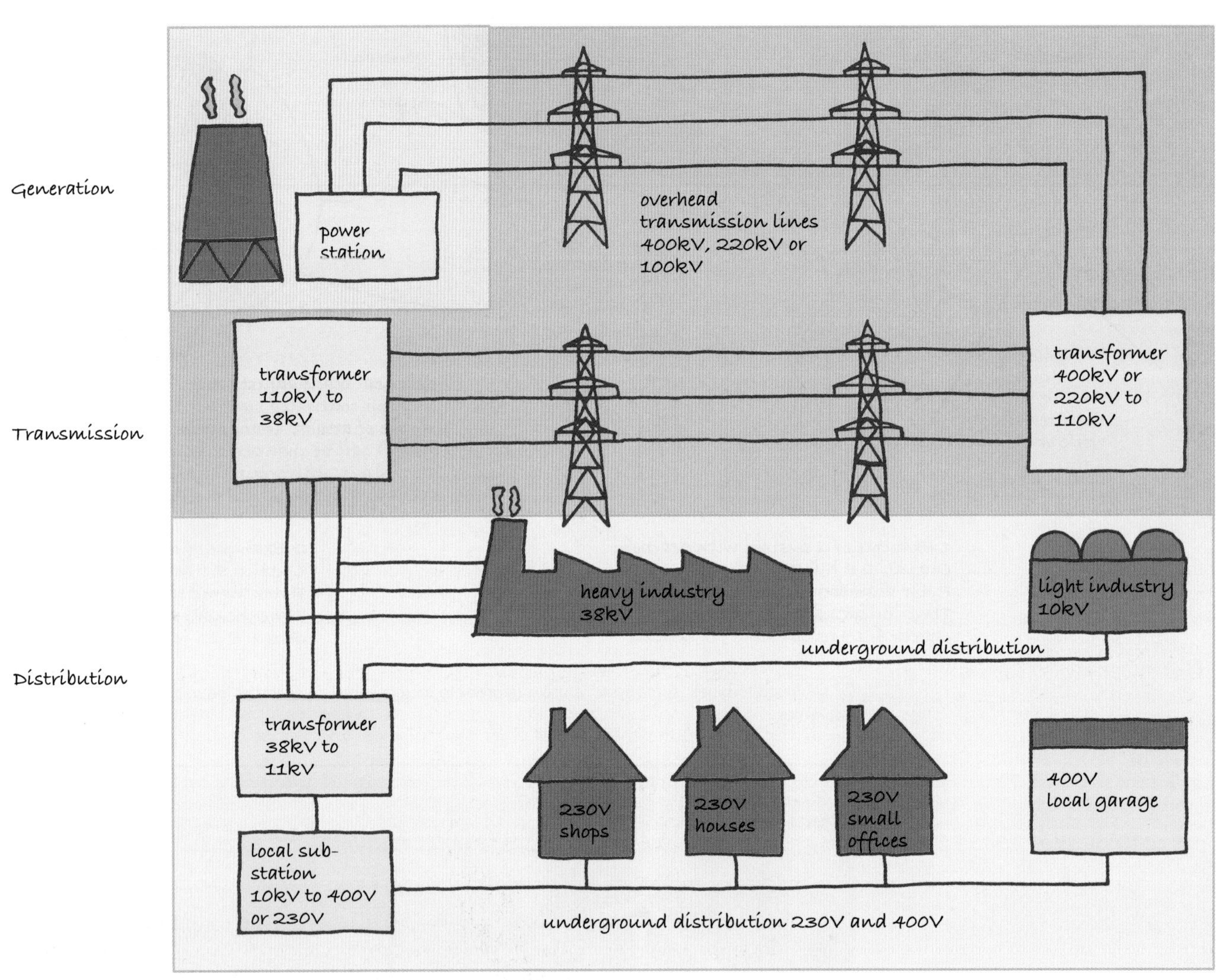

27.09 Electricity generation, transmission and distribution.

Intake

The mains supply of electricity usually enters the dwelling below ground. The mains cable must be encased in a red coloured protective plastic pipe and buried 600mm below finished ground level. This pipe is continued up through the external wall and into an outdoor meter cabinet. To facilitate access by the utility company for reading and maintenance, the meter cabinet must be directly accessible from the main entrance driveway and be positioned in the house wall facing the driveway or within 2m of either corner of the house wall facing the driveway. The utility company owns the equipment up to and including the meter.

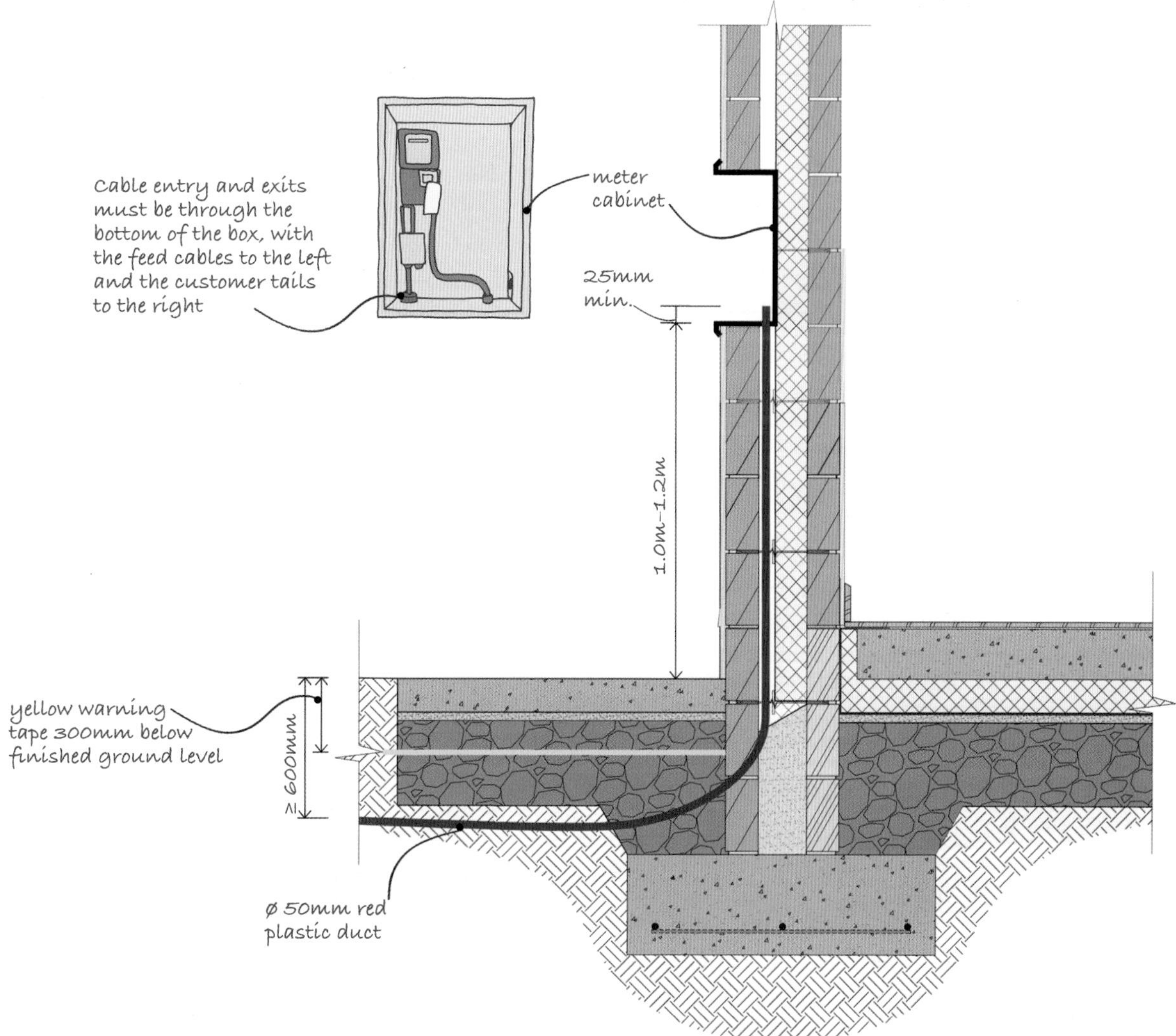

27.10 Electricity intake: safety measures to prevent accidental contact with buried cable.

Distribution of electricity in the home

The system for distributing electricity must be designed to meet a number of performance criteria, including:

- sufficient capacity for the needs of the occupants
- minimum wastage of current in the cables
- prevention of electrical injury
- prevention of fire
- means of isolation (cut-off supply)
- compliance with regulations and best practice.

From the meter, the supply is taken into the dwelling to the consumer unit. This is where the main supply is divided into separate circuits for sockets, lighting, cooker, etc. Each of these circuits is protected by a safety device that protects against electric shock.

Circuits

Every circuit comprises the following elements:

- energy source
- live conductor (brown) – feeds current to load
- switch – to control the circuit
- load – the device to be powered
- neutral conductor – returns current to source
- earth – protective conductor that protects user.

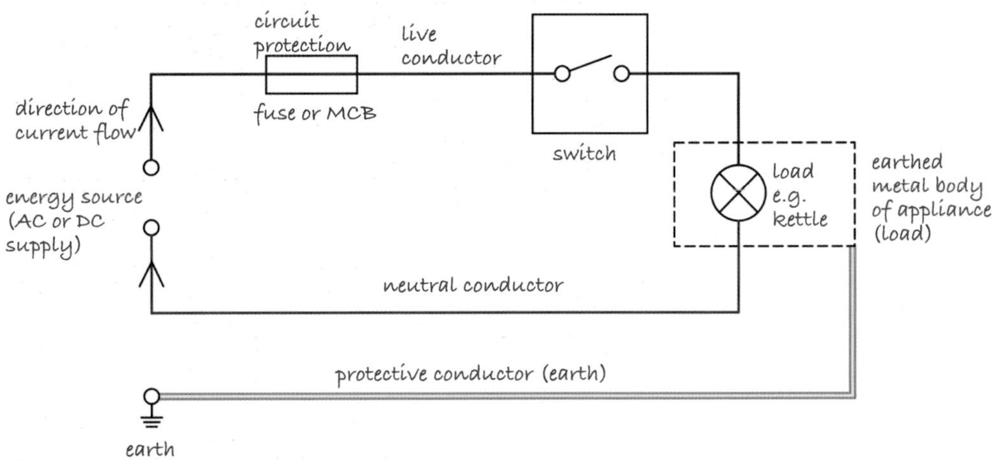

27.11 A simple circuit.

Conductors

Current is carried on copper wires called conductors. These wires are referred to as cables or cords. Cables are heavy wires used to create circuits (e.g. lighting/sockets):

- 1.5mm^2 for lighting loads
- 2.5mm^2 for heating loads
- 6.0mm^2 for cooking, shower or immersion heater loads.

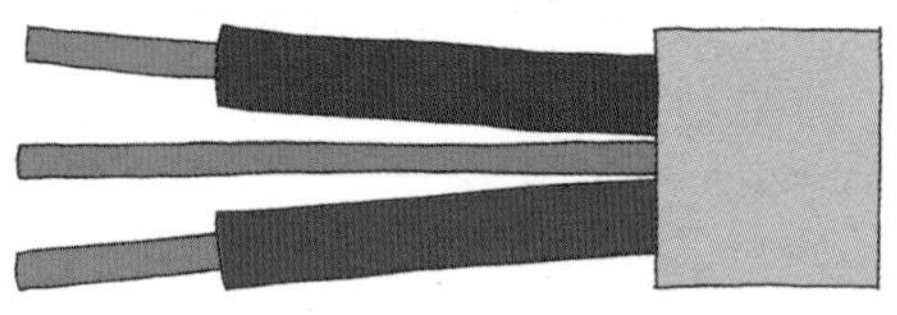

27.12 Cable: 1.5mm^2 to 6mm^2.

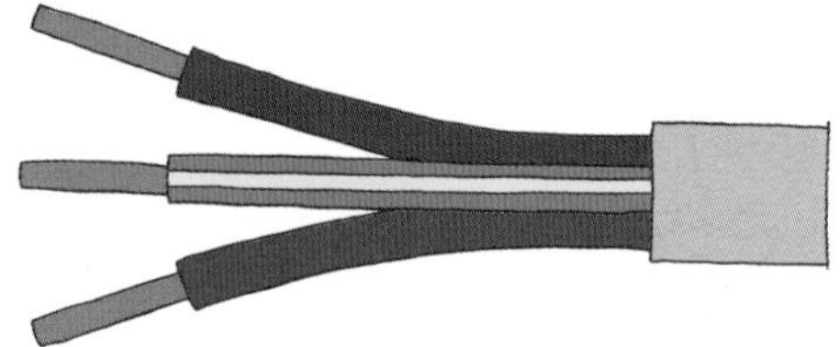

27.13 Cord: 0.75mm^2.

Cords are light, flexible wires used to carry electricity from sockets to appliances.

Circuit design

Electrical circuits are normally described as either radial or ring.

A radial circuit is one where power is transmitted from point to point by a single length of cable linking each point to the next.

- The circuit starts at the distribution board and stops at the last connected device.
- It is commonly used for lighting circuits.

A ring circuit starts at the distribution board and goes to each device in the same way as a radial circuit, but the last device is connected back to the supply so that the whole circuit forms a continuous ring.

- This means that there are two separate paths for the current to flow from the supply to every output. Ideally, the ring acts like two radial circuits proceeding in opposite directions around the ring.
- If the load is evenly split across the two directions, the current in each direction is half of the total, allowing the use of wire with half the current-carrying capacity.
- In practice, the load does not always split evenly, so thicker wire is used.

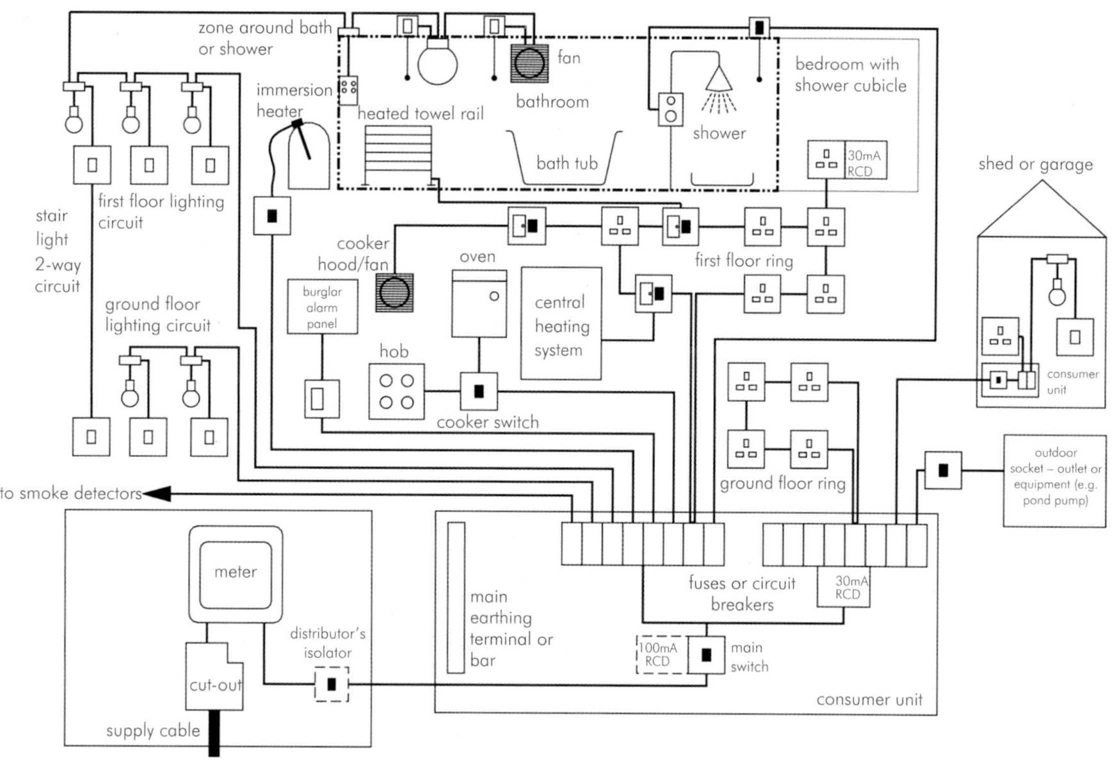

27.14 Electrical installation diagram: typical residential system.

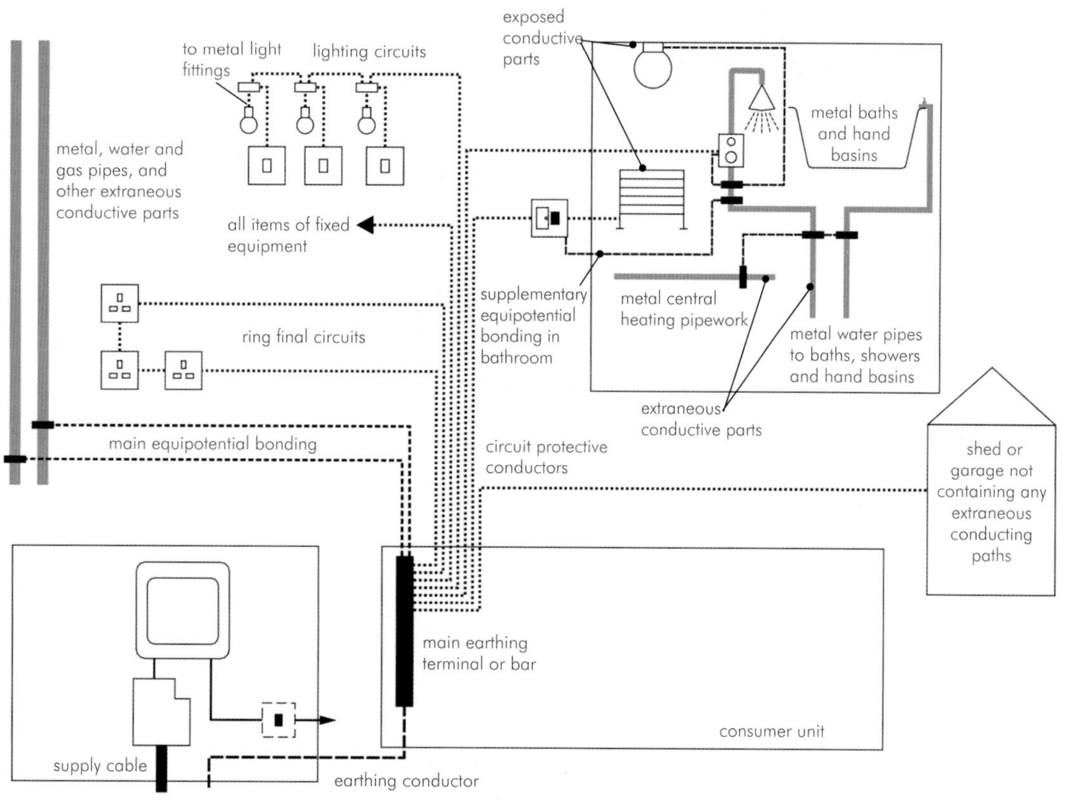

27.15 Electrical installation diagram: earthing and bonding conductors for a typical residential system.

Socket circuits

A ring circuit is commonly used to supply power to the sockets in a home. The sockets can be installed at any point on the circuit. The circuit forms a ring because it is connected to the distribution board at each end. This means that current is supplied to the sockets from both ends of the ring. This allows the use of lighter wiring (of lower current rating) than if it were connected at one end only, which means that less copper is used. Ring circuits are common in Ireland and the UK but are not widely used elsewhere. A ring circuit usually has a 36A miniature circuit breaker. When designing a system, two 20A radial circuits are a safer alternative to a single 36A ring circuit.

How is it possible to have an unlimited number of sockets on a ring circuit? Discuss this with your classmates

To prevent overloading, the following guidelines apply to the design of ring main circuits:

- a separate ring main circuit must be provided for every 100 m^2 of floor area
- a 2.5 mm^2 twin and earth double-insulated cable must be used
- there is no limit to the number of sockets
- radial spurs are allowed from 50% of sockets – a maximum of two sockets per spur.

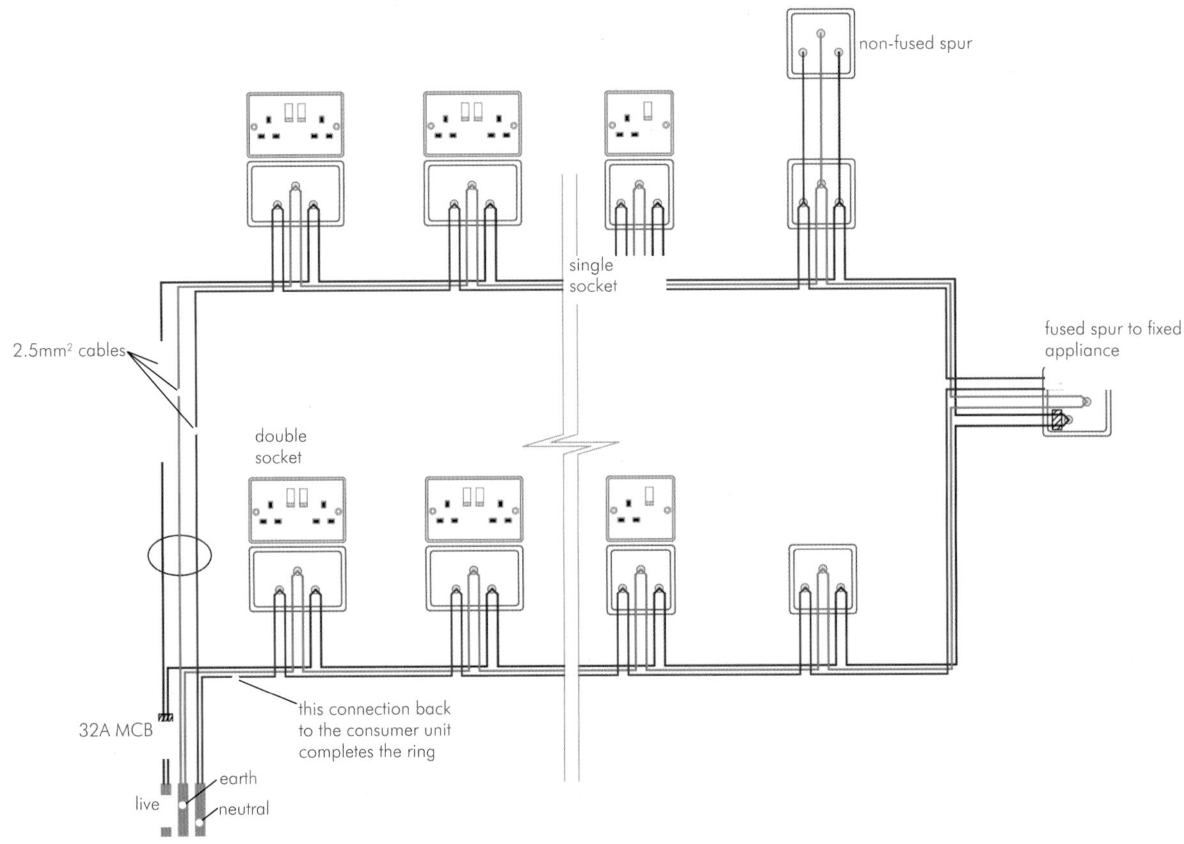

27.16 Ring circuit: typical 36A ring circuit for sockets.

A radial circuit may also be used to power sockets. Each point is fed from the previous one: live is connected to live, neutral to neutral and earth to earth at each outlet in the circuit. The final outlet in a radial circuit is not connected back to the distribution board.

For sockets, the maximum number of socket outlets per radial circuit is ten. A radial circuit for sockets should not supply more than two rooms. A kitchen should be supplied by at least two radial circuits. The 20A MCB should be fitted and conductors in the cable should be 40mm^2.

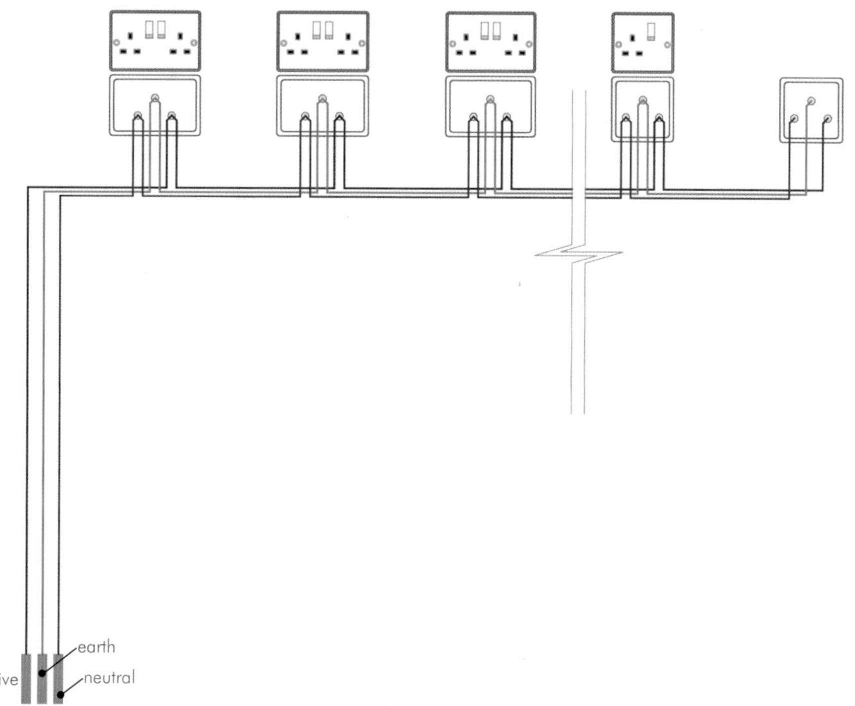

27.17 Radial circuit for sockets (4mm^2 twin and earth cable).

Lighting circuits

There are two basic lighting circuits used in residences: loop-in method; and joint box method. These circuits use 1.5mm^2 conductor cables. Lamps are placed in the centre of room ceilings except when more than one lamp is to be fitted. There should be no more than ten lighting points per circuit. There should be at least two lighting circuits per dwelling. This is to ensure that the entire house is not left in darkness if one lighting circuit fails.

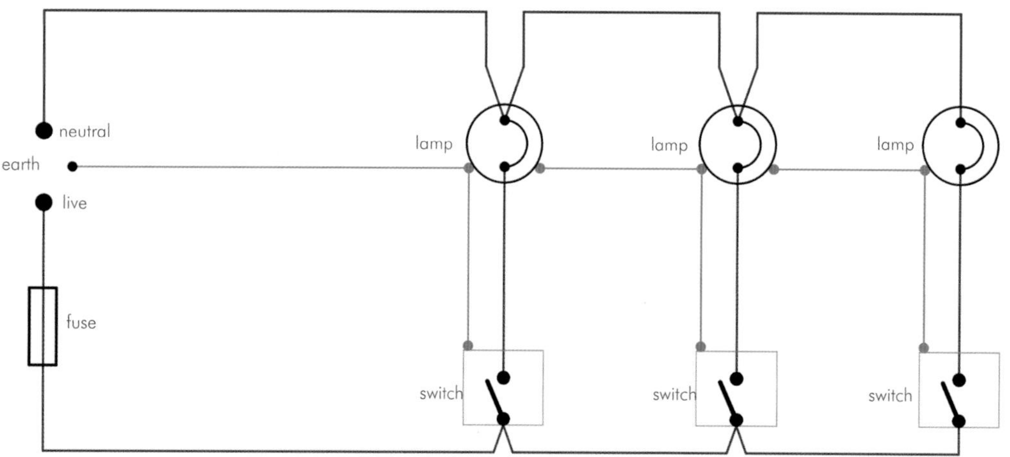

27.18 Radial circuit: typical 'loop-in' method for lighting – three lamps, individually controlled by one-way switches.

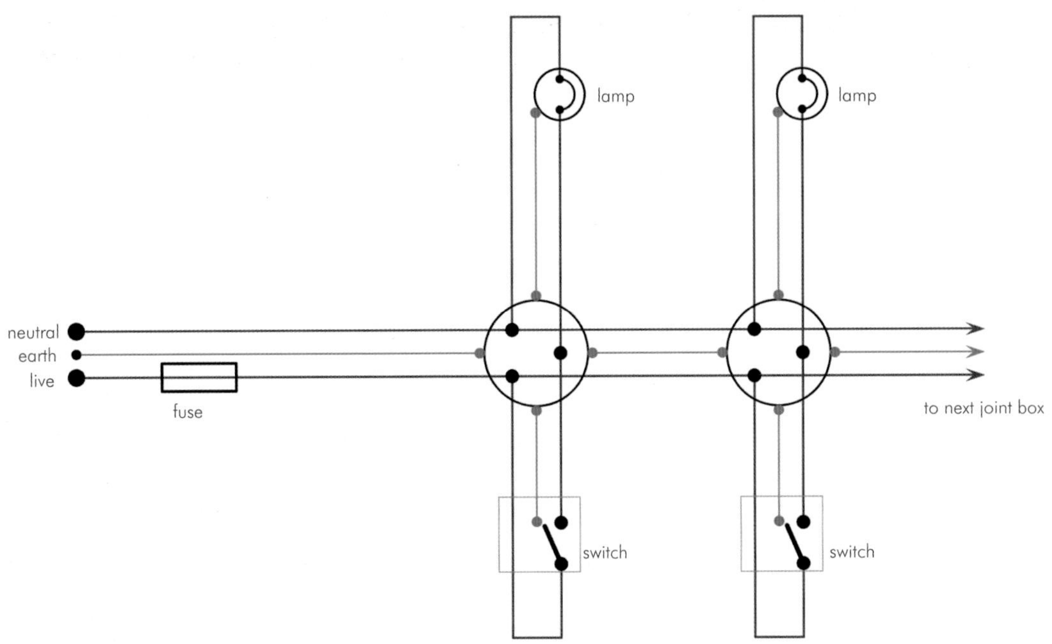

27.19 Radial circuit: typical junction box method for lighting – two lamps, individually controlled by one-way switches.

Light bulbs

Traditional incandescent lamps (i.e. bulbs) are no longer in use in Ireland and have been phased out in Europe since 2012. These have been mainly replaced by compact fluorescent lamps (CFLs). CFLs consume less energy and have a longer lifespan than traditional incandescent lamps.

There is a wide range of energy-saving lamps available. Tungsten halogen lamps are an alternative to CFLs. They are less energy efficient and have a shorter life span than CFLs, but they are suitable fc use in light fittings connected to a dimmer switch and they provide better colour rendering than CFLs

Lamp type	Sample image	Luminous efficacy (lm/W)	Colour appearance* (K)	Colour rendering (Ra)	Lamp life (hours)
Tungsten lamp		8 to 15	2,700	100	1,000
Tungsten halogen lamp		10 to 25	2,700 to 3,000	100	1,500 to 2,000
T8 linear fluorescent lamp		50 to 96	2,700 to 6,500	50 to 98	8,000 to 24,000
T5 linear fluorescent lamp		80 to 104	2,700 to 6,500	82 to 95	8,000 to 24,000
T2 linear fluorescent lamp		55 to 70	2,700 to 6,500	80 to 85	8,000 to 12,000
Plug-in compact fluorescent lamp		20 to 74	2,700 to 6,500	80 to 90	6,000 to 12,000
Pin-base compact fluorescent lamp		30 to 88	2,700 to 6,500	85 to 90	8,000 to 15,000
LED lamp		40 to 70	2,700 to 6,500	60 to 90	10,000 to 50,000

*Colour appearance can also be referred to as the colour temperature

27.20 Lamp types and features.

Switching

Most lighting circuits have a one-way switch. A two-way switch is used for stairs where the light can be turned off from either end (i.e. upstairs or downstairs).

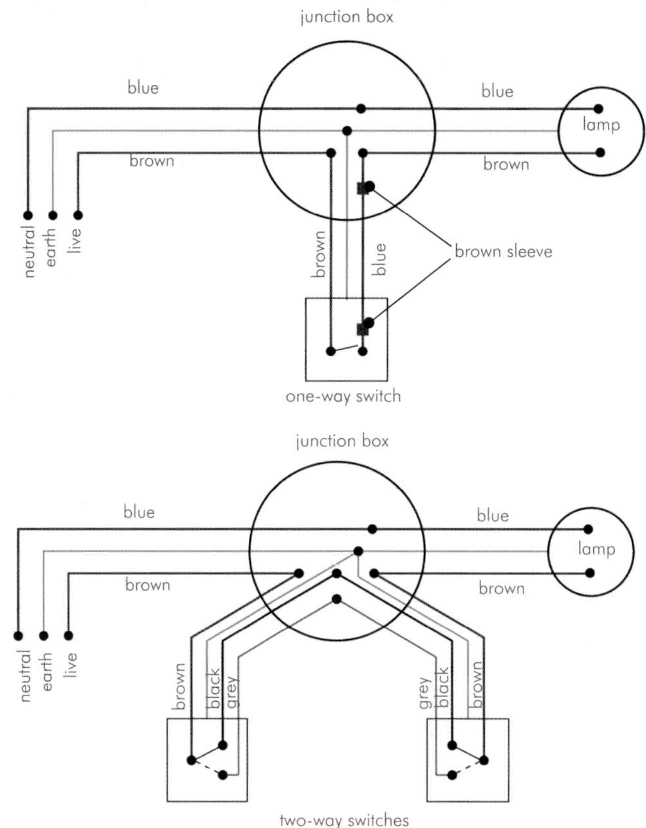

27.21 Switching: one-way and two-way switching for lighting. Note the colours used to identify each cable.

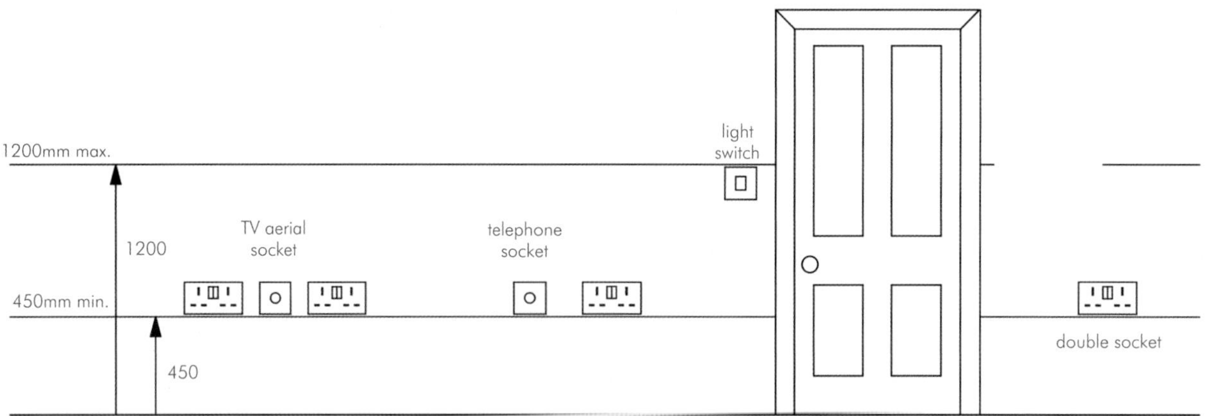

27.22 Installation of electrical points for universal access.

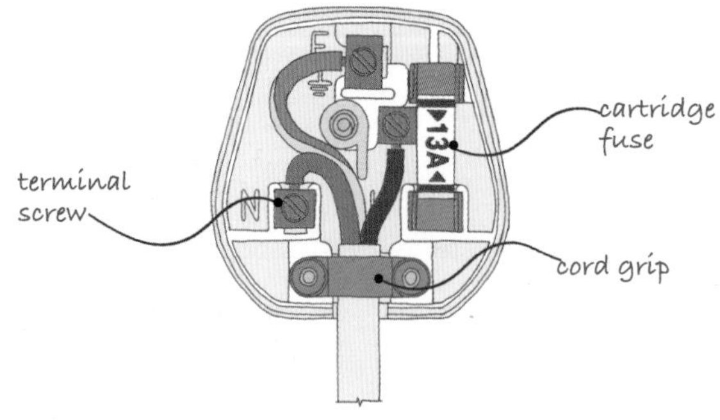

27.23 Plug: showing correct wiring and a 13 amp cartridge fuse.

Safety

The safe use of electricity is essential to everyday life. The potential of electricity to injure or kill should never be forgotten.

Electric shock

Electricity causes harm and injury at very low levels of current. Electric shock from a source above 0.1Amps (100mA) is fatal. Plugs are fitted with a 3Amp to 13Amp cartridge fuse, so the current flowing through all typical domestic appliances is potentially fatal.

The effect of an electric shock at different current levels

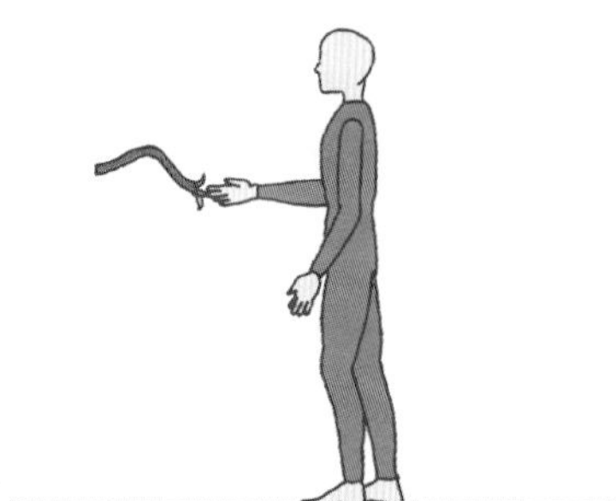

1–5 mA: discernible, but no danger

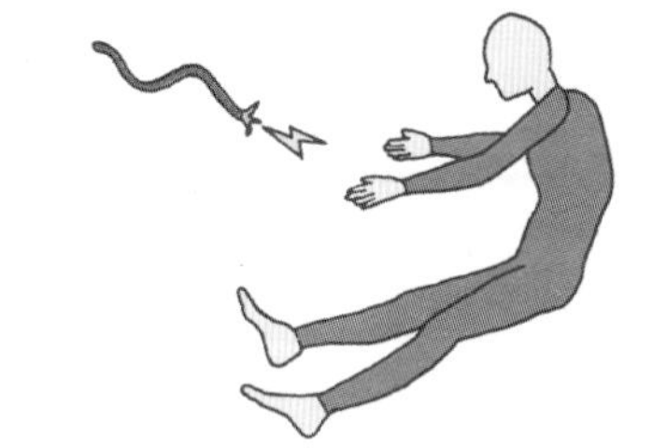

5–15 mA: pain and muscular contraction, which can repel the person; above approx. 15 mA it becomes impossible to let go

20–50 mA: impossible to release grasp; extreme pain and loss of consciousness

50–75 mA: paralysis with no pulse or respiration

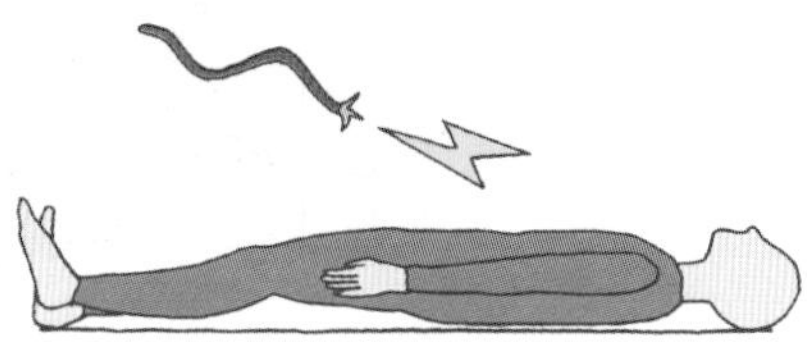

greater than 100 mA: ventricular fibrillation causing almost instantaneous death

27.24 Safe use of electricity: even low levels of current are fatal. Note that the current is shown in milliamps (mA).

Safety strategies

There are three main ways of ensuring an electrical system is safe:

- insulation of live parts – conductors are wrapped in PVC sheathing
- earthing and bonding metal components – the metal body of every appliance is connected to earth
- automatic disconnection using fuses and circuit breakers – cut off the supply if a fault occurs.

Earthing

Earthing is the connection of the exposed conductive parts of an electrical installation (e.g. the metal shell of a washing machine) to the main protective earthing terminal. The idea is that, should the body of an appliance become live, the current will have a safe path back to earth and a person touching the appliance will not be shocked.

If a faulty electrical appliance has been earthed, no shock is received because the fault current is able to flow directly to the installation's earth electrode, which is connected to the appliance. If fitted, a supplementary protective device will further minimise the risk of electric shock by disconnecting the supply in response to the earth fault.

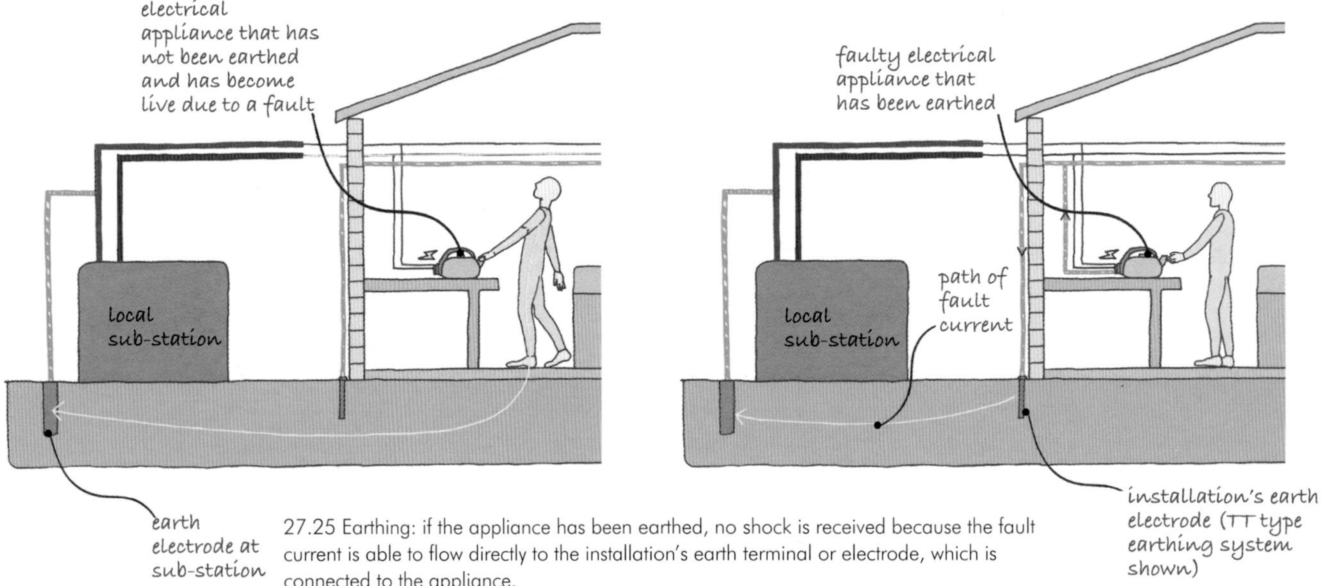

27.25 Earthing: if the appliance has been earthed, no shock is received because the fault current is able to flow directly to the installation's earth terminal or electrode, which is connected to the appliance.

Bonding

Bonding is the linking together of exposed metal components for the purpose of safety. In a typical home the pipework of the plumbing system and gas installation (if present) are bonded to the main earth terminal.

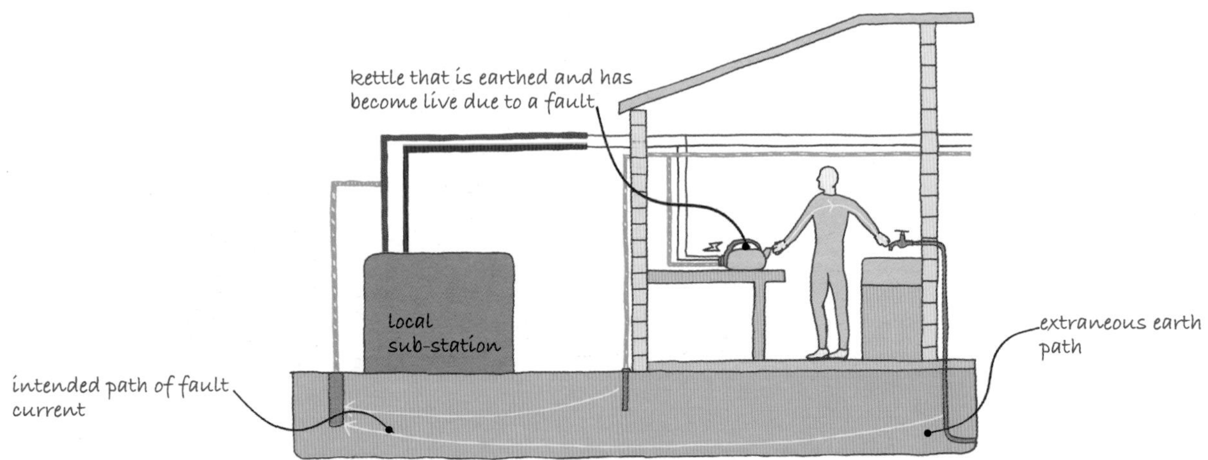

27.26 Bonding: a shock current passes through the body when the kettle and tap are touched simultaneously. The incoming water supply provides a much more effective earth path than the installation's earth electrode due to the amount of metallic pipework buried in the ground. If the incoming water supply is not bonded to the installation's earthing system a dangerous voltage may occur between the kettle and the tap.

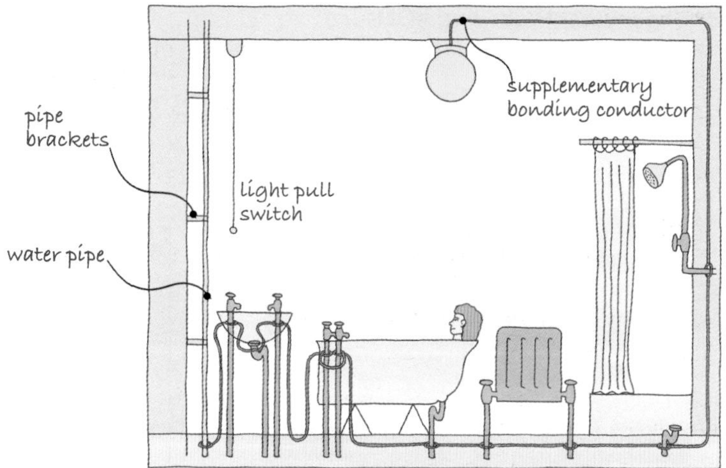

27.27 Bonding: supplementary local bonding in a high-risk area – the copper pipework of a typical bathroom.

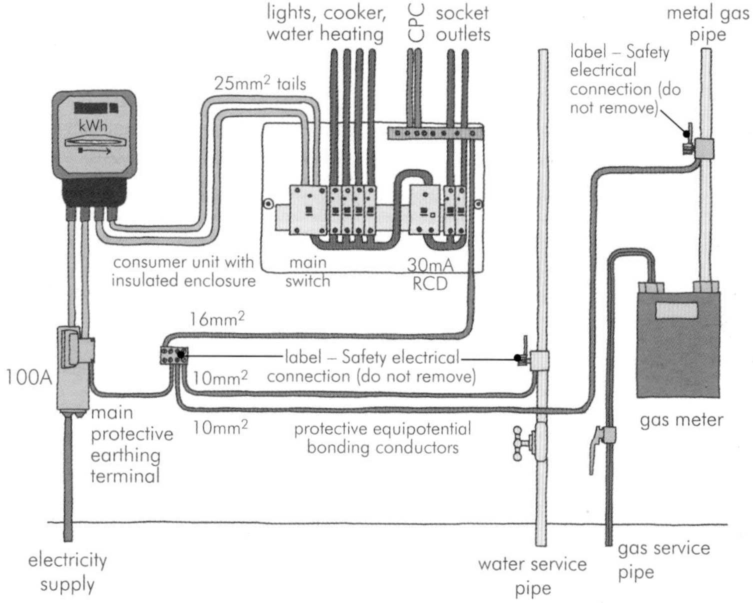

27.28 Electricity supply: TN-C-S (protective multiple earthing supply) earthing and bonding system used in urban areas.

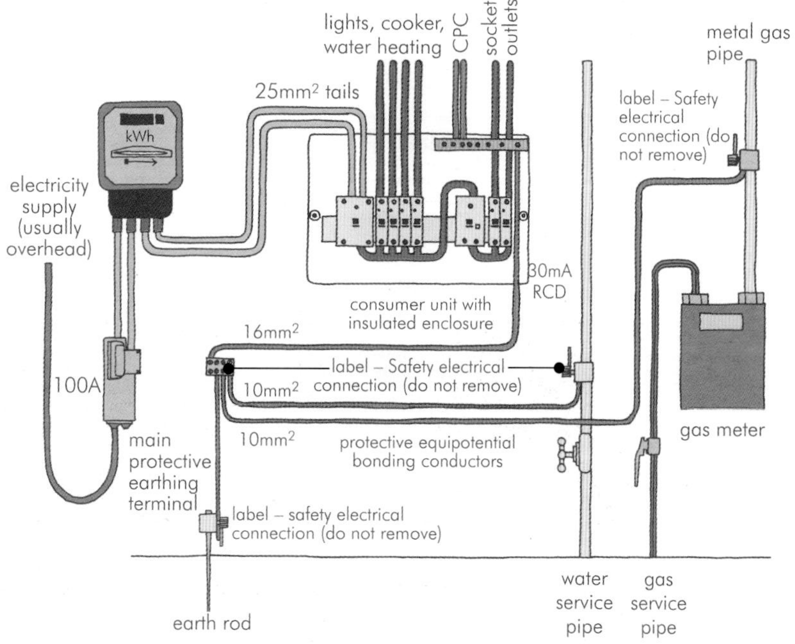

27.29 Electricity supply: TT (no earth supply) system used in rural areas.

Cartridge fuses, MCBs and RCDs

Cartridge fuses

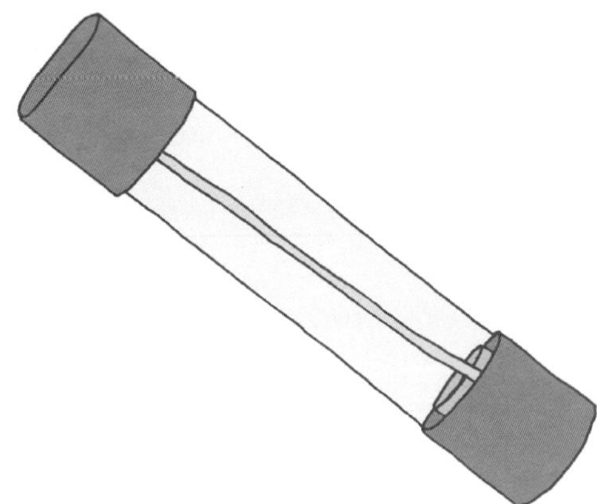

27.30 Cartridge fuses.

A cartridge fuse consists of a thin fuse wire encased in a ceramic tube and secured between end caps. The resistance of the wire is determined by its cross-sectional area. The smaller the cross-sectional area, the lower the rating. If a fault develops in the appliance and the flow of current exceeds the rating, the wire will melt, breaking the circuit.

Cartridge fuses are commonly installed in plugs to provide protection to individual appliances on a ring main circuit. This is because a typical ring main circuit can deliver more current than the flexibl power cords of small appliances can handle. The rating of the MCB on a ring main circuit is usuall 35A; the cartridge fuse allows a greater level of protection by reducing this to 3A, 5A, 10A or 13A (depending on the fuse chosen). Once a cartridge fuse blows it must be replaced.

Miniature circuit breaker

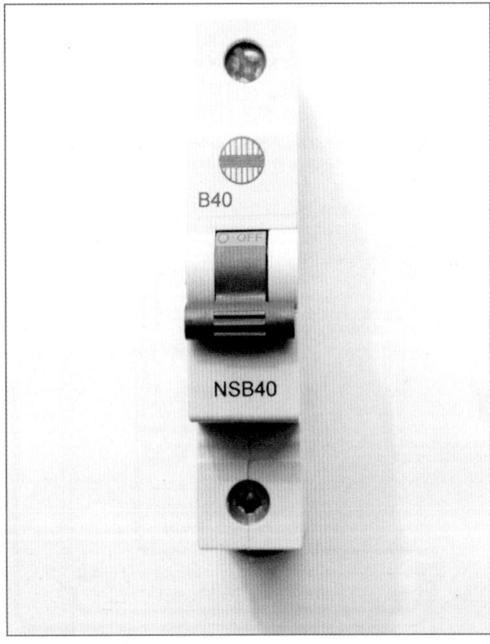

27.31 Miniature circuit breaker.

A miniature circuit breaker (MCB) is an automatic switch that instantaneously interrupts the flow of current in the event of an overload (too much current) or short circuit (accidental connection between the live conductor and the neutral conductor or between the neutral conductor and the earth conductor).

Residual current device

Residual current devices (RCDs) are mainly used to provide additional protection from receiving a shock by touching exposed parts that have become live due to a fault. During normal operation, the current flowing through the live conductor in a circuit will be the same as the current flowing through the neutral conductor. However, if an earth fault occurs there will be a difference in the current flow. The difference in current flow in the live and neutral conductors trips the RCD and breaks the circuit.

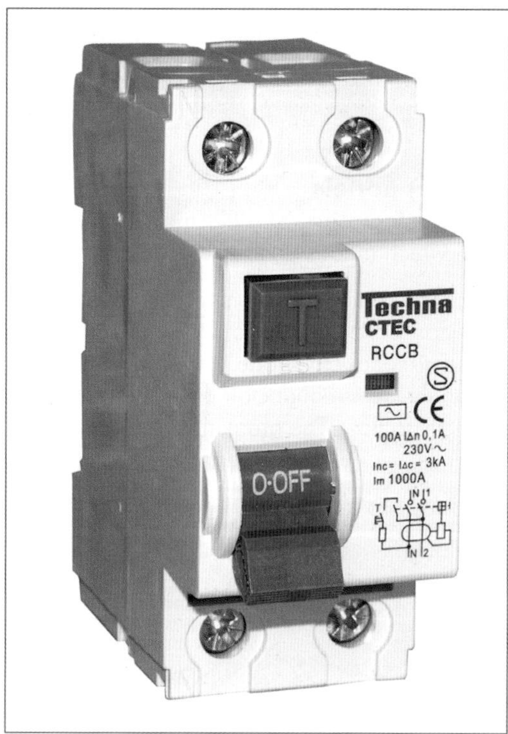

27.32 Residual current device.

Micro-generation

Micro-generation of electrical energy involves installing a small generator powered by a renewable source such as solar, wind, hydro or combined heat and power. Micro-generation is defined as less than 25 Amps for a typical home with a single phase connection – equivalent to a maximum output of 5.75kW. This is the maximum amount of electricity that the ESB permits a domestic user to export to the grid. This is in the context of the average Irish household using 5,300kW/h of electricity per year. A consumer exporting 5kW of power for three hours every day would break even over the course of a year. However, most micro-generation systems produce a lot less than 5kW. The SEAI maintains a database of micro-generation products.

TGD L (2011) requires that some of the energy consumed by a home is generated on site using renewable energy technologies. The minimum level required is:

- 10 kWh/m^2a contributing to energy use for domestic hot water heating, space heating or cooling; or
- 4 kWh/m^2a of electrical energy; or
- a combination of these which would have equivalent effect.

Appliance	Rating (W or kW)	Current (Amps) flowing at this power (single phase)
Microwave oven	600W	2.6
Television	200W	0.87
Hairdryer	2,200W (2.2kW)	9.57
Kettle	3,000W (or 3kW)	13.04
Electric shower	8,000W (or 9kW)	34.78

27.33 Load rating of typical appliances.

KEY PRINCIPLES

The benefits of micro-generation include:
- lower electricity bills –
  - consumer uses less electricity from the supplier
  - consumer receives payment (feed-in tariff) for power exported to the grid
- lower greenhouse gas emissions
- reduced reliance on fossil fuels
- reduced electrical losses on the distribution network
- building energy rating (BER) is improved
- protection against future electricity price rises.

Solar (photovoltaic) panels

Photovoltaic (PV) technology generates electricity from light. The term photovoltaic is a combination of the words photo, which means light, and voltaic, which refers to the production of electricity.

Certain materials, called semi-conductors, can be adapted to release electrons when they are exposed to light. Silicon is the semi-conductor material in most solar PV cells. All PV cells have at least two layers of semi-conductors: one that is positively charged and one that is negatively charged When light shines on the semi-conductor, the electrical field across the junction between these two layers causes electricity to flow. The greater the intensity of the light, the greater the flow of electricity.

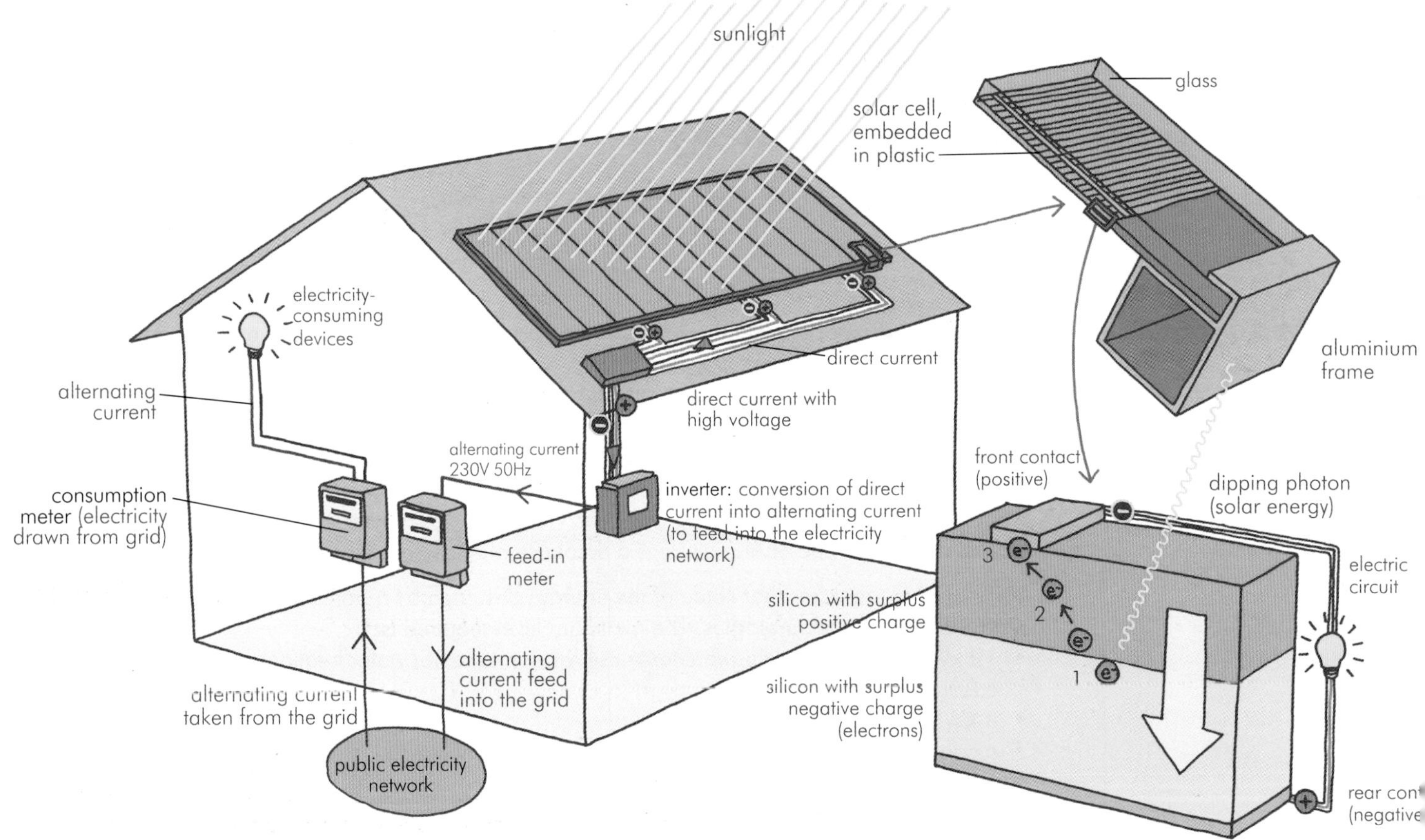

27.34 Photovoltaic panels: a simplified diagram of a PV installation.

Photovoltaic panels produce direct current electricity; this is converted to alternating current before it flows into the building's distribution system. Energy that is not consumed as it is generated can be exported to the grid. The consumer receives a payment for energy exported.

Power output

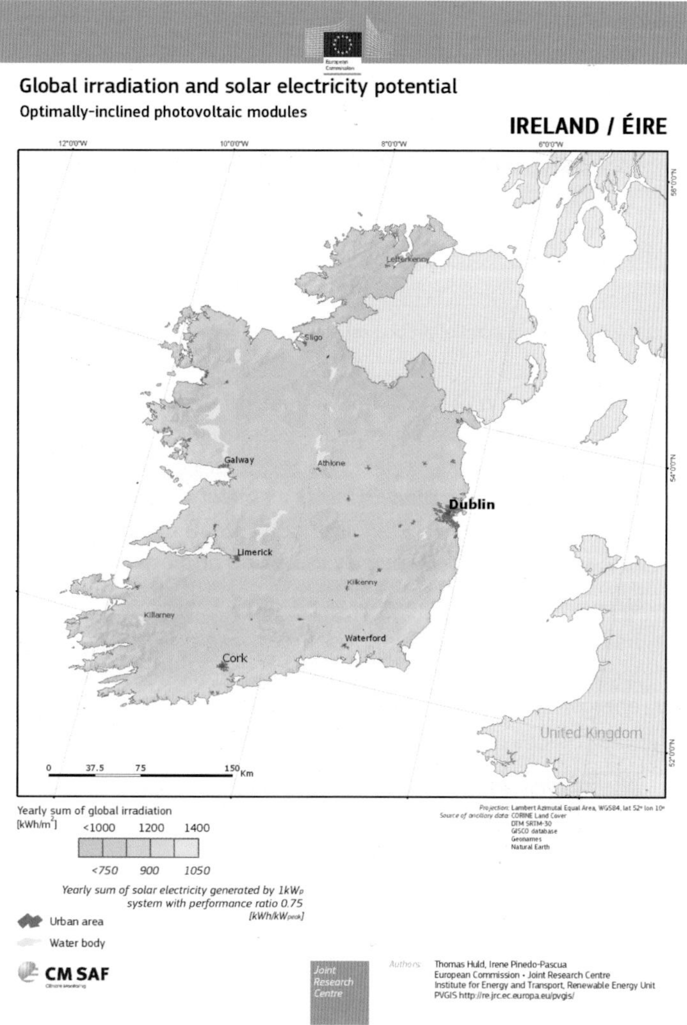

27.35 Annual solar irradiation Ireland: for panels installed at the optimum angle.

Ireland receives approximately 1,000 to 1,200 kWh/m2/year of solar irradiation. The ability of a solar panel to convert this light energy is determined by its efficiency:

$$\text{efficiency} = \frac{\text{nominal power}}{\text{light power*}}$$

*light power is assumed to be 1,000 W/m2

A typical system has an efficiency of 0.75 – it will produce power at a rate of 750W/m2 when the light intensity is 1,000W/m2. The nominal power of a unit is also called its peak power – the maximum power it can produce – and is indicated using the unit kWp. The nominal power is important for designing the system (selecting the correct size of cabling and other parts). However, it should not be used to compare panels. The output in kWh/m2 is a more appropriate metric for making comparisons. The power a module generates in real conditions can exceed the nominal power when the intensity of the sunlight exceeds 1,000W/m2.

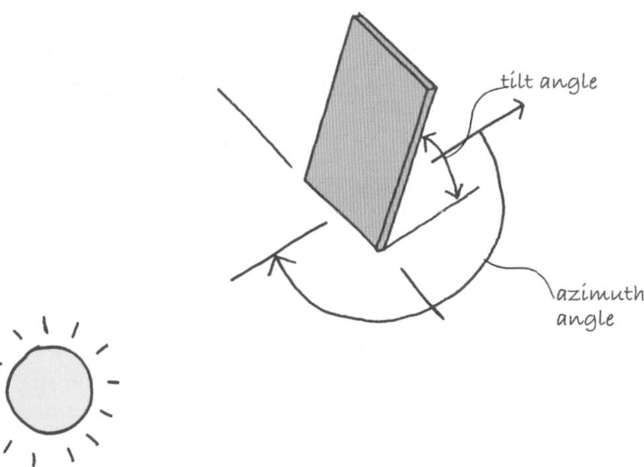

27.36 PV panel installation angles.

The output of a photovoltaic system varies with the intensity of the sunshine – the more intense the sunlight, the more power the PV panel will generate. However, performance will suffer if the panel is not correctly aligned in tilt and/or azimuth or if the panel is in shade or becomes dirty. The correct tilt angle (approximately 30°–40°) is determined by the latitude, while the correct azimuth angle (approximately 178°–182° (i.e. due south)) is determined by the longitude. However, these angles are usually predetermined by the slope and orientation of the roof on which the panels are installed

Wind turbines

Ireland has excellent wind resources. The amount of power available from the wind varies with location and elevation. Exposed sites on high ground offer the best opportunity for harvesting wind energy.

27.37 Horizontal (left) and vertical axis micro-generation wind turbines.

The ideal location for a micro-generation wind turbine is on a southwest-facing hill with gently slopin sides surrounded by clear countryside which is free from obstructions such as trees, houses or other buildings. Here the wind flows relatively smoothly and steadily, enabling it to drive wind turbines with greater efficiency. These sites are usually found in rural areas, which is why micro wind generation is rarely seen in urban settings.

27.38 Ideal wind turbine site.

The technology used in micro wind generation is similar to that used at large scale wind power stations. As the turbine is rotated by the wind, the generator produces electricity. An inverter converts the direct current output to alternating current, which is then either consumed or exported. Depending on size, turbines may be building-mounted or free-standing.

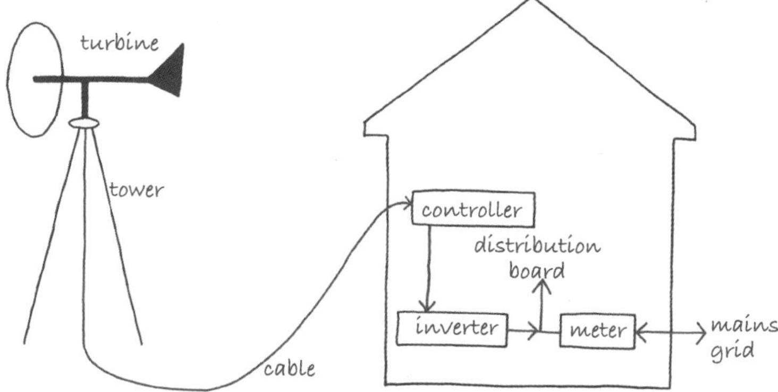

27.39 Micro wind turbine: a simplified diagram of a grid connected micro wind installation.

Power output

For horizontal axis turbines, the power generated by a wind turbine depends on:

- quality of the wind – wind speed, duration, turbulence
- area of the rotor – bigger blades capture more energy
- efficiency – proportion of the energy (typically 0.35) that can actually be captured
- efficiency of the generator
- transmission and conversion losses – heat losses in cables, etc.

Not all of the energy available in the airstream can be harvested by the turbine because the air would have no energy left to blow away downstream. The theoretical limit is 0.59 (the Betz limit). In addition to this is the ability of the rotor blade to capture the available energy – this is determined by the shape of the blade. Combining these two factors (Betz's law and rotor design), the maximum efficiency obtainable at optimal rotation speed is typically 0.35 – in other words, the turbine can capture 35% of the available wind energy.

Every wind turbine has a distinct power curve that illustrates the power output of the unit at a given wind speed. When the wind is blowing at a speed below or above the optimum the output is reduced. The optimum wind speed should be compared to climate data at the installation site so as to match the turbine to the local average wind speed.

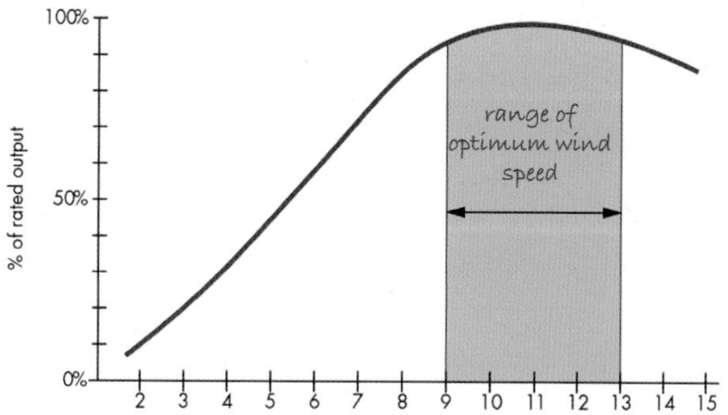

27.40 Power curve: allows optimum wind speed to be determined.

The power output of a turbine can be calculated using the formula:

power = CPoa x A x PA x G

where:

CPoa = aerodynamic power coefficient (efficiency of the rotor to capture energy)
A = swept area of the blade
PA = power density of the wind (0.6125 x S^3)
S = wind speed
G = generator efficiency

Worked example

Given the following data, calculate the output of the wind turbine.

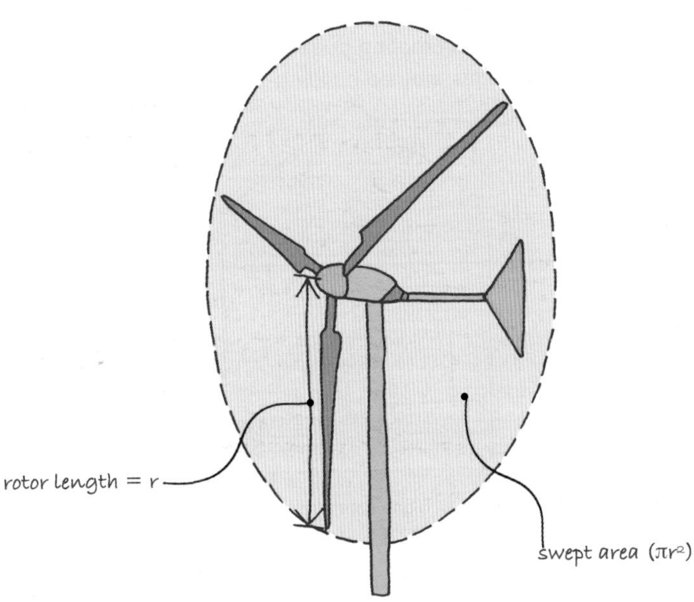

27.41 Wind turbine: dimensions.

Data:

rotor length:	1.75m
wind speed:	10m/s
CPoa:	0.35
G:	0.90

Calculate swept area:

area circle $= \pi (r^2)$
$= 3.14 (1.75^2)$
$= 3.14 (3.0625)$
$= 9.61625$
$= 9.62m^2$

Calculate power density of air:

PA $= 0.6125 \times (S^3)$
$= 0.6125 \times (10^3)$
$= 0.6125 \times 1{,}000$
$= 612.5$

Calculate power:

power = CPoa x A x PA x G
$= 0.35 \times 9.62 \times 612.5 \times 0.9$
= 1,856.06W
= 1.856kW

The power output is proportional to the square of the length of the rotor blade and the cube of the wind speed. So, for the calculation shown above, if the wind speed was halved to 5m/s the power output would be only 232W (i.e. $^1/_8$ of the output at 10m/s).

Combined heat and power

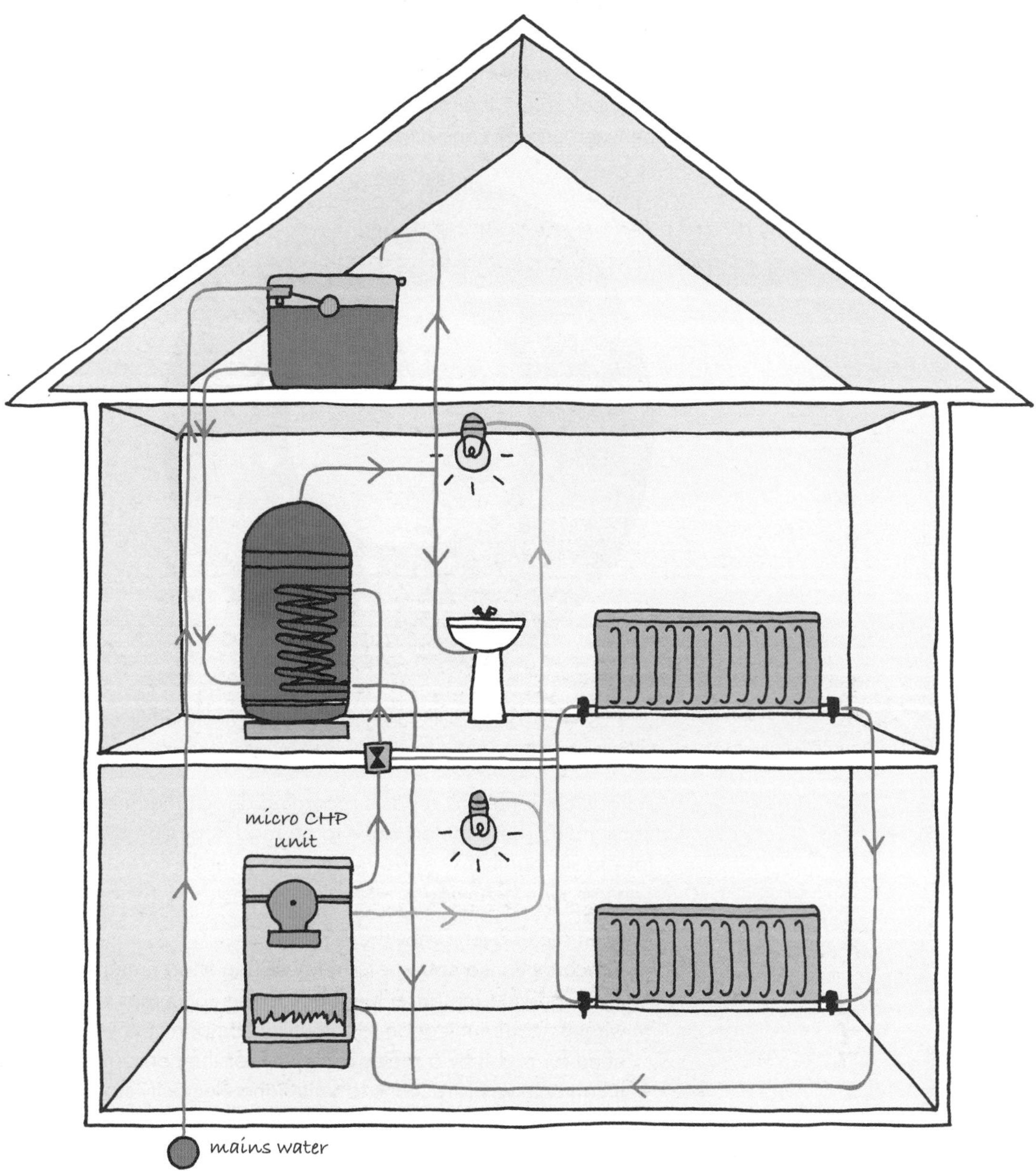

27.42 Combined heat and power (CHP): a simplified diagram of a CHP installation.

Combined heat and power (CHP) is a process in which both space/water heating and electricity are produced at the same time. CHP units usually burn natural gas or biomass (e.g. wood pellets/chips). When the fuel is burned the heat energy produced is used to provide space and water heating. Additional heat is used to drive a generator that produces electricity. Most homes that currently use a gas boiler could install a micro CHP unit.

Unlike traditional gas boilers, which are designed to heat water quickly and then shut down, micro CHP units are designed to run for long periods to maximise the amount of electricity generated. Micro CHP units have a relatively low heat output and will take longer to reach full temperature. They are best suited to situations where there is a demand over a relatively long period.

While most CHP units consume natural gas (a fossil fuel), because they generate electricity on-site, they do help to reduce the carbon emissions associated with electricity consumed from the national grid.

Smart metering

Smart metering is designed to make consumers more aware of their energy consumption behaviour. It shows the consumer, in real time, how much energy they are using and when they are using it. Smart meters can be used to monitor electricity and gas consumption.

The smart meter rate clock is a visual guide to the cost of energy around the clock. It highlights the peak rate – the most expensive time to cosume electricity. Knowing more about the link between energy consumption and cost reduces energy consumption in a typical household.

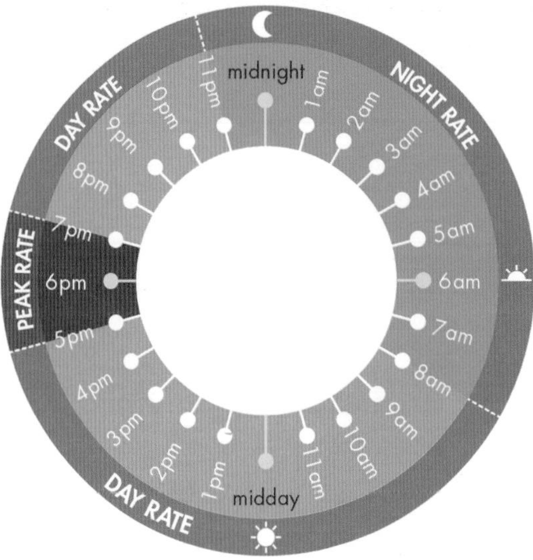

27.43 Smart meter rate clock: designed to increase awareness of the cost of consuming electrical energy over a 24-hour period.

A traditional meter is a basic recording device that measures the amount of electrical energy consumed. These meters have to be read in person by the energy company's representative every four to six months. They do not provide useful information to the consumer about their energy consumption behaviour.

A smart meter overcomes these problems:

- it records consumption of energy during short time periods
- it can provide real-time feedback to the consumer via an energy monitor unit
- wireless communication to the utility company allows readings to be transmitted without the need for a visit by a meter reader or for the consumer to submit a meter reading
- it can receive instructions to switch the electricity supply to the premises on or off
- it can distinguish between and record the import and export of electricity.

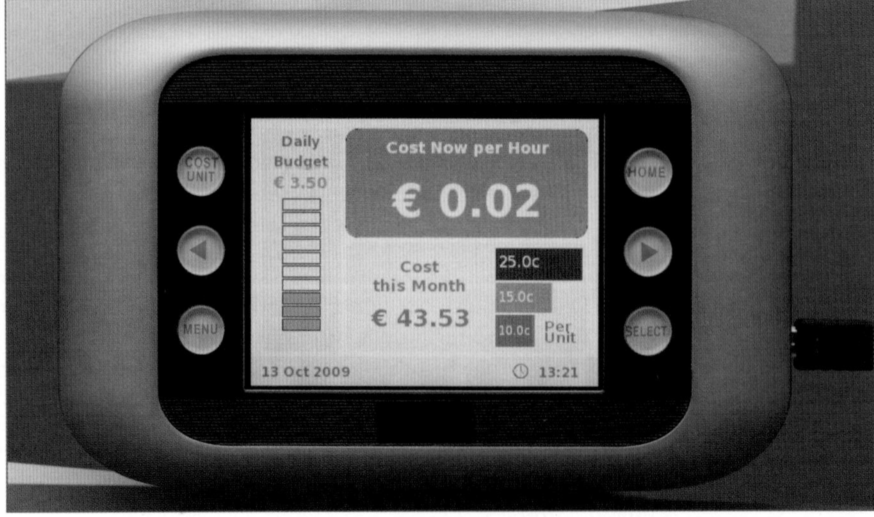

27.44 Smart meter: a typical residential smart meter. It provides detailed real-time feedback on energy consumption.

REVISION EXERCISES

1 Explain, using a neat annotated sketch, how a thermal power station generates electricity.
2 Describe, using a neat freehand sketch, how mains electricity is fed into a typical home.
3 Generate a neat annotated sketch of a circuit suitable for the supply of electrical energy to sockets in a typical home.
4 Explain how earthing and bonding contribute to electrical safety in the home.
5 Describe, using a neat freehand sketch, one micro generation system that can be used to generate electricity for a typical home.

CHAPTER 28

Water Supply

Water intake

This chapter should be read in conjunction with Chapter 3, where the broader issues relating to water consumption in the home and the sustainable use of water are examined.

Every home requires a constant supply of fresh clean water. In Ireland, 80% of the population is served by public water supplies. The remaining 20% is served by various group water schemes and private supplies (e.g. wells).

A typical domestic cold water supply begins with the connection to the water main. This is followed by an external stop valve and water meter, which are combined in a single unit. This is installed outside the property boundary to allow access for maintenance and meter reading by the water authority. The supply pipe is then fed into the dwelling via a protective insulated pipe.

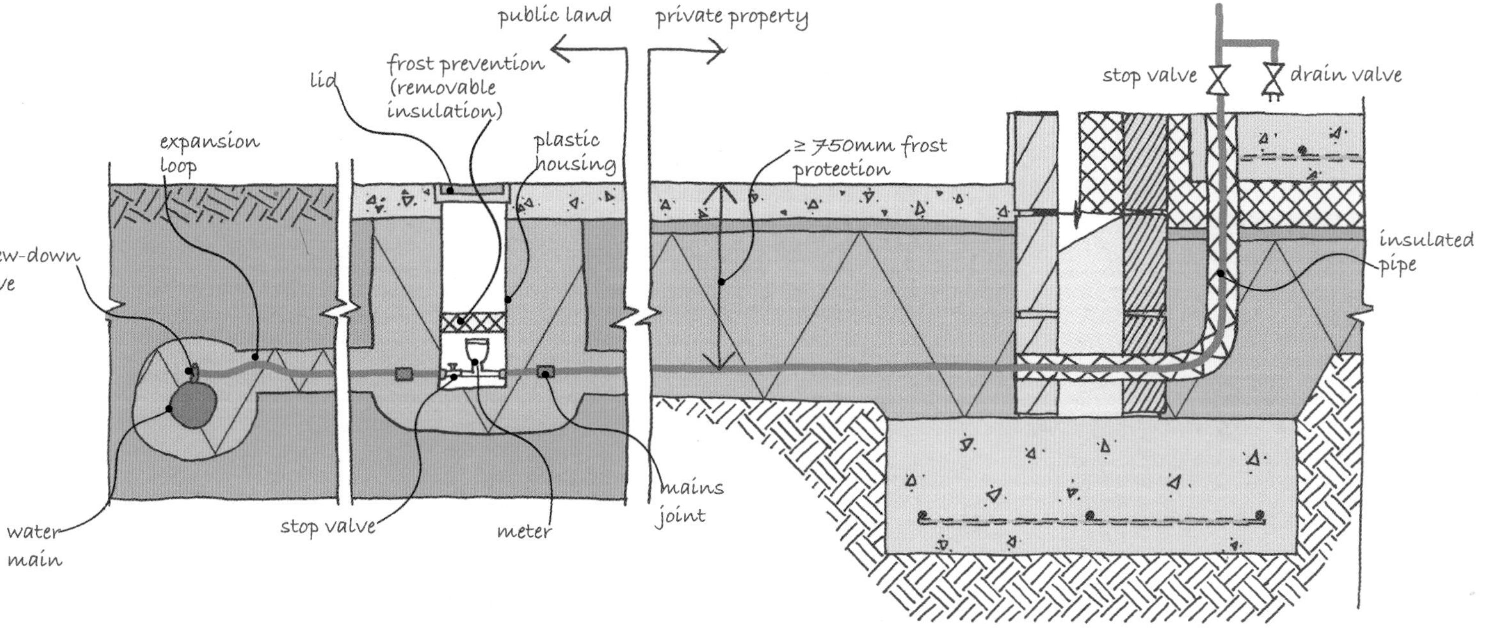

28.01 Water intake: mains connection, stop valve/meter and insulated feed into dwelling.

Water distribution

Water is distributed within a home via two systems: the cold water supply and the hot water supply.

Design criteria

The water supply system should meet the following design criteria:

- leak-proof – pipework must be capable of withstanding the stresses caused by changes in water pressure and temperature
- isolation – appliances (e.g. radiators) can be isolated to facilitate maintenance or replacement
- drainage – it should be possible to drain the system
- overflow – any appliance that stores water (e.g. cistern) should have an overflow device to prevent flooding.

ACTIVITIES

Check out the location of the external stop valve for your home. Open the cover and see if you would be able to turn off the supply if the need arose (older systems need a special tool).

Cold water supply

The main feed delivers water directly to the cold tap at the kitchen sink. This is the only source of drinking water in a typical home. All other cold water outlets are fed from a storage cistern (usually in the attic). Water is gravity-fed from the cistern to the appliances around the house. This type of system is called an indirect system.

The benefits of an indirect system include:

- reserve supply in case of mains failure
- balanced pressure to all appliances
- less demand on main supply during peak periods.

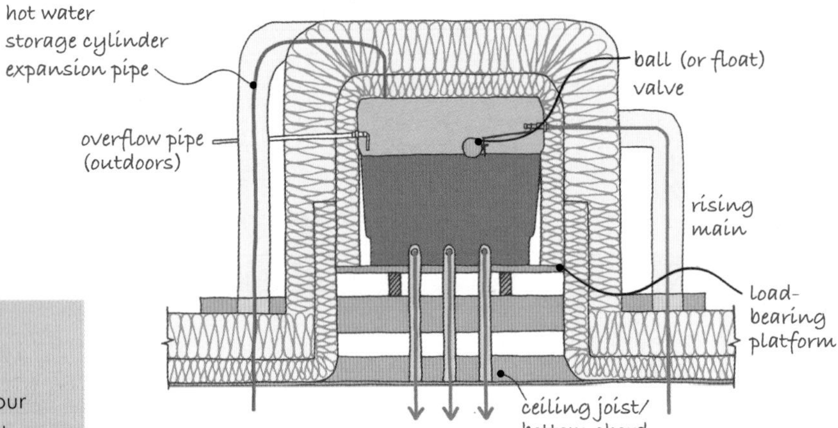

28.02 Storage cistern: the load (i.e. weight) of the cistern is spread by the supporting timbers and the pipework and cistern are insulated against freezing in winter.

ACTIVITIES

Find the location of the internal stop valve for your home. Turn on the cold tap at the kitchen sink and then turn off the internal stop valve: the water should stop flowing from the tap.

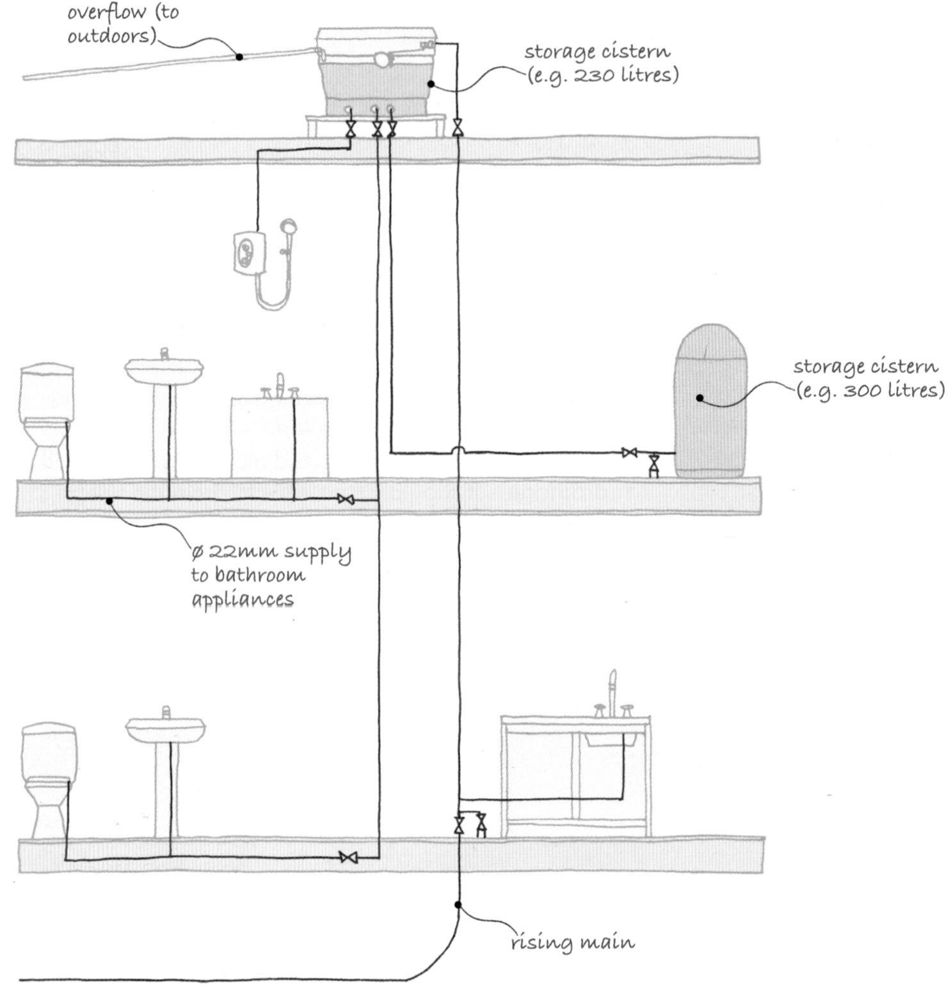

28.03 Cold water supply: typical indirect system.

Rainwater harvesting

Rainwater harvesting is the collection of water from the roof and paved areas of a building. This water would usually be lost to the drainage system, into the ground or to the atmosphere through evaporation. Instead the rainwater is collected, filtered and reused as a substitute for treated mains water. Water collected in this way cannot be used for drinking, bathing, showering or where there is any possibility of it being drunk. However, harvested rainwater is suitable for general cleaning, toilets, laundry, watering plants, washing cars and other outdoor uses.

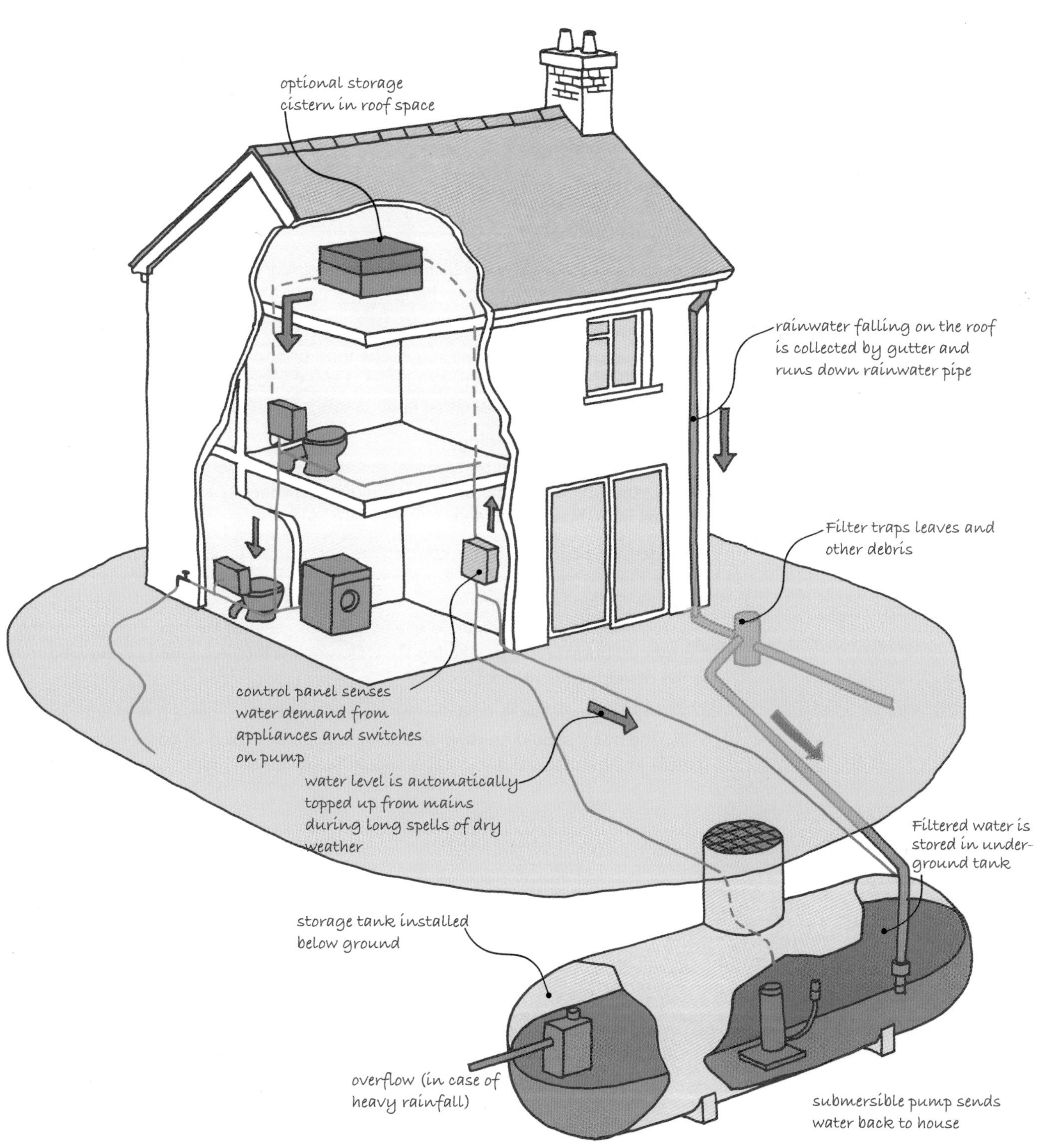

28.04 Rainwater harvesting: an integrated system that supplies harvested water to sanitary appliances.

Hot water supply: building regulations standard

In a typical home built to building regulations standard, the hot water system is used to provide both space heating and water heating:

- space heating – heating of the indoor spaces (i.e. rooms) usually via radiators or underfloor heating
- water heating – heating of the water supply (i.e. hot taps).

A typical hot water and central heating system consists of a heat source(s), thermal store and heat emitters.

- heat sources
  - boiler (oil, gas, solid fuel, biomass)
  - solar panels
  - heat pump (ground source, air source).
- thermal stores
  - hot water cylinder
  - solar cylinder.
- heat emitters
  - radiators
  - underfloor heating.

There are numerous ways in which these elements can be combined and interconnected. The most common approaches are shown here.

Heat sources

All heat energy comes from the sun in one form or another. Solar gain through windows is examined in detail in Chapters 17 and 21. Here the technology behind fossil fuel heat sources, solar thermal panels and domestic heat pumps is examined.

Condensing boiler technology

A boiler is a machine that burns a fuel to produce heat energy. Boilers used for domestic heating usually consume oil or natural gas. The major drawback of fossil fuels is that carbon dioxide is released when they are burned.

A condensing boiler is a boiler in which the hot exhaust gases are recycled to provide preheating for the intake water. When this happens the moisture in the exhaust gases condensates as the air cools, i.e. as the heat energy is transferred from the hot gases to the incoming water. The benefit of this type of boiler is that it is more energy efficient – less of the heat energy from the fuel is lost in the exhaust gases. Also, preheating the water means that less energy is required to bring the water to the desired temperature.

TGD L (2011) requires that oil- or gas-fired boilers must achieve a minimum seasonal efficiency of 90%. The boiler should be room sealed (intake air and exhaust gases should be sourced/vented directly to the outdoors) and the flue should be driven by a fan.

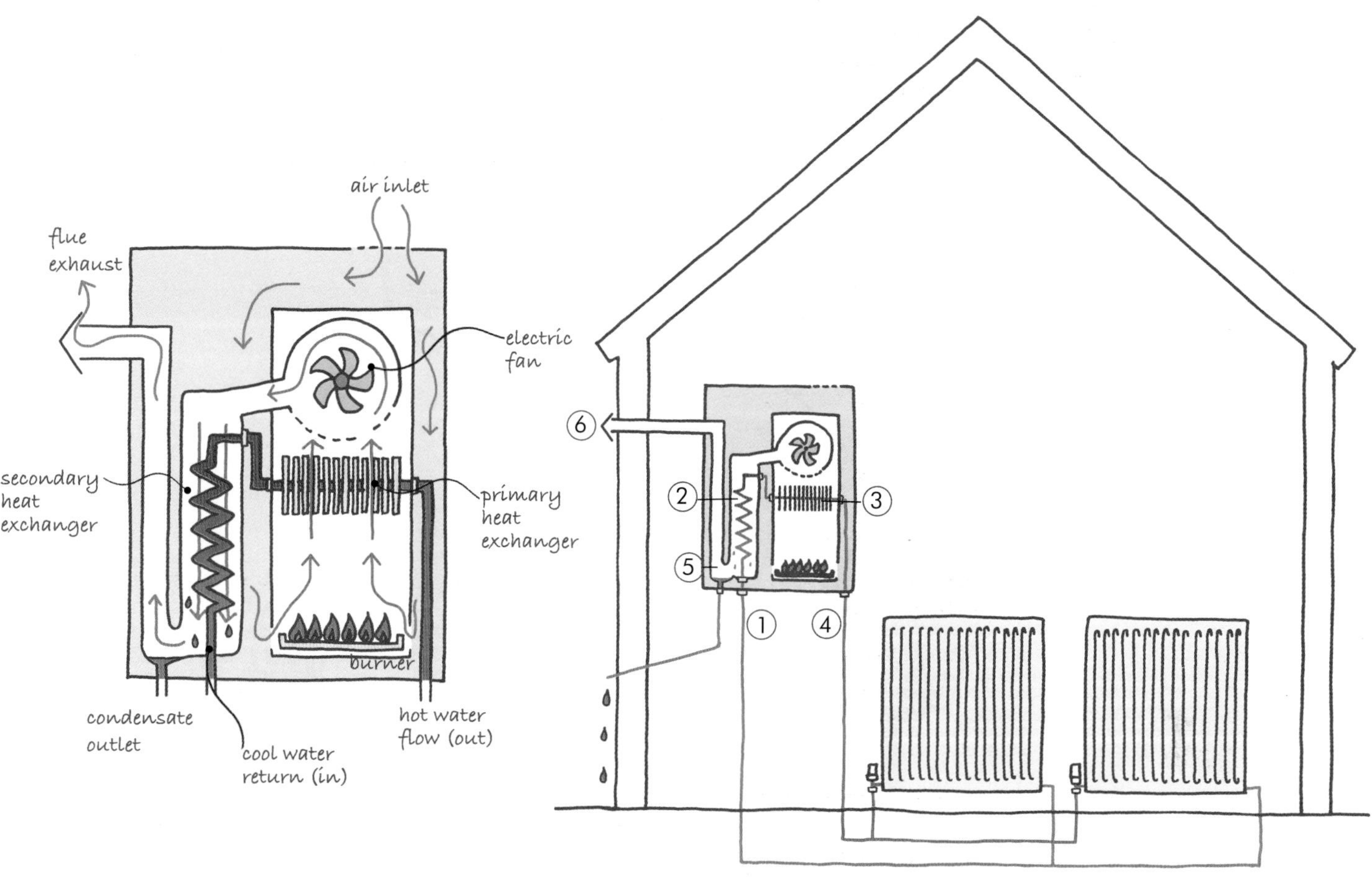

1 Cool water return
Cool water returns from the radiators around the house.

2 Secondary heating
The cool water is warmed by hot exhaust gases.

3 Primary heating
The water passes through the main heat exchanger where it is heated by the burner.

4 Hot water flow
The hot water leaves the boiler and is distributed to the radiators around the house.

5 Condensate
The water vapour condenses as the heat energy is transferred from the hot exhaust gases to the cool water.

6 Flue exhaust
The waste gases (including carbon dioxide) are pumped to the outdoor air.

28.05 Condensing boiler: a simplified schematic of a condensing gas boiler installation.

ACTIVITIES

Investigate the space and water heating system in your home.

- How is the hot water supply to the taps heated?
- How are the rooms heated (e.g. radiators, underfloor heating)?
- What energy source is used (e.g. oil, gas, etc.)?
- Is there a zoning system for space heating (e.g. downstairs/upstairs)?
- Are there temperature sensors for each room?
- Is there a renewable energy source (e.g. solar panel)?

Wood pellet boiler technology

The carbon released when wood is burned was originally captured by the wood during photosynthesis when the tree was growing. In this way, wood can be considered a fairly 'carbon neutral' fuel. While some embodied energy is linked to harvesting, processing and transport of the wood, compared to fossil fuels, wood from certified sources is a sustainable fuel.

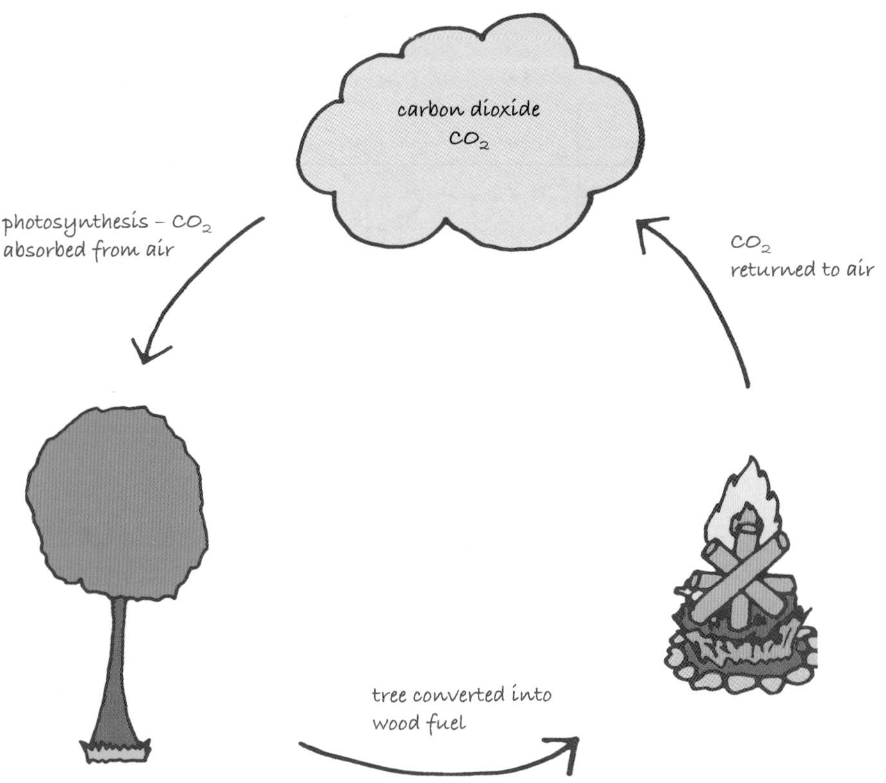

28.06 Wood: a sustainable fuel source.

Wood pellets can be bought in bags or in bulk. Bulk purchasing (i.e. more than 3,000kg at a time) is recommended because it is more economical. Wood pellet products should carry the WFQA (Wood Fuel Quality Assurance) label. Products with the WFQA label are independently tested to ensure the quality of the product (e.g. moisture content, calorific value) and that the wood is sourced sustainably and in compliance with EU regulations.

28.07 Wood pellets: a sustainable fuel.

28.08 Wood Fuel Quality Assurance label: wood pellets should be sourced from a certified supplier.

When storing wood pellets it is very important to keep them dry (less than 10% moisture content). Ready-made wood pellet storage tanks are available for this purpose. A storage space that can hold at least three tonnes (3,000kg) is recommended for a typical home. A home built to Passivhaus standard would require much less storage.

A typical wood pellet boiler has an integrated fuel hopper where the pellets are loaded. This can be done by hand or by an automated feed system. The boiler can be set up to run automatically based on room temperature, a timer or when linked to a whole-house system control unit. Wood pellet boilers are far more efficient than open fires and are a good replacement for an open fire in a typical house.

The relatively low output of a wood pellet boiler makes it an ideal heat source in a home built to the Passivhaus standard. Like any boiler, it should be room sealed (intake air and exhaust gases should be sourced/vented directly to the outdoors) and the flue should be driven by a fan. When used as part of an integrated Passivhaus heating system, the heat energy in the flue gases can be recovered and transferred to the thermal (e.g. water storage cylinder) store.

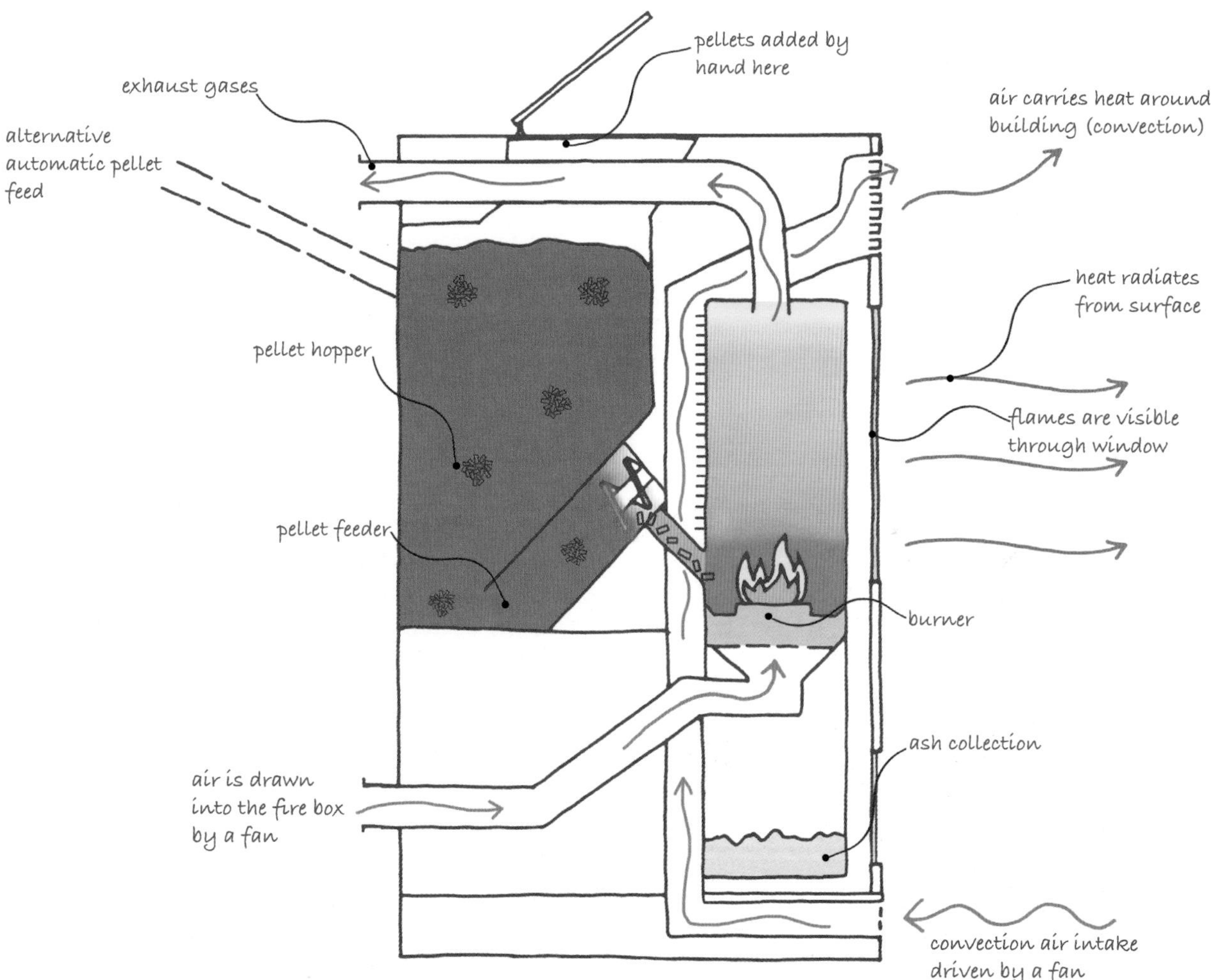

28.09 Wood pellet boiler: simplified section showing typical design features.

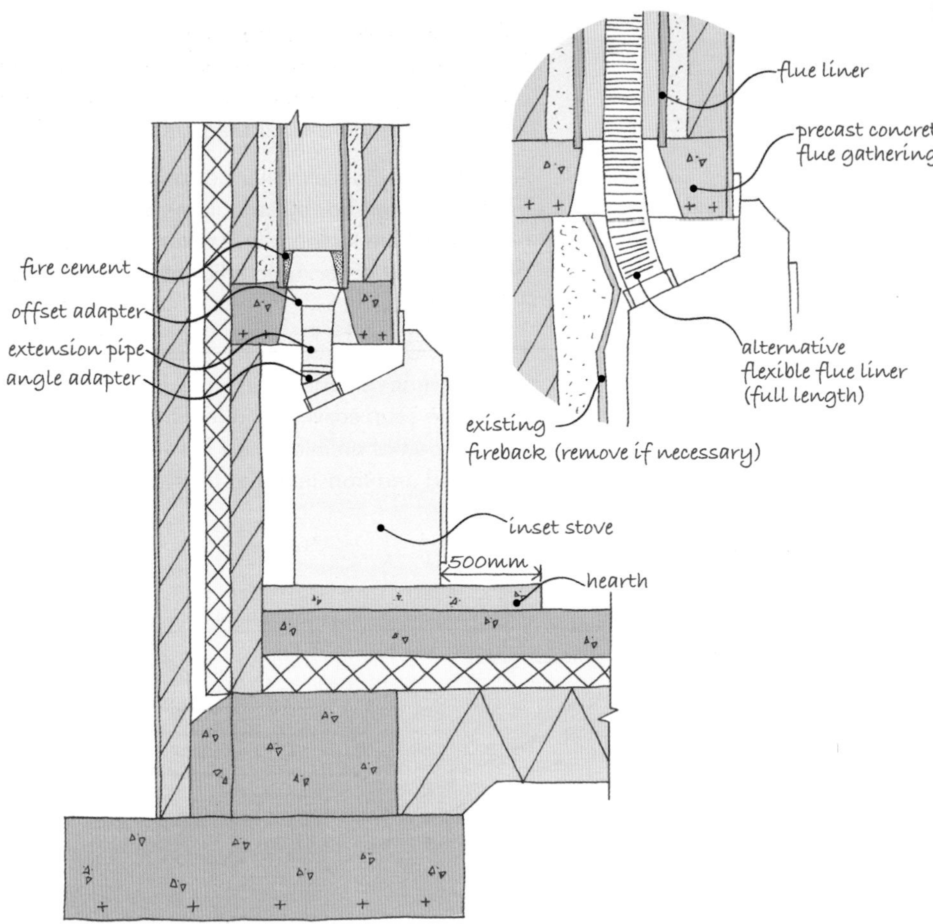

28.10a Wood pellet boiler: sample installation detail shown in traditional fireplace/chimney construction

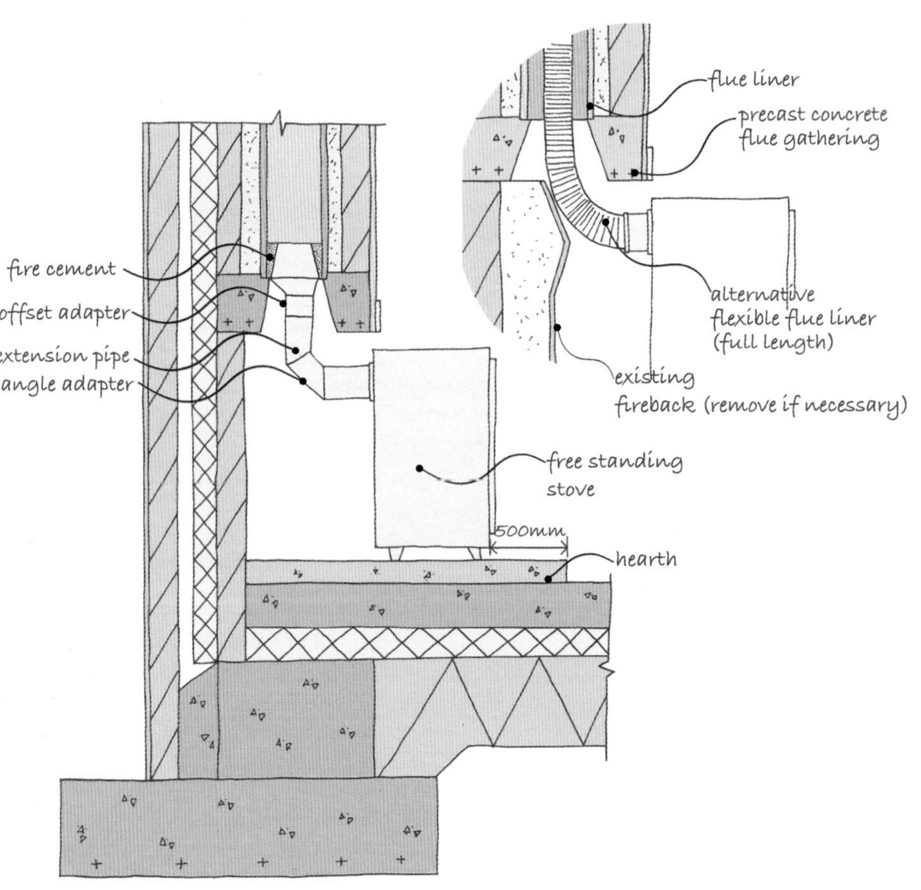

28.10b Wood pellet boiler: sample installation detail.

Solar thermal panel technology

Solar thermal panels are designed to provide heat energy which can be used for space heating or water heating. They should not be confused with solar photovoltaic panels which are designed to produce electricity (see Chapter 27).

There are two main types of solar thermal panel: flat plate collectors and evacuated tube collectors. The basic concept is the same for both. The solar energy that is absorbed by the pipes in the panel is transferred to the solar fluid in the pipes. When the temperature at the panel output is above the temperature at the thermal store, the pump is switched on by the controller and the fluid circulates. This fluid is pumped in a continuous loop from the panel to the thermal store (i.e. cylinder), where the heat energy is transferred to the water.

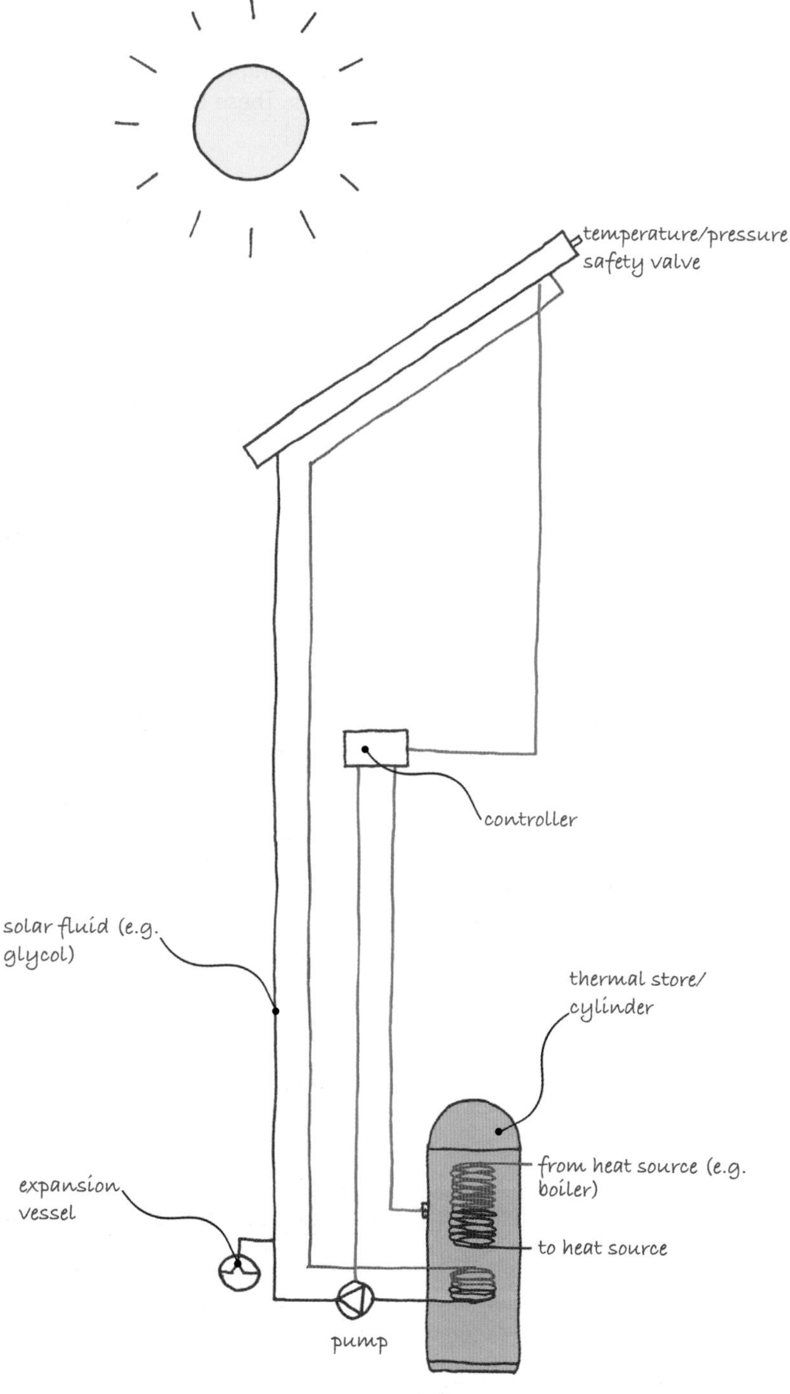

28.11 Solar panel: simplified schematic of a typical installation.

Heat pump technology

Heat pump technology is used in refrigerators. In a fridge the heat pump extracts heat from food and pumps it out into the kitchen air. Heat pumps that are used to provide space and water heating work on exactly the same principle. Heat is extracted from a warm place and transferred to a cold place. The source of heat is usually the ground or the air. Although the ground or air may not seem like a good source of heat, they are, because the ground temperature is consistently around 10°C below a depth of 600mm. Similarly the mean annual outdoor air temperature in Ireland is 10°C.

A heat pump consists of three independent loops. The outdoor loop contains a fluid (a water–anti-freeze mix). This fluid flows through a coil that is buried in the soil or held in a unit so that a fan can circulate air around it. The indoor loop provides heating (e.g. water heating/underfloor heating). The heat energy is transferred between these two loops via the third loop.

The third loop comprises a vapour compression cycle. This cycle is based on the scientific principle that when a gas or liquid is compressed its temperature rises. The gas or liquid in this case is a volatile evaporating and condensing fluid known as a refrigerant. (Most heat pumps use HFC (hydrofluorocarbon) refrigerants. These are harmful, greenhouse gases that require careful disposal when the unit is being replaced.)

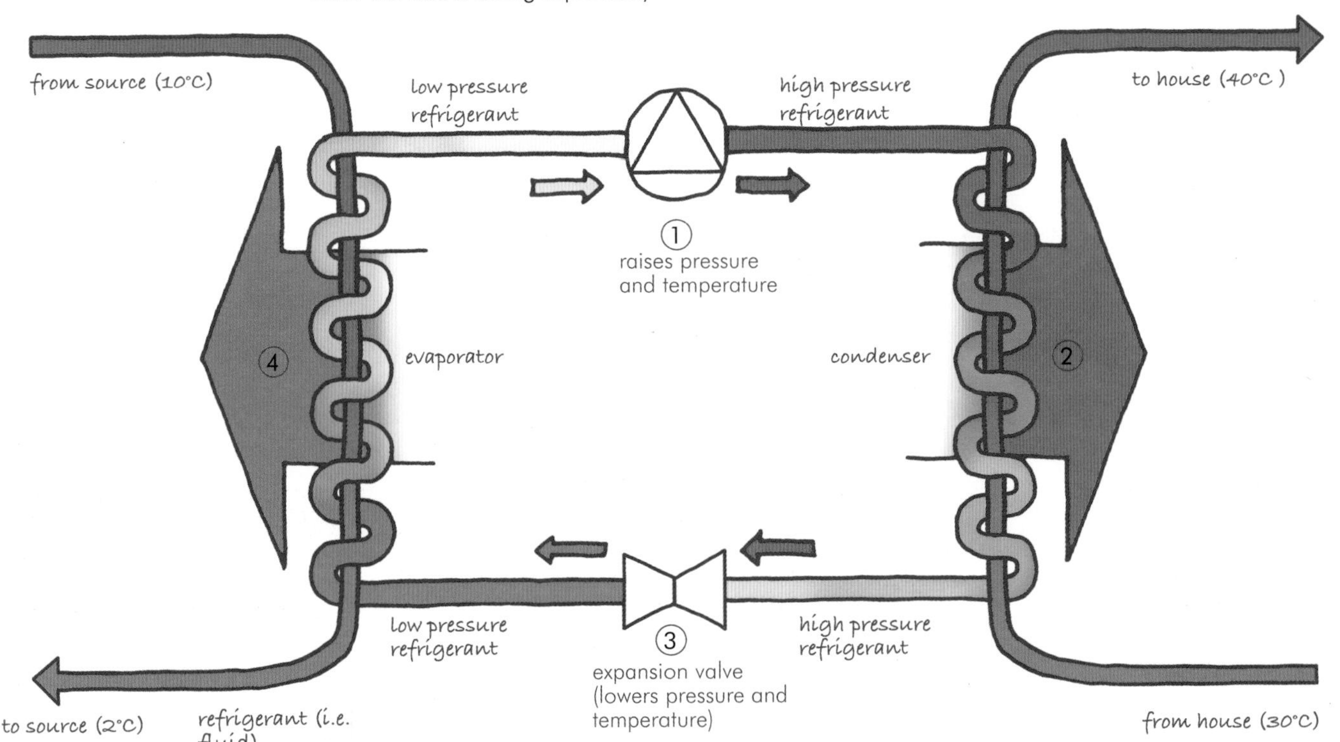

28.12 Heat pump: vapour compression cycle.

When the refrigerant passes through the compressor (1) its temperature rises. In the condenser (2), this heat is transferred to the indoor loop and the temperature of the refrigerant drops. The now cooler refrigerant passes through the expansion valve (3). This releases the pressure and causes the refrigerant to suddenly drop in temperature.The now cool refrigerant passes through the evaporator (4) where it warms up as heat energy is transferred from the heat source (ground/air) loop to the refrigerant and the cycle repeats as the refrigerant passes through the compressor again.

Even though the heat source is at a relatively low temperature (e.g. 10°C), it is warmer than the refrigerant, so heat energy is transferred.

The compressor is driven by electricity. However, heat pumps are quite efficient, so for every kilowatt hour of electrical energy consumed by the heat pump, two to four kilowatt hours of heat energy is produced. This ratio is called the coefficient of performance (COP).

Plumbing schematics

There are numerous layouts and designs that can used to supply space and water heating in a typical house. The schematics shown here are representative of two of the most common approaches. They are simplified to aid understanding.

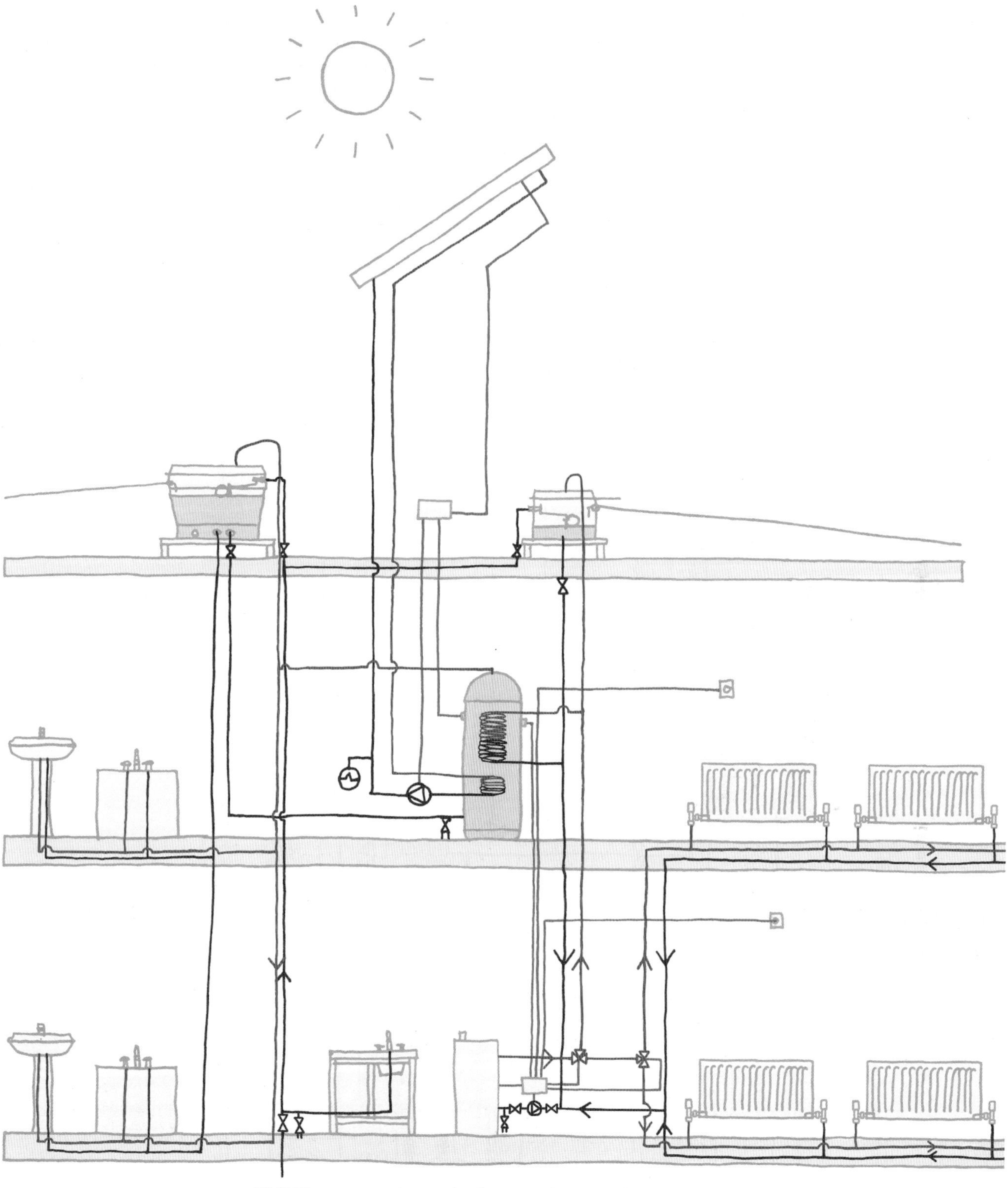

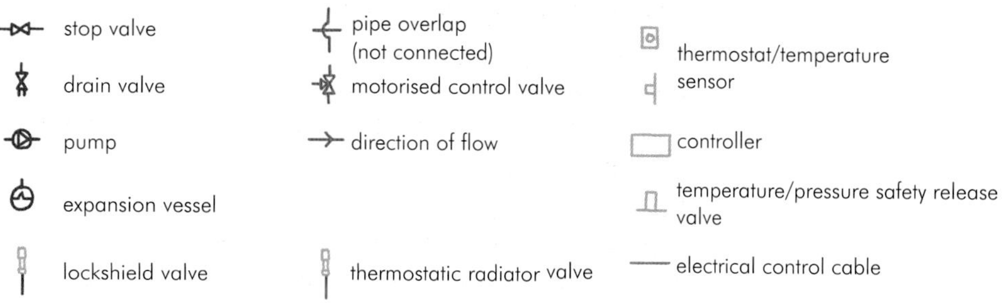

28.13 Hot water supply: typical indirect vented system with solar panel and boiler.

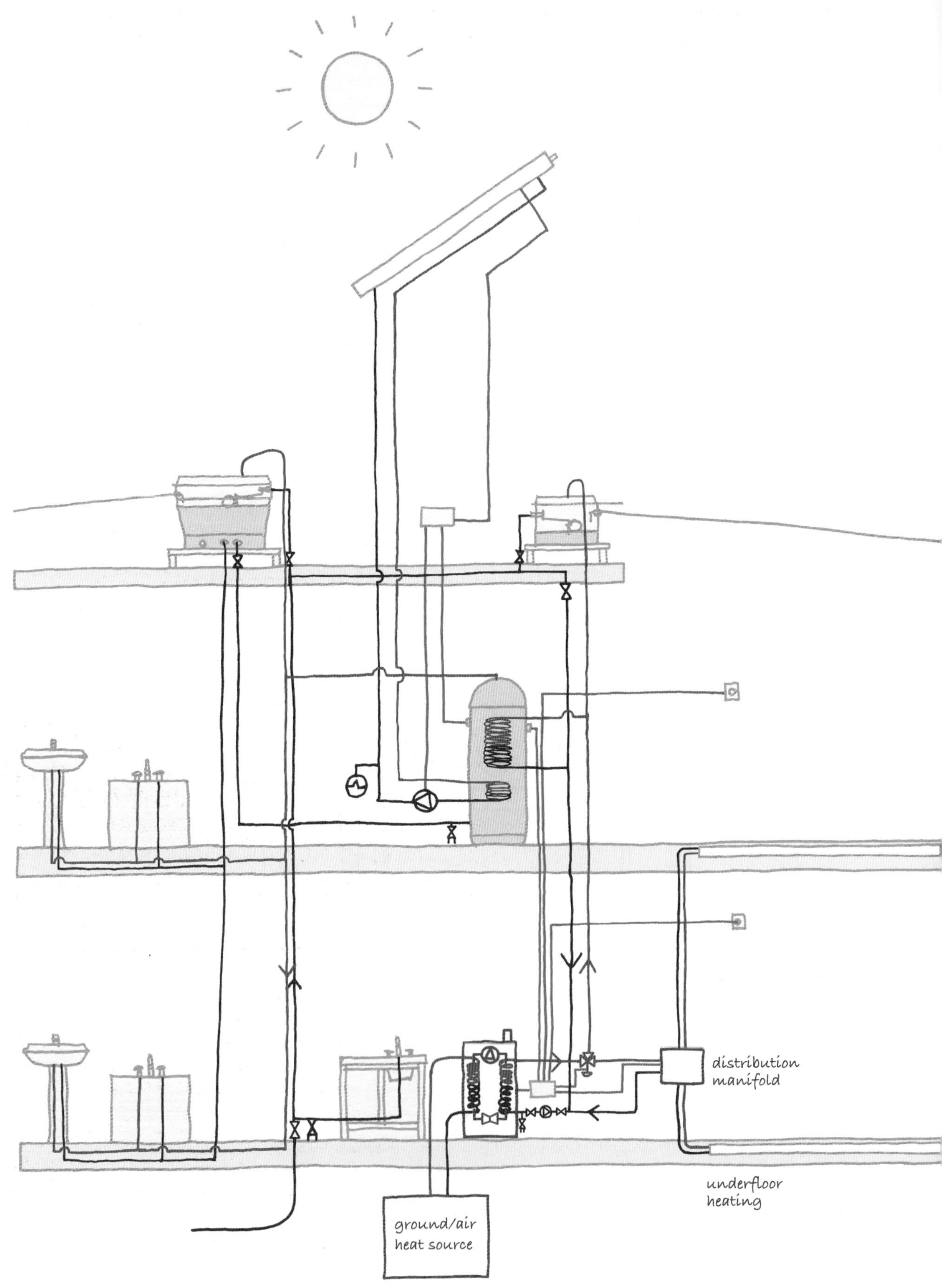

28.14 Hot water supply: typical indirect vented system with solar panel, heat pump and underfloor heating.

Hot water supply: Passivhaus standard

The space heating requirement of a home built to the Passivhaus standard is extremely low. In an average-sized home (e.g. 150m^2), the maximum space heating requirement in a worst-case scenario would be 1,500W. This could be met by leaving an ordinary hairdryer running! Traditional central heating systems are not required. In fact, one of the main challenges faced by early designers of passive houses in the 1990s was finding a heat source with a sufficiently low heat output; most boilers produce far too much heat for a Passivhaus.

Passivhaus heating concept

Most passive houses are heated using a compact heating system. This is a system that provides both space and water heating. It is also common for the MHRV system to be integrated with the space and water heating system. This type of 'all-in-one' system allows for heat energy to be shared between the various systems.

A useful way to think about this is to consider the Passivhaus as a closed loop in which heat energy travels from one part of the loop to another but never leaves. Of course, some energy is lost in a real system but the amount lost is very small; this is why it is possible to maintain year-round thermal comfort in a passive house without a traditional central heating system.

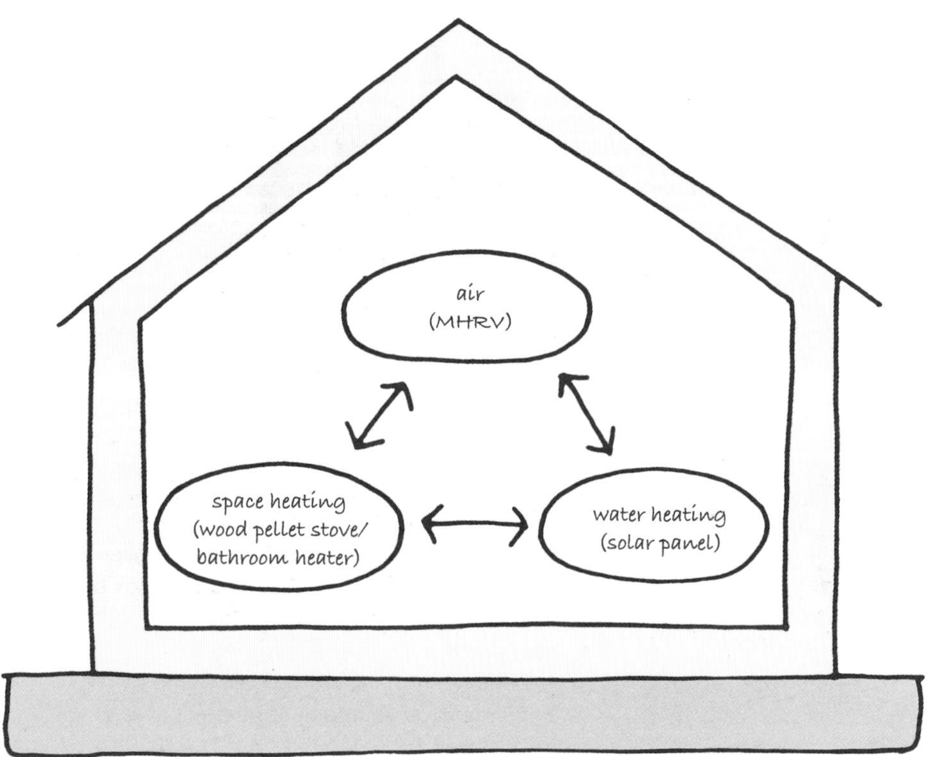

28.15 Passivhaus heating concept: heat energy is shared between systems.

A typical Passivhaus system uses similar components to those used in a traditional central heating system but on a much smaller scale. For example, a Passivhaus would usually have only one or two radiators in the entire building (usually in the bathrooms) and the boiler (if used) would be much smaller than a standard boiler.

As discussed in Chapter 26, it is possible to provide space heating solely by heating the fresh air intake; however, most home owners like to include a biomass boiler or bathroom radiator because people tend to like the 'idea' of having a fire as a focal point in a living room or they like a little extra heat in the bathroom.

Compact heating systems

Compact 'all-in-one' systems are housed in a single unit that is typically about the size of a large refrigerator. All the components are contained in this unit, including the heat source, heat exchange and the thermal store.

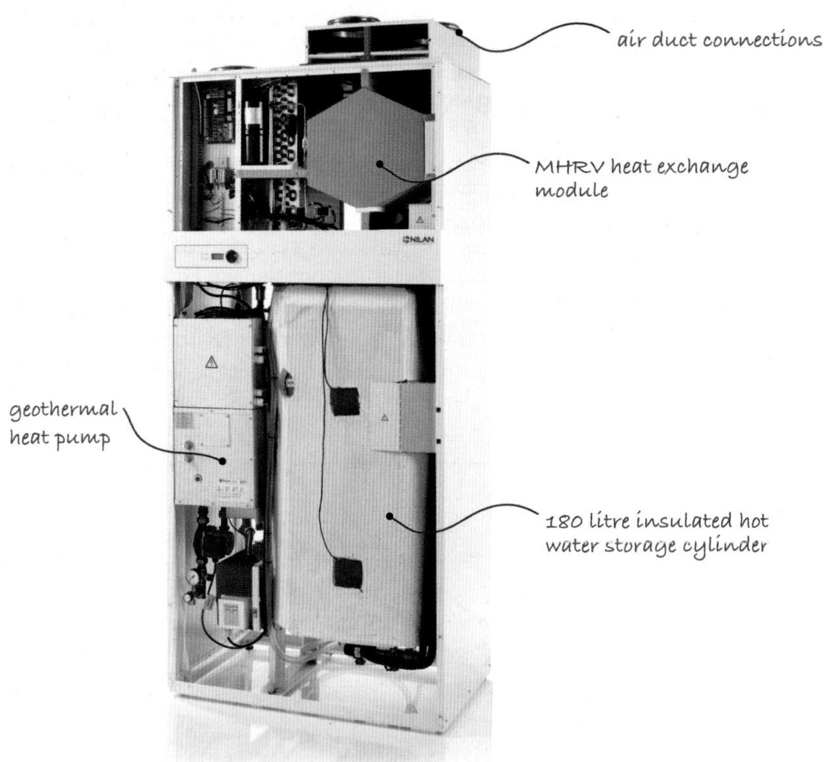

28.16 Compact heating system (dimensions 900x610x2,060). *Source:* Nilan.

A typical compact 'all-in-one' system consists of a heat source(s), thermal store and heat emitters.

- heat sources
  - boiler
    - biomass – low output wood pellet boiler
    - gas – compact condensing natural gas boiler
  - solar panels
  - heat pump
    - compact ground source heat pump
    - compact air source heat pump.
- thermal store
  - hot water cylinder – a large cylinder
  - solar cylinder – a secondary 'buffer' cylinder that uses water to store heat energy.
- heat emitters
  - MHRV system
  - radiators – usually in the bathroom only
  - underfloor heating – usually the bathroom floor only.

The explanations given below of how these systems might perform are simplified to make them easier to understand. In reality, the situation is very dynamic – the weather is constantly changing, as are indoor temperatures. These 'all-in-one' systems are constantly monitoring the entire system and making adjustments to keep the indoor temperature in the comfort zone and to provide sufficient hot water.

A typical 'all-in-one' compact system has several temperature sensors:

- outdoor air temperature
- supply air temperature (after heat exchange)
- supply air temperature (after post heater)
- exhaust air temperature

- top of the hot water cylinder
- bottom of the hot water cylinder
- heat pump condenser temperature
- heat pump evaporator temperature.

Careful consideration is given to the selection of an 'all-in-one' heating system for a Passivhaus to ensure that it matches the home properly – that is, that it suits the size of the home and the likely number of occupants. In addition, most designers choose to use Passivhaus-certified systems that they can be confident will perform as expected when installed.

Space and water heating via compact heat pump and solar panel

This 'all-in-one' system has two heat sources:

- solar panels capture solar energy to heat water in the thermal store (i.e. cylinder)
- compact heat pump captures heat energy from the exhaust air.

The small amount of heat energy left in the air after the heat recovery stage can be captured using a compact heat pump. This small amount of energy is sufficient to heat a Passivhaus. The really clever part of this design is the way the heat sources can support each other in various scenarios:

- during the summer the system has little work to do:
  - space heating is provided by solar gain through the windows and internal heat gains
  - water heating is provided by the solar panels.
- during the winter there are two possibilities:
  - low outdoor temperature (no clouds) but lots of sunshine – the ventilation system is in heat recovery mode, so the heat gain from the exhaust air is reduced but the solar panels are producing lots of heat, some of which can be used to post heat the supply air
  - milder outdoor temperature (overcast) but little sunshine – the solar panels are producing less heat energy, but the ventilation system is in bypass mode because the outdoor temperature is mild, so the compact heat pump can capture the heat energy from the exhaust air to provide hot water.

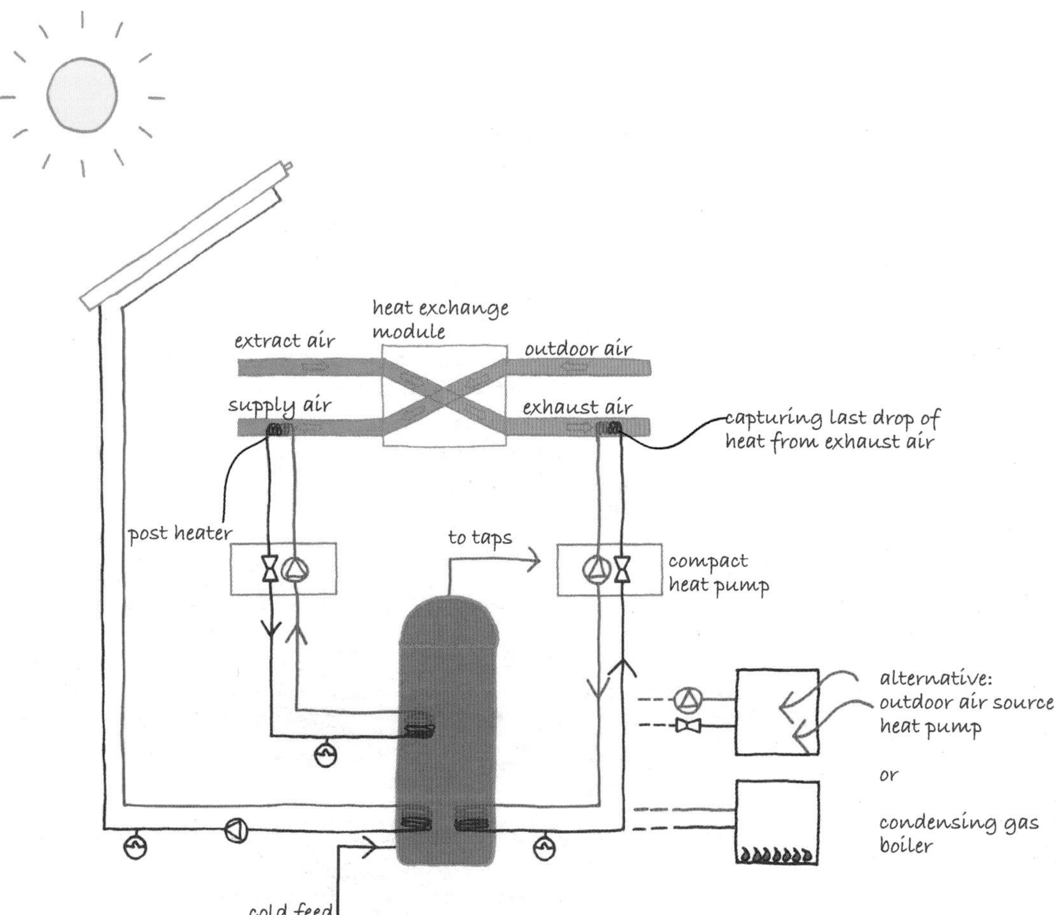

28.17 Passivhaus heating: space heating and hot water via MHRV system and solar panel (with alternative heat sources: condensing gas boiler or outdoor air source heat pump).

Space and water heating via biomass boiler and solar panel

This 'all-in-one' system has two heat sources:

- solar panels capture solar energy to heat water in the thermal store (i.e. cylinder)
- biomass boiler burns wood (e.g. pellets) to produce heat energy.

In this fully automated system the biomass boiler comes on when the control unit senses a drop in indoor temperature. The heat produced when the fuel burns is used in two ways:

- radiant heat from the unit warms the living space – this heat warms the air and travels throughout the building
- water is heated in the boiler and pumped to the storage cylinder, where it heats the stored water.

In addition, in a fully integrated system, the 'waste' heat in the exhaust gases from the boiler may be recovered and transferred to the thermal store. While this is the most energy-efficient use of a biomass boiler, in some installations the boiler is merely a stand-alone unit that produces radiant heat for the living space in the winter.

Similarly to the previous system, this system works in various scenarios:

- during the summer the system has little work to do:
  - space heating is provided by solar gain through the windows and internal heat gains
  - water heating is provided by the solar panels.
- during the winter there are two possibilities:
  - low outdoor temperature (no clouds) but lots of sunshine – the ventilation system is in heat recovery mode and the solar panels are producing heat for water heating and the biomass boiler provides backup
  - milder outdoor temperature (overcast) but little sunshine – the solar panels are producing less heat energy, and the ventilation system may be in bypass mode, so the compact heat pump can capture the heat energy from the exhaust air or the biomass boiler can switch on to provide hot water or space heating if required.

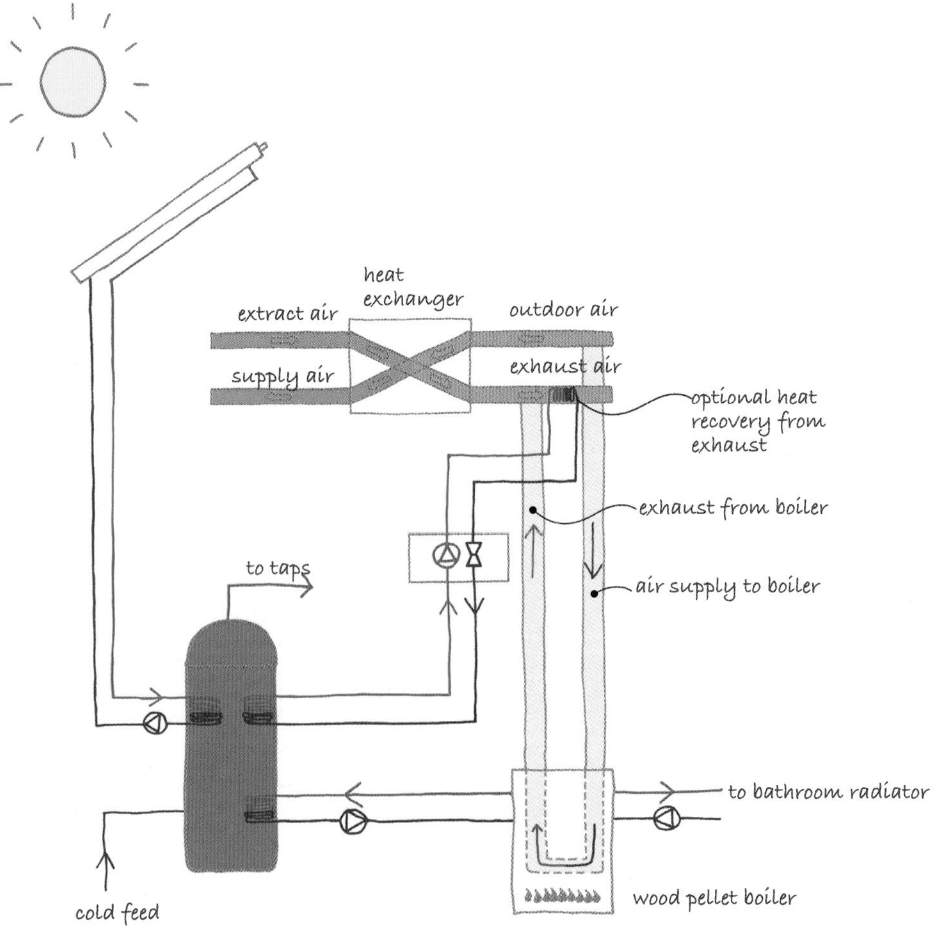

28.18 Passivhaus heating: space and water heating via biomass boiler (e.g. wood pellet) and solar panel.

REVISION EXERCISES

1 Describe, using a neat annotated sketch, how a typical home is connected to the mains water supply.
2 Describe, using a neat annotated sketch, how rainwater can be harvested for use in the home.
3 Generate a neat annotated sketch of the layout of a typical hot water supply system for a house designed to building regulations standard.
4 Generate a neat annotated sketch of a space and water heating system for a house designed to the Passivhaus standard.
5 Explain, using a neat annotated sketch, how a heat pump works.

CHAPTER 29

Drainage

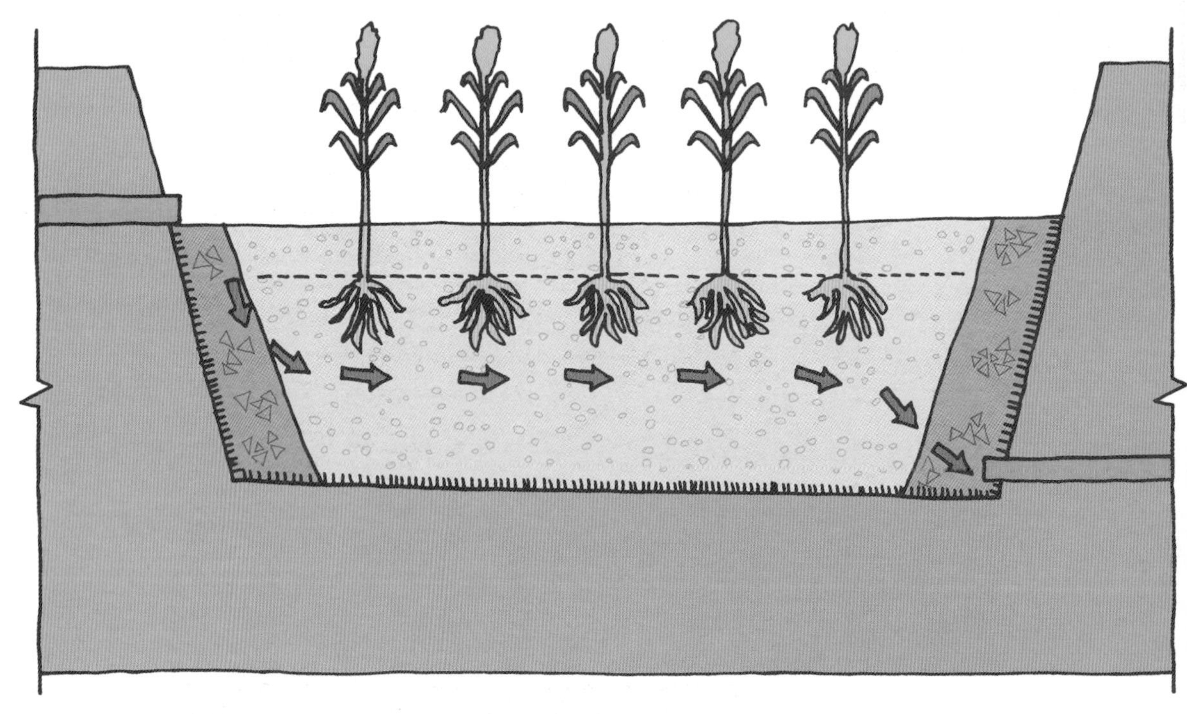

Wastewater is the term used to describe the water discharged from toilets, sinks, showers, baths, washing machines, etc. Surface water is rainwater collected from the roof and paved areas of a building. Drainage is the system of pipework (i.e. drains) used to carry wastewater and surface water from a building to a wastewater treatment facility. The treatment of wastewater may occur on site or off site, depending on the location of the home.

Wastewater is removed from a home via the drainage system. The drainage system should meet the following design criteria:

- leak-proof – pipework must prevent leakage inwards or outwards
- resist deposits of solids and blockages – the slope or gradient of the drains must be right. If the gradient is too steep the fluids will flow too quickly and the solids will be left behind, causing a blockage; if the slope is not steep enough the fluids won't flow readily.
- resist abrasion by grit (scouring) – especially storm drains
- resist corrosion by chemicals – e.g. cleaning products
- accommodate pressure – internal and external
- prevent the build-up of gases e.g. methane
- allow access for maintenance.

Above-ground pipework

Discharge stack

The pipework used to collect wastewater in a building typically comprises a discharge stack and branch pipes. The discharge stack is a vertical pipe into which each appliance is connected via a branch pipe. This vertical pipe is also called the soil vent pipe because it carries the soiled (i.e. toilet) water and the top of the pipe is open to the air to provide ventilation to the system. The ventilation prevents the build-up of gases. The length, slope and position of each branch pipe connected to the soil vent pipe is designed to ensure that the wastewater flows freely and blockages do not occur. These requirements are set out in TGD H (2010) Drainage and Wastewater Disposal. The discharge stack is commonly installed on the back wall of a dwelling, but it may also be positioned internally.

ACTIVITIES

Generate a neat freehand sketch of the floor plan(s) of your home. Indicate on the sketch the positions of all the appliances that generate waste water. Show how each appliance is connected to the main discharge stack/waste pipe.

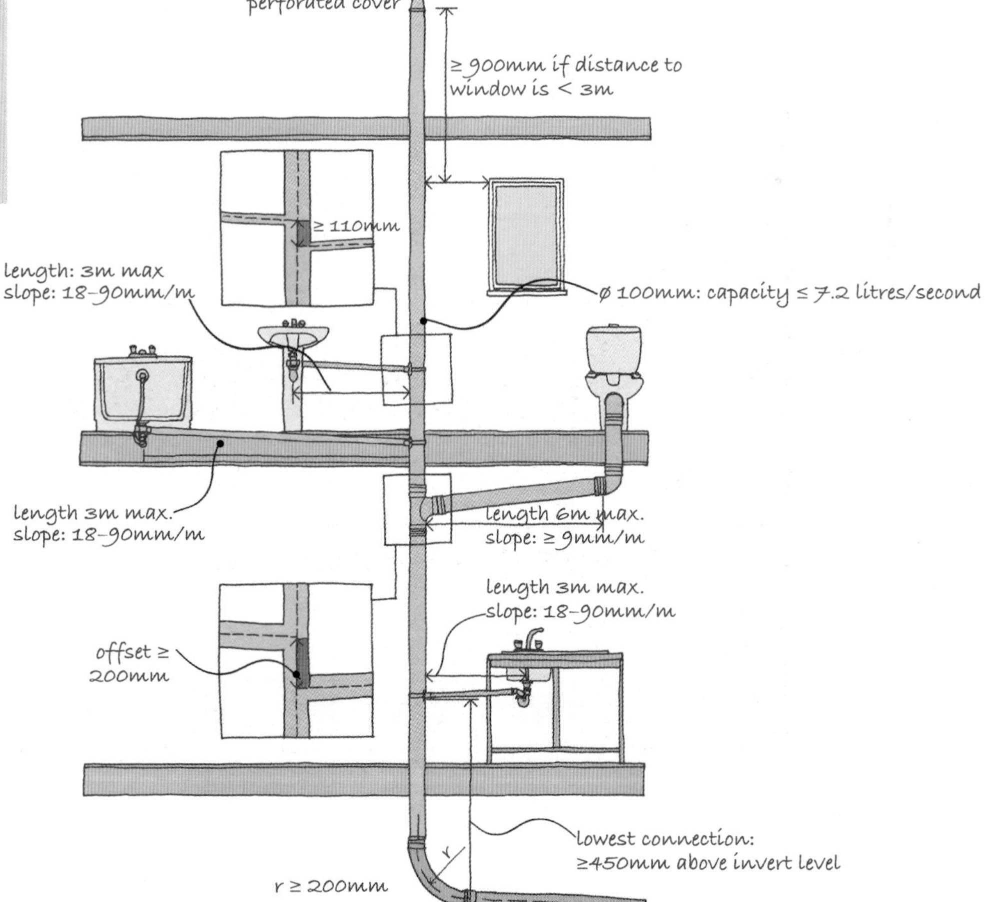

29.01 Discharge stack with branch pipes showing length, slope and offset requirements for installation. Based on ø100mm discharge stack and ø40mm branch pipes. Requirements differ for other pipe sizes.

Traps

A trap is used to connect each appliance (e.g. sink) to its branch pipe. The purpose of the trap is to prevent foul odours entering the home. A trap is simply a water-filled bend in the pipework. When an appliance is emptied the water flows away through the trap. The last portion of the water is left behind in the trap, creating a seal. Traps are available in a variety of shapes for different situations.

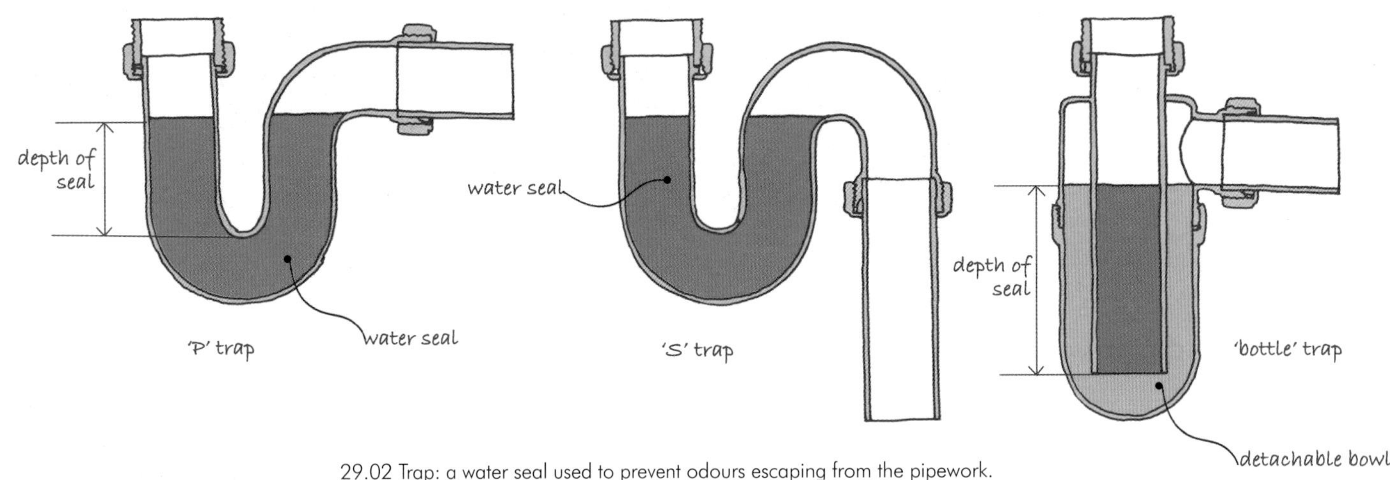

29.02 Trap: a water seal used to prevent odours escaping from the pipework.

Below-ground pipework

The pipework below ground continues from the bend at the bottom of the discharge stack and continues until it connects to a mains public sewer or on-site treatment system. Access junctions and manholes are installed to allow for connections and changes in direction or level along this path. It is essential that drains are laid at the correct depth and gradient to ensure that the wastewater flows smoothly.

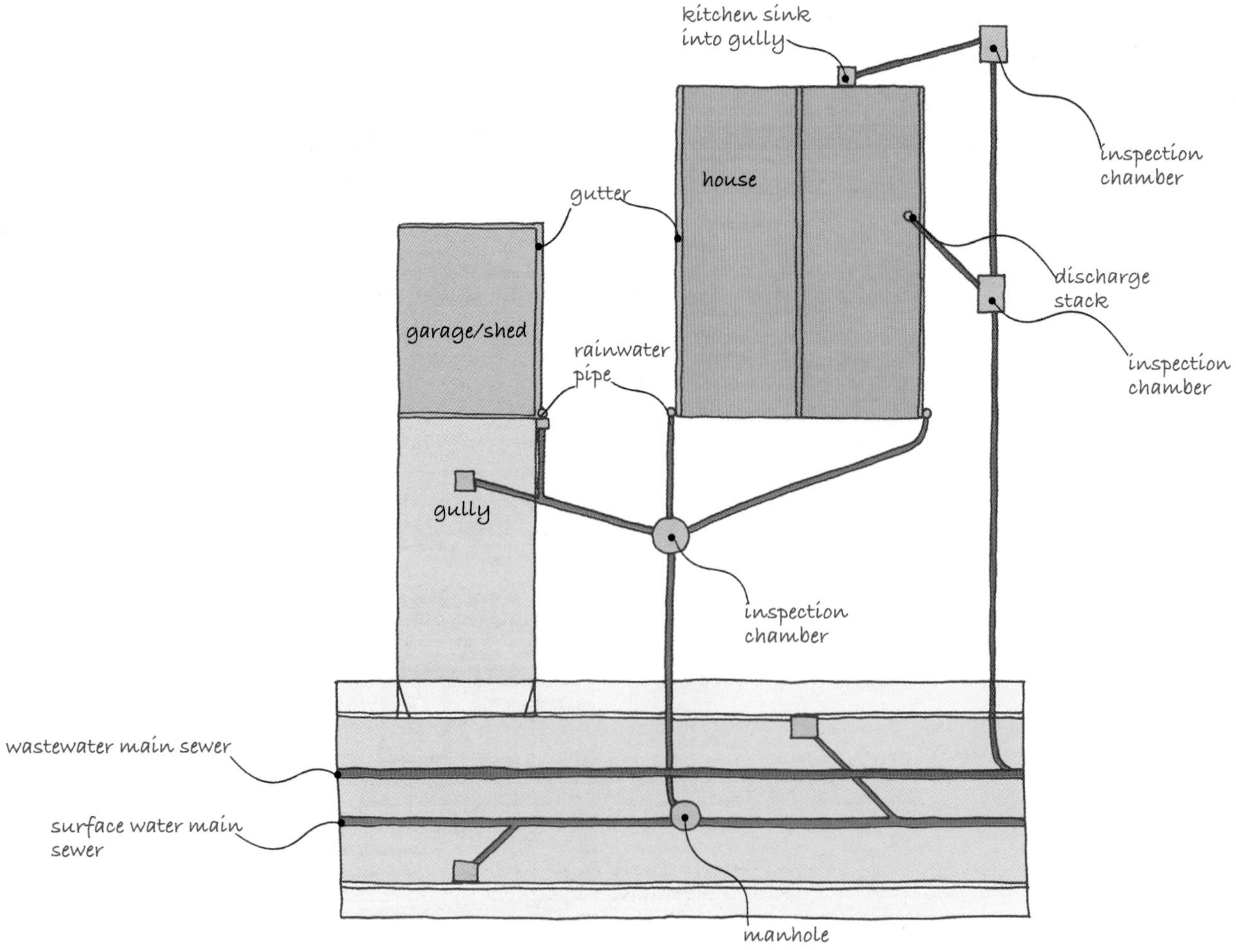

kitchen sink into gully
inspection chamber
house
gutter
discharge stack
garage/shed
rainwater pipe
inspection chamber
gully
inspection chamber
wastewater main sewer
surface water main sewer
manhole

29.03 Partial site plan showing wastewater and surface water drainage.

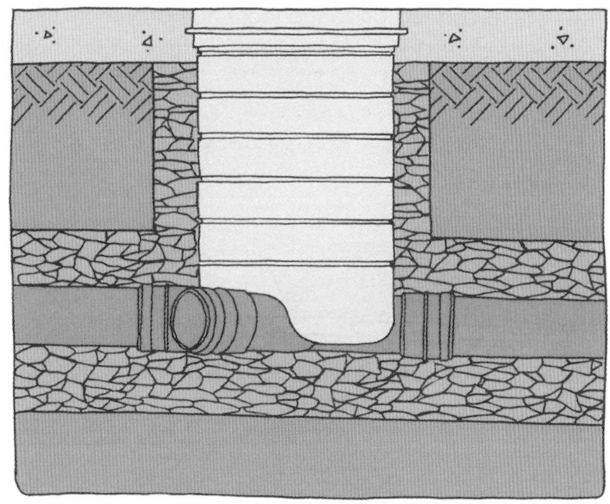

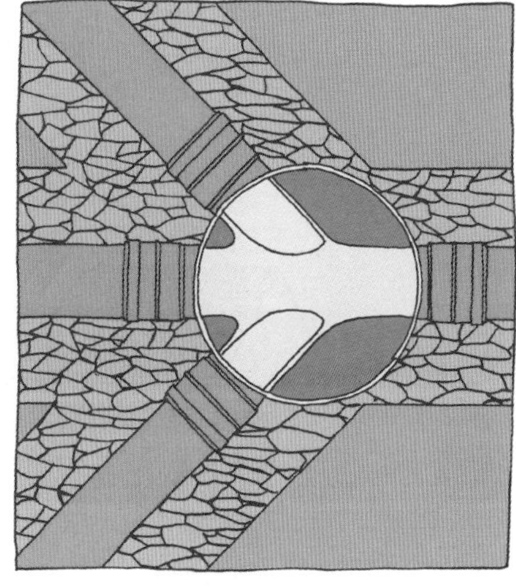

29.04 Access junction and inspection chambers allow shallow (<1,000mm) pipework junctions to be accessed for maintenance.

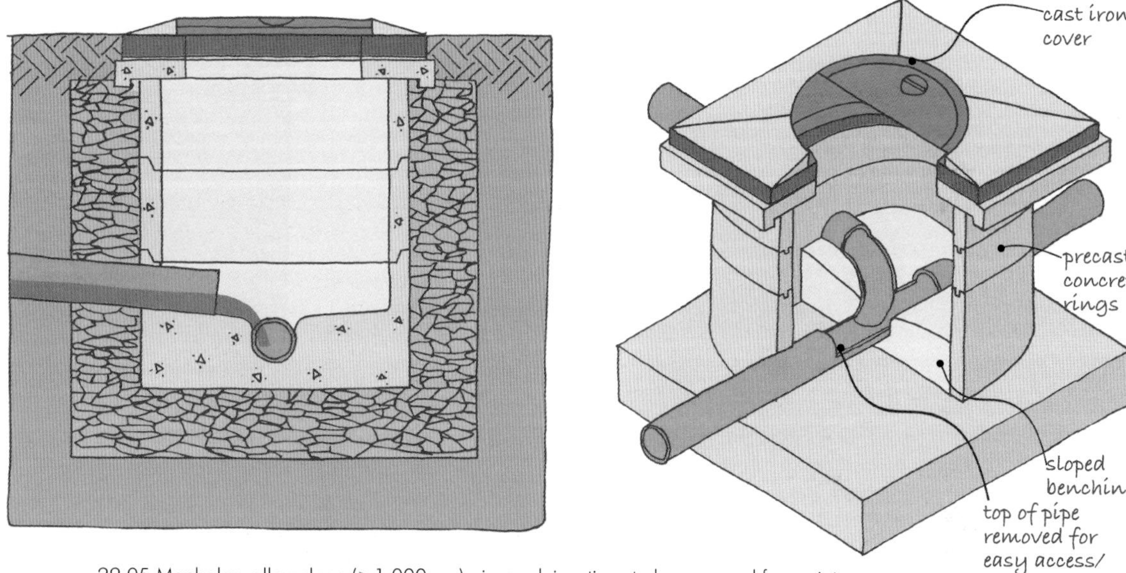

29.05 Manholes: allow deep (>1,000mm) pipework junctions to be accessed for maintenance.

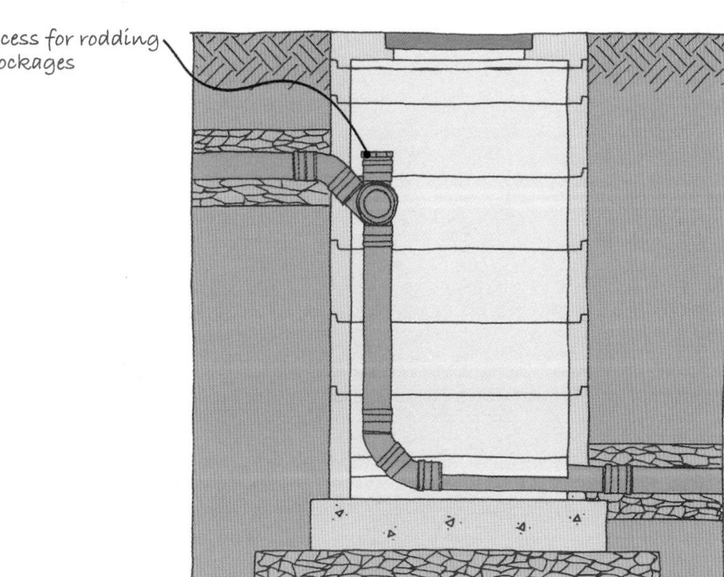

29.06 Backdrop manhole: used to maintain correct slope on very steep sites.

On-site wastewater treatment

In rural settings, where connection to the local authority main sewer is not possible, each house has its own separate wastewater treatment system. Surface water is diverted to a soakage pit.

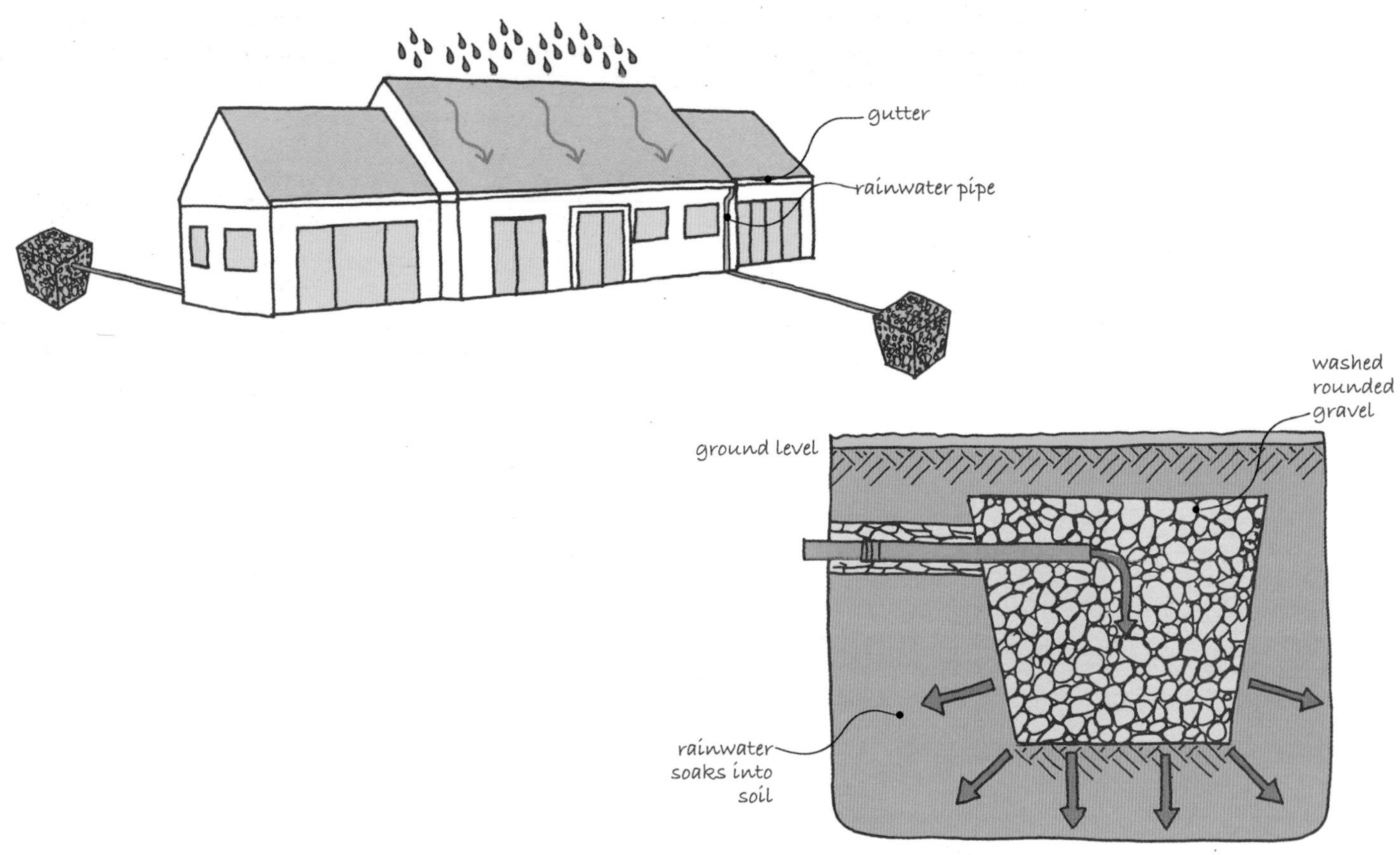

29.07 Surface water is diverted to a soakage pit, where it seeps into the soil.

Septic tanks

A septic tank is simply a separation chamber for solid waste (i.e. faeces). Solid wastes sink to the bottom of the tank, becoming part of the sludge layer. The middle layer contains the liquid waste, which will flow to the percolation area. On top floats the scum layer, composed of less dense liquids such as cooking oil and grease. Over time, the scum layer forms a seal on the surface of the effluent. This allows naturally occurring anaerobic (without oxygen) bacteria to break down the solids and gradually reduce the amount of sludge.

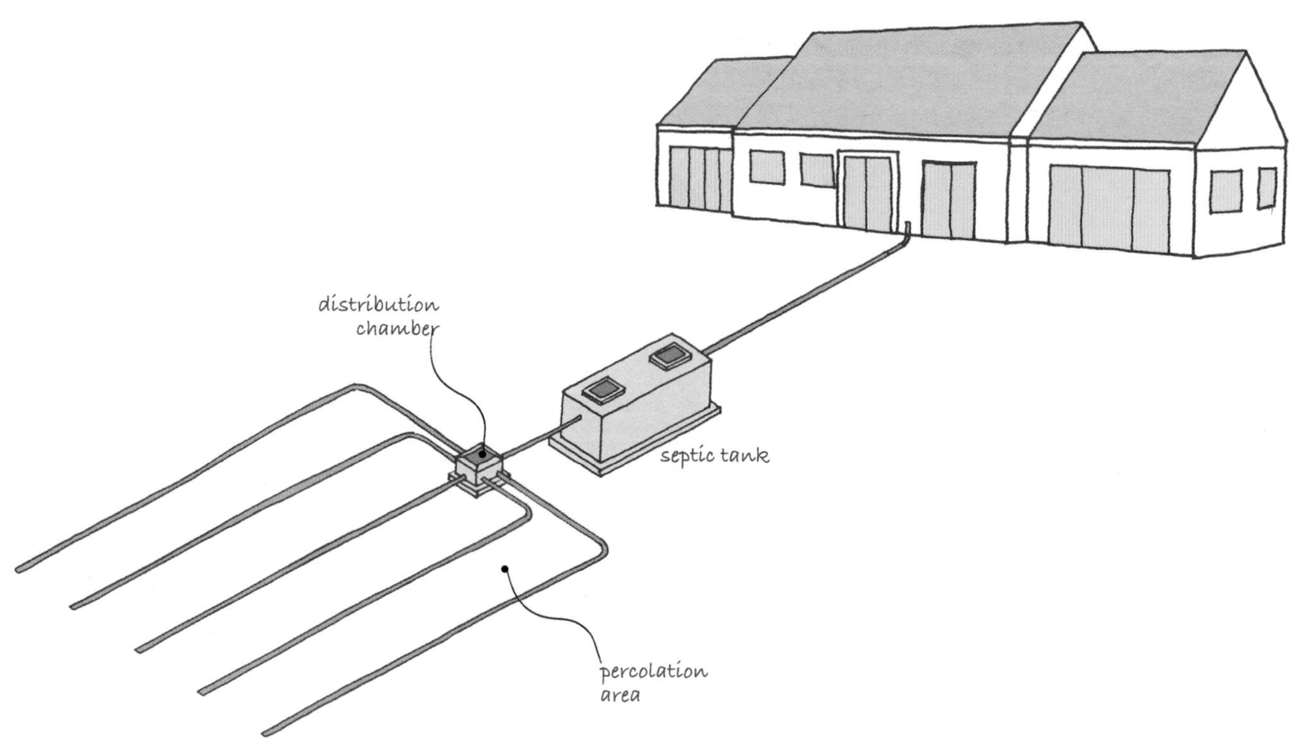

29.08 Septic tank system: a typical system comprising the septic tank, distribution chamber and percolation area.

29.09 Trial hole: exposes the subsoil for inspection

The function of a wastewater treatment system is to:

- treat the wastewater to minimise contamination of groundwater
- protect humans from contact with wastewater
- keep animals, insects and vermin from contact with wastewater
- minimise the generation of foul odours
- prevent pollution – discharge of untreated wastewater to groundwater or surface water.

Site analysis

A visual inspection, trial hole and percolation test must be carried out to determine whether a site is suitable for on-site wastewater treatment. The visual inspection involves looking for nearby resources that may be at risk of pollution (e.g. streams, rivers, lakes, wells). A trial hole measuring 1m × 6 m and 1.2m deep is dug to establish the depth of the water table, the depth to bedrock and the subsoil characteristics.

Groundwater contamination and septic tanks

Groundwater can become contaminated when hazardous liquids soak down (e.g. waste water) through the soil or rock into the groundwater. While groundwater is generally less easily polluted than surface water, it tends to remain polluted for much longer once pollution occurs.

Approximately one in three of the two million homes in Ireland are individual houses built in rural areas. Each of these houses has its own septic tank. These tanks provide a very basic level of wastewater treatment and rely on the quality of the subsoil to clean the effluent. If the soil conditions are not ideal or if a septic tank is not maintained and emptied regularly the level of treatment will not be adequate to clean the wastewater before it reaches the groundwater.

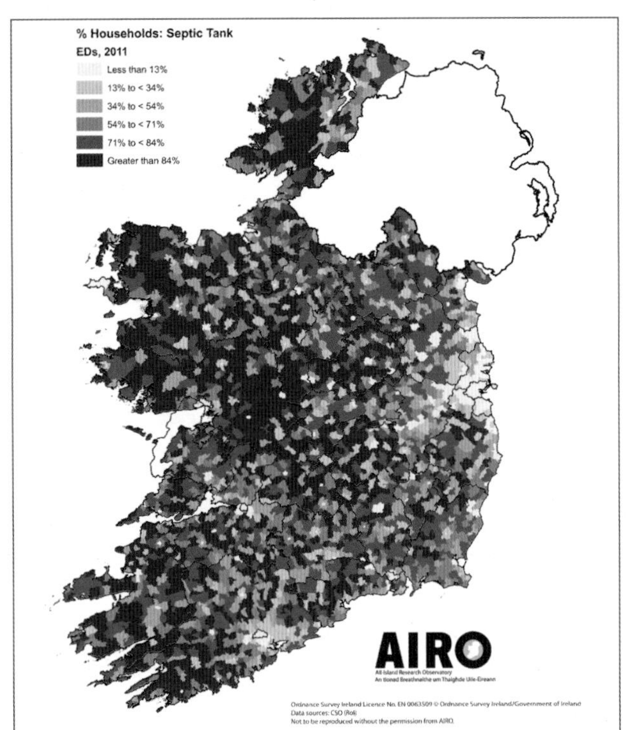

29.10 Percentage of households with an individual septic tank. *Source:* AIRO Census 2011.

DEFINITION

Percolation test
A measure of the time taken for a specific volume of water to be absorbed by the soil at a defined depth.

Percolation test (T test)

A percolation test examines whether the soil on site is good at absorbing water. This test is carried out on sites in rural areas where it will not be possible to connect to a mains sewer. This is necessary because an on-site wastewater treatment system releases wastewater into the subsoil – so it's important that this wastewater can soak away.

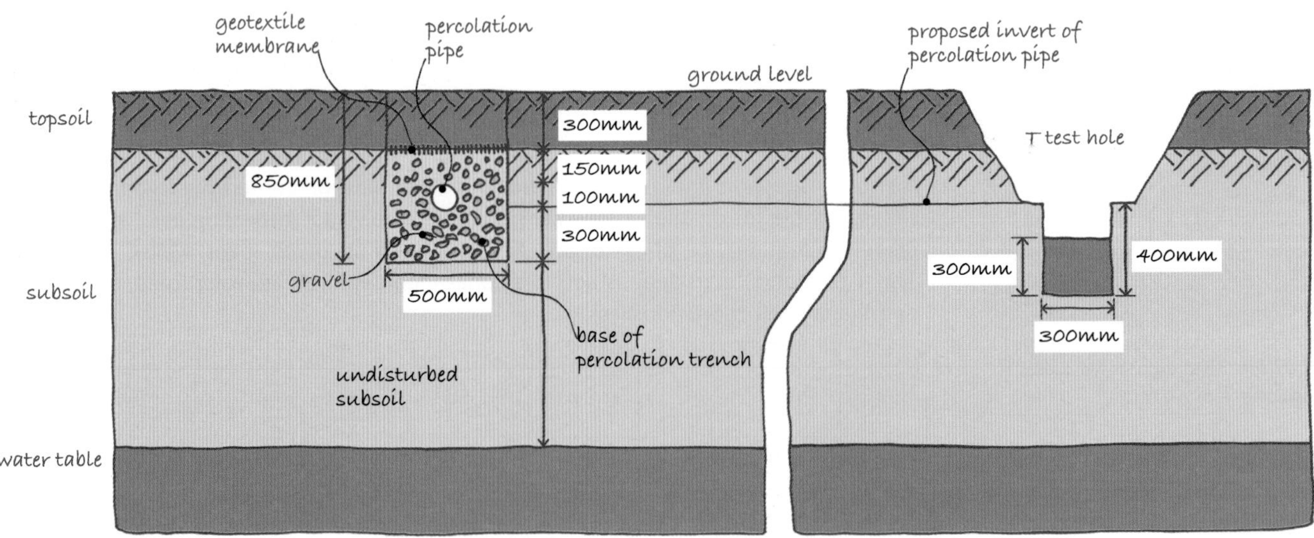

29.11 Percolation test: the proposed depth of the percolation pipe (left) determines the position of the test hole (right).

The test involves excavating a hole in the area of the site where the proposed percolation (soakage) area is to be installed. The hole is filled with water and the percolation time (T) in minutes is noted. If the water is absorbed too slowly or too quickly (less than 3 minutes or more than 50 minutes) this indicates that the soil is not suitable for a standard wastewater treatment system. If the time is between 50 and 75 minutes a septic tank combined with a secondary treatment system is required.

Procedure

Day 1

1 Two percolation test holes should be dug in the proposed percolation area and the following procedure carried out in both. Each hole should be 300mm × 300mm and 400mm deep below the proposed invert level of the distribution pipe (minimum depth 2.1m).
2 The bottom and sides of the hole are scratched with a wire brush to remove any compacted or smeared soil surfaces and to expose the natural soil surface.
3 Clean water is carefully poured into the hole at about 10.00 a.m. in order to fill it to the full height of 400mm.
4 The water is allowed to percolate.
5 At about 5.00 p.m. the hole is once again filled to the full height of 400mm and allowed to drain overnight.

Day 2

1 The hole is filled with clean water at about 10.00 a.m. and the water allowed to drop until there is 300mm of water in the hole.
2 Then the time in minutes required for the water to drop 100mm (i.e. from 300mm to 200mm) is recorded.
3 The hole is then refilled to the 300mm level, the water allowed to drain to the 200mm level and the time recorded again.
4 Step 3 is repeated. The drainage time has now been recorded three times in total.
5 The average value in minutes of the three recordings is calculated.
6 This average time is divided by four to give the time required for a fall of 25mm – this is called the percolation value or T value.

Once the soil investigation, water table investigation and percolation test have been completed, the next steps to be taken will depend on the results obtained.

Location

The wastewater treatment system must be installed in accordance with the current regulations issued by the Environmental Protection Agency.

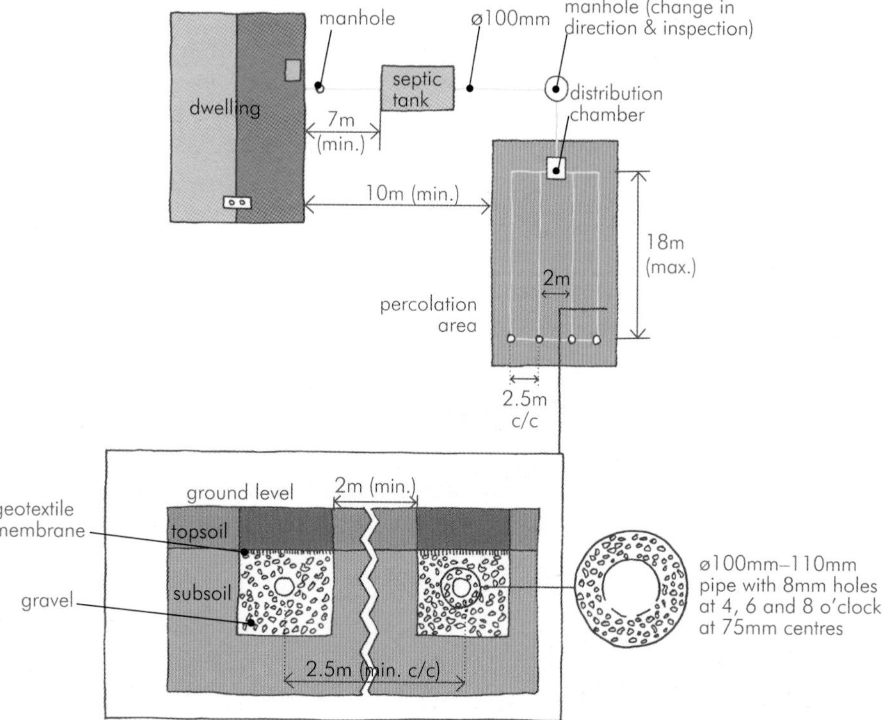

29.12 Wastewater treatment system location on site and construction of percolation trenches.

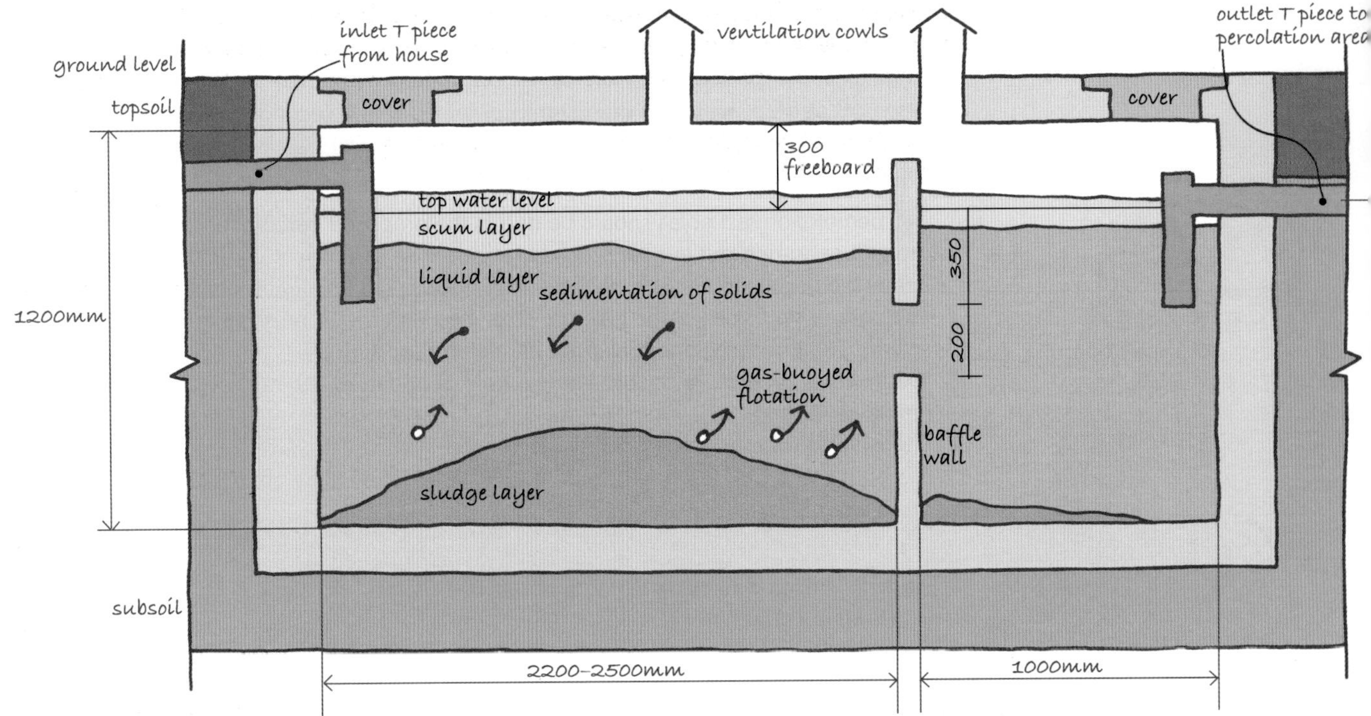

29.13 Septic tank: section showing design criteria.

Nominal septic tank capacity for various design populations	
Number of persons served	Nominal capacity (m³)
2–5	3
6–10	4

Percolation trench length	
Number of people in the household	Minimum combined length of trenches*
4	72
5	90
6	108
7	126
8	144
9	162
10	180

29.14 Septic tank sizing and percolation trench lengths.

* Individual trench length 18m max, trench width 500mm.

Secondary treatment systems

Secondary treatment is required on a site where the result of the percolation test (T test) is between 50 seconds and 75 seconds. This means that the subsoil is non-cohesive and the wastewater will drain too quickly. This could lead to pollution of the groundwater.

When this is the case a second treatment stage is required after the primary treatment provided by the septic tank. There are numerous ways this can be done, including:

- raised soil/sand filter systems – this involves building a raised mound of soil or sand on the site and pumping the wastewater up to the top of the mound so that it can percolate down through the additional layer of soil/sand
- mechanical biological systems – these proprietary systems use various mechanical and biological methods to treat the wastewater
- natural systems – constructed wetlands that mimic nature to provide wastewater treatment.

Constructed wetland (reed bed)

Constructed wetland is a general term used to describe both horizontal and vertical flow reed bed systems. Constructed wetlands have several advantages over proprietary systems:

- gravity fed – no electricity required
- no moving parts – low maintenance
- natural system – no chemicals required
- biodiversity – provides a habitat for wildlife
- aesthetically pleasing – can be designed to blend into the landscape.

29.15 Constructed wetland – a newly built reed bed and the same bed two years later.

A constructed wetland can be gravel-, sand- or soil-based, depending on what best suits the site conditions. A constructed wetland typically comprises a pit containing a growing medium (e.g. gravel) and vegetation (e.g. reeds).

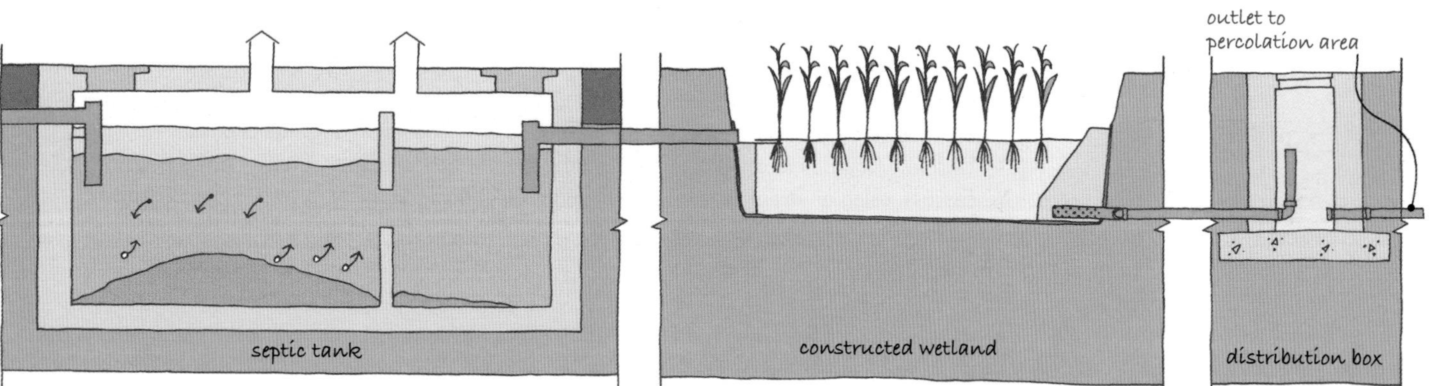

29.16 Secondary treatment system – installed between the septic tank and the percolation area.

Reeds are used because their thick roots provide a pathway for the transfer of oxygen from the the atmosphere to the root zone (rhizosphere). The plants used are macrophytes, the most popular of which is the common reed (*Phragmites australis*). Other plants species used are *Iris*, *Typha*, *Sparganium*, *Carex*, *Schoenoplectus* and *Acorus*. Planting should be done in blocks of plant species at a density of four to five plants per metre squared. A mixing of plant species is encouraged to promote diversification in the system.

In the reed bed, physical, chemical, and biological processes combine to remove contaminants from the wastewater. Treatment occurs as the wastewater passes through the wetland medium and the plant rhizosphere. A thin film around each root hair is aerobic due to the release of oxygen from the roots. Aerobic and anaerobic micro-organisms decompose the organic matter in the wastewater. Ammonia (and other nitrogen-based compounds) is removed by the action of microbes – this is very important because ammonia is toxic to fish if discharged into watercourses. Suspended solids are physically filtered out by the medium (i.e. gravel) and harmful bacteria and viruses are reduced by filtration and adsorption by biofilms on the gravel.

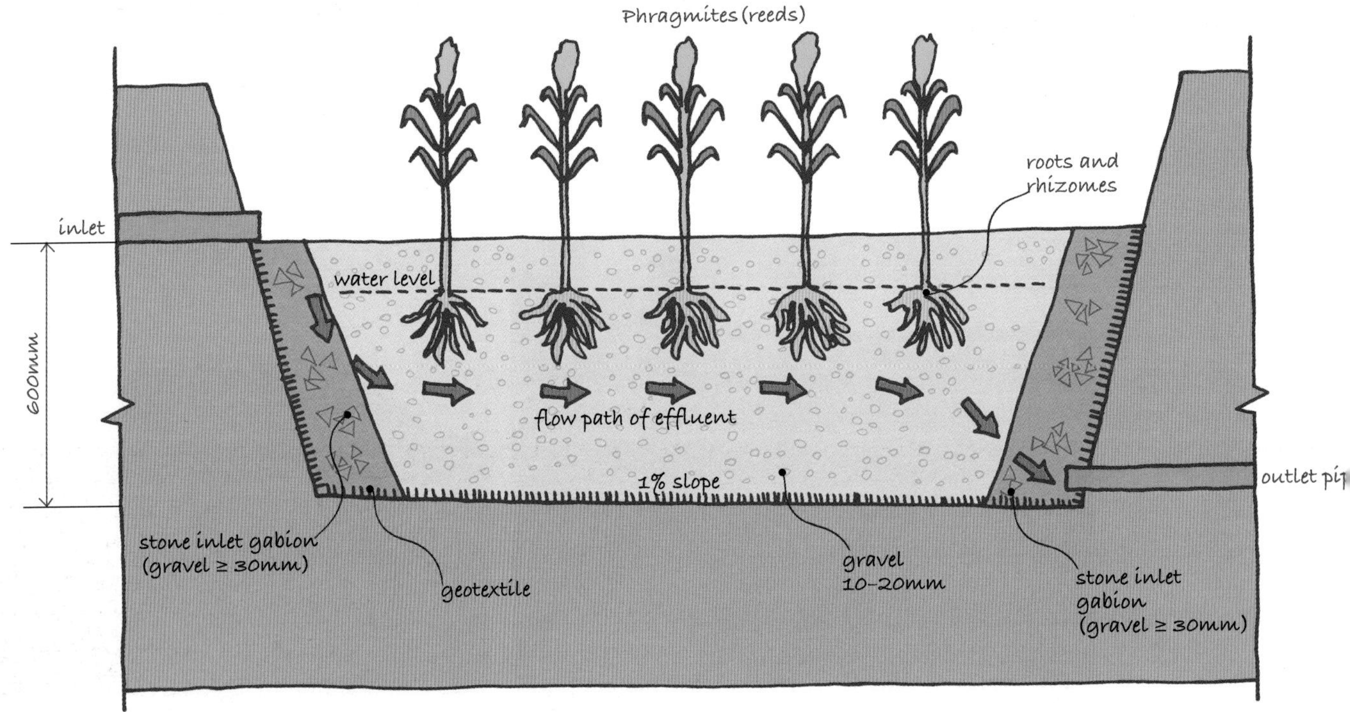

29.17 Constructed wetland – horizontal sub-surface flow reed bed.

REVISION EXERCISES

1 Describe, using a neat annotated sketch, the design requirements for a typical discharge stack.
2 Explain, using neat freehand sketches, the different ways in which storm water is handled in rural and urban areas.
3 Summarise the problems associated with ground water pollution and septic tanks.
4 Explain, using a neat annotated sketch, how a septic tank works.
5 Discuss, using an example, the importance of secondary treatment for wastewater treatment systems in a rural setting.

CHAPTER 30

Sound

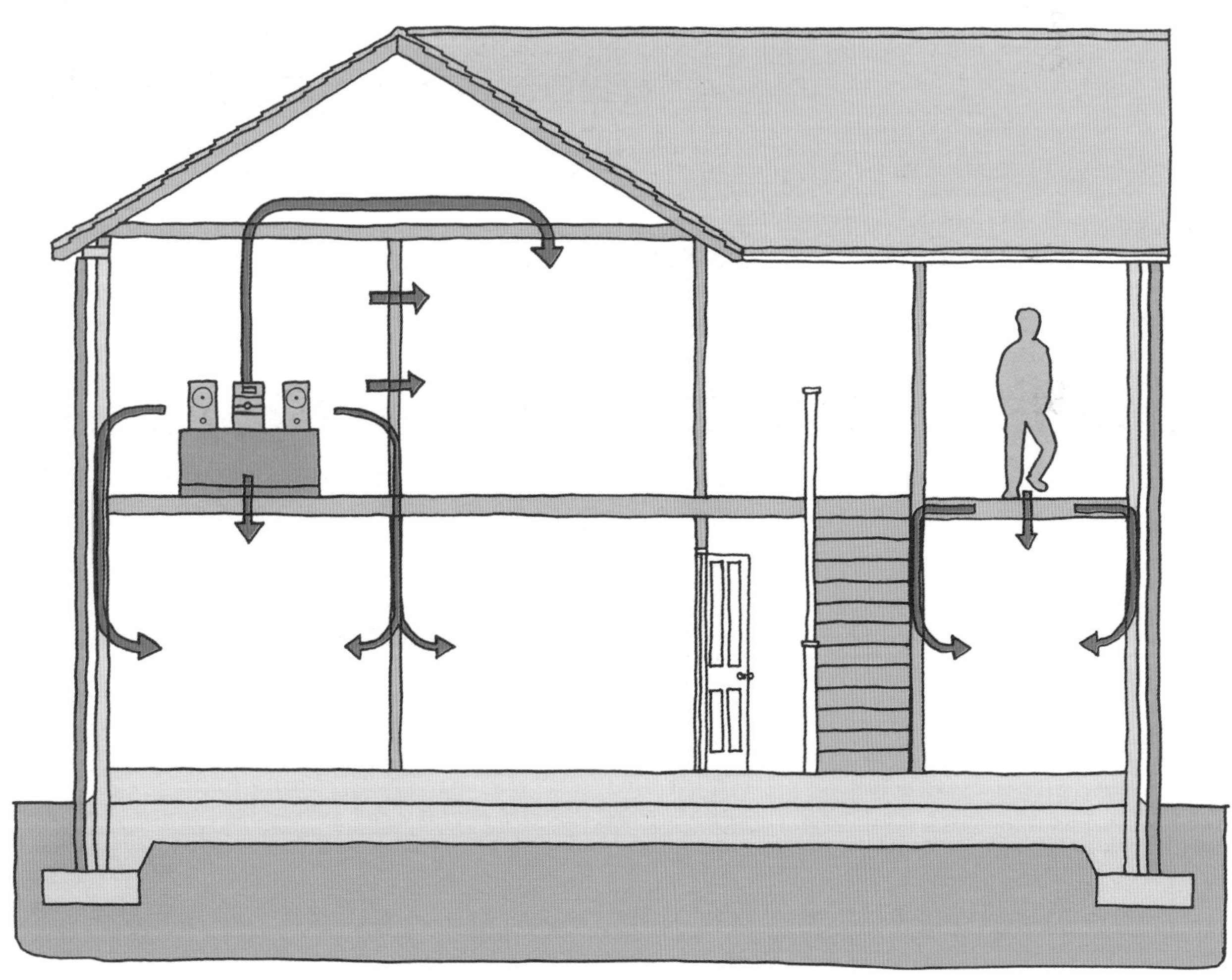

Sound energy

Sound is a form of energy that causes vibrations of the air which the ear detects. Sound energy can be transferred through the air or through a solid object:

- airborne sound travels through the air (e.g. singing)
- impact sound travels through a structure (e.g. knocking on a door).

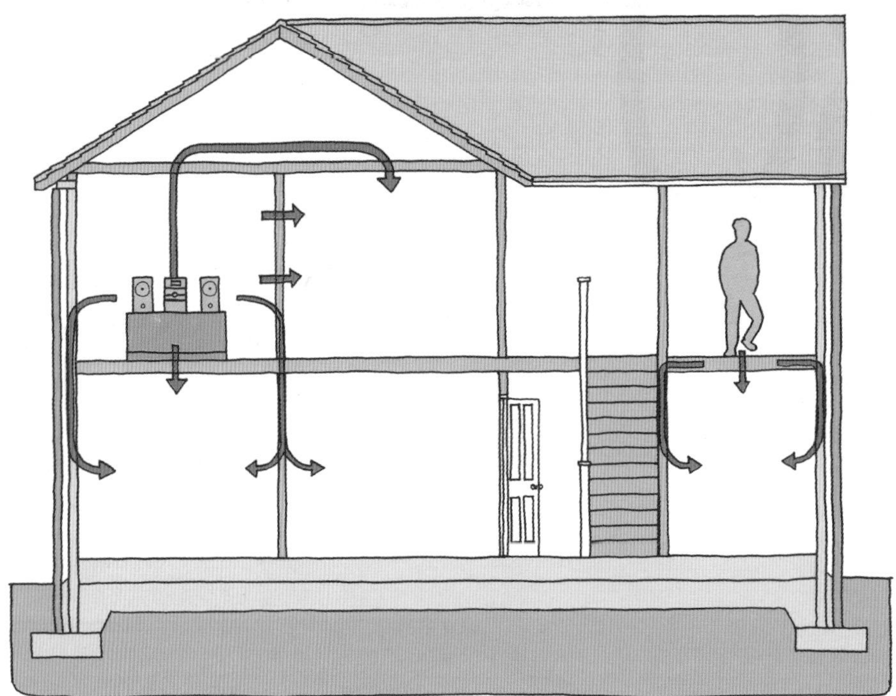

30.01 Sound transmission routes: sound energy can be transmitted directly or indirectly.

Principles

Measurement

Human perception of sound is determined by the sound pressure level and is measured in decibels (dB). The threshold of hearing is assigned a value of zero decibels and rises to 130dB – the threshold of pain.

Source of sound Sound in air	Sound pressure (pascal, Pa)	Sound level (decibels, dB)
Theoretical limit for undistorted sound at 1 atmosphere environmental pressure	101.325	194
Stun grenades	6,000–20,000	170 – 180
Jet engine at 1m	632	150
Threshold of pain	63.2	130
Vuvuzela horn at 1m	20	120
Risk of instantaneous noise-induced hearing loss	**20**	**approx. 120**
Jet engine at 100m	6.32–200	110 –140
Non-electric chainsaw at 1m	6.32	110
Pneumatic (e.g. Kango) hammer at 1m	2	100
Traffic on a busy roadway at 10m	0.2–0.6	80 – 90
Hearing damage (over long-term exposure, need not be continuous)	0.356	85
Car at 10m	0.02 – 0.2	60 – 80
TV (set at home level) at 1m	0.02	60
Normal conversation at 1m	0.002 – 0.020	40 – 60
Very calm room	0.0002 – 0.0063	20 – 30
Light leaf rustling, calm breathing	0.000063	10
Threshold of hearing at 1kHz	0.00002	0

30.02 Sound pressure/sound level of common events.

Inverse square law

The inverse square law states that the sound intensity from a point source decreases in inverse proportion to the square of the distance from the sound. In other words, if the distance to the sound source is doubled, the sound intensity level is quartered i.e. $(\frac{1}{2})^2 = \frac{1}{4}$. This happens because the same energy is spread over a larger area as the sound spreads out. This law applies to both sound and light.

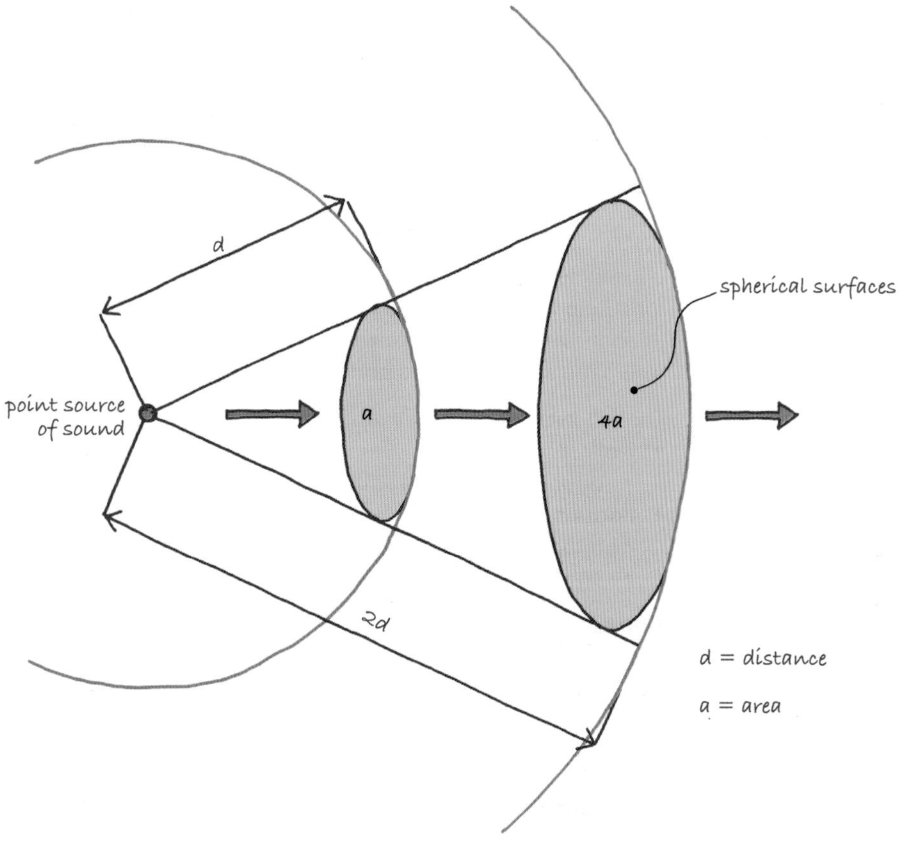

30.03 Inverse square law: intensity from a point source decreases in inverse proportion to the square of the distance from the source.

Reverberation

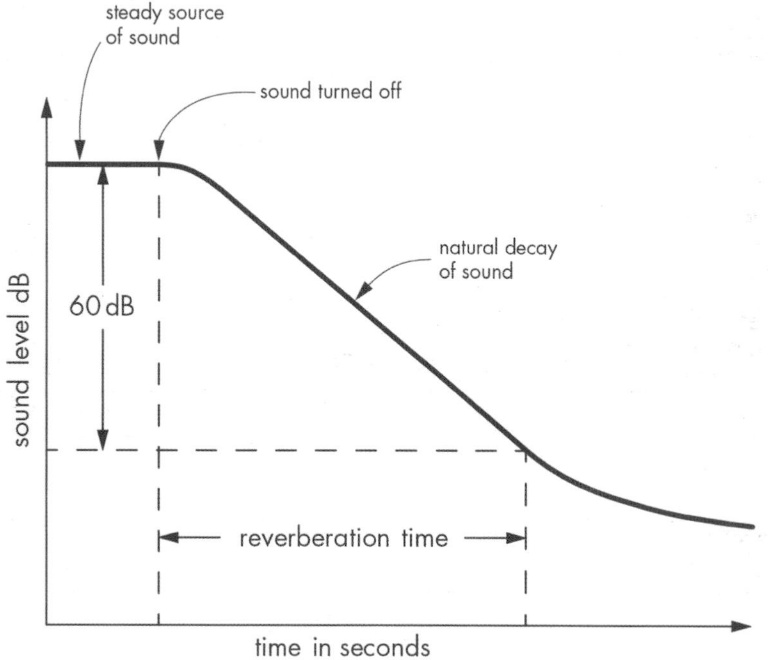

30.04 Reverberation time.

Reverberation is the term used to describe the continuation and enhancement of a sound caused by rapid multiple reflections between the surfaces of a room. Reverberation is not the same as echo because the reflections reach the listener too rapidly for them to be heard as a separate sound – instead they are heard as an extension of the original sound.

The reverberation time of a sound is defined as the time taken for a sound to decay by 60dB from its original level. This depends on the floor area of the room, the sound absorption of the surfaces of the walls, floor and ceiling, and the frequency of the sound.

The ideal reverberation time varies: speech requires short reverberation times for clarity (excessive reverberative sound will mask the next syllable), whereas longer reverberation times are thought to enhance the quality of music.

Sound insulation

Sound insulation or acoustic insulation is the reduction of sound energy transmitted into an adjoining air space. Sound insulation is important in buildings where large numbers of people live and/or work in close proximity, for example apartment buildings or hotels. In home design it is unusual to consider sound insulation as a requirement for ordinary houses. The only requirement for sound insulation stated in the current building regulations relates to the prevention of noise through the party wall of a semi-detached or terraced house or through the floor of a dwelling where the space below is part of another dwelling (e.g. duplex/flat/apartment).

The following minimum levels of sound insulation should be achieved:

- walls
  - airborne sound – 45dB min. sound insulation value
- floors
  - airborne sound – 45dB min. sound insulation value
  - impact sound – 62dB min. sound insulation value.

Sound insulation principles

Sound insulation is based on four basic principles.

1 heaviness – heavyweight structures (e.g. concrete) with high mass transmit less sound energy than lightweight structures.

2 completeness
  - airtightness – airborne sound will travel through any gaps in the structure
  - uniformity – sound will take the 'path of least resistance'. A small, poorly insulated area can significantly reduce the performance of the whole structure (e.g. when a window is slightly ajar the sound insulation of the whole wall drops dramatically).

3 flexibility – flexible materials (e.g. quilted insulation) tend to absorb sound energy. The level of insulation provided by a structure (e.g. plasterboard stud partition) can be affected by resonance and coincidence:
  - resonance – if the natural frequency of the material from which the partition is constructed is the same as the frequency of the sound, the insulation performance of the partition drops
  - coincidence – if the frequency of the sound matches the frequency of the bending in the material, the insulation performance of the partition drops.

4 isolation – discontinuous construction (e.g. double/triple glazing) is effective in reducing sound transmission. Sound energy is lost when it travels from one medium to another (e.g. glass to air).

ACTIVITIES

Considering the everyday activities in your home, can you think of examples of situations where noise has been a problem?

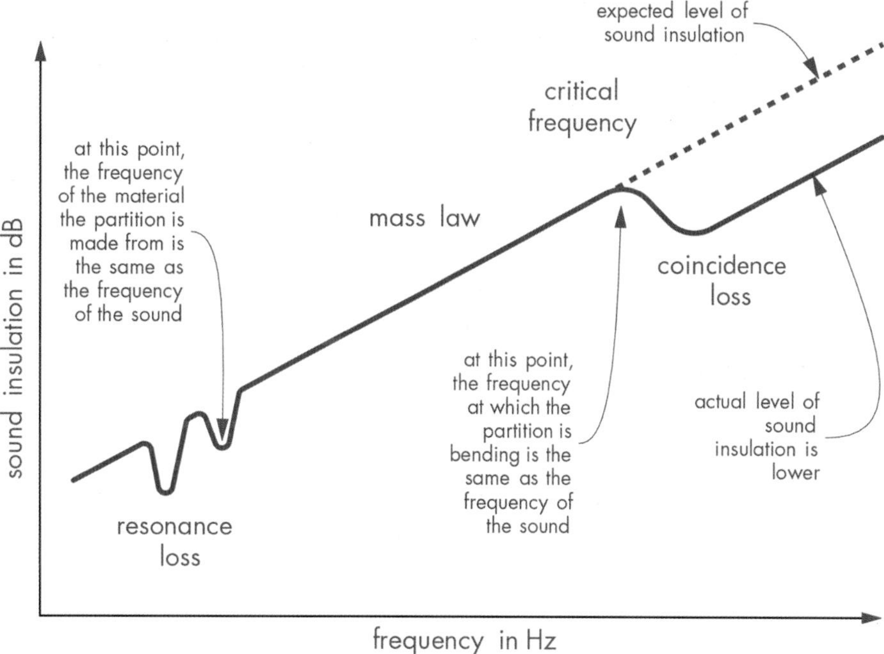

30.05 Flexibility: resonance and coincidence loss.

Sound insulation construction

Dwellings generally require sound insulation in:

- the external envelope – to reduce noise from outdoor sources
- party walls – to reduce noise between semi-detached/terraced dwellings
- internal floors – to reduce impact noise (i.e. footfall) between levels.

The weak link in the external envelope is where the windows and doors are installed (i.e. the uniformity principle). Sound insulation at the window – wall junction depends greatly on airtightness, so Passivhaus dwellings will perform better than dwellings built to building regulations standards.

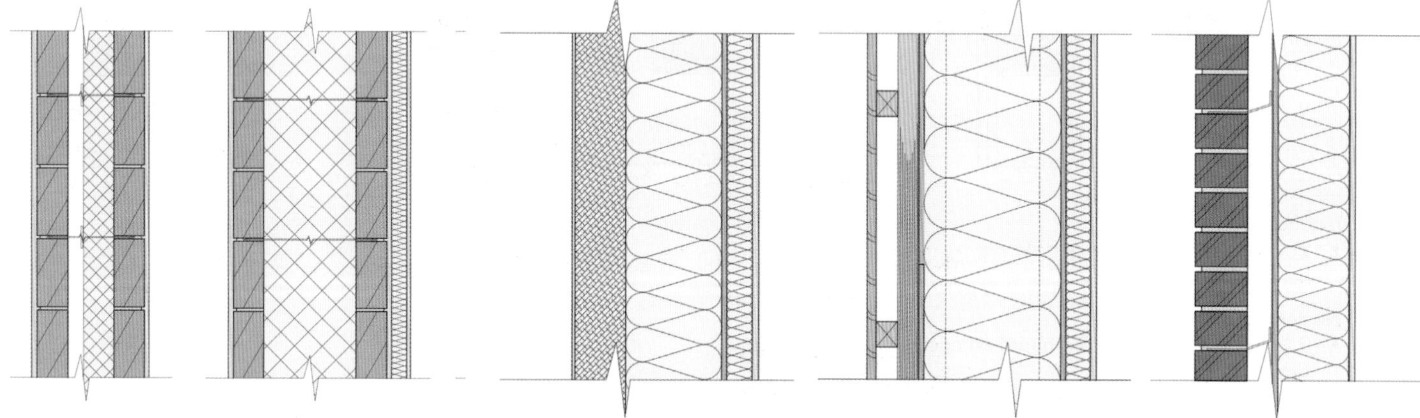

30.06 Sound insulation – external envelope: heaviness and completeness provide sound insulation.

30.07 Sound insulation – external envelope: flexibility and completeness provide sound insulation in the Passivhaus walls; mass, isolation and flexibility provide sound insulation in the building regulations wall.

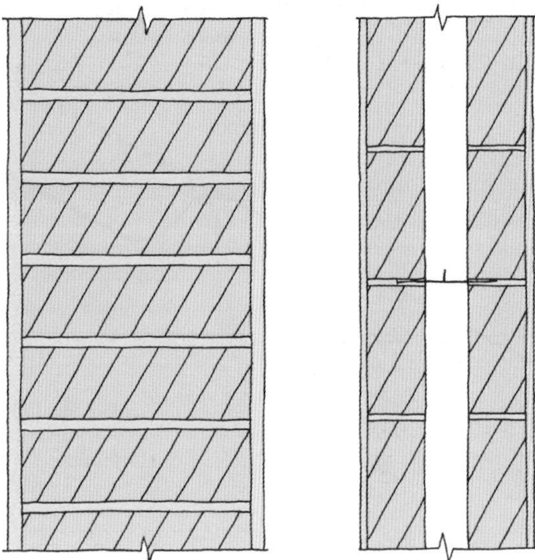

30.08 Sound insulation – party wall: typical block 'on flat' or cavity wall construction will provide adequate sound insulation between dwellings.

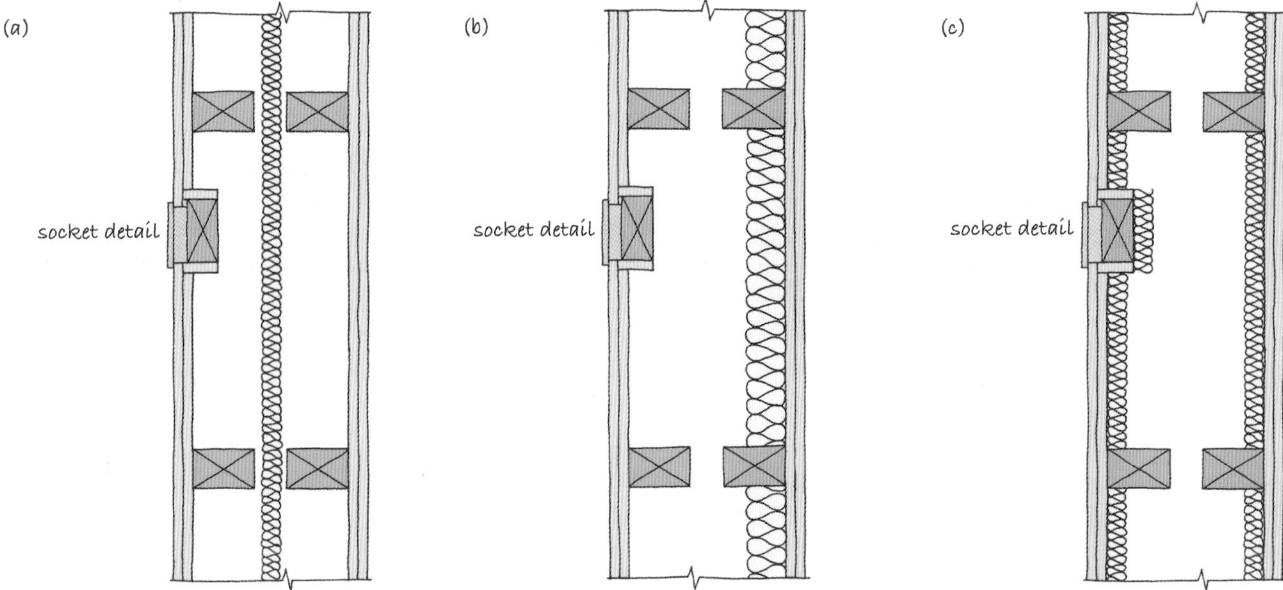

requirements:

- 200mm minimum internal distance between faces

plasterboard:

- 2 layers of 12.5mm plasterboard on each side
- unfaced quilted or batt insulation (10kg/m^3 min. density)

insulation:

- 25mm thickness if suspended in cavity or fixed to each frame
- 50mm if fixed to one frame

30.09 Sound insulation – horizontal section of party wall: timber frame walls (stud partitions) with double layers of plasterboard and absorbent material.

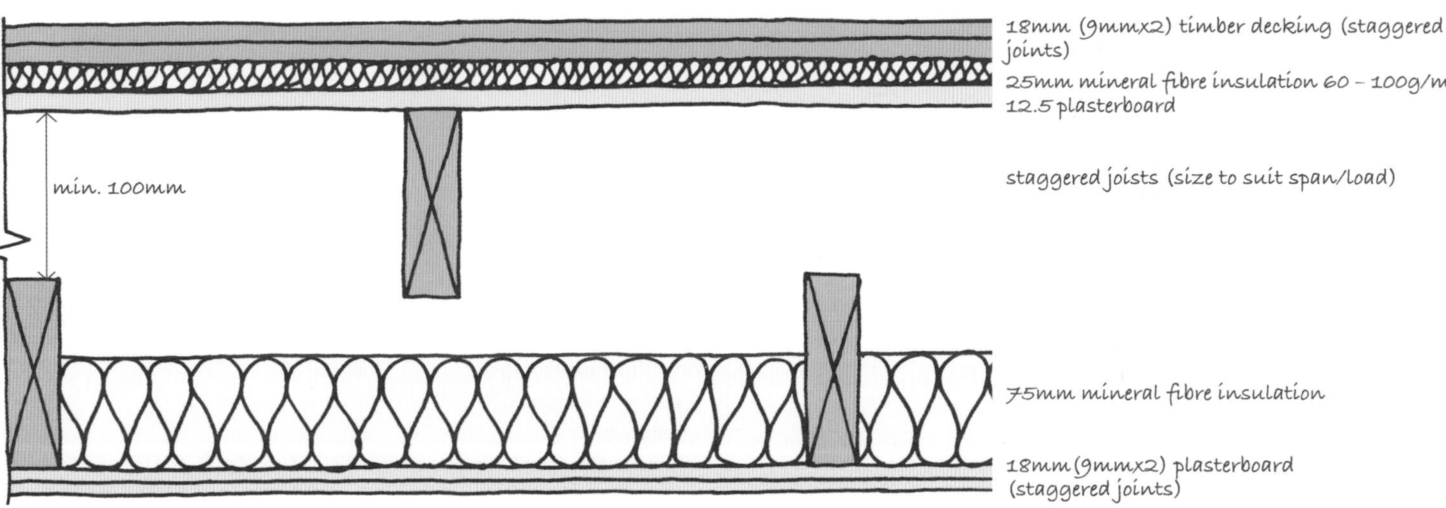

30.10 Sound insulation – upper floor: platform floor comprising a floating layer on a resilient layer, supported on a staggered joist structure.

REVISION EXERCISES

1 Describe, using a neat annotated sketch, how sound travels through a home.
2 Explain the four principles of sound insulation.
3 Outline the minimum level of sound insulation required for the walls and floors of a typical home.
4 Explain how noise is prevented from travelling across the party wall of a pair of semi-detached houses.
5 Explain how noise is prevented from travelling through a timber upper floor.

Index